WITHDRAWN

PHYSICAL METHODS IN CHEMICAL ANALYSIS

VOLUME II

PHYSICAL METHODS
IN
CHEMICAL ANALYSIS

Edited by

WALTER G. BERL

Applied Physics Laboratory, Johns Hopkins University, Silver Spring, Maryland

VOLUME II

1951

ACADEMIC PRESS INC. PUBLISHERS
NEW YORK

ACADEMIC PRESS INC.
111 Fifth Avenue, New York, New York 10003

United Kingdom Edition published by
ACADEMIC PRESS INC. (LONDON) LTD.
Berkeley Square House, London W.1

First Printing, 1951

Second Printing, 1967

PRINTED IN THE UNITED STATES OF AMERICA

CONTRIBUTORS TO VOLUME II

WALTER G. BERL, *The Applied Physics Laboratory, Johns Hopkins University, Silver Spring, Maryland*

H. T. S. BRITTON, *Washington Singer Laboratories, University College of the South West of England, Exeter*

BENJAMIN B. DAYTON, *Distillation Products, Inc., Rochester, New York*

MALCOLM DOLE, *Department of Chemistry, Northwestern University, Evanston, Illinois*

H. W. HERMANCE, *Bell Telephone Laboratories, Inc., New York, New York*

JAROSLAV HEYROVSKÝ, *University of Prague, Czechoslovakia*

GEORGE JURA, *Department of Chemistry, University of California, Berkeley, California*

A. R. KAUFMANN, *Department of Metallurgy, Massachusetts Institute of Technology, Cambridge, Massachusetts*

H. A. LAITINEN, *Department of Chemistry, University of Illinois, Urbana, Illinois*

ALOIS LANGER, *Westinghouse Research Laboratories, East Pittsburgh, Pennsylvania*

J. SHERMAN, *Philadelphia Naval Shipyard, Philadelphia, Pennsylvania*

H. V. WADLOW, *Bell Telephone Laboratories, Inc., New York, New York*

E. R. WEAVER, *National Bureau of Standards, Washington, D. C.*

PREFACE

The contributions included in this volume continue the aims set forth in Volume I to describe those physical methods that have either proved of considerable value in analytical work or are destined to play an important role in the future. Electrical, magnetic, and miscellaneous techniques are discussed. In addition, a chapter on the statistical analysis of experimental data is included.

In carrying out an analysis the analyst usually performs two major tasks:

1) preliminary operations that bring the system under investigation into physical states suitable for analysis,
2) measurement of physical constants that can be compared with known systems for identity or can be interpreted in terms of structure and organization.

Among the preliminary operations are included such changes in structure and phase as may be necessary for the subsequent physical measurement (ionization in the mass spectrometer, vaporization and heating in emission spectroscopy, etc.) and the many techniques of separation (distillation, distribution between immiscible solvents, separation of ions in a magnetic field, etc.). The determination of physical constants leads to identification as to type and nature of the structure under investigation (qualitative analysis). If a definite relation between physical constant and concentration can be established, quantitative results are obtainable. Measurement of nonspecific colligative properties of the system (mass, volume, ionization current, etc.) also lead to quantitative results, provided a separation from all interfering admixtures has been accomplished. Such separations are not required if a characteristic property can be measured (intensity of spectral lines in emission or adsorption, discharge current in polarography) where difficulties due to overlapping by interfering substances are absent or can be taken into account.

The discussions of analytical procedures in these volumes deal primarily with nonchemical methods and techniques useful in establishing the qualitative nature of unknowns. In addition, a number of methods are discussed that measure nonspecific properties only but are of great value in obtaining quantitative information on relatively simple systems (conductometric titration, radioactive tracer methods). Preliminary operations are not described unless they are essential steps in the over-all procedure.

It is indeed a great pleasure and privilege to express my thanks here to all the contributors for their splendid help and advice, and to the publishers, who cooperated in every way possible.

WALTER G. BERL

CONTENTS

ix

Gas Analysis by Methods Depending on Thermal Conductivity

By E. R. WEAVER, *National Bureau of Standards, Washington, D. C.*

The Measurement of Radioactivity for Tracer Applications

By ALOIS LANGER, *Westinghouse Research Laboratories, East Pittsburgh, Pennsylvania*

Statistical Analysis

By J. SHERMAN, *Philadelphia Naval Shipyard, Philadelphia, Pennsylvania*

Chromotographic Analysis

By WALTER G. BERL, *The Applied Physics Laboratory, Johns Hopkins University, Silver Spring, Maryland*

Metallurgical Polarographic Analysis; Polarometric Titrations

BY

JAROSLAV HEYROVSKÝ

University of Prague, Czechoslovakia

CONTENTS

1. HISTORY

The polarographic method applied to technical analysis uses automatically recorded current-voltage curves, obtained in electrolysis with a slowly dropping mercury electrode. From the shape of the ensuing curves constituents in the solution are determined qualitatively and quantitatively even in large dilutions and in a small volume with economy of time and material.

In its simplest form the method uses G. Lippmann's capillary electrometer as applied to the study of the surface-tension of polarized mercury. A thick-walled glass capillary, of 0.05 to 0.1 mm. inside diameter and 5–10 cm. in length is joined by rubber tubing to a mercury reservoir M (Fig. 1). Lippmann (1876) observed the position of the mercury meniscus in the capillary, keeping the reservoir at I; B. Kučera (1903) modified this method by lifting the reservoir to II, letting the mercury drop slowly out of the capillary and weighing the drops to determine the surface tension. J. Heyrovský (1922) used this arrangement for measurements of current-voltage curves, having introduced a sensitive galvanometer G. His theoretical investigations of electrode reactions at the dropping mercury electrode have disclosed the applicability of this arrangement for general analysis.

2. THEORY

The role of the capillary electrode is similar in its function to that in Lippmann's arrangement, i.e., to act as the polarizable electrode during the passage of current, the large mercury pool at the bottom of the electrolytic vessel remaining unpolarized. The term "polarizable" means that the electrode is capable of counterbalancing the external e.m.f. by reaching a back-potential or "polarization voltage" π_c, while the large electrode maintains its potential π_a constant throughout electrolysis. This contrasting behavior is primarily due to the difference in size of the electrodes. The current density is high at the dropping mercury electrode, but very small at the bottom electrode, the area of which is several hundred times larger than the surface area of an individual drop. The unpolarizability of the bottom electrode is further enhanced when used as anode. If the electrolyte consists of 1 N potassium chloride, calomel is produced during electrolysis, which imparts to the anode the definite potential of the normal calomel electrode. The mercury pool then acts as a standard electrode.

If one branches off a voltage E from the battery B by slide contact S, and a current i flows through the cell and galvanometer, the following relation holds: $E = \pi_a - \pi_c + ir$, where r is the resistance in the circuit SGCAD.

In polarography the current i rarely exceeds 10^{-5} amp. and since r is less than 100 ohms, ir is of the order of millivolts and may be neglected. π_a is the potential of the unpolarizable reference electrode and may be taken as zero so that $\pi_c = -E$. This is the condition of the polarizability of the dropping electrode and indicates that the applied voltage is equal to the potential of the dropping electrode. (The negative sign means that the dropping electrode is used as the cathode.)

To acquire the potential π_c, each drop of the capillary electrode has to be charged to the respective potential by a charging (or capacity) current i_c whose value, however, does not exceed 10^{-7} amp. This is neglected in most cases but it has to be taken into account when using high galvanometer sensitivity.

The method is best illustrated when the applied voltage E is increased by shifting the sliding contact S (Fig. 1) from D towards F and noting, after each increase of E, the corresponding current i. When using a solution of 1 N potassium chloride as electrolyte, the graph showing the dependence of the current i on the applied voltage E, the "current voltage curve," has the shape of curve 1 (Fig. 2). It represents the charging current, which shows a sudden increase at $E = 1.86$ volt due to the electrolytic current, by which the potassium ions are electrodeposited on mercury, forming a dilute amalgam. If one adds small amounts of lead, cadmium, and zinc salts to the electrolyte, so as to make the solution 10^{-4} normal in each component one observes an increase of current at

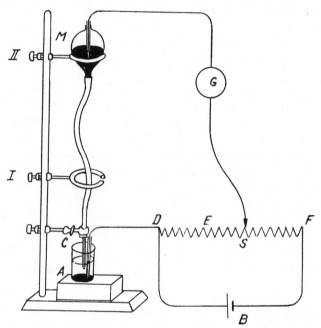

Fig. 1.   Schematic diagram of a polarographic arrangement.

0.45 volt, another at 0.60 volt and a third at 1.05 volt.   The first increase is due to the electrodeposition of lead, the second to cadmium and the third to zinc.   The current changes are called "waves" and denote by their potential the nature, and by their height the quantity of the ions in solution.

The horizontal parts of the curve are due to "diffusion currents," where the current is limited by the rate of diffusion of the cations to be deposited.   The magnitude of the diffusion current i_d is given by the equation of Ilkovič (18):

$$i_d = 0.627(\nu)FD^{\frac{1}{2}}m^{\frac{2}{3}}t^{\frac{1}{6}}C,$$

where ν is the number of charges exchanged, D the diffusion constant of the diffusing ion, F the Faraday equivalent, C the concentration of the reducible constituent, m the rate of flow of mercury and t the drop time. Thus i_d increases linearly with C.   The position and shape of the "wave" is given by the relationship deduced by Heyrovský and Ilkovič (13):

$$\pi_c = \frac{RT}{\nu F} \ln \frac{id - i}{i} + K.$$

Here R and T are the gas constant and temperature respectively, and K is a constant specific for the electrodeposited ions.   This characteristic

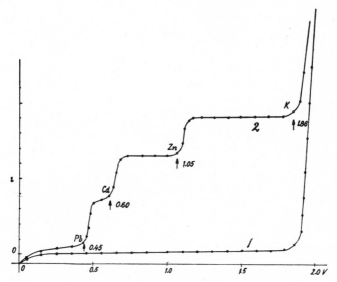

FIG. 2.   Current-voltage curves for 1 N KCl (1) and Pb^{++}, Cd,$^{++}$ Zn^{++} ions in 1 N KCl (2).

value of K is obtained from the curve at the point, at which the half-wave current is reached, i.e., when $i = i_d/2$; then $\pi_c = K$ and this value is called the "half-wave potential."   It is independent of the concentration of the reducible cation and of the properties of the capillary.   When the cation enters into a complex, e.g., plumbous and zinc ions in an alkaline solution or cadmium and zinc ions in ammoniacal solutions, the half-wave potentials are considerably changed (see Table I).   Not only cations are electrodeposited in polarography, but many ions are reduced, as, for example, $Fe^{+++} \rightarrow Fe^{++}$, $Cr^{+++} \rightarrow Cr^{++}$, $NO_3^- \rightarrow NH_3$, $BrO_3^- \rightarrow Br^-$, $CrO_4^= \rightarrow Cr^{+++}$ etc., and numerous molecular species, both inorganic and organic, are reduced, as, for example, oxygen, hydrogen peroxide, sulfur dioxide, dicyan, aldehydes, nitro derivatives, unsaturated compounds etc.   When the dropping electrode is made the anode,

TABLE I
Half-Wave Potentials (in Volts) of Metal Ion Deposition Referred to the Normal Calomel Electrode

Cation	In neutral or acid solutions	In 1 N alkali	In 1 N NH$_4$OH 1 N NH$_4$Cl	In 1 N KCN	In 10% tartarate or citrate	In 0.1 N KOH 0.30 M triethanol amine
Ca^{++}	-2.23	-2.23	—	—	—	—
Li$^+$	-2.38	-2.38	—	—	—	—
Sr^{++}	-2.13	-2.13	—	—	—	—
Na$^+$	-2.15	-2.15	—	—	—	—
K$^+$	-2.17	-2.17	—	—	—	—
Rb$^+$	-2.07	-2.07	—	—	—	—
Cs$^+$	-2.09	-2.09	—	—	—	—
NH$_4^+$	-2.07	-2.17	—	—	—	—
Ba^{++}	-1.94	-1.94	—	—	—	—
Ra^{++}	-1.89	-1.89	—	—	—	—
Al^{+++}	-1.76	—	—	—	—	—
Mn^{++}	-1.55	-1.74	-1.69	-1.37	-1.7	-1.65
Cr^{++}	-1.42	-1.98	-1.74	—	—	—
Fe^{++}	-1.33	-1.56	-1.52	—	—	—
H$^+$	-1.6	—	—	—	-1.6	—
Co^{++}	-1.23	-1.44	-1.32	-1.2	—	—
Ni^{++}	-1.09	—	-1.14	-1.42	—	-1.40
Zn^{++}	-1.06	-1.53	-1.38	—	-1.19	-1.49
In^{+++}	-0.63	-1.13	—	—	—	—
Cd^{++}	-0.63	-0.80	-0.85	-1.15	-0.68	-0.82
Sn^{++}	-0.47	-1.26	—	—	-0.68	-1.43
Pb^{++}	-0.46	-0.81	—	-0.74	-0.54	-0.88
Tl$^+$	-0.50	-0.50	-0.52	—	-0.52	—
Sb^{+++}	-0.21	-1.2	—	-1.17	-1.04	—
Bi^{+++}	-0.03	-0.6	—	—	-0.74	-0.78
Cu^{++}	-0.03	-0.52	—	—	-0.11	-0.53
Cu$^+$	—	—	-0.54	—	—	—
Au$^+$	—	-1.3	—	-1.5	—	—
Au^{+++}	—	-0.6	—	—	—	—

electro-oxidation of cations takes place, for example, $Cr^{++} \rightarrow Cr^{+++}$, $Fe^{++} \rightarrow Fe^{+++}$, etc., as well as oxidation of many organic compounds, notably the redox systems. All substances that undergo electrolysis at the dropping mercury electrode are designated as "depolarizers," since in their presence the polarization voltage (back e.m.f.) cannot increase until the "depolarizer" is exhausted at the interphase of the dropping electrode and thereby gives rise to concentration polarization.

3. APPARATUS

3.1. Capillary

The capillary is an ordinary, thick-walled glass tube as used for thermometer stems. When the inner bore is narrow, 0.05 mm. or less, the length must not exceed 6 cm. otherwise the dropping rate is too slow and the resistance of the capillary too great. The wider the bore the longer the capillary should be to give a drop time t of about three seconds. The drop time depends on the surface tension of mercury and on the outflow velocity of mercury m. Since $m = k \dfrac{h \cdot r^4}{l}$, i.e., directly proportional to the pressure of mercury (height of the reservoir) h and to the 4th power of the radius, and inversely to the length l of the capillary the surface-tension of mercury is constant at any fixed potential of the dropping electrode and hence the drop-weight $m \cdot t$ is also constant and independent of the height of the mercury reservoir. Since m is proportional to h, t is inversely proportional to the height of the reservoir. For example with a 1 N potassium chloride electrolyte, place the sliding contact S (Fig. 1) on D, so that the applied e.m.f. is zero and adjust the height of the mercury level to obtain the required drop time of about 3 seconds. If the inside bore r is approximately 0.1 mm., and the length of the capillary l is 10 cm., the height h is small, i.e., 10 to 15 cm. If r is 0.07 to 0.08 mm., h becomes 30–40 cm. and the length l 7–8 cm. Capillaries of smaller radius than 0.05 cm. are not suitable, as they offer electrical resistance of several ohms and, according to the Ilkovič equation, give small diffusion currents.

The drawn-out capillary recommended originally has the advantage that at its wide end rubber tubing is easily attached and little solution adheres at its narrow tip (approximately 2 mm. wide) when the capillary is transferred from one solution into another. The disadvantage of such capillaries is their poor reproduciblity and fragility.

A standardization of capillaries was introduced by Maas, by using thermometer capillaries of uniform bore. However, for repeated analyses the danger of contaminating the solution with small quantities of the previous sample exists unless the capillary is thin. The thin capillary, however, presents difficulties in attaching it to the rubber tube.

To use the advantages of both the old and new type of capillaries Novák (35) recommends the following adjustment: a narrow thermometer capillary 2 to 3 mm. thick and with an inside bore of 0.08 mm. (or between 0.1 and 0.07 mm.) is fused on or attached by a short rubber tube to a tube 6 mm. wide, 8 to 10 cm. long and 3 mm. inside diameter. The narrow capillary is cut off 4 to 5 cm. from the tube seal. This capillary is preferentially used in the "universal vessel" arrangement (page 10).

The advantages of the dropping mercury electrode technique are:

1. Every drop offers a fresh surface unaffected by the previous history of the preceding drop and surrounded by a fresh layer of solution, so that the surface conditions are well defined and time effects excluded.
2. The large overvoltage of hydrogen on the mercury electrode prevents evolution of hydrogen even in the deposition of the alkali metals from neutral solutions, so that the study of primary electrode processes may be extended to -2.6 volt (using the $1\ N$ potassium chloride-calomel electrode potential as reference base).
3. The changes in the composition of the solution are negligibly small owing to the small value of the current, so that current-voltage curves may be measured repeatedly with identical results.
4. The constancy of dropping rate leads to reproducible results and permits an exact mathematical treatment of the curves.
5. The small dimensions of the dropping electrode allow very small volumes of solutions (0.01 to 0.005 ml.) to be analyzed.

3.2. Polarograph

To shorten the time of obtaining current-voltage curves an apparatus has been constructed that automatically registers the current-voltage curves and produces diagrams called polarograms (14). A diagram of the polarograph is shown in Fig. 3. The sliding contact C moves along the potentiometer wire AB as the wheel is turned by clockwork or electric motor. The terminals A and B are connected to a 2 or 4 volt lead storage battery or dry cell. The contact C is connected to the mercury reservoir. One end of the potentiometer wire A leads to the large mercury electrode and to the positive pole of the dry cell. As the wheel moves, it drives a cylinder F bearing photographic paper surrounded by a fixed cover with a horizontal slit S. The circuit connecting the mercury electrodes passes a sensitive mirror galvanometer G. The mirror deflection is recorded on the photographic paper by means of a light beam falling on the horizontal slit S. An Ayrton shunt R regulates the sensitivity of the galvanometer. As the wheel moves, the voltage acting on the mercury electrodes increases and the corresponding current curve is registered on the photographic paper, the abscissa denoting the voltage and the ordinate the current.

The automatic registering of the current-voltage curves represents a substantial improvement in the method since a continuous record reveals much more detail than discontinuous manual plotting.

Recently various types of polarographs have been developed using a current amplification and recording the curves by ink or pencil on tracing paper. These diagrams are called polarograms.

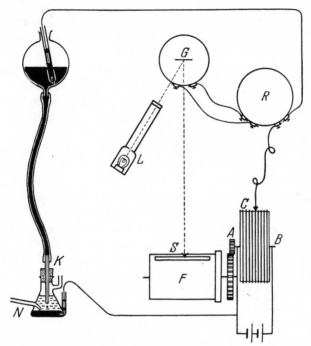

FIG. 3. Diagram of the polarograph.

3.3. Galvanometer and Shunt

The optimum sensitivity of the mirror galvanometer gives a deflection of about 300 mm. per microamp. or 3×10^{-9} amp. causes a deflection of 1 mm. This is too high for the majority of cases investigated in polarography, and the sensitivity has to be reduced by means of the Ayrton shunt. It is important that the resistance of the shunt and galvanometer are chosen to keep the critical resistance for aperiodic damping constant. The shape of the current-voltage curve largely depends on the damping, since it is merely the mean current during the formation of the mercury drop which is registered. An equally important factor is the period of swing of the galvanometer mirror. This should be somewhat longer than the drop time. The best conditions exist when the half period of swing, $T/2$, is from 4–6 seconds. The damping of the galvanometer may be effected also by connecting an electrolytic condenser of large capacity (several thousands microfarads) in parallel with the terminal of the galvanometer. In commercial polarographs the damping, period of swing and sensitivity scale are already adjusted.

3.4. Electrolyte Vessels

The electrolyte vessels have various shapes according to the volume of liquid available and allow for conditions where atmospheric oxygen must be eliminated or where the mercury pool serving as the reference electrode must be separated from the solution surrounding the dropping mercury electrode.   When examining the solutions open to air, ordinary beakers (Fig. 4a) of 5 to 20 ml. capacity are satisfactory, containing a layer of mercury approximately 3 mm. deep.   The solution to be examined is poured in to fill three-fourths of the vessel.   Small volumes of 0.005 to 0.1 ml. are conveniently investigated in the vessel shown in Fig. 4b, for which a finely drawn-out capillary is used as the dropping electrode; the wide arm of the vessel serves to keep the level of mercury constant in the narrow arm.   The tube sealed on at right-angles to the two arms contains a platinum wire at its lower end and makes electrical connection with the larger electrode.   The vessels shown in c and d serve to remove atmospheric oxygen from the electrolyte solution by bubbling an inert gas (nitrogen, hydrogen, or carbon dioxide) through the solution.

For repeated analyses the "universal vessel" of Novák (35) is suitable (Fig. 5).   It consists of two parts: the outer cylindrical jacket C and the inner electrolyte vessel N.   The cylindrical jacket C is fixed to an iron stand by a clamp so that its lower edge is 25 to 30 cm. above the base of the stand.   The long tube passing into the cylinder serves as inlet for an inert gas.   The gas is passed in from a gas tank through a rubber tube connected to the horizontal tube with the stopcock.   The capillary of the dropping electrode is inserted through the neck of the jacket, so that the exit of the capillary reaches almost to the exit of the gas tube. The capillary is fastened at the neck by means of a short piece of rubber tubing h.

The dimensions of the jacket C are: inside diameter 18.5 to 19 mm., thickness of the glass wall 1.5 mm., length of the cylinder 9 to 10 cm., length of the vertical gas tube 7 to 8 cm.

The electrolyte vessel N is a glass tube 18 mm. in outside diameter fused to a narrow capillary tube of 5 mm. outside and 2 mm. inside diameter.   A solid rod base n is sealed on to the narrow tube.   The wide part is 8 cm. long and the glass walls are 1 mm. thick.

It is sufficient to provide one jacket cylinder for each polarograph. A dozen electrolyte vessels should be available.

The procedure for a polarographic determination is as follows:

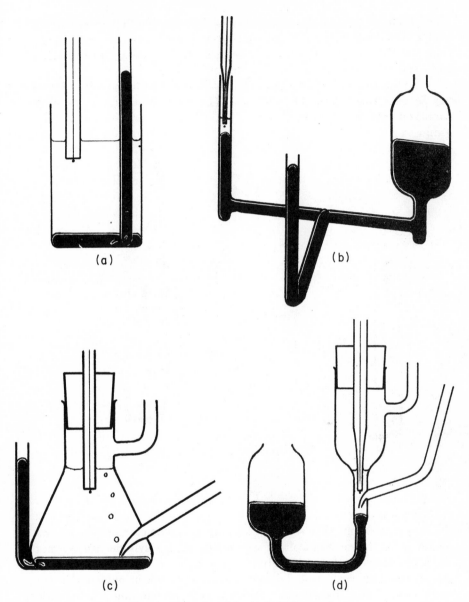

Fig. 4. Polarographic electrolysis vessels.

Place about three-quarters of a milliliter of mercury into the electrolyte vessel N, taking care to remove all air bubbles from the side tube k, then 2 to 10 ml. of the solution to be examined are added and vessel N is pushed into the cylinder C.   The vessel N is fixed in position by spring p.   The position of the vessel N is adjusted to allow the bubbles of inert gas to pass freely into the solution.   The inner tube of the vessel N should fit into the cylinder C of the jacket to leave a clearance of about ½ mm.

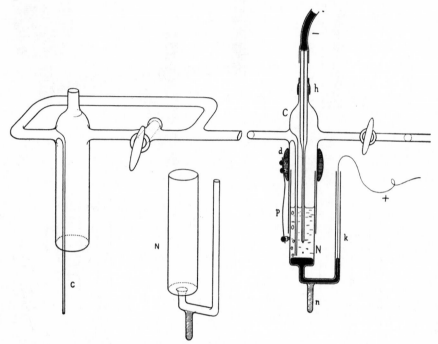

FIG. 5.   Universal electrolysis vessel.

Oxygen is removed from the solution by passing the inert gas through the by-pass tube into the solution, keeping the stopcock closed.   During recording of the current-voltage curve, the stopcock is opened so that the atmosphere in the jacket above the solution is filled with the inert gas, which escapes through the space between the two cylindrical tubes without disturbing the solution.   Diffusion of outside air into the solution is prevented.

The connection to the anode is made by inserting a stainless steel contact wire into the mercury of the side arm k.   A similar contact is made to the cathode through the mercury reservoir.   Stainless steel wires are as satisfactory as platinum wire.

After having recorded the curve of one solution another vessel, filled with the subsequent solution, is inserted into the jacket and, after two or three minutes of vigorous bubbling is ready for polarographic examination. For a large series of solutions a wooden block should be provided with holes to support the electrolyte vessels on the rod n.

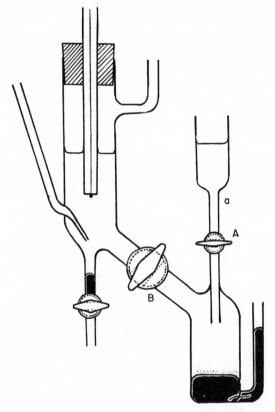

FIG. 6. Electrolysis vessel with a separate unpolarizable reference electrode.

To obtain anodic and cathodic currents and to determine the corresponding half-wave potentials it is necessary to have a reference electrode separate from the solution to be examined. A suitable vessel for such measurements is shown in Fig. 6. The mercury pool is placed in the side vessel, separated from the electrolyte vessel by a stopcock with wide bore, to ensure good electric conductivity. A standard electrode is chosen to impart a positive potential to the mercury layer; this is effected by using a 2 N sodium sulfate solution slightly acidified with sulfuric acid with solid mercurous sulfate acting as depolarizer. This electrode maintains a potential of +0.4 volt compared to the 1 N potassium chloride-calomel electrode. The sulfate solution is poured in through tube a, the taps A and B being open. As soon as the solution rises above the tap B, it is closed and the side vessel is filled above tap A. This tap is then closed and any bubbles remaining in the vessel are driven out through the main tap B. When the side tube is filled, the main vessel is rinsed with water and the electrolyte poured in. During the recording of curves tap B must be opened. Otherwise the large ohmic resistance in the tap would considerably alter the current-voltage curves owing to the large drop of potential ir.

Continuous anodic-cathodic polarization can be effected also without the introduction of a separate unpolarizable electrode when the arrange-

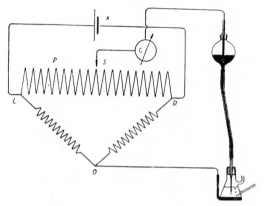

FIG. 7.   Scheme for continuous anodic-cathodic polarization.

ment shown in Fig. 7 is used. This is found in commercial polarographs. As long as the sliding contact moves in the left part of the bridge, the external e.m.f. imparts a more positive potential to the dropping mercury electrode than to the mercury pool. When the contact moves to the right side of the potentiometer wire, the direction of the applied voltage is inverted, making the dropping electrode more negative than the potential of the mercury layer at the bottom of the electrolytic vessel.

4. TECHNIQUES OF INVESTIGATING SOLUTIONS

The substance to be investigated polarographically has to be present in true solution. The procedure of dissolving the sample is given in the experimental section and is often critical for obtaining well-defined current-voltage curves. The solution must be electrically conducting. A supporting electrolyte in a concentration from 0.1 to 1 N should be present. The nature of the electrolyte has an influence on the depolarization potentials of the components that are polarographically active, since the potentials change according to the stability of the complexes formed between the depolarizer and the electrolyte. This effect is illustrated in Fig. 8. Curve 1 is due to 10^{-4} N thallium sulfate in 0.1 N nitric acid. After the addition of an equivalent amount of plumbous ions the waves for lead and thallium ions coalesce, because their half-wave potentials practically coincide. Addition of an excess of alkali produces curve 2 which now shows two distinct waves; the first caused by thallium ions, which do not form complexes with hydroxyl ions, the second wave at a potential more negative by 0.3 volt due to lead, which is now in the form

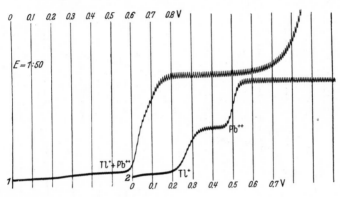

FIG. 8. Resolution of interference. Curve 1 is due to 0.001 N Pb^{++} + 0.001 N Tl$^+$ in 0.1 N HNO$_3$; curve 2 is due to 0.001 N Pb^{+++} + 0.001 N Tl$^+$ in 0.1 N NaOH. Sensitivity of galvanometer, 1:50. Nitrogen atmosphere.

of plumbite ions. Thus a suitable choice of the composition of the electrolyte may resolve coincidences. Besides alkaline solutions, polarographically suitable complexes are obtained in ammoniacal, cyanide, tartarate, or citrate solutions. The cyanide complexes are of particular value, when minor constituents, of basic character, e.g. nickel, manganese, cadmium, have to be determined in the presence of excess of ions of a noble metal, e.g., copper. In an excess of cyanide the waves of copper, zinc, or iron do not appear and the minor constituents, which form waves in the cyanide solution, i.e. nickel, manganese, and cadmium, are measurable with high sensitivity. Similarly, in the determination of traces of sodium in aluminium an alkaline solution prevents the formation of the aluminium wave, and a wave of sodium may be obtained. The indifferent electrolyte recommended has to be one of high decomposition voltage, i.e., lithium hydroxide, calcium hydroxide, or a hydroxide of a quaternary amine, $N(C_2H_5)_4OH$ or $N(CH_3)_4OH$.

Sulfite is often added to ammoniacal and alkaline solutions when the solution is to be freed from oxygen. Atmospheric oxygen, present in all solutions in a concentration of about 8 mg. per liter, i.e., 0.001 N (at ordinary room temperature) produces a double wave, the first step of which is due to the reduction $O_2 \rightarrow H_2O_2$ and the second to the reaction $H_2O_2 \rightarrow H_2O$ (Fig. 9). The addition of sulfite in a 0.1 N concentration (about 1%) or 30 to 40 bubbles of sulfur dioxide (55) removes the oxygen wave completely (curve 2). Cupric ions accelerate the reaction between oxygen and sulfite, otherwise likely to be retarded by ammonia and many organic substances. It is therefore advisable to add a trace of a cupric salt, if copper is not already in the solution to be analyzed.

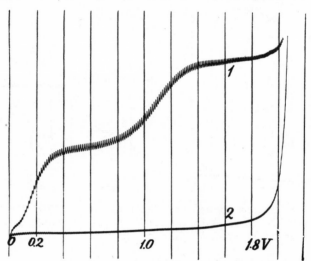

FIG. 9. Curve 1: 0.1 N NaOH + 0.02% gelatin, open to the air. Curve 2: the same solution after addition of 2 drops saturated Na_2SO_3 to 10 ml. Sensitivity, 1:32.

Another substance to be added to the solution before polarographic examination is gelatine, or a similar colloid, which removes maxima from the current-voltage curves and makes diffusion currents reproducible and well measurable. Figure 10 shows a curve obtained before (1) and after (2) the addition of 0.02% gelatine. The function of the colloid is to damp the streaming of electrolyte around the polarized mercury drop, caused by the inhomogenous electric field close to the capillary. Such streaming, observable with a microscope, transports the depolarizer to the surface of the dropping electrode so quickly that the current is often several times larger than under normal conditions of diffusion. The charges of the colloids counterbalance the inhomogenous electric field and stop the motion of the electrolyte.

The solution, freed from air and containing the indifferent electrolyte and colloid, is ready for polarographic examination.   After adjusting the sensitivity of the galvanometer to obtain measurable waves, the curve is recorded.   From the polarogram the half-wave potentials have to be ascertained, if qualitative determinations are required.   These are found, if a standard electrode (e.g., the saturated potassium chloride-calomel electrode) is used as separate anode.   If both electrodes are in the same solution and vessel, a depolarizer is added (e.g., a trace of thallium sulfate), whose half-wave value is well known (-0.5 volt based on the 1 N potassium chloride-calomel scale, -0.46 volt based on the saturated calomel electrode scale).   From this value other half-wave

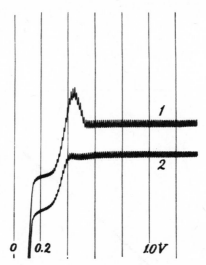

Fig. 10.   Curve 1: 0.002 N CuCl$_2$ in 0.1 N HCl; curve 2: the same solution containing 0.02% gelatin.   Nitrogen atmosphere.   Sensitivity, 1:64.   (Curve 2 shifted below curve 1.)

potentials are determined (Fig. 11).   In routine analysis, however, the components are known and have to be determined only quantitatively.

Quantitative determinations are carried out either by means of a calibration curve or by the method of "standard addition."   The principle of the determination from a calibration curve is shown in Figs. 12 and 13.   If a component in a sample, for example, cadmium in zincblende, has to be determined, known cadmium solutions are made up with a suitable indifferent electrolyte, i.e., 2 N ammonium hydroxide and 2 N ammonium chloride containing 0.01% gelatine and 0.01 N sodium sulfite, and the curves are recorded (Fig. 13).   The heights of the waves are then plotted on a graph giving the dependence of the diffusion current on the concentration of cadmium (Fig. 12).   The samples to be analyzed

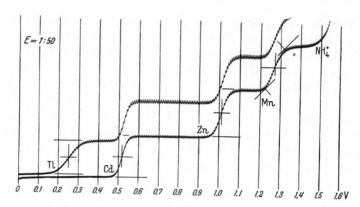

Fig. 11.   Lower curve: 0.1 N NH$_4$OH, 0.1 N NH$_4$ Cl, 0.1 N Na$_2$SO$_3$ 0.01 % gelatin with 0.001 N Cd^{++}, Zn^{++}, Mn^{++}.   Upper curve: the same solution with 0.001 N Tl$^+$. Sensitivity, 1:50.

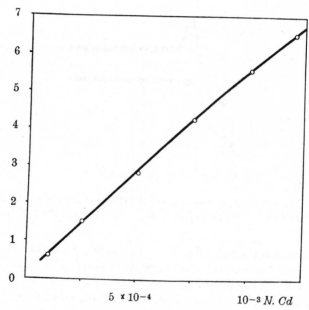

Fig. 12.   A calibration curve for Cd in zincblende.

are dissolved in the same solution used for the calibration values and the polarographic curves are recorded under exactly the same conditions, i.e., with the same capillary, the same pressure of mercury, the same sensitivity of the galvanometer and at exactly the same temperature. The electrolytic cell with the reservoir should be placed in a thermostat. To avoid this inconvenience one may register the polarographic curves of several samples on one polarogram and add one curve of a standard solution, taking for granted that the temperature of the room and solutions has not changed by more than 0.5°C. The temperature coefficient of the diffusion currents is 1.6%. If the standard curve has a wave height near those of the samples, the concentration x of the unknown is calculated from simple proportionality as $x = \dfrac{100ah_x}{hw}$ %, where a is the weight of the component in the standard solution, h_x the height of wave for the solution of the sample, h the height of the wave for the standard and w is the weight of the sample.

The assumption that the temperature does not change during recording is best fulfilled if a standard addition is made at once to each sample

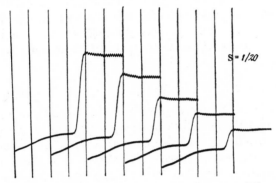

FIG. 13.   A calibration polarogram showing the increase of the wave due to an increasing concentration of Cd^{++} ions in 0.1 N NH_4OH, 0.01 N NH_4Cl in nitrogen atmosphere. Sensitivity, 1:20.

after its curve has been taken. When a ml. of the standard solution is added to v ml. of the solution and the polarographic wave is increased from h to h', the unknown concentration x of the sample is given by $x = \dfrac{hc}{h' + (h' - h)^{a/v}}$, where c denotes the concentration of the standard solution.

Spálenka (41) uses a more exact procedure by removing two equal volumes from the dissolved sample. One portion is diluted to 100 ml. with the indifferent electrolyte. A known amount of the component to be determined is added to the other portion and diluted with the indifferent electrolyte to the same volume as the first portion. The second solution gives a higher wave, h, than the first solution, which gives a wave of height h_x. The concentration x of the component in the sample is given as $x = \dfrac{100ah_x}{(h - h_x)w}$ %, where a is the weight of the standard addi-

. tion and w that of the sample. This method has an advantage in that the component in both the standard and the sample solution are mixed with the other components, so that possible losses due to adsorption, which should be almost identical in both solutions are eliminated.

The procedure of "quotient of two waves" is independent of temperature (6). A known quantity of a certain depolarizer is added to each solution if another depolarizer is to be determined. It is assumed that the ratio of the two waves is independent of the temperature, viscosity, rate of flow of mercury, etc. One needs only to determine the calibration curves, giving the dependence of the ratio of the two waves on the concentration of the depolarizer to be determined, if the concentration of the other depolarizer is kept constant. This relation gives practically a straight line.

The methods here described offer but little advantage for analysis, if only one sample of an unknown composition is to be examined. They are, however, of great value in series analyses of samples of similar composition.

5. Sensitivity and Accuracy of the Method

The sensitivity of the polarographic method is limited partly by the oscillations of the galvanometer caused by the dropping of mercury and partly by the capacity (condenser) current which charges the dropping electrode to the applied potential. The latter is of the order of 10^{-8} to 10^{-7} amp. Depolarizers in a 10^{-4} N concentration give a wave corresponding to 3×10^{-7} amp., i.e., about 10 cm., if the greatest sensitivity of the galvanometer is used. A depolarizer in a concentration of 10^{-6} N would give a diffusion current of 3×10^{-9} amp., i.e., a wave 1 mm. high indistinguishable from the capacity current.

The compensation method of Ilkovič and Semerano (19) partly counterbalances the capacity current, so that it remains almost constant: In this case one can estimate depolarizer concentrations as low as 5×10^{-6} N.

Since polarographic measurements may be carried out with liquid volumes as small as 0.01 ml., the sensitivity is sufficient to measure about 5×10^{-9} g. of an unknown depolarizer.

Regarding accuracy, it is advantageous to have waves in the form of easily measurable steps, which is the case in the concentration range between 10^{-4} N and 10^{-3} N. The height of the wave is measurable to 1%, which represents the limit of the accuracy of polarographic measurements. To obtain exactly reproducible results, all the physical factors determining the diffusion current have to be kept strictly constant, which requires care particularly in regard to temperature changes.

If small quantities of the depolarizer are present, the shape of the waves is sometimes indefinite, so that an exact measure of the height of wave is impossible. The waves become disfigured especially when applying the compensation of the capacity current (Fig. 14). In such cases it is recommended the direction of the lines before and behind the wave be extended and an ordinate be drawn at the half-wave potential;

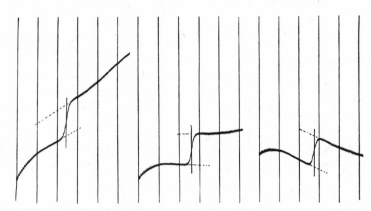

FIG. 14. Evaluation of the height of wave when using compensation of the charging current. $5 \cdot 10^{-5}$ N PbCl$_2$ in 0.1 N NaOH. Sensitivity, 1:5. Nitrogen atmosphere.

the distance between the points at which the lines intersect the ordinate is regarded as the true height of the wave.

6. TABLES OF DEPOLARIZATION POTENTIALS

Although polarography is rarely used for qualitative determinations of the components in solution, it is necessary to have a summary of the half-wave potentials in order to recognize the wave of the depolarizer and to avoid coincidences, especially when trying to develop a special method.

The values of the half-wave potentials are given on p. 6 for various solutions of different electrolytes. The values are also represented in tables III and IV as "polarographic spectra" to serve for comparison with real polarograms. When comparing the positions of the half-waves, it must be borne in mind that if another diffusion current of value i_d precedes a curve its half-wave value is shifted towards greater voltage by the drop of potential $i_d \cdot r$ across the cell, where r is the resistance of the cell. As r is usually of the order of 100 ohms, and i_d approximately 10^{-4} amp., the shift may be larger than 10 mv. The values in the tables are referred to the potential of the normal potassium chloride-calomel electrode, whereas the half-wave values obtained from the polarograms are referred to the potential of the unpolarizable electrode used in the electrolysis. The values in the tables are obtained when the value of the potential of the unpolarizable electrode is added, to the experimental

TABLE II
Reduction Potentials of Inorganic Substances

Reduction process	Potential			
	In acid	In neutral	In ammo-niacal	In alka-line
	Electrolyte, containing monovalent cations, like Na^+, K^+, NH_4^+, H^+			
$O_2 \rightarrow H_2O_2$	$+0.05^a$	0^a	-0.17^a	-0.20^a
$H_2O_2 \rightarrow H_2O$	-0.8	-1.1	-1.1	-1.2
$(CN)_2 \rightarrow 2CN^-$	—	-1.15^a	—	—
$SO_2 \rightarrow S_2O_4^-$	-0.31	-1.13	—	—
$NO(HNO_2) \rightarrow NH_3$	-0.76^a	—	—	—
NO_3^-, $NO_2^- \rightarrow NH_3$	—	$-1.3^{a,b}$	—	—
$BrO_3^- \rightarrow Br^-$	-0.97	-1.85	-1.72	-1.85^a
$IO_3^- \rightarrow I^-$	-0.30	-1.3	-1.2	-1.25
$IO_4^- \rightarrow IO_3^-$	$+0.15^a$	-0.4	—	—
$ReO_4^- \rightarrow Re^-$	-0.45	-1.20^a	—	-1.40^a
$UO_2^{++} \rightarrow /U^V/U^{IV}$	-0.1	$-0.28, -1.08$	$-0.8, -1.4$	—
$Eu^{+++} \rightarrow Eu^{++}$	-0.77	—	—	—
$Yb^{+++} \rightarrow Yb^{++}$	-1.48	—	—	—
$Ti^{++++} \rightarrow Ti^{+++}$	-0.98	—	—	—
$VO_3^- \rightarrow /V^{++}/V^{+++}$	-0.83	—	-1.23	-1.66
$Co^{+++} \rightarrow Co^{++}$	—	—	-0.41	—
$Cr^{+++} \rightarrow Cr^{++}$	-0.78	-0.96	-1.46	—
$CrO_4^- \rightarrow Cr^{+++}$	—	$-0.30, -1.00$	-0.36	-0.89
$MoO_4^- \rightarrow Mo^{+++}$	-0.3	—	—	—
$WO_4^- \rightarrow W^{+++}$	-0.46	—	—	—
$OsO_4^- \rightarrow OsO_2$	—	—	—	-0.44
$OsO_2 \rightarrow Os_2O_2$	—	—	—	-1.20
$SeO_3^- \rightarrow Se$	-0.1	—	-1.43	—
$TeO_3^- \rightarrow Te$	-0.48	—	-0.65	—

^{a} Foot of wave, otherwise half-wave potentials.
^{b} In 0.1 N LaCl$_3$.

half-wave potentials, e.g., $+0.4$ volt in the case of sulfuric acid and sulfate solutions, or -0.2 volt in normal alkalies. Only values found from the curves determined in 1 N chloride solution coincide with those in the tables, both being referred to the same potential, i.e., to that of the 1 N potassium chloride-calomel electrode. The values found empirically when the reference electrode is the saturated potassium chloride-calomel electrode have to be made more negative by 40 mv. to be referred to the 1 N calomel electrode.

TABLE III
Anodic Depolarization Potentials

Concentration of anions 0.001 N	Foot of wave	Process	Half-wave potential
$Hg + Cl^- \rightarrow HgCl$	$+0.17$	$Fe^{++} \rightarrow Fe^{+++}$ (0.1 N KHF$_2$)	$+0.08$
$Hg + CNS^- \rightarrow HgCNS$	$+0.10$	$Fe^{++} \rightarrow Fe^{+++}$ (NH$_4$OH, NH$_4$Cl)	-0.38
$Hg + Br^- \rightarrow HgBr$	$+0.04$	$Mn^{++} - Mn^{+++}$ (2 N KOH with tartarate)	-0.40
$Hg + 2OH^- \rightarrow HgO + H_2O$	$+0.00$	$Sn^{++} \rightarrow Sn^{++++}$ (HCl)	-0.06
$Hg + 2SO_3^- \rightarrow Hg(SO_3)_2$	-0.07	$Sn^{++} \rightarrow Sn^{++++}$ (Tartarate or citrate buffer, pH = 7)	-0.48
$Hg + I^- \rightarrow HgI$	-0.11	$Sn^{++} \rightarrow Sn^{++++}$ (0.1 N KOH)	-0.61
$Hg + 2S_2O_3^- \rightarrow Hg(S_2O_3)$	-0.30	$Ti^{+++} \rightarrow Ti^{++++}$ (HCl)	-0.18
$Hg + 2CN^- \rightarrow Hg(CN)_2$	-0.42	$V^{++++} \rightarrow V^{+++++}$ (1 N KOH)	-0.46
$Hg + S^- \rightarrow HgS$	-0.70	$Sb^{+++} \rightarrow Sb^{+++++}$ (0.5 N KOH)	-0.34
		$As^{+++} \rightarrow As^{+++++}$ (0.5 N KOH)	-0.25

TABLE IV
Half-Wave Potentials of Some Inorganic Redox Processes

Process	Electrolyte	$\kappa_{1/2}$
$Cu^+ \rightleftarrows Cu^{++}$	0.1 N Na$_2$SO$_4$	-0.06
$Cu^+ \rightleftarrows Cu^{++}$	1 N NH$_4$OH, 1 N NH$_4$Cl	-0.25
$Cu^+ \rightleftarrows Cu^{++}$	Citrate buffer pH = 7	-0.21
$Cr^{++} \rightleftarrows Cr^{+++}$	Saturated with CaCl$_2$	-0.55
$Fe^{++} \rightleftarrows Fe^{+++}$	1 N sodium oxalate	-0.30
$Fe^{++} \rightleftarrows Fe^{+++}$	Citrate buffer pH = 7	-0.49
$Fe^{++} \rightleftarrows Fe^{+++}$	1 N KOH	-0.9
$Ti^{+++} \rightleftarrows Ti^{++++}$	Saturated with CaCl$_2$	-0.15
$Ti^{+++} \rightleftarrows Ti^{++++}$	0.1 N KCNS	-0.49
$Ti^{+++} \rightleftarrows Ti^{++++}$	Citric or acetic acid	-0.48
$V^{++} \rightleftarrows V^{+++}$	1 N H$_2$SO$_4$	-0.55

7. APPLICATIONS

The chief operation preceding the polarographic investigations is the preparation of the sample. As there is, however, no general rule for dissolving a solid and since the reagents that have to be used depend largely on the components to be determined, the procedure is in each case adapted to the species present. It is customary in polarography to use the simplest possible operation and to avoid lengthy quantitative operations such as fusion, filtration, washing of precipitates, centrifuging, etc. The best way is to dissolve the weighed sample directly in a measuring flask and to dilute it to a known volume with a suitable indifferent electrolyte. For nobler metals nitric acid or aqua regia is suitable, for baser metals hydrochloric acid should be used since nitrates and nitrites produce unwanted polarographic effects, especially troublesome when di- or trivalent metallic cations are present in solution.

If an excess of a nobler constituent or a coinciding depolarizer interfere with a particular determination they have to be chemically removed by precipitation or extraction. It is significant for the polarographic method that the interfering substances need not be removed entirely for it suffices if they are present in a lower concentration than the constituent to be determined.

Lithium has the most negative half-wave potential of the alkali group and its value differs enough from the potentials of sodium, potassium, rubidium, caesium, strontium, and barium to give a distinctly separate wave. These ions, however, must not be present in concentration of more than 20 times that of lithium. The most suitable indifferent electrolyte is 0.1 N $N(CH_3)_4OH$ or $N(C_2H_5)_4OH$. The presence of atmospheric oxygen does not interfere with the determination, although with small amounts of lithium present, greater sensitivity is obtained in the absence of oxygen.

Sodium and potassium cannot be determined separately, as their half-wave potentials almost coincide. Thus the height of the wave gives their sum. For the determination in water 1 drop of 1 N phosphoric acid, 1 ml. of 0.5 N $N(CH_3)_4OH$ and 1 ml. of distilled water is added to 1 ml. of the sample and the mixture polarographically investigated in contact with air (31).

Sodium in ceramic material in the presence of high aluminium content: 5 to 20 mg. of the finely powdered substance is dissolved by heating with 0.3 ml. 1 N sulfuric acid and 0.5 ml. 40% hydrofluoric acid in a platinum crucible. After evaporation the residue is dissolved in 1 drop 1 N phosphoric acid and 1.0 ml. 0.5 N $N(CH_3)_4OH$ or $N(C_2H_5)_4OH$. After the addition of 0.5 ml. water the solution is transferred into a small electrolytic vessel and polarographed open to air (Fig. 15).

Sodium in magnesium: A small piece of the metal is burned in a closed vessel, and the oxide is extracted with saturated lime-water or 0.1 N $N(C_2H_5)_4OH$. The curve of this solution shows a distinct wave of the sodium.

Sodium in aluminum or its salts: 15 mg. of the metal are dissolved in a few drops of hydrochloric acid and the solution evaporated almost to dryness. Two-tenths of a milliliter of water and the requisite amount of

0.5 N N(C₂H₅)₄OH to redissolve the aluminum salt as aluminate are added with 1 ml. water. This solution is polarographed open to air. If an aluminum salt is to be examined, 0.2 ml. of its 0.5 N solution is used and enough 0.2 N N(C₂H₅)₄OH is added to redissolve the precipitate. The solution is diluted exactly to 2 or 3 ml. by adding water and polarographed. Urech and Sulzberger (53) have modified the above method to determine traces of sodium in very pure aluminum. A concentrated solution of aluminum chloride is precipitated by passing hydrogen chloride gas through it. The remaining liquor is concentrated by evaporation, the residue dissolved by adding dilute hydrochloric acid and the solution is precipitated with ammonium hydroxide. The clear solution is evaporated to dryness, the residue dissolved in 0.2 N

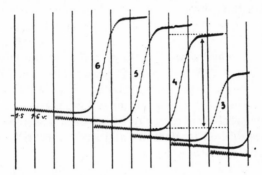

FIG. 15.   Waves due to 0.001 N K⁺ and Na⁺ in 0.1 N N(CH₃)₄OH, open to air.

N(CH₃)₄OH and polarographed. As little as 0.001% sodium in aluminium can be determined in this way.

Alkaline earths: According to Kimura (21) the three alkaline earths give distinct and separate waves in alkaline solution. Zlotowski and Kolthoff (57, 58) have worked out a method to determine calcium, strontium, and barium in neutral solutions in a mixture of 50 to 80% ethyl alcohol and water, the indifferent electrolyte being 0.2 to 0.3 N N(C₂H₅)₄I. Since calcium tends to form a maximum, the solution has to contain some barium ions.

Magnesium and beryllium when depositing in aqueous solutions are accompanied by evolution of hydrogen, which prevents their polarographic determination.

Aluminum offers difficulties, since it hydrolyzes in solution and the wave due to the deposition of hydrogen ions closely precedes that of aluminium. Thus the pH of the solution must be carefully kept between 2.6 and 2.7. The procedure of Hövker (15, 40) considers the presence of iron and effects its reduction to the divalent form by hydrazine. The determination is carried out as follows: 5 ml. of the solution of clay, diluted so that 40 ml. would contain about 20 mg. aluminum, are evaporated to dryness in a porcelain dish with 3 ml. concentrated sulfuric acid. Dilute sulfuric acid is added and again evaporated to dryness. After cooling the residue is dissolved in 8 ml. 0.1 N sulfuric acid and warmed with 40 ml. water to bring all basic salts into solution. This solution is filtered into a 100 ml. measuring flask and diluted to the mark. The pH of this solution lies between 1.70 and 1.80. For polarographic examination 30 ml. of the indifferent electrolyte solution are added to 10 ml. of this solution having the following composition: 1.5 g. lithium oxide, 2.0 g. lithium sulfate, 50 g. tylose, 1.0 g. hydrazine sulfate in 1000 ml. of water. The pH of the final solution is between 2.60 and 2.70. The curve is recorded with the solution open to air and shows the waves due to the reduction of oxygen, deposition of ferrous and hydrogen ion, and of aluminium at −1.7 volt.

Aluminum in magnesium (7): 0.2 to 0.5 g. of the alloy is dissolved in a slight excess of 2 N hydrochloric acid. After cooling bromphenol blue indicator is added and the solution is neutralized first with calcium hydroxide until the color changes from yellow to greenish-yellow. Calcium hydroxide solution is carefully added until the color is light-green. This solution is diluted to 1000 ml. and a small portion of it is polarographed in a nitrogen atmosphere.

Aluminum in steel is determined by extracting the iron as ferric chloride with ether. The sample (500 mg.) is dissolved in 10 ml. hydrochloric acid (1:1), oxidized by hydrogen peroxide and finally with potassium chlorate. The solution is evaporated to dryness, heated at 130°C. in an oven to effect the separation of silica. The residue is dissolved in a small amount of water, more water is added and silica is filtered off. The filter paper is thoroughly rinsed with dilute hydrochloric acid. The filtrate is again condensed to a few milliliters, mixed with 30 ml. hydrochloric acid (1:1), and extracted with ether. When the greenish-yellow coloration disappears, 5 ml. hydrogen peroxide and 5 ml. hydrochloric acid (1:1) are added and extracted further until no color remains. The etherial layer is separated from the aqueous solution in a funnel and the aqueous solution is evaporated to a few milliliters in a beaker and transferred to a 100 ml. measuring flask. To this solution are added 5 ml. of 5 N lithium chloride with methyl orange as indicator, neutralized with lithium hydroxide, 2 ml. of 0.1 N hydrochloric acid are added and the solution diluted to the mark with water. From this solution a small volume is used for the polarographic record, starting from 1 volt of the applied e.m.f. The small amount of iron that remains in the solution does not interfere with the wave of aluminum.

Manganese belongs to the polarographically most easily determined elements since its salt solutions are not hydrolyzed and produce well developed waves; complexes with ammonium hydroxide, cyanide, and thiocyanide are also suitable, as well as the tartarate complex which give an anodic wave. In alkaline solutions the manganous ion is readily oxidized to the manganic ion, and atmospheric oxygen must be carefully eliminated. As sodium sulfite is not sufficient, "Metol" (monomethyl paramidophenol sulfate) has to be present to keep manganese in its divalent form.

Determination in ammoniacal solutions: 5 ml. of a neutral or acid solution, which should contain less than 0.1 to 0.2% manganese, is freed from oxygen by carbon dioxide. Then 0.5 ml. of a solution containing 0.2 g. "Metol" in 100 ml. 1 N hydrochloric acid and 0.2 g. gelatin is added and finally 1 ml. of concentrated ammonium hydroxide. After allowing 5 minutes for cooling the solution is examined, open to air, starting from 1 volt with the manganese wave appearing at 1.4 volt.

Manganese in aluminum alloys (44): the accurately weighed sample (0.5 g.) is placed in a 50 ml. measuring flask and dissolved in 8 ml. of hydrochloric acid (1:1). Five to twenty drops of 30% hydrogen peroxide are added and the mixture is brought to boiling to dissolve traces of copper. Then 2 ml. of a saturated sodium sulfite solution and 3 ml. of a "Metol" solution (consisting of 0.1 g. "Metol," 2 ml. saturated sodium sulfite and 5 ml. concentrated hydrochloric acid in 100 ml. water) are added to the warm solution and well stirred. Fifteen milliliters of a tartarate solution (containing 500 g. potassium tartarate·$4H_2O$ and 10 ml. saturated sodium sulfite in 1000 ml. water) and 10 ml. of a cyanide solution (164 g. potassium cyanide, 200 g. sodium hydroxide, and 10 ml. saturated sodium sulfite in 1000 ml. water) are added, the contents of the flask well shaken and cooled down quickly to room temperature. After addition of 1 ml. of a gelatin solution (0.5 g. gelatin, 3 ml. concentrated hydrochloric acid in 100 ml. water) the solution is diluted to the 50 ml. mark and well shaken. A small portion of this solution is placed in a small open beaker and polarographed from 0 volt to 1.2 volt.

Manganese in zinc is determined (44) in an ammoniacal cyanide solution, to prevent the formation of the zinc wave. The sample is dissolved as described above for the aluminum alloy. After the addition of sodium sulfite and "Metol," 10 ml. of ammonium hydroxide (500 ml. saturated ammonium hydroxide and 20 ml. saturated sodium sulfite in 1000 ml. water) are added and the solution cooled. Fifteen milliliters of a cyanide solution (326 g. potassium cyanide and 20 g. sodium hydroxide in 1000 ml. water) and 5 ml. sodium hydroxide (40 g. sodium hydroxide and 5 ml. saturated sodium sulfite in 100 ml. water) are added, the contents well mixed and diluted to the 50 ml. mark with water. This solution open to air gives the manganese wave at −1.36 volt.

Manganese in steel: When the sample contains an excess of iron, the amount of manganese absorbed on ferric hydroxide might cause losses, although they are largely eliminated in the method of standard additions. Cyanide dissolution is recommended, which keeps the iron in solution and from which it is not electrodeposited at the dropping electrode.

Determination in cyanide solution (54): 50 mg. of steel, which contains 0.1 to 1% manganese, are dissolved in the smallest required amount of concentrated hydrochloric acid and evaporated to a semisolid mass. After cooling the residue is dissolved in several ml. of water and a few crystals of sodium sulfite are added to reduce the iron. The solution is brought to boiling and 2 g. potassium cyanide are added under a hood. Boiling is continued until the solution clears. The solution is transferred to a 25 ml. measuring flask and diluted to the mark with water. A part of this solution is polarographed and gives the manganese wave at −1.3 volt. This determination is not interfered with by copper, chromium, and zinc but the electrodeposition of nickel (at −0.9 volt) precedes the manganese wave, and that of cobalt (at −1.3 volt) coincides with it. To distinguish between nickel, cobalt, iron, and manganese a concentrated potassium thiocyanide solution is added to bring the thiocyanide concentration to 1 N in another portion of the weakly acidic solution of manganese, containing sodium sulfite. A few drops of 1 N potassium hydroxide are added to make the solution faintly alkaline. The polarogram of this solution shows nickel at −0.9 volt, cobalt at −1.3 volt and manganese and iron at −1.7 volt. The heights of the nickel and cobalt waves show what portion of the manganese wave in 1 N potassium cyanide is to be attributed to those elements. However, if much more nickel and cobalt than manganese are present in the sample the manganese should be determined from the anodic wave due to its tartarate complex in strongly alkaline solution, in which it is oxidized to manganic ion. One proceeds, according to Verdier (55), by diluting 5 ml. of the weakly acidic manganese solution, containing sodium sulfite, to 25 ml.; this is mixed with 5 ml. of 4 N potassium hydroxide containing 5% of tartaric acid in an atmosphere of nitrogen or hydrogen, and the curve is recorded. Manganese produces an anodic wave at −0.4 volt, for which the arrangement of anodic-cathodic polarization is used or a separate mercury anode with mercurous sulfate, 2 N sodium sulfate (Fig. 6) is applied. In the presence of a large excess of iron, the redox wave due to the process $Fe^{++} \rightarrow Fe^{+++}$ interferes, so that the manganese wave cannot be obtained with suitable sensitivity. In such a case a stream of air is slowly passed through the alkaline tartarate solution, which oxidises Fe^{++} to Fe^{+++} and consequently diminishes the anodic wave due to iron. When the anodic wave of Fe^{++} at -0.9 volt does not hinder the observation of the manganese wave at -0.4 volt, the current of air is stopped, the inert gas added, and the curve recorded with suitable sensitivity (Fig. 16).

Another method is given by Stackelberg and co-workers (45), who separate iron from manganese in a weakly acidic solution by precipitation with barium carbonate and determine manganese in a neutral solution of barium chloride.

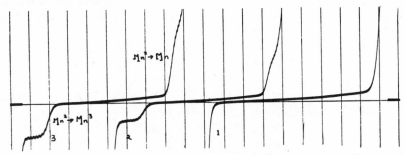

FIG. 16.   Anodic wave due to the oxidation of Mn^{++} to Mn^{+++}.   Curve 1: 2 N KOH with 5% tartarate.   Curve 2: with 0.001 N MnCl$_2$.   Curve 3: with 0.002 N MnCl$_2$; in atmosphere of hydrogen.   Sensitivity, 1:20.

A neutral calcium chloride solution is the medium for the determination of manganese in limestone, according to Straumanis and Dravnicks (48), while Hohn uses an ammoniacal solution (17).

Iron is determined by its redox wave due to $Fe^{+++} \rightarrow Fe^{++}$, which, in solutions of strong acids (nitric and sulfuric acid), occurs at the positive potential of about $+0.2$ volt, so that it coincides with the wave of oxygen, mercury, chloride, bismuth, and Cu^{++}; in an oxalate buffer of pH 7 the half-wave potential is -0.30 volt, in a citrate buffer of pH 7 at -0.49 volt, and in an alkaline tartarate solution at -0.9 volt. The wave of deposition of $Fe^{++} \rightarrow Fe$ coincides with that of cobalt and is near the deposition of hydrogen ions. According to Novák 100 mg. of sample is dissolved in 2 ml. concentrated hydrochloric acid and diluted to 100 ml. Two milliliters of this solution are placed in a small open beaker and to this is added 2 ml. of a stock solution with the following composition: 5.3 g. sodium carbonate, 100 ml. 0.5 M oxalic acid, and 5 ml. 0.5% gelatin. Mercury is added to cover the bottom of the beaker and carbon dioxide is bubbled through for 1 minute to free the solution from oxygen. The dropping mercury electrode is inserted into the solution and the curve is registered. In the presence of copper its wave is likely to coincide with that of iron. In this case a citrate buffer of pH 7 is used as electrolyte, and the excess of copper precipitated by the addition of hydroxylamine or hydrazine. In the presence of aluminium Novák places the 2 ml. of the iron solution (which must not contain more than 0.2% iron) into a small open beaker, adds 0.4 ml. 1 M tartaric acid and, after stirring, 2 ml. of a very concentrated alkali (50 g. sodium hydroxide dissolved in 100 ml. water). The curve is registered both anodically and cathodically; the waves are smaller, owing to the high viscosity of the concentrated alkali.

According to hitherto unpublished results of J. Mojžiš the best separation of the waves of copper and iron is effected in the solution of 0.6 N sodium hydroxide and 0.1 N triethanolamine; the latter compound has

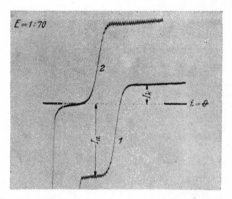

Fig. 17. The $Fe^{++} - Fe^{+++}$ redox wave. Curve 1: 0.001 N Fe^{++} in oxalate buffer of pH 6. Curve 2: the same solution oxidized by air. I_A is the anodic current, I_K the cathodic current.

been suggested for the polarographic determination of iron by Wolfson (55a) and for a number of other heavy metals by Jessop (19a).

Kamegai (20) uses concentrated phosphoric acid as the electrolyte producing the iron complex. According to Okáč (36), the oxalate complex is very suitable for the determination of iron in soil extracts. In all these determinations the concentration of ferrous ion is given by the height of the wave measured above the galvanometer zero line, and the concentration of ferric ion by the height below the zero line. If the ratio $Fe^{++}:Fe^{+++}$ is to be determined, care must be taken to avoid atmospheric oxygen in the solution (Fig. 17).

Nickel and cobalt may be determined simultaneously in solutions when their deposition potentials differ at least by 0.2 volt, i.e., in solutions containing ammonium hydroxide and ammonium chloride (46), ammonium thiocyanide (11), or in pyridine containing pyridine hydrochloride (4). In these solutions cobalt cannot be determined exactly if there is a

10- to 15-fold excess of nickel whose potential is more positive. If nickel is to be determined in a large excess of copper, zinc, or iron, a 1 N potassium cyanide solution with sodium sulfite is suitable; however, the nickel wave coincides with that of cobalt and manganese. In ammoniacal solution the cobalt wave coincides with that of zinc.

For the determination of cobalt in steel, iron may be removed by shaking the solution of the sample with barium carbonate. Ammonium hydroxide and ammonium chloride is added and cobalt allowed to be oxidized by atmospheric oxygen to the cobaltamine; the polarogram of this solution is recorded. Nickel, when present in excess, hinders the precision.

Nickel in steel and in nickel ore using a sodium fluoride electrolyte (56): 1 g. of steel is dissolved in hydrochloric acid (1:1), 5 ml. concentrated nitric acid is added and the solution is boiled until the nitrogen oxides are dispelled, evaporated to small volume, poured into a 50 ml. measuring flask, and diluted with distilled water. From this solution 5 ml. is pipetted into a second 50 ml. flask, 25 ml. of 1.0 N sodium fluoride and 1 ml. of 0.2% gelatin are added and after diluting to the mark and mixing, the solution is filtered. The first 10 ml. is discarded and a suitable quantity of the filtrate is analyzed polarographically in an atmosphere of nitrogen.

When nickel ore is to be analyzed, 0.5 g. is weighed out and digested for 20 minutes in 25 ml. hydrochloric acid (1:1). The excess hydrochloric acid is evaporated, the residue extracted with hot water, and any silica filtered off. The filtrate is diluted to 50 ml.; from this 10 ml. is pipetted into a 50 ml. measuring flask, 25 ml. 1.0 N sodium fluoride and 0.5 ml. of 0.2% gelatin are added and diluted to 50 ml. From this solution a portion is filtered, the first 10 ml. is rejected, and the remainder is examined polarographically after the removal of air.

Cobalt interferes only where present in the same concentration as nickel.

Chromium in steel is best determined (44) as chromate in an alkaline solution: The sample is dissolved directly in the measuring flask in a mixture of concentrated hydrochloric acid and 25% sulfuric acid. If, according to the amount of chromium, 1 to 2 g. is weighed out, the solution is diluted to 100 or 250 ml. accordingly. If the sample contains tungsten or molybdenum or both, the solvent should be concentrated hydrochloric acid and phosphoric acid (1:1). From this solution two equal volumes are placed into measuring flasks (100 ml.). To one a known amount of potassium chromate is added, to serve as the standard addition. To each measuring flask 3 ml. of a 30% hydrogen peroxide solution is added and, after mixing, 40 ml. of 2 N sodium hydroxide is

slowly added; the hydrogen peroxide in solution is decomposed on prolonged boiling. During boiling two glass beads should be added and the
solution often stirred until rapid boiling ensues. After cooling 3 ml. of
0.5% gelatin is added and the flasks diluted to the mark. The curves
of both solutions are recorded in an atmosphere of inert gas (Fig. 18).

Vanadium in steel is determined in the form of vanadate in an ammoniacal solution (45). Four tenths of a gram of steel, or 0.8 g. if the
sample contains less than 0.5% vanadium, is dissolved in a 200 ml.
beaker in 10 ml. concentrated hydrochloric acid (1:1), with warming.
Nitric acid (d = 1.4) is added and the liquid evaporated to about 2 ml.
Thirty milliliters of hot water are added, brought to boiling, and poured

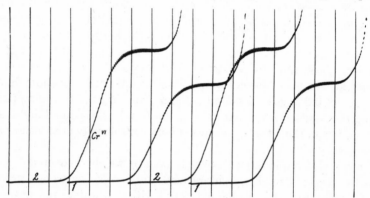

Fig. 18. Determination of chromium in steel. Curves 1: sample. Curves 2: sample
with standard addition.

into a 100 ml. measuring flask which contains 3 g. sodium hydroxide
dissolved in 30 ml. of hot water. After heating the solution is cooled
to 20°C. and the solution diluted to the mark. The solution is shaken
and filtered through a dry, folded filter paper; 50 ml. is transferred into
a dry 100 ml. measuring flask. The alkaline solution is neutralized with
hydrochloric acid (d = 1.19) and 1 g. ammonium chloride is added;
concentrated ammonium hydroxide is added, the solution cooled down to
20°C. and diluted with ammonium hydroxide to the 100 ml. mark with
vigorous shaking. Ammonium vanadate is slowly formed as the blue
color disappears. A few milliliters suffice for the polarographic examination. The wave due to the vanadate appears at −1.23 volt and is not
affected by other components of the alloy.

Vanadium in steel and other ferro-alloys (29). According to Lingane
and Meites it is convenient to determine vanadium by its anodic wave
in the oxidation step $V^{++++} \rightarrow V^{+++++}$ in a strongly alkaline supporting
electrolyte. Iron and other interfering elements are removed by elec-

trolyzing a solution of the sample in a phosphoric acid and sulfuric acid bath with a mercury cathode. The residual solution is treated with hydrogen peroxide and with excess sulfite to convert the vanadium to the +4 state and is diluted to a known volume. An aliquot portion of this solution is added to air-free 1 N sodium hydroxide in a polarographic cell and the polarogram is recorded. The method claims to be as accurate as the classical methods for steels containing a few per cent of vanadium and even more reliable with very small amount of vanadium.

Molybdenum may be polarographically estimated as molybdate in a solution of nitric acid (52), giving two waves, at −0.37 volt and −0.55 volt or (45) in a solution of sulfuric acid (1:1) at −0.3 volt. These procedures involve several separations and are lengthy. The original papers should be consulted. A simultaneous determination of molybdenum and of chromium has been worked out by Thanheiser and Willems (51). Chromium is determined by the chromate wave in 2 N sodium hydroxide at −0.8 volt.

Tungsten in steel is determined (45) by precipitating the tungstic acid and redissolving it after separation in hydrochloric acid; the wave appears at −0.4 volt.

Zinc is determined either in weakly acidic solutions of ammonium chloride in hydrochloric acid (at −1.06 volt) or in ammoniacal solutions (at −1.38 volt); a well developed wave appears also in solutions of alkali hydroxides at −1.41 volt, if ammonia is present. Nickel coincides with zinc in acidic solutions and precedes zinc in ammoniacal solutions; in cyanide solutions no zinc wave appears.

Zinc in the presence of nickel (47) is determined in 0.1 N ammoniacal ammonium acetate of pH 9, in which the waves of nickel and zinc are about 0.3 volt apart. At pH 4.5 the waves of nickel and zinc coincide, but that of cobalt is more negative by 0.3 volt. This procedure is of value especially when concentration by extraction with "Dithizon" is applied. To separate the nickel, zinc, and cobalt waves an electrolyte consisting of 0.1 N ammonium acetate and 0.025 N potassium thiocyanate is used (Cummings and Reed, 3).

Simultaneous determination of zinc and chromium (43) proceeds as follows: the weighed sample, which should not contain more than 8 mg. chromium and 1 to 6 mg. zinc is placed into a 50 ml. measuring flask and after dissolving in hydrochloric acid, 4 ml. hydrochloric acid (1:1), 2 ml. saturated sodium sulfite, and 5 ml. of 0.5% gelatin solution (in $N/3$ hydrochloric acid) are added. The solution is shaken and after the addition of 15 ml. ammonium hydroxide (1:1) and cooling the solution is diluted to the mark with distilled water. A small portion of this solution is polarographed open to air from 0.8 to 1.7 volt. The curve of the pure trivalent chromium shows two waves, in a ratio of 1:2. For quantitative determination of chromium only the height of the second wave is measured, since the first coincides with that of zinc. Thus, to determine zinc, half of the height of the second wave is subtracted from the height of the first wave (Fig. 19).

Zinc in aluminum alloys containing copper: if less copper than zinc is present, approximately 0.3 g. is dissolved in a 100 ml. measuring flask in 10 ml. hydrochloric acid (1:1); the undissolved portion (copper) is brought into solution by adding hydrogen peroxide and boiling. The

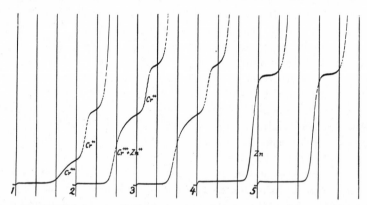

Fig. 19. The determination of chromium and zinc in electrolytic baths. 1 N NH$_4$OH, NH$_4$Cl solution with 0.02% gelatin and Na$_2$SO$_3$ open to the air. Curve 1: addition of Cr^{+++}. Curves 2 and 3: the same solution after addition of Zn^{++}. Curves 4 and 5: the solution containing Zn^{++} alone. Curves start at 0.7 volt.

solution is diluted with water to about 50 ml., 25 ml. of ammonium hydroxide (1:1) is added, the mixture well stirred and cooled to room temperature. One milliliter of saturated sodium sulfite, 1 ml. of gelatin (0.5 g. with 3 ml. concentrated hydrochloric acid in 100 ml water) are added and the solution diluted to the mark. The clear layer is polarographed open to air between 0.8 and 1.4 volts.

If the zinc content is considerably smaller than that of copper, 0.5 g. of the alloy is dissolved in a 50 ml. measuring flask with 10 ml. 3.5 N sodium hydroxide (140 g. in 1000 ml. water) with boiling, leaving the residue (copper, magnesium, nickel, manganese and iron) undissolved. Ten milliliters of water is added and the solution cooled.

Determinations of cadmium are based on its wave in neutral and acid solutions at -0.63 volt, in ammoniacal solution at -0.85 volt, in tartarate solution at -0.80 volt, and in cyanide solutions at -1.14 volt. In neutral and acid solutions the indium wave coincides with cadmium.

Cadmium, zinc, lead, and copper in crude zinc ore (26), (a) cadmium, copper, and zinc: 1 g. of finely powdered zinc ore is dissolved in a 50 ml. measuring flask by boiling with 10 ml. concentrated hydrochloric acid and addition of 5 ml. nitric acid.   After cooling 10 drops of a freshly saturated sodium sulfite solution and 20 ml. of concentrated ammonium hydroxide containing 10 drops of sodium sulfite are added.   One milliliter of 0.5% gelatin solution is added and the mixture diluted to the 10 ml. mark with 0.01 N sodium sulfite.   Five milliliters of this solution, in which all lead and iron is precipitated, are polarographed in a small beaker open to air.   The polarogram (Fig. 20) shows the cadmium wave at -0.6 volt next to the double-wave of copper at a more positive potential.

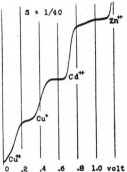

FIG. 20.   Determination of copper and cadmium in zincblende.

To determine zinc, the solution prepared in the 50 ml. beaker is diluted 100-fold with a 2 N ammonium hydroxide, ammonium chloride solution containing sodium sulfite.   This solution is examined open to air.

(b) Lead and cadmium: If the content of copper is considerable, cadmium and lead are determined by dissolving 1 g. of the zinc ore in 10 ml. hydrochloric acid in a 50 ml. measuring flask with the addition of nitric acid.   After cooling 0.2 g. of a thin aluminium sheet is immersed, which reduces all trivalent iron to the divalent stage and precipitates practically all copper.   When the aluminium is dissolved the solution is diluted to the 50 ml. mark with boiled water.   Five milliliters of the solution with 4 drops of 0.5% gelatin are freed from air by nitrogen and polarographed.   The lead wave appears at 0.45 volt and the cadmium wave at 0.60 volt (Fig. 21).

Alternatively, after dissolving the aluminium, one adds 30 ml. of a 10% sodium citrate or tartarate solution, neutralizes with sodium hydroxide to a faintly acidic reaction, dilutes to the 50 ml. mark, and takes the curve in an atmosphere of nitrogen.   The lead and cadmium waves are now at 0.6 and 0.8 volt respectively.

Cadmium, lead, and copper in zinc or zinc salts: 1 g. of zinc is dissolved in 10 ml. concentrated hydrochloric acid and examined in an hydrogen atmosphere.   The curve (Fig. 22) shows the wave of copper at 0 volt, lead at 0.4 volt, and cadmium (plus indium) at 0.6 volt.   If zinc salts are to be examined, their concentrated solution is freed from oxygen either by passage of nitrogen (or hydrogen) out of contact with the atmosphere, or of carbon dioxide in an open beaker.

Lead: lead deposits at -0.45 volt from neutral or acidic plumbous solutions. Normal alkali plumbite ions produce a wave at -0.81 volt and in tartarate or citrate solution a wave appears at -0.67 volt. In neutral and acidic solutions the coincidence with thallium and stannous

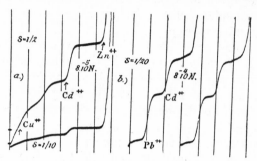

Fig. 21. Analysis of zincblende: a) for copper, cadmium, and zinc in ammoniacal solution, b) for lead and cadmium in acid solution.

ions has to be considered and resolved by the addition of excess alkali, by which the lead wave is shifted to -0.81 volt, the stannous wave to -1.18 volt, while the thallium wave remains unchanged at its potential of -0.48 volt. Moreover, stannites are easily oxidized so that their wave becomes indistinct or disappears.

Lead in bronzes (42): 0.1 g. of the alloy is weighed out and dissolved in a 100 ml. measuring flask by boiling with 5 ml. nitric acid (1:3) and

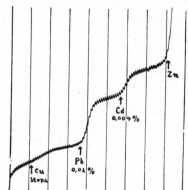

Fig. 22. Traces of copper, lead, and cadmium in chemically pure zinc.

diluting with 20 ml. of water. Twenty milliliters 2 N sodium hydroxide added and stirred well. Three and a half milliliters of a 2 N potassium cyanide, 0.1 N sodium hydroxide solution are added. After stirring until the solution clears 1 ml. 0.5% gelatin (in 0.5 N nitric acid) and 1 ml. of a fresh saturated sodium sulfite solution are added and the flask is filled to the 100 ml. mark. A small part of this solution is polarographed open to air by recording the anodic-cathodic curve, starting from a small e.m.f. at the anodic side, so as to record the foot of the lead wave, which appears at 0.1 volt on the cathodic side (Fig. 23). The cyanide solution is used whenever the appearance of the wave of copper, zinc, or iron has to be avoided.

Lead in copper, brass, and zinc alloys (42): 2.5 g. is dissolved in 15 to 20 ml. nitric acid (1:1) in a 50 ml. measuring flask, boiled, cooled, and diluted to the mark with water. From this solution exactly 20 ml. is pipetted into each of two 100 ml. flasks and to the first a solution of

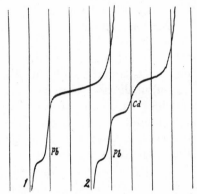

FIG. 23. Determination of cadmium and lead in copper. Solution 1.5 N KCN, 0.1 N NaOH, 0.02% gelatin with Na_2SO_3. Curve 1: sample contains 0.090% lead. Curve 2: sample contains 0.060% lead and 0.024% cadmium.

known lead content (e.g., 5 ml. of a 0.02 N lead nitrate solution) is added. Each solution is diluted with water to about 40 ml. To each of the solutions 30 ml. of 2 N sodium hydroxide is added as well as a 5 N potassium cyanide, 0.5 N sodium hydroxide solution; 10 ml. is added in the case of zinc alloys, 13 ml. for brass, and 15 ml. for copper alloys. After thorough mixing 1 ml. of 0.5% gelatin (in 0.5 N nitric acid) and 2 ml. of a freshly saturated sodium sulfite solution are added to each flask, the solutions diluted to the 100 ml. mark with water, and the contents well mixed. The solutions are polarographed open to air. The standard containing g grams produces in the first solution an increase in the wave height of $h' - h$ and from this difference the per cent content of lead in the sample is given as $x = \dfrac{100h}{h' - h} \dfrac{g}{m}$ % Pb where h' denotes the height of the wave due to the solution with the standard addition, h the wave without standard, and m the amount of the sample transferred by pipette into the measuring flask. This procedure will determine lead in concentration of 0.05%.

Simultaneous determination of traces of lead and cadmium in zinc specimens or zinc alloys (42): 7.5 g. zinc is dissolved in a 50 ml. measuring flask using 10 ml. hydrochloric acid (1:1), 15 ml. concentrated hydrochloric acid, and 3 to 5 ml. concentrated nitric acid. The solution is boiled, cooled, and diluted to the mark with water. Ten milliliters of this solution (containing 1.5 g. of the sample) is placed in each of two 50 ml. measuring flasks. To one of these a standard is added consisting of several milliliters of a dilute solution of lead nitrate and of cadmium nitrate, the concentrations of which are known. To each flask 5 ml. of water, 18 ml. of 10 N sodium hydroxide, and 7.5 ml. of 5 N potassium cyanide, 0.5 N sodium hydroxide are added and stirred until the precipitate is redissolved. To each flask are added 3 ml. of a freshly saturated sodium sulfite solution, 0.2 ml. of weakly acidic 0.5% gelatin and enough water to dilute the solutions to about 49 ml.; the flasks are then filled up to the mark with a 6% sulfur dioxide solution. Each solution is stirred well and after some minutes polarographed open to air. From the results the content of lead and cadmium is calculated as given by the above formula. In this way traces of lead and cadmium to 0.001% are determined.

If the alloy contains copper, the concentration of the cyanide has to be increased and the alkalinity decreased. Instead of 18 ml. only 11 ml. 10 N sodium hydroxide is used and 10 ml. 5 N potassium cyanide, 0.5 N sodium hydroxide is added.

Tin: The wave of the electrodeposition of divalent tin coincides with that of plumbous and thallium ion at -0.47 volt, stannic ion forms a redox wave $Sn^{++++} \rightarrow Sn^{++}$ at 0.06 volt in strongly acidic solutions. Cozzi (1) reduces the solution to obtain tin in solution in the unhydrolyzed stannous form. Seith and v. d. Esche (39a) determine traces of tin in zinc by dissolving 0.5 g. zinc in concentrated hydrochloric acid, adding chlorine water and evaporating to a small volume. From the stannous and plumbous wave at -0.47 volt the sum of the two coinciding components is obtained. Another solution of 0.5 g. zinc in concentrated hydrochloric acid is evaporated to dryness and the residue dissolved in water, slightly acidified with hydrochloric acid, and polarographed. The wave at -0.47 volt in this case is due only to plumbous ion, since all stannous ion is oxidized and hydrolyzed. From the difference of the wave heights the amount of tin is estimated to concentrations as low as 0.0015% tin. Lingane (30) determines tin simultaneously with lead, nickel, and zinc in copper base alloys. The metal is dissolved in 6 ml. 12 N hydrochloric acid, 4 ml. water, and with warming in 1 ml. concentrated nitric acid. The excess of copper is removed by electrolysis. In the remaining solution tin is tetravalent and forms the redox wave as well as the wave due to $Sn^{++} \rightarrow Sn$, coinciding with lead. The latter is determined in 1 N sodium hydroxide.

Thallium: The half-wave potential of thallium is unchanged in the presence of practically all electrolytes, remaining at -0.49 volt in neutral, acid, alkaline, ammoniacal, tartarate, or citrate solutions. The thallium wave thus coincides in neutral and acidic solutions with that of stannous and plumbous ions, and is distinguished from them in alkaline solutions. In the presence of ammonium hydroxide the thallium wave coalesces with the second wave of copper ($Cu^+ \rightarrow Cu$). For the simultaneous determination of cadmium and thallium reference (5) should be consulted.

Antimony in hard lead: In strongly acidic solutions antimonous ion is deposited at -0.2 volt, antimonic ion at 0 volt, which coincides with the deposition of copper while the wave of antimonous ion is near that of bismuth. However, in cases where the content of copper and bismuth is very small, as in hard lead, the wave at -0.2 volt, according to Kraus and Novák, gives precise indication of antimony (27). Two tenths gram of the lead sample is dissolved in a 50 ml. flask on warming in 15 ml. concentrated hydrochloric acid and the residual antimony is brought into solution by adding a few drops of bromine; the excess bromine is boiled out and the solution cooled. The flask is filled with hydrochloric acid (2:3) so that the concentration of hydrochloric acid is 8 N; 5 ml. of this solution with 0.1 ml. 0.5% gelatin are polarographed after having been freed of oxygen. The wave at -0.2 volt gives the antimony content.

Bismuth: The wave due to bismuth overlaps in acid solutions with that of copper at -0.2 volt. This coincidence is removed in weakly acid tartarate or citrate solutions, the bismuth wave being shifted to -0.4 volt.

Copper: The copper wave is best shown in citrate, tartarate or in ammoniacal solutions, in the absence of oxygen. The latter is conveniently removed in ammoniacal solutions by sulfite, which also reduces some of the divalent copper to its monovalent stage. This, however, does not invalidate the measurement of the height of the second copper wave at -0.54 volt due to the process $Cu^+ \rightarrow Cu$, as this corresponds to the total copper content. In sulfuric, nitric, and perchloric acid solutions the cupric ion wave is easily measurable, but coalesces with that of bismuth, iron (III), and antimony (III).

Copper and nickel in steel: 0.1 g. of steel is dissolved in 3 to 5 ml. hydrochloric acid (1:1) in a 50 ml. beaker. Iron is oxidized by a few drops of concentrated nitric acid and the solution evaporated to dryness. The dry residue is dissolved in exactly 1 ml. hydrochloric acid (1:1) and

1 drop of concentrated nitric acid. This solution with the insoluble silicic and tungstic acid is transferred to a 50 ml. measuring flask and diluted with water to a 10 ml. mark. The iron is precipitated by adding, in two portions, 20 to 25 ml. 2 N ammonium hydroxide containing ammonium chloride and mixed thoroughly in the cold. After the addition of sulfite and gelatin the solution is diluted to the 50 ml. mark and a portion of it is polarographed open to air (Fig. 24).

Traces of copper and nickel are determined similarly in technical iron specimen containing less than 0.05% copper and nickel. One gram of iron is dissolved in 25 ml. of the ammoniacal solution. The presence of cobalt does not interfere with the determination of nickel as long as the nickel content is small.

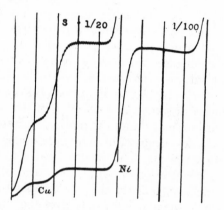

Fig. 24.   Determination of copper (3.55%) and nickel (13.8%) in steel.

Analysis of brass (16, 39): 0.1 g. brass filings are dissolved in 2 ml. concentrated nitric acid in a small beaker and covered with a watch glass. The contents are rinsed into a 50 ml. measuring flask and diluted to the mark with water. Exactly 5 ml. of the solution is pipetted into 10 ml. of 2 N ammonium chloride, 2 N ammonium hydroxide which contains fresh sulfite and gelatin, and polarographed. The double wave of copper appears at 0 volt and 0.4 volt, that of zinc at 1.2 volt. If nickel is present, its wave coincides to some extent with that of zinc; in this case a solution in 1 N potassium cyanide, 0.1 N potassium hydroxide shows only the wave of nickel.

Copper in aluminum alloys (42): 0.3 g. is dissolved in a 100 ml. measuring flask by 10 ml. hydrochloric acid (1:1) and the insoluble copper residue is brought into solution by boiling with a few drops of hydrogen peroxide. The solution is diluted with distilled water to 50 ml., 25 ml. of ammonium hydroxide (1:1) is added, stirred well, and cooled to room temperature.   One milliliter of a freshly saturated sodium sulfite solution and 1 ml. of 0.5% gelatin are added, and the flask is filled to the mark with water.   After thorough mixing a small portion of the solution is polarographed open to air.

Uranium: hexavalent uranium forms a double wave in acidic solutions (9) and in solutions of ammonium carbonate but only a single wave in 0.1 N sodium carbonate.   Trivalent iron and copper interfere in the polarographic determination in acidic solution and have to be removed. This is effected according to Strubl (49) by hydroxylamine, which reduces ferric and cupric ions.   One milliliter of a 0.1 N hydrochloric acid solution containing uranium, which may contain an excess of iron, is heated with 1 ml. of a 4 N hydroxylamine hydrochloride solution to boiling for one minute.   A part of this solution is cooled in an electrolytic vessel in a stream of hydrogen and polarographed.   The height of the first uranium wave is used for its estimation.

Determination of low-melting alloys (1) is carried out by dissolving the alloy in concentrated hydrochloric acid and potassium chlorate and evaporating the solution almost to dryness.   The residue is dissolved in dilute hydrochloric acid.   In a known volume of the solution, i.e., 10 ml., the tetravalent tin is reduced to the divalent stage by sodium dihydrogen hypophosphite and diluted to 50 ml.   A part of this solution, in a hydrogen atmosphere, is polarographed; the wave at -0.5 volt is due to the sum of plumbous and stannous ions.   To another known volume of the acid solution, i.e., 10 ml., 20 ml. of a 20% tartaric acid solution, a few drops of methyl orange and enough 40% sodium hydroxide solution are added to change the indicator color (pH 4.0).   A few drops of a 1% fuchsin solution are added, the solution diluted to the 50 ml. mark and a part of the solution polarographed in a nitrogen atmosphere. The curve shows the wave of bismuth at -0.34 volt, of lead at -0.60 volt, and of cadmium at -0.80 volt.

The content of tin is given by the difference of the wave due to tin and lead, and that due to lead alone.

Copper, lead, and zinc in flotation processes (2): Treat 1 g. of a finely ground copper or zinc tailing containing less than 1% of the metal to be determined with a mixture of 3 ml. concentrated hydrochloric acid and 1 ml. concentrated nitric acid.   Evaporate to dryness on a steam plate. Treat the residue with 3 drops of hydrochloric acid and 3 ml. distilled water.   Transfer the solution and residue to a 50 ml. measuring flask containing 25 ml. 2 N ammonium hydroxide, 2 N ammonium chloride and 3 ml. 0.2% gelatin solution.   The precipitates do not affect the results.   Dilute to 50 ml. mix and filter 5 ml. for the polarographic examination, which has to be carried out in an atmosphere of nitrogen or to which freshly saturated sulfite is added. The curve of this solution shows the waves of copper and zinc as in the case of brass. To determine lead 1 g. of finely ground sample is treated with 5 ml. of concentrated hydrochloric acid. After the initial reaction, the mixture is heated to boiling, cooled, and transferred to a 50 ml. measuring flask containing 3 ml. of 0.2% gelatin solution. The flask is filled to the mark with distilled water. The polarographic analysis is run on a 5 ml. portion of the solution, after bubbling for 5 minutes with nitrogen.

8. POLAROMETRIC (AMPEROMETRIC) TITRATIONS

The accuracy of polarographic determinations reaches 1% of the total amount of the component in favorable cases. The determinations can be made exact to 0.1% or better if a titration is carried out in which the diffusion current passing through the dropping mercury cell is used as an indicator of the titration. The titrations may involve precipitations, neutralizations, complex formations or redox reactions.

As an example the polarometric titration of lead is described, suggested by Heyrovský (10, 12) and refined by Majer and Spálenka (32). A simple polarographic arrangement is sufficient (Fig. 25) to show the galvanometric deflection at a constant applied voltage, in this example at 1.0 volt. A microammeter or a galvanometer measuring to 10^{-7} amp. is suitable. The presence of air interferes only in special cases, but the bubbling of an inert gas through the solution has the additional advantage of producing the necessary vigorous stirring after each addition of reagent. In most cases the mercury pool at the bottom of the electrolyte vessel serves as the reference electrode. Where the large surface of mercury would affect the solution or acquire a redox potential, a separate standard electrode (calomel or mercurous sulfate) should be used. One of the two solutions necessary for the titration i.e., the sulfate solution or that containing lead ions, is placed into the electrolytic vessel and the other is added from a burette. After each addition the solution is well stirred by the inert gas and two minutes are allowed for the formation and settling of the precipitate. The galvanometer reading at 1.0 volt is recorded. As long as all lead ions are being precipitated, the current is very small. As soon as there is an excess of lead ions, the current at the dropping mercury electrode increases due to the deposition of lead. The equivalence point of the titration is obtained according to Kolthoff (24) from a graph (Fig. 26) in which the abscissae represent the volume of added reagent and the ordinates the galvanometer deflection. The intersection of a line through two points before the equivalence point with a line connecting two points after the equivalence point, gives the

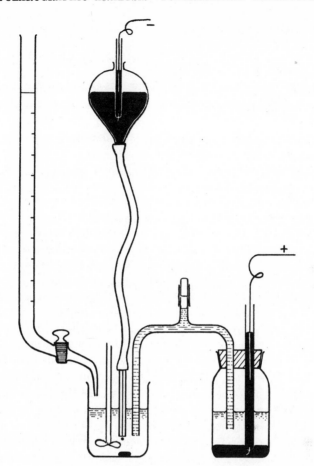

Fig. 25. Arrangement for polarometric titrations.

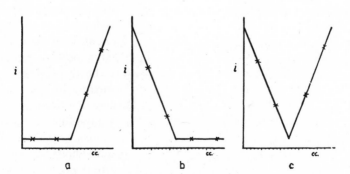

Fig. 26. Typical polarometric titration curves.

volume required for neutralization. It is not necessary to titrate exactly to the point of equivalence.

The galvanometer deflection, i, has to be corrected for the dilution by multiplying i by the ratio $\dfrac{V + v}{V}$, where V is the original volume of the solution in the electrolyte vessel and v the volume added from the burette (50).

Polarometric titrations were further developed by Neuberger (33, 34) who introduced organic reagents, such as dimethylglyoxime, salicylaldoxime, and 8-oxyquinoline for precipitations of nickel and copper. Later on many additional applications of polarometric titrations were developed by Kolthoff and coworkers.

The advantages of polarometric titrations are:

1) Very dilute solutions can be titrated with a high degree of accuracy.

2) Precipitation titrations can be performed when the solubility of the precipitate is relatively great and under conditions where the potentiometric or indicator methods do not yield good results.

3) Foreign electrolytes, whose presence is harmful in conductometric titrations, do not interfere in polarometric titrations.

4) Substances that are not depolarizers can be titrated, if the reagent yields a diffusion current.

5) The titrations are carried out rapidly because only two measurements before and after the point of equivalence are needed.

6) The temperature does not have to be known as long as it is constant during the titration.

There are some limitations to the method:

1) As a rule depolarizers, which produce a current at a more positive potential than the substance to be titrated, must not be present in concentrations many times larger than that of the substance titrated.

2) The solubility equilibrium, or in general the establishment of the equivalence equilibrium, must be attained relatively quickly (in a few minutes).

Kolthoff has shown that in the place of a dropping mercury cathode a rotating platinum electrode may be used with special advantage at more positive potentials than that of the calomel electrode, at which the mercury electrode would dissolve anodically. Such electrodes enable one to titrate silver, mercury, the halides, and the cyanides (28).

In all titrations of heavy metals gelatin has to be present to ensure a steady diffusion current.

Titration of lead and of barium: For lead ions Abresch (33) recommends chromate ions, which produce a diffusion current at 0.8 volt similar to the lead ions. Thus, as long as any of the two ions are in excess, a galvanometric deflection is observed. The deflection is a minimum at the equivalence point. The plot of deflection versus reagent added has the form shown in Fig. 26c. However, when the titration is carried out in acid solution, in which the chromate ions are reduced at the potential of the calomel electrode, one obtains another diagram when measuring the deflection at 0.0 volts. As long as there is an excess of lead ions there is no deflection at the potential of 0.0 volt, excess chromate ions are shown by a deflection at that voltage (Fig. 26a). If, on the other hand, the solutions are interchanged so that the lead solution is added from the burette into a solution of the chromate ions, the diagram Fig. 26b is obtained.

Kolthoff and Pan (25) found that the lead titration is best carried out in an acid acetate buffer or in a 0.01 to 0.1 N perchloric acid solution. It is sufficient to connect a separate calomel electrode directly to the dropping electrode through the galvanometer, without need of removing oxygen, which does not interfere at that voltage (Fig. 27).

The same authors recommend the chromate titration for barium ions (24). For lead ions oxalate in aqueous solution may be used (25).

Titrations of zinc: According to Spálenka (41) zinc ions are best precipitated by potassium ferrocyanide in a hydrochloric acid solution at 1.2 volt or, according to Neuberger (49), by oxine (8-oxiquinoline).

Titrations of nickel, cobalt, and copper: Kolthoff and Langer (22) titrate nickel ions in 0.0001 to 0.01 N concentrations, using 0.1 N ammonium chloride, 0.5 N ammonium hydroxide and gelatin as the electrolyte. The titration is carried out in absence of air by adding an alcoholic 0.1 N dimethylglyoxime solution. After each addition inert gas is passed for 30 seconds and the deflection is noted after 3 minutes at -1.85 volt. At this voltage both reagents produce a wave so that a V-shaped plot is obtained. Cobalt must not be present in concentration of more than 5% of the nickel, or else must be removed by potassium cobalti nitrite.

According to Langer (23), cobalt ions are titrated in a 0.2 N acetic acid and 0.2 N sodium acetate solution with a solution of α-nitroso-β-naphthol in concentrated acetic acid. The point of equivalence is given by a sharp minimum at -1.5 volt.

Cupric ions are titrated (33, 34) in dilute acetic acid and potassium chloride by a 1% salicylaldoxime solution.

Kolthoff and Langer (23) recommend α-nitroso-β-naphthol either in an acetate buffer or in a solution of ammonium hydroxide and ammonium chloride for copper titrations. Under the same conditions palladium ions are determined also.

Titrations of cadmium and iron: Cadmium ions are precipitated by naphthoquinone in an acidic potassium iodide solution and the deflection is obtained at -1.0 volt (Sandberg, 38). The same author suggested bromoxine (5,7-dibromo-8-hydroxyquinoline) in 0.1 N hydrochloric acid at 0 volts for the titration of ferric ions.

Titration of potassium: Sandberg (38) has found a suitable reagent for potassium in sodium dipicryl aminate at pH 12, producing a large diffusion current at -1.6 volt. Best results are obtained when the

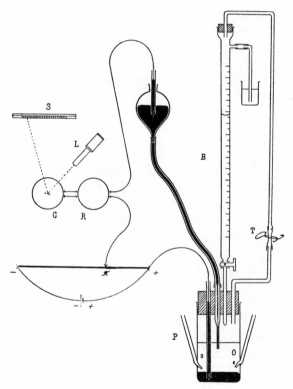

FIG. 27.   Polarometric cell for titrations using the reference calomel electrode as the unpolarizable electrode.

solution to be titrated is kept in an ice thermostat. The titration is carried out as follows: 10 ml. of a monosodium phosphate-sodium hydroxide buffer of pH 12, in which the potassium ions should have a concentration of from 0.01 to 0.15 N, is freed from atmospheric oxygen by nitrogen at 0°C. A separate calomel electrode is used as anode and the voltage is kept at 1.6 volt. A 0.07 N sodium dipicryl aminate solution is added from the burette. After the first addition the solution is stirred for about 5 minutes by nitrogen bubbles to complete crystallization.

After further additions shorter duration of bubbling suffices. In this way solutions containing from 4 to 120 mg. of potassium can be titrated with an accuracy of 0.4%. The content of sodium may be 15 times that of potassium. Lithium salts interfere even less. Ammonia, on the other hand, is objectionable. Other metals, such as magnesium, manganese, zinc, aluminum, and iron have to be removed. This is done best by oxine, first at pH 4.5, afterwards at pH 9.5, in an acetate buffer.

Titration of calcium and of aluminum: For cases where the diffusion current is not well developed, as for example, by simultaneous hydrogen deposition in the case of calcium or aluminum ions, Ringbom (37) suggests the addition of a trace of a substance having practically the same solubility as that of the ions to be precipitated, but depolarizing at a more positive potential. Thus the addition of cadmium ions is suggested when precipitating calcium ions with oxalate. When all the calcium ions are precipitated by the oxalate ions, the diffusion current due to the deposition of cadmium ions begins to be diminished, which denotes the end point of the titration. This titration is carried out at −1.0 volt. Similarly ferric ions may indicate the end point of the titration of calcium ions by fluoride, but in this case the voltage can be maintained at 0 volt, i.e., at the potential of the calomel electrode, which is used as the separate anode.

Aluminum ions may be titrated by fluoride but the indicator here is the diffusion current of the ferric ions, which again is measured by the deflection of the galvanometer at 0.0 volt. "Indicator" ions are those that behave similarly to the ions to be titrated, and thus may be used to indicate their presence.

Titration of molybdenum: Thanheiser and Willems (51) determine molybdenum in steel polarometrically after precipitating the iron by alkali. The molybdate solution is titrated with lead acetate, which forms an insoluble lead molybdate at pH between 5 to 6. At 0.6 volt no galvanometric deflection is observable until there is a slight excess of lead ions, which indicates the end point of the titration. This titration is best carried out at 80°C.

Titration of bismuth: Gillis *et al.* (8) have worked out the polarometric titration of bismuth by precipitation with oxine (8-oxyquinoline), which is dissolved in 1 N acetic acid. To 10 ml. of a 0.05 N bismuth solution in 10% nitric acid 2 g. of sodium tartarate are added, the solution neutralized with 1 N sodium hydroxide and 7.33 g. sodium acetate and 1 ml. of 1 N acetic acid are added. This solution has a pH of 6 and shows the wave of bismuth at −0.7 volt. An aqueous solution of oxine is added containing 2 g. oxine and 5 ml. of glacial acetic acid in 100 ml. water. After each addition the solution is stirred for 30 seconds and after an additional 30 seconds the galvanometer deflection is determined at 0.85 volt.

REFERENCES

1. Çozzi, D., *Ann. chim. applicata* **29**, 442 (1939).
2. Crowe, G. A., and Bishop, W. T., *Am. Inst. Mining Met. Engrs.*, Tech. Pubs. 2010 (1946).
3. Cummings, R. W., and Reed, J. F., *Proc. Am. Soc. Soil Sci.* **5**, 167 (1940).
4. Devoto, G., and Ratti, A., *Gazz. chim. ital.* **62**, 887 (1932).
5. Ensslin, F., Dreyer, H., and Abraham, K., *Metall u. Erz* **39**, 184 (1942).
6. Forche, E., *Mikrochemie* **25**, 217 (1938).
7. Geller, B. A., and Sanko, A. M., *Zavodskaya Lab.* **8**, 1030 (1939).
8. Gillis, J., Eeckhout, J., and Standaert, G., *Mededeel. Koninkl. Vlaam. Acad. Wetenschap. Belg.* No. 7, **2**, 1 (1940).
9. Harris, W. E., and Kolthoff, I. M., *J. Am. Chem. Soc.* **47**, 1484, 1488 (1945).
10. Heyrovský, J., *Bull. soc. chim.* **41**, 1224 (1927).
11. Heyrovský, J., in Böttger, Physikalische Methoden der Analytischen Chemic Akademische Verlagsgesellschaft, Leipzig, 1936, Vol. II, p. 299.
12. Heyrovský, J., and Berezický, S., *Collection Czechoslov. Chem. Commun.* **1**, 19 (1921).
13. Heyrovský, J., and Ilkovič, D., *Collection Czechoslov. Chem. Commun.* **7**, 198 (1935).
14. Heyrovský, J., and Shikata, M., *Rec. trav. chim.* **44**, 496 (1925).
15. Hövker, G., Dissertation, Hamburg, 1938.
16. Hohn, H., *Z. Elektrochem.* **43**, 127 (1937).
17. Hohn, H., in Zintl, Anleitungen für die chemische Laboratoriumspraxis. J. Springer, Berlin, 1937, Vol. III.
18. Ilkovič, D., *Collection Czechoslov. Chem. Commun.* **6**, 498 (1934).
19. Ilkovič, D., and Semerano, G., *Collection Czechoslov. Chem. Commun.* **4**, 176 (1932).
19a. Jessop, G., *Nature* **158**, 59 (1946).
20. Kamegai, S., *J. Biochem. Japan* **29**, 285 (1939).
21. Kimura, G., *Collection Czechoslov. Chem. Commun.* **4**, 492 (1932).
22. Kolthoff, I. M., and Langer, A., *J. Am. Chem. Soc.* **62**, 211 (1940).
23. Kolthoff, I. M., and Langer, A., *J. Am. Chem. Soc.* **62**, 3172 (1940).
24. Kolthoff, I. M., and Pan, Y. D., *J. Am. Chem. Soc.* **61**, 3402 (1939).
25. Kolthoff, I. M., and Pan, Y. D., *J. Am. Chem. Soc.* **62**, 3332 (1940).
26. Kraus, R., and Novák, J. V., *Collection Czechoslov. Chem. Commun.* **10**, 534 (1938).
27. Kraus, R., and Novák, J. V., *Die Chemie.* **56**, 302 (1943).
28. Laitinen, H. A., and Kolthoff, I. M., *J. Phys. Chem.* **45**, 1061, 1079 (1941).
29. Lingane, J. J., *J. Am. Chem. Soc.* **67**, 182 (1945).
30. Lingane, J. J., *Ind. Eng. Chem. Anal. Ed.* **18**, 429 (1946).
31. Majer, V., *Z. anal. Chem.* **92**, 321, 401 (1933).
32. Majer, V., and Spálenka, M., *Z. Elektrochem.* **42**, 123 (1936).
33. Neuberger, A., *Z. anal. Chem.* **116**, 1 (1939).
34. Neuberger, A., *Arch. Eisenhüttenw.* **13**, 171 (1939).
35. Novák, J. V., *Collection Czechoslov. Chem. Commun.* **12**, 237 (1947).
36. Okáč, A., *Forschung Bodenkunde* **8**, 206, 227 (1944).
37. Ringbom, A., *Tek. Tid.* **77**, 755 (1947).
38. Sandberg, B., *Svensk Kem. Tid.* **58**, 197 (1946).
39. Schwarz, K., *Z. anal. Chem.* **115**, 161 (1934).

39a. Seith, W., and Esche, W. v. d., *Z. Metallkunde* **33**, 81 (1941).
40. Semerano, G., and Ronchi, I., *Chem. Centr.* **1943**, I, 2618.
41. Spálenka, M., *Collection Czechoslov. Chem. Commun.* **11**, 146 (1939).
42. Spálenka, M., *Metallwirtschaft* **23**, 341 (1943).
43. Spálenka, M., *Metallwirtschaft* **23**, 346 (1943).
44. Spálenka, M., unpublished.
45. Stackelberg, M., Klinger, P., Koch, W., and Krath, E.   *Forschungsber. Techn. Mitt. Krupp* **2**, 59 (1939).
46. Stout, P. R., and Levy, J., *Collection Czechoslov. Chem. Commun.* **10**, 136 (1938).
47. Stout, P. R., Levy, J., and Williams, L. C., *Collection Czechoslov. Chem. Commun.* **10**, 129 (1938).
48. Straumanis, M., and Dravnieks, A., *Z. anal. Chem.* **120**, 168 (1940).
49. Strubl, R., *Collection Czechoslov. Chem. Commun.* **10**, 466 (1938).
50. Strubl, R., *Collection Czechoslov. Chem. Commun.* **10**, 475, (1938).
51. Thanheiser, G., and Willems, J., *Arch. Eisenhüttenw.* **13**, 73 (1939).
52. Uhl, F. A., *Z. anal. Chem.* **110**, 102 (1937).
53. Urech, P., and Sulzberger, R., *Helv. Chim. Acta* **27**, 1074 (1944).
54. Verdier, E. T., *Collection Czechoslov. Chem. Commun.* **11**, 216 (1939).
55. Verdier, E. T., *Collection Czechoslov. Chem. Commun.* **11**, 233 (1939).
55a. Wolfson, H., *Nature* **153**, 375 (1944).
56. Zentler-Gordon, H. E. and Roberts, E. R., *Trans. Electrochem. Soc.* **90**, 27 (1946).
57. Zlotowski, I., and Kolthoff, I. M., *J. Am. Chem. Soc.* **66**, 1431 (1944).
58. Zlotowski, I., and Kolthoff, I. M., *J. Phys. Chem.* **48**, 386 (1945).

Conductometric Analysis

BY

H. T. S. BRITTON

Professor of Chemistry, Washington Singer Laboratories, University College of the South West of England, Exeter

CONTENTS

1. THEORY AND TECHNIQUE

1.1. Electrical Conductance

If two platinum electrodes of the same size and shape are placed immediately opposite to one another in a solution of an electrolyte they will enclose a volume of solution, the electrical resistance, R ohms, of which will be determined by:

(i) the distance, l cm., between the electrodes,

(ii) the area, a sq. cm., of one electrode,

(iii) the concentration, c of the electrolyte,

(iv) the degree of ionization and the ionic mobilities,

(v) the temperature.

The true resistance, $R = \rho \frac{1}{a}$, where ρ, the proportionality factor is the specific resistance, i.e., the resistance of a unit cube, 1 cc., of the solution when electricity passes directly through it from face to face. According to Ohm's law, the current, i, is equal to E/R, E being the potential difference (volts) between the two electrodes. Confining our attention to the unit centimeter cube of resistance, ρ ohms, and letting the potential difference between the two opposite faces be 1 volt, we find that the current which passes through the cube is $1/\rho$ amperes. This is the *specific conductance*, κ, i.e., $\kappa = 1/\rho$ amperes. As specific conductance is the reciprocal of the specific resistance, it is therefore only necessary to measure the specific resistance, the reciprocal of which gives the specific conductivity in *amperes*. As the specific resistance is measured directly in *ohms*, the specific conductivity is assigned the unit $\frac{1}{1 \text{ ohm}}$ or 1 *reciprocal ohm*, 1 r.o., 1 mho. These units are actually amperes.

The equivalent conductivity, $\Lambda_c = \dfrac{\kappa_c \times 1000}{c}$, where κ_c is the specific conductivity of a solution which contains c gram-equivalents of electrolyte per liter. It was originally introduced to give the specific conductance of a solution in each cubic centimeter of which 1 gram-equivalent of electrolyte is dissolved. Kohlrausch, however, found that the equivalent conductivity varies with the concentration, so that Λ_c indicates the specific equivalent conductivity computed from the observed specific conductivity, κ_c, of a solution of concentration, c.

According to the Arrhenius theory of incomplete ionization, which, although largely discredited still provides a satisfactory basis for the study of conductometric titrations, the degree of ionization, $\alpha = \dfrac{\Lambda_c}{\Lambda_0}$ where Λ_0 is the so-called equivalent conductance at infinite dilution, or zero-concentration, which is found by extrapolation of the equivalent conductance at low concentrations by means of the Kohlrausch square root law.

For an electrolyte, $BA \rightleftharpoons B^+ + A^-$, Kohlrausch's law of independent migration holds, i.e.,

$$\Lambda_0 = l_{B\cdot} + l_{A'}$$

and therefore
$$\Lambda_c = \alpha(l_{B\cdot} + l_{A'})$$

where $l_{B\cdot}$ and $l_{A'}$ represent the equivalent conductivities of the respective ions, $B^{\cdot}$ and A', but which are more generally known as ionic mobilities. According to the Arrhenius theory these ionic mobilities are independent of the concentration, but though this is not quite true, their slight variations will not invalidate the fundamental theory of conductometric titrations.

In attempting to measure the resistance of a solution by passing direct current through it, substantial sources of error may arise owing to the polarization of the electrodes through the occurrence of electrolysis and the consequent setting up of cathodic and anodic processes which may even involve electrodeposition or electrodissolution. To minimize this risk, Kohlrausch employed an alternating current of high frequency. According to Kohlrausch and Holborn (39), the passage of an alternating current, i, between the electrodes is determined by:

$$E_0 \sin pt = Ri + P \int i \, dt$$

where E_0 = maximum e.m.f. applied,
   P = the polarization e.m.f. and
   $\dfrac{p}{2\pi}$ = the frequency of the alternations.

From this expression, it can be shown that the apparent resistance is equal to

$$\sqrt{\left\{1 + \frac{P^2}{p^2R^2}\right\}},$$

so that if the method of measurement can be arranged such that P^2/p^2R^2 becomes negligible when compared with unity, then the *apparent resistance becomes equal* to the true resistance, R. To do this the polarization, P, must either be eliminated altogether or else reduced to a minimum, and the frequency, $\frac{p}{2\pi}$, must be as high as possible.

To reduce the polarization to negligible dimensions: (1) high frequencies are necessary, but if they are increased much beyond 1000 c.p.s. errors due to capacity and inductance may become appreciable; (2) relatively large electrodes are an advantage. They may be made effectively larger by depositing on them adherent coatings of either platinum or palladium black, the latter being preferred by some when dealing with solutions of high concentrations. Kohlrausch and Holborn consider that polarization effects become negligible when the resistance to be measured is less than 50/(area of the platinized electrode) ohms. To obtain an accuracy of 0.1% with bright unplatinized platinum electrodes the limiting resistance, R, is given by 2500/(area of electrode).

It is important that, if the specific conductance of the solution should be less than 4×10^{-4} r.o., polarization must be avoided, as its presence will lead to a poor and indistinct null point. If a telephone be employed the minimum noise will extend over a considerable range of the Wheatstone bridge wire and even when the point of minimum noise is located that point will not be the same as the one obtained when polarization is absent.

Parker (51) maintains that the distance between the electrodes is a matter of importance and suggests that the expression:

$$R = \frac{160 \sqrt{\text{distance (cm.)}}}{\text{area of electrode (cm.}^2)}$$

should be satisfied in the case of platinized platinum electrodes in the construction of conductivity cells.

In some solutions the use of platinum black on the electrodes has deleterious effects which may be caused by (a) catalytic activity, though this is reduced by using high frequencies, (b) adsorption, (c) errors produced by the retention of electrolytes of previous solutions, while in conductometric titrations such retention might cause a lag in the indication of accurate conductances which, with dilute solutions, may be appreciable. In ordinary titrimetric work adsorption errors are usually very small. To minimize such errors Whetham advocates the use of gray platinum electrodes which are prepared by heating platinum black electrodes to dull redness (76).

1.1.1. Platinizing Electrodes. The bright platinum electrodes are thoroughly cleaned in a warm solution of potassium dichromate and concentrated sulfuric acid, followed by several washings with distilled water. The platinizing solution (Lummer and Kurlbaum, 1895) contains 3 g. platinic chloride and 0.02–0.03 g. lead acetate per 100 cc. water. The electrodes are placed in the solution in an inclined position to enable bubbles of gas to leave the electrodes as soon as they are formed, and electrolysis is allowed to occur, using two lead accumulators and a resistance adjusted to permit a moderate evolution of gas only. The current is reversed every half minute and electrolysis is allowed to proceed for 10–15 minutes, when a good black velvety coating of platinum black should have been deposited on each electrode.

Adsorbed substances, e.g., chlorine, are removed from the electrodes by electrolyzing in either dilute sulfuric acid solution or one of sodium acetate for $\frac{1}{2}$ hour, reversing every minute.

The electrodes are washed with distilled water and finally with "conductivity water" and kept therein until required. To test the electrodes it is advisable to use them in repeated determinations of the conductance of "conductivity water" until reproducible data are obtained.

1.1.2. Removal of Platinum Black. This is best done by electrolysis in aqua regia for a few minutes, with current reversal every minute until bright surfaces are obtained.

1.2. Sources of Alternating Current

1.2.1. The Induction Coil. Although the induction coil has been used extensively in the past, it is being superseded by vacuum tube oscillators. It is noisy and must be placed some distance from the measuring apparatus if induction effects are to be avoided. The noise can be reduced by inserting a resistance in its primary circuit. The chief disadvantage of the induction coil is that the alternations produced are unsymmetrical and possess a definite unidirectional component. The induction coil described by Kohlrausch consists of a soft iron core, 8 cm. by 1 cm., a primary of 200 turns of 0.5 mm. copper wire and a secondary of 2000 turns of 0.25-mm. copper wire. It is fitted with a Neeff hammer, the contacts of which should be of platinum.

1.2.2. Vacuum Tube Oscillators. These are now generally available and can be obtained from scientific instrument makers. They have been widely adopted for conductometric titrations. They have the distinct advantage that the frequency of the A.C. can be varied at will while making conductance measurements. If polarization of the conductivity cell has been eliminated, then the observed resistances should be independent of the frequencies of the A.C. used and the oscillator thus makes it possible to prove at any time that the measuring apparatus is in good working order. Oscillators should be thoroughly screened and grounded. Sometimes it is found that interchanging the connections from an oscillator to a Wheatstone Bridge may result in a change in the position of balance. This may be caused by differences in capacity between the oscillator and its leads to ground; if this should be so the error can be eliminated by inserting a small variable condenser between one lead wire and ground and varying the capacity until no difference in the null point occurs whichever way the oscillator is connected to the bridge. When an oscillator is used for highly resistant solutions, e.g., dilute nonaqueous solutions, it will be necessary to balance accurately not only the resistances but the capacities in the Wheatstone bridge circuit. Except for titrimetric work in nonaqueous media this will usually be unnecessary.

For details of constructing oscillators the original literature must be consulted (14, 24, 25, 28, 34, 36, 59, 60, 70, 77).

1.3. Conductometric Titration Cells, Cell Constants

In making cells it is essential that vessels of insoluble glass, viz., borosilicate glass of the Pyrex or Jena type, should be used and the two electrodes, each about 1 sq. cm. in area, should be securely placed at a suitable distance apart. Larger electrodes may be used with advantage. The distance between the electrodes is determined by the conductance of the solutions to be tested; if the conductance is low the electrodes should be closer to one another than when highly conducting solutions are involved. In any case the platinum electrodes should be sufficiently thick to be rigid, and they should be so mounted that the distance between them is absolutely fixed and is not affected by any mechanical agitation of the solution. A method of making electrodes rigid is to back and mount them on glass plates. Types of conductometric titration cells are illustrated in Fig. 1 (9, 18, 37, 40, 63, *see also* 57).

1.3.1. *Calibration.* In the foregoing discussion we have said nothing about the precise dimensions of the electrodes and their exact distance apart. Instead, we use electrodes of such size and in such relative positions that lead to the most accurate conductivity measurements. Provided the electrode system is of rigid construction it is possible to calibrate the cells by inserting in them accurately prepared solutions of potassium chloride, the specific conductances of which have been determined by Kohlrausch, Parker and Parker (52) and Jones and Bradshaw (35) with exceptional precision.

Table I records the specific conductances reported by Parker and Parker.

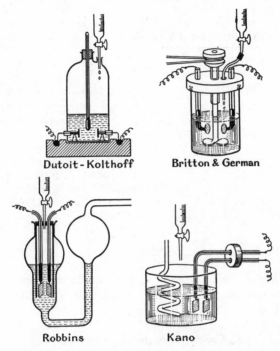

Dutoit - Kolthoff   Britton & German

Robbins   Kano

FIG. 1.   Some conductometric titration cells.

We saw that $R = \rho \dfrac{1}{a}$ and that $\kappa = \dfrac{1}{\rho}$, whence

$$\frac{1}{R} \times \frac{1}{a} = \frac{1}{\rho} = \frac{1}{\rho} = \kappa$$

As l and a are of any convenient magnitude and are, moreover, probably incapable of precise measurement, $\dfrac{1}{a}$ is put equal to C, the cell constant, i.e., $\dfrac{1}{R} \times C = \kappa$ whence $C = \kappa \times R$. If, therefore, one of the KCl solutions given in Table I is inserted in the cell, the resistance, R, of the volume of solution between the electrodes can be directly measured, and as the specific conductance, κ, is known, the cell constant, C, can be calculated. If the electrode system remains undisturbed and a solution of unknown conductance is placed in the cell, it follows that the reciprocal of its resistance *multiplied* by the cell constant will give its specific conductance. For analytical work a knowledge of the cell constant may not be needed, but it will be required when it is desired to interpret the precise conductivities prevailing during a conductometric titration.

TABLE I

Specific Conductances of Solutions of KCl at Various Temperatures

G. KCl in 1000 g. H_2O	76.6276	7.47896	0.746253
Sp. g. of solution at 0°C.	1.0480	1.00489	1.00037
Temperature, °C.	Specific conductances, κ mhos.		
0	0.06510	0.007130	0.0007728
5	0.07388	0.008206	0.0008920
10	0.08289	0.009316	0.0010151
15	0.09213	0.010460	0.0011422
18	0.09779	0.011164	0.0012202
20	0.10161	0.011639	0.0012731
25	0.11132	0.012852	0.0014079
30	0.12127	0.014100	0.0015466

In determining the cell constant it is advisable to select a KCl solution which has a specific conductance comparable with those of solutions undergoing test.

1.4. Conductivity and Equilibrium Water

For conductometric work involving strong electrolytes, solutions prepared with good distilled water will be satisfactory, but if weak electrolytes are involved, a purer water will be desirable. The chief impurity in distilled water is carbon dioxide, although water exposed to the air of chemical laboratories will often contain ammonia and possibly hydrogen chloride and sulfur dioxide, while water stored in soda-glass vessels will contain traces of alkali. Water so contaminated is generally unsuitable.

According to Kendall (38) water having a specific conductance of ca. 0.8×10^{-6} mho at 25° may be regarded as a solution of carbon dioxide that is saturated under the partial pressure of carbon dioxide normally present in the atmosphere. Washburn (73) calls such water "*equilibrium water*" whereas the κ of "*ultra pure conductivity water*" is less than 0.1×10^{-6} mho. For conductometric work "equilibrium water" should be used. Stills for the preparation of equilibrium water have been described (2, 3, 4, 48, 66, 71, 72, 75).

1.5. Measurement of Conductance

1.5.1. Wheatstone Bridge. For general conductometric analysis the simple Wheatstone meter bridge with which a low resistance earphone is used as the null-point indicator will be satisfactory. The earphone indicator is necessary because A.C. has to be employed (Fig. 2). If increased accuracy is needed the meter wire can be effectively lengthened by inserting a resistance coil at each end, preferably wound with the same wire as that used in the construction of the bridge wire; the resistance of each coil being exactly $4\frac{1}{2}$ times that of the bridge wire. The effect of inserting these two coils will be to convert the length of the bridge from 1 meter to 10 meters and in so doing each millimeter of the extended wire

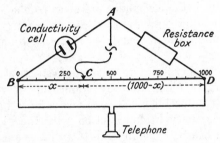

FIG. 2.   Wheatstone bridge method of measuring electrical conductance.

will correspond to one-tenth of the resistance indicated by the same length when the extension coils are omitted. As Table I shows, temperature has a considerable effect on conductivity so that when a conductometric titration is to be performed for purely analytical reasons, it will suffice if it is carried out in a room in which the temperature is sensibly constant, but if it is desired to interpret the precise conductivities set up at different stages of the titration, the conductivity cell should be inserted in a carefully controlled thermostat.

By removing a resistance plug from the box in the arm AD which is of similar magnitude to that of the cell, r, and then moving the sliding contact, C, minimum noise will be heard in the earphone when C is somewhere near the middle of the wire BD. If BD is of uniform resistance throughout its whole length, then

$$\frac{\text{Resistance of conductivity cell}}{\text{Resistance in box}} = \frac{r}{R} = \frac{BC}{CD} = \frac{x}{1000 - x}$$

where x is the number of scale divisions represented by BC, BD representing 1000 divisions. Hence the "apparent" specific conductance

$$= \frac{1}{r} = \frac{1000 - x}{x} \times \frac{1}{R}$$

and as the cell-constant is C, the true specific conductance,

$$\kappa = \frac{1000 - x}{x} \times \frac{C}{\text{R}}$$

For analytical work only, it is unnecessary to calculate κ for each addition of titrant, but merely to plot $\dfrac{1000 - x}{x}$ (it being directly proportional to κ) against the volume of titrant added.

If the minimum noise given by the earphone is easily detectable, it can be safely assumed that errors, which may enter into conductivity measurements, have been eliminated.

It is important that the smallest current should be employed. Large currents, especially if the electrodes are close to one another, are apt to heat the enclosed liquid and thereby lead to errors, a point which has to be borne in mind when visual instruments are used as null-point indicators.

Capacity effects may interfere with the location of the balance point. They can be largely eliminated by connecting a variable condenser across either the conductivity cell or the resistance box, i.e., in parallel, and varying its capacity in conjunction with the sliding contact until the least sound is heard. Usually this is an unnecessary refinement.

A direct method of measuring the resistance, r, of the conductivity cell is to use two fixed equal resistances, say 100 ohms, in place of the two sections of the meter wire and to dispense with the sliding contact. In the third arm of the Wheatstone bridge network, place the conductivity cell, and in the fourth arm, a resistance box having four rheostats, viz., 0–12 ohms, graduated in tenths; 0–10 ohms, graduated in ohms; 0–100, in 10 ohm steps; and 0–1000 in 100 ohm steps. To balance the bridge the pointer of the first rheostat is set at, say, 6 ohms and the pointers of the other rheostats rotated until minimum noise is heard; the balance is then completed by rotating the first dial until the true minimum noise is obtained. The resistance indicated by the dials of the resistance box must be that of the cell (62).

1.5.2. Null-Point Indicators: a. Earphones. The telephone is probably the most accurate null-point detector in that with it the smallest currents can be used to operate the Wheatstone bridge, thereby avoiding many errors that are inherent in the employment of larger currents. Its sensitiveness can be enhanced if the frequency of its diaphragm is the same as that of the A.C. used, preferably 1000 c.p.s. Tunable earphones may be obtained commercially. By using a tube amplifier, Jones and Josephs (36), were able to measure resistances up to 60,000 ohms. Loudspeakers have also been employed (25).

b. A.C. Galvanometers. These instruments necessitate the use of appreciable alternating currents but they have nevertheless received much attention during the last sixty years. Jander and Schorstein (33) have, however, applied them to conductometric titrations successfully.

1.6. Special Methods of Measurement

Various methods have been devised by which the alternating current, which ordinarily passes through the indicating instrument of the Wheatstone bridge, may be rectified and then made to operate D.C. instruments. Thus a crystal detector (31) has been used to operate a D.C. galvanometer and a copper-cuprous oxide-lead rectifier (27) has been used in conjunction with a microammeter. Another ingenious method of Jander and Pfundt (32), is one in which the primary coil of a transformer takes the place of the earphone. The secondary coil is connected with the two ends of a short constantin wire at the middle of which is attached an iron wire in the form of a cross which is enclosed in an atmosphere of hydrogen. A sensitive galvanometer is connected to the constantin and iron wires, the galvanometer circuit thus including the constantin-iron junction. As the heat generated in the constantin wire is proportional to the square of the current, it follows that when the bridge is nearly balanced, very little heat will be developed and so the *Thermo-Cross* (as it was designated by Jander and Pfundt) is not very sensitive in the region of the null point. In consequence, bridge readings on each side of the balance point are taken at points that give equal deflections of the galvanometer; the null point is assumed to be the mean of these two values.

1.6.1. A.C. Galvanometer Method: Thermo-Cross. The circuit used by Jander and Schorstein is given in Fig. 3. The method makes use of the exceedingly sensitive A.C. galvanometer described by Weibel (74) and Gollnow (26).

By varying the comparison resistance, R, both well-conducting and poorly-conducting solutions may be titrated. As a source of A.C. the main supply is connected directly to the primary coil of a 1:1 transformer and the alternating current in the secondary is reduced to 110 volts by passing through an "iron-hydrogen" resistance. It then excites the electromagnet of the A.C. galvanometer across which a shunt is placed. The A.C. to operate the Wheatstone bridge is tapped off from a potentiometer which is inserted in the lead from the secondary coil and regulated by means of a voltmeter, *V*.

1.6.2. Vacuum Tube Methods. As a rule these methods are based on the principle employed by Treadwell and Janett (68) in 1923 to carry out conductometric titrations of alkaloids with hydrochloric acid.

They used the Whetham commutator for the dual purpose of passing A.C. through the conductivity cell and rectifying the A.C. therefrom in order to actuate a millivoltmeter. The commutator gave alternations of 4–8 per second and the current was a few milliampères with an e.m.f. of 8 volts.

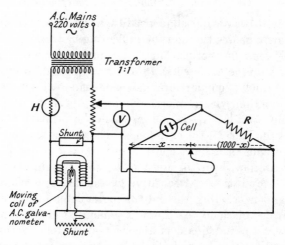

Fig. 3.   Jander and Schorstein's method of conductometric titration using an alternating current galvanometer.

In 1925 Treadwell and Paoloni (69) substituted a vacuum tube for the commutator and placed the conductivity cell in the grid circuit through which A.C. from the mains was passed.   Figure 4 depicts Callan and Horrobin's (15) modification of their circuit in which a step-down trans-

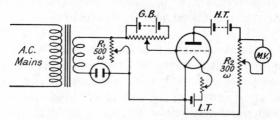

Fig. 4.   Treadwell-Callan-Horrobin's circuit for conductometric titrations, using vacuum tube and millivoltmeter.

former is placed across the main supply in order to give A.C. at 8 volts. Sufficient negative grid bias is provided to bring the variation in voltage to the "bend" in the characteristic curve of the valve and away from the straight section of the curve.   To bring the readings during a titration within the range of the millivoltmeter in the anode circuit either the resistance, R, or the resistance, R_2, may be adjusted, or else the steady anode current through the millivoltmeter may be balanced out initially and thus allow only the variations caused by the changing resistance of the conductometric cell in the grid circuit to be indicated by the millivoltmeter (cf. 21).

Circuits which employ crystal detectors and dry rectifiers instead of valves (15, 56) have also been described.

An apparatus embodying a Wheatstone bridge circuit with vacuum tube amplification in which a cathode-ray tube, known as the "magic eye," is incorporated as the null-point indicator is now available commercially. It is particularly serviceable in conductometric titrations.

2. CONDUCTOMETRIC TITRATIONS OF ACIDS AND BASES

2.1. Conductometric Titrations: Basic Principles

2.1.1. Acidimetry and Alkalimetry. If to a solution of a strong acid, a solution of an alkali is added in small volumes and after each addition either the specific conductance or some other quantity $\left(\text{e.g., } \dfrac{1000 - x}{x}, \right.$ which is directly proportional to the specific conductance) be measured, it will be found that the conductance will rapidly fall to a minimum value and that immediately afterwards each fresh addition of alkali will cause a further increase in conductance. The alkali which produced the minimum conductance will be that required to neutralize the amount of acid originally present in the solution. But unless special precautions have been taken regarding the concentrations of the acid and alkali solutions used, neither the initial decrease in conductance nor the subsequent increase will be represented by straight lines when the *conductance* is plotted against the *volume of titrant added.* Lack of rectilinearity would thus render it difficult to locate the position of the end point by producing the initial and final curves to the point of intersection. For this purpose, then, it is imperative that wherever possible in conductometric analysis, changes in conductance should be represented by straight lines.

Figure 5 shows the relationship at 25°C. between the specific conductance and concentration (in gram equivalents per liter) of three typical *strong* electrolytes from 0 to 0.1 N, which is the range of concentration usually encountered in titrimetric work. It will be noticed that the graphs are almost rectilinear, from which it follows that to obtain straight line relationships it will be necessary that each addition of titrant should be made in such a way that the volume added is directly proportional to the concentrations of the acid and the salt formed in the first part of the titration, and to those of the salt and the excess of alkali

added after the end point has been passed.   In Fig. 6 curve A represents
the specific conductances of solutions of sodium hydroxide that contain
the volumes of sodium hydroxide indicated by the abscissae in each
100 ml.   As the final volume is the same in each case, then the volumes of

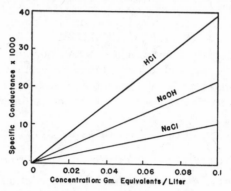

FIG. 5.   The approximate rectilinear relationship between specific conductance and
concentration.

normal sodium hydroxide (or 0.1 *N* NaOH) are directly proportional to
the respective concentrations and consequently A is a straight line.   To
keep the total volume constant during a single titration, however, is not

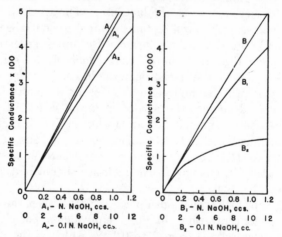

FIG. 6.   To show that the rectilinear relationship can be maintained by using a titrant
of a suitable concentration.

practicable.   The nearest approach that can be made is to carry out the
titration with a relatively large volume of a dilute solution and to use a
concentrated solution of the titrant so that the total volume of the

reacting solutions change but little as the titration proceeds. Curve A_1 shows the effect of adding 1.3 ml of N NaOH to 100 ml. of water, the volume thereby changing from 100 to 101.3 ml. Curve A_2 refers to the addition of the same weight of caustic soda to 100 ml. of water, but being added as 0.1 N NaOH, 13 ml. were necessary, whereby the volume changed from 100 to 113 ml. Whereas A_1 is straight, A_2 is slightly curved. In the case of A_2, owing to the progressively large increase in total volume, the volume of 0.1 N sodium hydroxide added is not proportional to the concentration of alkali in the resulting solution.

Curves B, B_1 and B_2 are comparable with the exception that they refer to 10 ml. instead of 100 ml., as for the A curves. Thus B_1 refers to

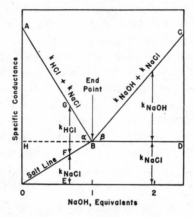

FIG. 7.   Conductometric titration of a very dilute solution of hydrochloric acid with a concentrated solution of sodium hydroxide.

the addition of 1.3 ml. of 1 N sodium hydroxide to 10 ml. of water, and a consequent change in volume from 10 ml. to 11.3 ml., an increase of 13%, whereas B_2 refers to the addition of 13 ml. of 0.1 N sodium hydroxide to 10 ml. of water by which the total volume increases by 130%, i.e., from 10 to 23 ml. Curves B_1 and B_2 are appreciably curved, the curvature of B_2 being greater than that of B_1 owing to the greater increase in volume. *In general, the concentrations of the reactants should be so chosen that the increase in volume of the mixed solutions should not exceed 5%.*

2.1.2. Titration of a Strong Acid with a Strong Base. Figure 7 illustrates the type of conductometric graph obtained by titrating 100 ml. of approximately 0.01 N hydrochloric acid with 1 N sodium hydroxide; the endpoint being reached when ca. 1.0 ml. of alkali has been added. For the complete titration only 2 ml. of alkali are required, so that the effect of dilution becomes negligible. But so small a titer can be accurately found only by using a good microburet. An accurate buret having

1 ml. scale divisions 5-cm. apart, and reading to 0.01 ml. is necessary. Furthermore, it is essential that the solution undergoing titration be thoroughly stirred before each conductance reading is made.

2.2. Errors in the Titration of Strong Acids

a. *Dilution.* Righellato and Davies (62) point out that if the usual assumption be accepted regarding the graphical extrapolation of the end point when the concentration of the titrant is 10 times that of the solution being titrated that the end point in conductometric titrations may occur 2% too early. Thus if 100 ml. of 0.01 N hydrochloric acid were titrated with 0.1 N sodium hydroxide the end point would occur at about 9.8 ml. instead of at 10 ml. That such an error might arise becomes obvious from the lack of rectilinearity of A_2 in Fig. 6, for if the alkali curve obtained after passing the end point of the titration were considered to be straight in such circumstances, and then produced to intersect the neutralization line, and the end point were assumed to be indicated by the point of intersection, the titer would certainly be too low. Working on the assumption that, within the range of concentrations involved in a titration that necessitates a 10% dilution, the specific conductance is directly proportional to the concentration they correct for dilution by multiplying each observed conductance by the factor:

$$\frac{\text{Total volume of the solution corresponding to that measurement}}{\text{Initial volume of the solution to be titrated}}$$

Such a correction is sufficient for practical purposes, despite the fact that it ignores any slight changes in ionic mobilities due to the diffusion of the ionic atmospheres as postulated by Debye and Hückel.

b. *Presence of Carbon Dioxide.* If "equilibrium water" is used and the alkali is free from carbon dioxide, errors will, of course, not be caused by carbon dioxide. But if carbon dioxide be present Poetke (55) states that such errors will be negligible in the titration of a strong acid with a strong base, but that when carried out in the reverse manner the end point will appear too early and in place of a sharp "break" the titration graph will be curved in the vicinity of the end point. In titrating weak acids with alkali, carbon dioxide will lead to too high titers and to too low titers when the titration is carried out in the reverse way.

2.3. Theory of Titration

As the sodium hydrochloride is added to the hydrochloric acid the hydrogen ions are progressively replaced by sodium ions:

$$H^{\cdot} + Cl' + Na^{\cdot} + OH' \rightarrow Na^{\cdot} + Cl' + H_2O$$

so that when the equivalence point is reached the replacement is complete and only the ions of sodium chloride remain. The line OB, called the "salt line" represents the increase in conductance due to the increasing concentration of sodium chloride whereas the vertical distance between AB and OB corresponds to the conductance caused by the decreasing concentration of hydrochloric acid. BD indicates the contribution by the sodium chloride to the total conductance after the end-point, B, is passed, whereas BC represents the contribution to the conductance made by the excess of sodium hydroxide.

The diminution in conductance, indicated by AB, is caused by the removal of the highly mobile hydrogen ions and the substitution of the much less mobile sodium ions. Thus the equivalent conductance, Λ_{C_a}, of a solution of hydrochloric acid containing C_a gram equivalents per liter is related to the ionic mobilities, $l_{H^.}$ and $l_{Cl'}$:

$$\Lambda_{C_a} = \frac{1000\kappa_a}{C_a} = \alpha(l_{H^.} + l_{Cl'})$$

κ_a being the specific conductance and α the degree of ionization. As the solutions that are conductometrically titrated are preferably very dilute, we can put $\alpha = 1$, whence

$$\kappa_a = \frac{C_a}{1000} \times (l_{H^.} + l_{Cl'})$$

Similarly for sodium chloride solutions,

$$\Lambda_{C_s} = \frac{1000\kappa_s}{C_s} = \alpha(l_{Na^.} + l_{Cl'})$$

so that
$$\kappa_s = \frac{C_s}{1000} \times (l_{Na^.} + l_{Cl'})$$

As both acid and salt are present during neutralization, the concentration of acid, C_a, will decrease and thereby produce a decrease in its specific conductance, κ_a, while that of the salt formed, C_s, will increase with a corresponding increase in κ_s, as shown by the "salt line." At any point, E, the observed specific conductance κ will be equal to $\kappa_a + \kappa_s$, i.e., to $EG = GF + FE$ in Fig. 7. Hence

$$\kappa = \kappa_a + \kappa_s = \frac{C_a}{1000}(l_{H^.} + l_{Cl'}) + \frac{C_s}{1000}(l_{Na^.} + l_{Cl'})$$

$$= \frac{1}{1000}\{C_a l_{H^.} + C_s l_{Na^.} + (C_a + C_s).l_{Cl'}\}$$

If the initial concentration of the hydrochloric acid be C, and *if we can ignore the small dilution that occurs in a titration*, then $C = C_a + C_s$, so that when the fraction of hydrochloric and neutralized is x, then $C_s = xC$, and $C_a = (1 - x)C$, whence it follows that

$$\kappa = \frac{C}{1000}\{(1 - x)l_{H^.} + xl_{Na^.} + l_{Cl'}\},$$

showing that the difference, AH, between the specific conductance observed at the beginning of a titration and at the end point, i.e., when $x = 0$ and $x = 1$, is equal to

$$\frac{C}{1000} \times (l_{\text{H}} - l_{\text{Na}'})$$

The *slope* of the neutralization graph AB is $\tan \alpha = \dfrac{AH}{HB}$, and if the titer, OI, ($= HB$) be expressed in terms of the concentration, C, then

$$\tan \alpha = (l_{\text{H}} - l_{\text{Na}}) \cdot \frac{C}{1000} \Big/ C = \frac{l_{\text{H}} - l_{\text{Na}}}{1000}$$

The slope of the alkali graph, BC, is

$$\tan \beta = \frac{l_{\text{Na}} + l_{\text{OH}'}}{1000},$$

i.e., provided that the dilution is negligible and the extended "salt line," BD, remains horizontal to the x-axis, the increase in conductance then resulting from the increasing excess of alkali added. If appreciable dilution occurs BD will slope downwards towards the x-axis and the slope of BC will be accordingly reduced.

2.3.1. Influence of Ionic Mobilities. As ionic mobilities, or more precisely, the equivalent conductances of ions, are of fundamental importance in conductometric titrations, Tables II and III are inserted to show the magnitudes of the mobilities of ions and their great dependence on temperature.

TABLE II

Ionic Mobilities at 18 and 25°

Kations				Anions		
Ion	Temperature			Ion	Temperature	
	18°	25°			18°	25°
H·	316.6	349.7		OH′	175	196
Li·	33.3	38.7		Cl′	65.5	76.6
Na·	43.5	50.1		Br′	67.6	77.7
K·	64.4	73.5		I′	66.1	—
NH₄	64.4	74.8		CNS′	56.5	—
Ag·	54.4	61.9		NO₃′	61.8	71.4
½Ca··	51	61		½SO₄″	68	80
½Sr··	51	61		½C₂O₄″	63.0	73.5
½Ba··	55	65		½CO₃″	70.0	83.3
½Pb··	60.8	71.2		HCO₃′	40.5	47.0
½Mg··	45	53		CH₃COO′	35.0	40.8
½Zn··	46	54		½CrO₄″	72	—

TABLE III

Ion	0°	18°	25°	50°	100°
H·	229	317	350	465	633
Na·	26	44	50	82	155
K·	40	64	74	115	206
Ag·	33	54	62	101	188
$\frac{1}{2}$Ba··	33	55	65	104	200
OH'	105	175	196	284	439
Cl'	41	66	77	116	207
$\frac{1}{2}$SO₄''	41	68	80	125	234

These figures reveal that at all temperatures the mobilities of the hydrogen and hydroxyl ions are very much higher than those of any other ions and it is this fact of which use is made in acid-base conductometric titrations.

2.4. Conductometric Titrations of Acids of Different Strengths with Strong Bases

We have seen in the previous paragraph that, owing to the high mobility of the hydrogen ion, the exceptional conductance of a solution of an acid is to be attributed to the concentration of the hydrogen ions which it yields through dissociation. In the case of a strong acid the ionization is almost complete. Moreover when its ionization is regarded from the classical theory of Arrhenius, it is found that the variation in the degree of dissociation with concentration cannot be accounted for by the law of mass action. On the contrary, the ionization of weak acids and bases at varying concentrations is in remarkable accordance with both the Arrhenius theory and the law of mass action. It is true that dissociation constants of weak acids, computed on the basis of the Arrhenius theory, display a tendency to decrease for solutions of increasing dilution, but the extent is insufficient to discard the Arrhenius theory for our present purpose. Fig. 8, which is diagrammatic only, gives the conductometric graphs of weak acids (0.0156 N), having the dissociation constants indicated, with potassium hydroxide (1 N). Proceeding downwards from the uppermost graph, which for the sake of comparison is that of hydrochloric acid, the curves are those of acids of diminishing strength, viz., trichloracetic acid, $K = 3 \times 10^{-1}$; dichloracetic acid, $K = 5 \times 10^{-2}$; monochloracetic acid, $K = 1.6 \times 10^{-3}$; formic acid, $K = 2 \times 10^{-4}$; acetic acid, $K = 1.8 \times 10^{-5}$; and paranitrophenol, $K = 5.6 \times 10^{-8}$. In constructing this diagram the data have been so plotted that the specific conductances of the solutions of the salts of each acid, formed at the end points, were identical. Through the small differences between the ionic mobilities of the anions of the various acids this is not quite the case.

It will be observed that as the strength of the acids decreases the specific conductances become lower and the neutralization curves depart from the rectilinearity of the strong acid. Though the curvature of the neutralization graphs of the acids, of which $K = 3 \times 10^{-1}$ and 5×10^{-2}, is not large, that of the weaker acids become increasingly great until the acids become so weak, as is the case with acetic acid, $K = 1.8 \times 10^{-5}$,

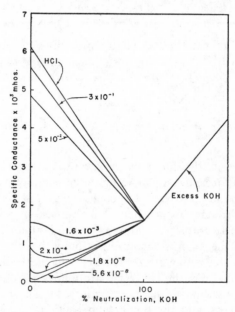

FIG. 8.　The effect of the dissociation constant of an acid on its conductometric graph during neutralization with a strong base.

that a slight curvature is produced in the initial section of the curve while the final section is practically straight. For yet weaker acids the curvature becomes less and the final straight section becomes longer. A very slight initial bend is just perceptible in the paranitrophenol ($K = 5.6 \times 10^{-8}$) graph. The curves for still weaker acids, such as boric acid, $K = 6 \times 10^{-10}$, arsenious acid, $K = 5.5 \times 10^{-10}$ and phenol $K = 6 \times 10^{-10}$, are perfectly straight. As in Fig. 7 the straight line joining the origin to the point of intersection of the acid-alkali graphs is the "salt line." The weakest acids, e.g., boric, are incapable of producing sufficient concentrations of hydrogen ions to affect the specific conductances of their solutions. On neutralization, however, they form alkali salts which render their solutions increasingly conducting until the acids are completely neutralized, e.g., arsenious acid, $HAsO_2 + KOH \rightarrow K^{\cdot} + AsO_2' + H_2O$; the result being that their neutralization graphs coincide with their respective salt lines.

The neutralization graphs of the stronger acids, for which K is of the order of 10^{-3} and 10^{-4}, in showing that the specific conductances first fall, then pass through minima, and finally tend to approach the "salt lines," are interesting in that they reveal the gradual depression of the ionization of the diminishing concentration of unneutralized acid by the increasing concentration of the anions of the sodium salt formed as the neutralizations proceed. Bruni and coworkers (13) have shown that the location of these minima depend on the ionic mobilities, the dissociation constants of the acids, and their concentrations.

2.4.1. Moderately Strong Acids. $K = 10^{-1}$–10^{-4}. Owing to the comparatively large curvature of the neutralization graphs of the stronger acids, $K = 10^{-3}$, especially when titrated at certain concentrations, the exact location of the equivalence-point is sometimes difficult. Thus in curve A in Fig. 9, which represents the conductometric titration of 100 ml. of 0.01 N salicylic acid with 0.56 N NaOH, the precise end point is not easily located. To find the end point Kolthoff (41) constructs the "salt line," B, by adding 0.05 N sodium salicylate to 100 ml. of water and determining the conductances. The point indicated by the arrow is the true end point. The difficulty about Kolthoff's method is that it presupposes that the acid being titrated is known. Righellato and Davis (62) therefore, devised two methods which obviate this requirement; one of which will be described. A conductometric titration of the acid is first performed with ammonia, and a second one on a solution of the acid of the same concentration is carried out with potassium hydroxide of exactly the same concentration as that of the ammonium hydroxide previously used. As the ammonium and potassium ions have almost the same mobilities the neutralization graphs will be nearly coincident up to the end point. Thereafter, the excess of potassium hydroxide will give an oblique straight line, whereas the excess of ammonium hydroxide will be represented by a straight line parallel with the x-axis, owing to the ammonium ions, originating from the ammonium salt, depressing the trifling ionization of the free ammonium hydroxide. The point of

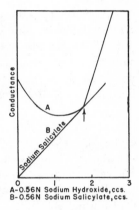

A-0.56N Sodium Hydroxide, ccs.
B-0.56N Sodium Salicylate, ccs.

Fig. 9. Location of the titration end point of a moderately strong acid.

intersection of the potassium hydroxide and ammonium hydroxide lines
denotes the titer of the acid.

2.4.2. Weak Acids. K < 10⁻⁵. As already shown, the final part
of the neutralization graph is straight and is coincident with the "salt
line." But when this straight portion is not sufficiently long to produce
it with certainty so as to intersect the "alkali line" produced, the precise
determination of the end point may not be easy and this difficulty is
aggravated by the large angle between these two lines which may interfere with accurate extrapolation. Another point to remember is that
in the final stage of the neutralization of a weak acid some hydrolysis
of the alkali salt occurs, thereby giving slightly higher conductances
than would be caused by the salt alone. This leads to a rounding of the
titration curve in the vicinity of the end point. Unless the acid be very
weak, this curvature at the end point does not create insurmountable
difficulties.

Kolthoff suggests that at least one-quarter of the neutralization
graph should be straight for the satisfactory extrapolation of the end
point. As already stated, during the process of neutralization of an
acid, $\kappa_{obs} = \kappa_{salt} + \kappa_{acid}$, and by assuming that the neutralization graph
will begin at 75% neutralization to coincide with the salt-line when κ_{acid}
is equal to $\kappa_{salt}/100$, Kolthoff arrives at the expression:

$$K = 6.7 \times 10^{-3} \times C,$$

giving the relationship which must exist at 25° between the dissociation
constant, K, and the initial concentration of the acid, C, for this to occur.
Hence to titrate a decinormal solution of an acid at 25°, i.e., $C = 0.1\ N$,
the dissociation constant must be equal to, or less than 6.7×10^{-4}; a
centinormal solution, $C = 0.01\ N$, $K \lessgtr 6.7 \times 10^{-5}$; a millinormal solution, $C = 0.001\ N$, $K \lessgtr 6.7 \times 10^{-6}$. At 18° for $0.1\ N$ acid, $K < 5
\times 10^{-4}$; $0.01\ N$ acid, $K < 5 \times 10^{-5}$; and for $0.001\ N$ acid $K < 5 \times 10^{-6}$.

2.4.3. Very Weak Acids. K < 10⁻⁷. The difficulty in conductometrically titrating very weak acids with strong bases arises from the
relatively large amounts of hydrolysis of the alkali salts, resulting in
enhanced conductances, that may occur when insufficient free acid
remains in the solution to prevent their hydrolytic decomposition from
becoming appreciable. Hydrolysis will cause the neutralization graph
to diverge from the "salt line" as soon as it is sufficient, by substituting
the highly conducting OH′ ions for the much less mobile acid anions, to
raise the conductance by 1% above that due to the salt formed. It can
be shown that the neutralization graph of a centinormal solution of an
acid will coincide with the "salt line" during the first half of the neutralization if $K > 5 \times 10^{-10}$; for three quarters of the neutralization if

$K > 1.1 \times 10^{-9}$ and for 90% of the neutralization if $K > 2.6 \times 10^{-9}$. These figures show that it is possible to titrate very weak acids conductometrically having dissociation constants as small as 10^{-10}. This brings very weak acids, e.g., phenol, boric, and arsenious acid, within the scope of conductometric titration in a manner which is more accurate than either potentiometric or volumetric methods. Their conductometric graphs consist simply of "salt lines" and "alkali lines" and production of the initial straight sections of the salt lines to intersect the alkali lines produced renders it easy to locate the end points. Provided that a weak base is capable of neutralizing the very weak acid in question, a more satisfactory angle between the "neutralization line" and the "excess base line" is obtained, in that it facilitates the location of the end point (cf. Fig. 10).

2.5. The Titration of Weak Acids with Weak Bases

Cases have already been cited in which the titrations of acids with ammonium hydroxide lead to more satisfactory "breaks" corresponding

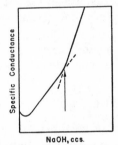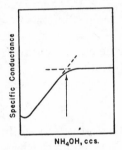

FIG. 10. Location of the end point of a titration of a weak acid (acetic) with (a) NaOH, (b) NH₄OH.

with the end points. This is clearly demonstrated by the titration graphs of acetic acid in Fig. 10. But the strength of the weak base used as the titrant must be taken into consideration for it may happen that the hydrolysis of the resulting salt may be so large and the graph may therefore become so curved in the vicinity of the end point that the accurate extrapolation of the end point may become impossible. As Fig. 10 shows, this is not the case when acetic acid is titrated with ammonia although it is the case when much weaker acids, such as boric, arsenious, and hydrocyanic, are titrated.

It can be shown that the pH range within which 1 to 99% of a weak acid can be neutralized is $pK_a - 2$ to $pK_a + 2$, whereas the pH range for the neutralization of a weak base (1 — 99%) is given by $pK_w - pK_b + 2$ to $pK_w - pK_b - 2$; K_a being the dissociation constant of the weak acid; K_b, that of a weak base, and K_w, the ionic product of water (6). Thus the dissociation constant of acetic acid is 1.8×10^{-5}, and therefore $pK_a = 4.74$, so that in order to neutralize acetic acid with a pH range of pH 2.74 to pH 6.74, it is necessary that the base shall be able to set up a pH somewhat higher than pH 6.74 when the base itself is at least 99% neutralized. As K_b of ammonium hydroxide is 1.8×10^{-5}, i.e., $pK_b = 4.74$, and as $pK_w = 14$, it follows that ammonium hydroxide is 1% neutralized at pH 9.24 and 99% neutralized at pH 7.24.

In the neutralization of acetic acid with ammonium hydroxide, the formation of ammonium acetate necessitates that both conditions, regarding the neutralization of the weak acid and of the weak base, shall simultaneously be satisfied. These conditions are satisfied in this particular titration, for acetic acid is 99% neutralized at pH 6.74 and ammonium hydroxide is 99% neutralized at pH 7.25. Some hydrolysis of the ammonium acetate occurs before, at, and after the end point as shown by Fig. 10. Soon after the end point, the hydrolysis is depressed and so is the ionization of the ammonium hydroxide which has been added in excess by the ammonium acetate already formed. This is manifested by the fact that the excess of the weak base causes no change in conductance.

The conductometric titration graph of boric acid with ammonium hydroxide exhibits no "break" and is so curved that graphical extrapolation of the end point is not possible.

$$HBO_2 + NH_4OH \rightleftharpoons NH_4{}^{\cdot} + BO_2{}' + H_2O$$

The pK_a of boric acid is 9.24 so that for 99% neutralization the attainment of pH 11.24 is required, whereas the pH when only 1% of ammonia is neutralized is 11.25. This means that NH_4BO_2 can only exist in solution when the ratio of the *excess of ammonia* to the *ammonium borate* is in the molecular ratio of 99:1; this large excess being needed to depress the hydrolysis of the ammonium borate. Under such conditions conductometric titration is clearly impossible. The use of ammonia as a titrant is therefore restricted to strong and weak acids, the dissociation constants of the latter being not much less than 10^{-5}.

2.6. Titration of Mixtures of Acids and Di- and Tribasic Acids

Pyridine, $K_b = 1.2 \times 10^{-9}$, $pK_b = 8.9$, is a weak base and is often used in conductometric analysis for the simple reason that it is too weak to react with very weak acids, e.g., phenol, $pK_a = 10$, boric acid, $pK_a = 9.24$, but is sufficiently strong to neutralize strong and moderately strong acids. It is therefore used to determine conductometrically such acids in mixtures of very weak acids.

Figure 11 illustrates the titration of a mixture of mandelic acid, $K_a = 4.3 \times 10^{-4}$, and phenol, $K_a = 10^{-10}$, with (i) sodium hydroxide, (ii) ammonium hydroxide (iii) pyridine. In the sodium hydroxide graph the mandelic acid neutralization curve merges into the phenol section without giving any definite "break" although the end of the neutralization of the mixed acids is clearly defined. The ammonium hydroxide graph shows that ammonia is able partly to neutralize the phenol, while in the pyridine graph a "break" indicates the complete neutralization of the mandelic acid only, pyridine being much too weak to react with phenol. The composition of the mixture can thus be found from the

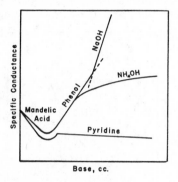

FIG. 11. Use of a very weak base (pyridine) to determine the end point of the neutralization of a moderately strong acid in the presence of a very weak acid.

sodium hydroxide and pyridine titrations. Calculation shows that 99% neutralization of pyridine is only possible in acid solutions of pH 3.1, whereas phenol requires a pH of 12.0 for 99% neutralization. Hence pyridine cannot neutralize phenol, but is able to neutralize the comparatively strong acids.

If the mixture consists of a strong acid and a weak acid, it is sometimes possible to extrapolate the end point of the neutralization of the strong acid by producing the strong acid and weak acid sections until they intersect, whereas the end point of the titration of the mixture will be indicated by a "break." Such a method presupposes that the strong acid is sufficiently strong to give a straight line change in conductance on neutralization and the weak acid is sufficiently weak that the major portion of its neutralization graph follows its "salt line." This method may be illustrated by a neutralization graph of oxalic acid (Fig. 12). In its ionization and neutralization oxalic acid behaves as if it were a mixture in equivalent proportions of a strong acid,

$$H_2C_2O_4 \rightleftharpoons H^\cdot + HC_2O_4{}'$$

and a fairly weak acid,

$$HC_2O_4' \rightleftharpoons H\cdot + C_2O_4''$$

Extrapolation from the first two rectilinear sections gives the titer at which sodium or ammonium bioxalate are formed in solution. Chromic acid, H_2CrO_4, gives a similar graph, the first "break" corresponding to the formation of $NaHCrO_4$, and the second to Na_2CrO_4. In very dilute solution the neutralization of the first stage of phosphoric acid gives a rectilinear graph which is terminated by a well-defined "break" (NaH_2-PO_4). In its second stage phosphoric acid is weak and very weak in its third stage. Owing to the slight difference in the mobilities of the HPO_4'' and PO_4''' ions there is but a slight change in the slopes of the

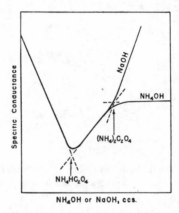

FIG. 12. The conductometric titrations of the dibasic acid (oxalic) with (a) NaOH, (b) NH₄OH.

second and third sections of the graph. Unless a solution of phosphoric acid of concentration greater than 0.05 M be titrated, this difference in slope is insufficient to permit the location the point corresponding to Na_2HPO_4. Owing to the extreme weakness of the third stage:

$$HPO_4'' \rightleftharpoons H\cdot + PO_4'''$$

the considerable hydrolysis which occurs in very dilute solutions prevents the extrapolation of the third end point, although with solutions more concentrated than 0.05 M such extrapolation becomes possible.

Figure 13 (left) illustrates the titration of a mixture of a strong acid and moderately strong acid, K about 10^{-4}. By neutralizing with 1 N sodium hydroxide, the final "break" at A', corresponding with a titer of OP, is obtained, but no "break" is given at R when the neutralization of the strong acid is complete, i.e., with a titer equal to OQ. Righellato and Davies, however, had devised a method by which OQ can be indirectly computed. It consists of titrating the neutralized solution, i.e., corresponding to A', with 1 N hydrochloric acid, whereby the graph AD (Fig. 13 right) is obtained. The initial section of this curve refers to the replacement of the moderately strong acid HM, from its salt, NaM, thus

$$NaM + HCl \rightarrow NaCl + HM,$$

while the oblique section, MD, ultimately becomes rectilinear owing to the excess of hydrochloric acid, the ionization of the released HM having

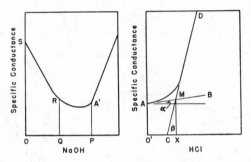

FIG. 13. Righellato and Davies' method of estimating the titer of a strong acid in the presence of a weak acid.

previously been depressed. It can readily be shown that the

$$\frac{\text{Slope of } DC}{\text{Slope of } AB} = \frac{\tan \beta}{\tan \alpha} = \frac{l_{H^.} + l_{Cl'}}{l_{Cl'} - l_{M'}}.$$

The angle, β, can be measured directly, and if the mobilities, $l_{H^.}$, $l_{Cl'}$ and $l_{M'}$, are known, the angle, α, can be calculated. The line AB can then be constructed. Its point, M, of intersection with DC gives the titer, $O'X$, of the moderately strong acid, HM. As $O'X = PQ$, therefore $OQ = OP - O'X$.

2.7. Replacement Titration Reactions

The graphs in Fig. 14 are typical of titrations in which weak acids or bases are replaced from their salts by strong acids or strong bases respectively. It very often happens that this form of titration results in sharper "breaks" being obtained. The graphs, marked CH_3COONa, $Na_2C_2O_4$, K_2CrO_4, Na_3PO_4, and Na_2S, represent the change in specific conductance when dilute solutions of these salts are progressively treated with hydrochloric acid. In every case it is the weak stages of the acids involved that are replaced, and where there is more than one weak stage, the weakest stage is first replaced to be followed by the next weakest acid stage and

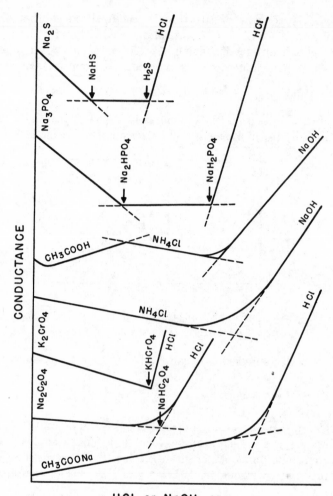

FIG. 14. Typical replacement conductometric titrations.

so on. Thus in the Na_3PO_4 graph, the first section refers to the replacement reaction:

$$Na_3PO_4 + HCl \rightarrow NaCl + Na_2HPO_4$$
$$K_{HPO_4''} = 10^{-12}$$

the second section to:

$$Na_2HPO_4 + HCl \rightarrow NaCl + NaH_2PO_4$$
$$K_{H_2PO_4'} = 10^{-7}$$

while in the third section the comparatively strong acid stage:

$$H_3PO_4 \rightleftharpoons H^{\cdot} + H_2PO_4'$$
$$K_{H_3PO_4} = 10^{-2}$$

becomes involved. Owing to its greater strength the reaction:

$$NaH_2PO_4 + HCl \rightleftharpoons NaCl + H_3PO_4$$

requires considerably more than 1 equivalent of hydrochloric acid to drive it completely from left to right, with the consequence that no "break" appears in the third section of the conductometric graph. Similar remarks apply to the second sections of potassium chromate and sodium oxalate graphs.

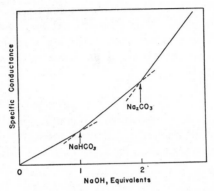

Fig. 15. The conductometric titration of 100 cc. of 0.006 M H_2CO_3 with 0.56 N NaOH.

The curve, marked NH_4Cl, typifies the changes in conductance produced when NaOH is added to a solution of NH_4Cl by the reaction:

$$NH_4Cl + NaOH \rightarrow NH_4OH + NaCl$$

the specific conductance during the replacement of the weak base being caused by the concentrations of the remaining ammonium chloride and the sodium chloride formed.

The graph immediately above that of NH_4Cl is that of solution containing acetic acid and ammonium chloride with sodium hydroxide. The first "break" marks the completion of the neutralization of the acetic acid while the second "break" indicates when the ammonium hydroxide is completely liberated from the ammonium chloride.

2.8. The Titration of Carbonic Acid

Carbonic acid, H_2CO_3, is quite a weak acid in its first stage, $K = 3 \times 10^{-7}$, and a very weak acid in its second, $K_2 = 6 \times 10^{-11}$. On neutralization with a concentrated solution of sodium hydroxide the specific conductance will follow the salt line, i.e., of sodium bicarbonate, during the first stage, and the sodium carbonate salt line during the second stage, except that the hydrolysis of the Na_2CO_3 will cause the conductometric graph to depart somewhat from the salt line towards the end of neutralization. As the mobility of the bicarbonate ion is 40, while that of the carbonate ion is 70, it follows that the slope of the sodium carbonate salt line will be greater than that of the sodium bicarbonate salt line, as is shown to be the case in Fig. 15 which refers to a titration of 100 ml. of 0.006 M sodium carbonate with 0.56 N sodium hydroxide (42). As Kolthoff pointed out, the "breaks" are not very pronounced and in order to find them at all it is necessary to make very accurate measurements of the specific conductance.

By inserting calcium chloride in the carbonic acid solution and then titrating with alkali, an accurate end point, corresponding with the second "break," can be obtained on account of the precipitation of calcium carbonate.

2.9. The Titration of Phenols in Aqueous-Alcohol Media

As phenol is a very weak acid its conductometric titration graph coincides with the salt line until its neutralization is complete, after which the excess alkali is represented by a straight line having a greater slope.

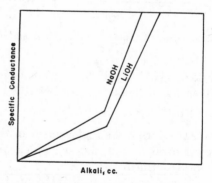

Fig. 16. The conductometric titration of an aqueous solution of phenol with (a) NaOH, (b) LiOH.

Using very dilute solutions the hydrolysis of the alkali salt will cause a rounding in the region of the end point, which, however, will not detract from the accuracy by which the end point can be detected by extrapolation. As the mobility of the lithium ion is appreciably lower than that of the sodium ion, the use of lithium hydroxide instead of sodium hydroxide as titrant, as shown in Fig. 16 will result in a larger angle at the end point, thereby making its extrapolation more precise. It happens that the phenols are such weak acids that they render their titration either volumetrically, with indicators, or potentiometrically inaccurate. Moreover, some phenols are sparingly soluble in water although they will dissolve in alcohol. Solutions in alcohol-water media (the alcohol being about 40% by volume) can be titrated with an accuracy greater than 1% with lithium hydroxide, after making a correction for the slight reaction between the lithium hydroxide and the alcohol (about 0.03 ml.). Vanillin, isovanillin, bourbonal, isobourbonal, and protocatechuialdehyde have been so titrated.

In salicylic acid the phenolic group is so feeble an acid, K = ca. 10^{-13}, that it cannot be conductometrically titrated. But in its esters, e.g., methylsalicylate and phenylsalicylate, the phenol groups function as acids which are sufficiently strong for conductometric titration. Owing to their slight solubility in water the titrations must be performed in 50–60% alcohol-water solutions.

2.10. Conductometric Titration of Alkaloids and Their Salts

Alkaloids are usually very weak bases that are sparingly soluble in water. Hence, during the titration of the acid present in their salts with alkali, using phenolphthalein as indicator, it often happens that the free base undergoes precipitation, and so renders difficult the detection of the color-change. In some instances, the free bases are strong enough to give an alkaline reaction to phenolphthalein. Many free alkaloid bases can be titrated directly with hydrochloric acid to either methyl red or dimethyl yellow, though some very weak alkaloids, such as papaverine and hydrastine, cannot be so titrated. In these volumetric estimations, however, even in the presence of alcohol there is a distinct tendency to get indefinite end points and the results consequently are erroneous. It is not surprising, therefore, that other methods have been sought, and considerable success has been obtained by the use of conductometric methods.

The first conductometric titrations were carried out by Küster, Grüters and Geibel in 1904 who adopted the replacement method by dissolving the free alkaloid (quinine, cinchonine, quinidine, and cinchonidine were tested) in hydrochloric acid and titrating back with barium hydroxide. This was followed, in 1916, by the work of Dutoit and Meyer-Levy (19), who made an extensive investigation of the subject. They found the direct neutralization of the alkaloid to be unsuitable for quantitative work, but found the "replacement method" in which the salts were titrated with sodium hydroxide to be satisfactory, provided that the liberated alkaloidal bases are insoluble. Soluble bases gave indefinite results. Titration with reagents which precipitate alkaloids gave the following results:

(a) *Chloroplatinic acid* was satisfactory only in the presence of sodium acetate.

(b) *Picric acid* gave useful results of the concentration of the alkaloid solution when between 0.01 and 0.002 N, to which was added sodium acetate, equal to 2 to 3 times the weight of alkaloid, the picric acid solution in alcohol being approximately 0.5 N.

(c) *Phospho-tungstic acid* was very unsatisfactory, owing to the fact that it precipitates substances other than alkaloids, and also that its decomposition, especially in slightly acid solutions, causes the conductivity to alter with time. Errors of several per cent were always obtained.

(d) *Potassium dichromate* is suitable for a few alkaloids, the dichromates of which are insoluble in water, e.g., brucine and morphine, if the titrations are carried out in strictly neutral solution.

(e) *Silico-tungstic acid* yielded very good results in the presence of sodium acetate. The two parts of. the conductivity curve are straight and their intersection gives the end point within 1%. The concentration of the alkaloid should be 0.01 to 0.002 N and that of the silico-tungstic acid should be 0.5 to 0.05 N. The reagent may be standardized either gravimetrically, weighing as $SiO_2,12WO_3$, or preferably by conductometric titration against a known amount of pure salt of some alkaloid. Dutoit and Meyer-Levy found strychnine salts to be quite satisfactory. Sodium acetate in concentration of two to three times that of the alkaloid should be added.

Dutoit and Meyer-Levy showed that the salts of veratrine, strychnine, brucine, cocaine, narcotine, morphine, aconitine, papaverine, aspidospermine, and emetine could be estimated by conductometric titration, and more recently Kolthoff (42) has added to the list salts of the following alkaloids: tropacocaine, atropine, codeine, and novocaine. Unlike Dutoit and Meyer-Levy, Kolthoff was able to titrate conductometrically, with accuracy, some alkaloidal bases with strong acids. Thus excellent titrations were performed on hydrastine with 0.1 N HCl, using 0.01 M solution in 50% alcohol, and on codeine. A brief outline of Kolthoff's work follows.

Although quinine is a diacid base, the quinine hydrochloride of commerce is the monochloride. The two basic constants of quinine are $K_{b_1} = 10^{-6}$ and $K_{b_2} = 10^{-9.7}$. It should therefore be possible to check the purity of the commercial product by following the replacement reaction with alkali or by conductometric titration of the salt with hydrochloric acid, so as to bring the weaker base into combination. Both methods have been shown by Kolthoff to yield accurate results. Similarly, strychnine is a diacid base, $K_{b_1} = 10^{-6}$ and $K_{b_2} = 10^{-11.7}$. The second base is too weak for conductometric titration, but the monohydronitrate usually supplied can be satisfactorily titrated conductometrically with alkali. Cocaine hydrochloride is the salt of a weak base, $K_b = 10^{-5.6}$, and owing to the insolubility of the free base, the salt can only be titrated with alkali to phenolphthalein either if alcohol is added to keep the cocaine in solution, or else carbon tetrachloride, or chloroform is added with shaking to precipitate it completely. Conductometrically, however, a sharp end point can be obtained without any of these substances being added. Following the "replacement reactions" from tropacocaine hydrochloride and novocaine with alkali by means of conductivity lead to accurate results. Novocaine also contains an amino group, but its constant, $K_b = 10^{-11.8}$, is too small to permit a very accurate conductometric titration with hydrochloric acid,

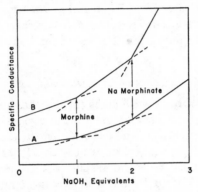

FIG. 17. Conductometric titrations of an ampholyte:
A. 25 cc of 0.05 M morphine hydrochloride with 1.035 N NaOH,
B. 25 cc. of 0.05 M morphine hydrochloride $+25$ cc 96 % alcohol with 1.035 N NaOH.

although Kolthoff has shown that a fairly good titer may be obtained by using solutions not less dilute than 0.05 M. Atropine hydrosulfate gave reasonably good results with both sodium and barium hydroxides. Fig. 17 is particularly interesting in that it represents the titration with alkali of the salt of an ampholyte, and also illustrates what an important effect alcohol may sometimes have on a conductometric titration. As an acid, morphine is very weak, $K_a = 10^{-9.85}$, whereas as a base it is somewhat stronger, $K_b = 10^{-6.13}$. It happens, therefore, that the titration of morphine hydrochloride with alkali interferes with the phenolphthalein end point through the liberation of the base, which although it is sparingly soluble, does not separate completely from the solution. Curve A represents the conductometric curve of the salt, but owing to the disturbing influence of the precipitated morphine, satisfactory readings were not easily obtained, and the end points were not accurate. Morphine, however, is soluble in alcohol, and so it was possible to obtain accurate results in the titration represented by B.

The first half of each of the titrations is one of replacement and the second half one of neutralization of a very weak acid. Dionine (ethyl morphine hydrochloride) and heroin can be similarly titrated. Morphine can be titrated in 50% alcohol as a base with hydrochloric acid, and as an acid with baryta.

Nicotine can be estimated accurately in aqueous solution, as it behaves as a diacid base; the first "break" is not sharp, but the second is quite satisfactory.

Kolthoff has also shown that it is possible to estimate amounts of theobromine and caffeine in a mixture by dissolving it in alkali and titrating back with N-hydrochloric acid. As an acid caffeine is very weak, K_a being less than 10^{-14} whereas theobromine is stronger, $K_a =$ ca. 10^{-10}. The first section terminating with an extrapolated end point, corresponds to the caffeine, and the second, ending with a sharp break, to the theobromine.

2.11. Titration of Bases with Acids

To the titration of bases with acids exactly the same principles apply as when the titrations are carried out in the reverse order. The effect of the dissociation constant of the base, K_b, on the shape of the titration curve with hydrochloric acid, with respect to its particular salt line, is shown in Fig. 18 which gives the graphs of a moderately strong base, methylamine, $K_b = 5 \times 10^{-14}$, and a weak base, ammonium hydroxide, $K_b = 1.8 \times 10^{-5}$, over a large range of dilutions, v representing the number of liters of aqueous solution in which 1 gram-equivalent of the base is contained. In the titration of very weak bases such as urotropine, $K_b = 6.5 \times 10^{-10}$, and pyridine, $K_b = 1.2 \times 10^{-9}$, with a strong acid, e.g., hydrochloric acid, the neutralization graph will be coincident with the salt line, although when extremely dilute solutions of the bases are titrated some little divergence from the salt lines will occur towards the end of neutralization owing to the hydrolysis of the salt. This is shown in graph A (Fig. 19) which refers to the titration of 25 ml. of 0.0096 N urotropine with 0.10 N hydrochloric acid, whereas the effect of hydrolysis is not apparent in graph B which refers to the use of solutions that were 10 times more concentrated, viz., 25 ml. of 0.096 N urotropine titrated with 1 N hydrochloric acid. (N.B. It must be realized that the graphs given in the figures in this Chapter are typical only of the different titrations, and that as the conductances observed vary widely with the concentrations of the solutions undergoing titration, the scale used as the ordinate of one graph in a figure will generally be very different from that employed for another graph. This applies to graphs A and B, in Fig. 19, with respect to the ordinate, marked "Specific Conductance.")

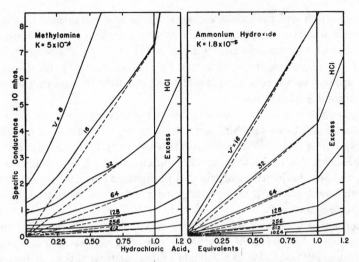

FIG. 18.   The effect of the dissociation constant of a base on the change in specific conductance during neutralization with a strong acid at different dilutions, v being the number of liters which contain 1 gram-equivalent.

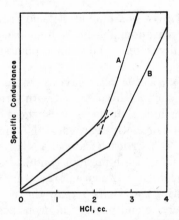

FIG. 19.   Conductometric titrations: effect of concentration:
   A. 25 cc. of 0.0096 N urotropine with 0.1 N HCl,
   B. 25 cc. of 0.096 N urotropine with 1 N HCl.

2.12. Conductometric Titrations of Acids in Acetone-Water Mixtures

Various workers (53, 62) have demonstrated the particular advantages accruing from the conductometric analysis of leather extracts, vegetable tan liquors and chrome tan liquors.   Owing to the deleterious actions of strong acids; particularly sulfuric acid, on leather it is desirable to have a method that not only will give the total quantity of acid present but one which will provide a measure of the concentrations of the acids and their relative strengths. This Airs and Balfe (1) have endeavored to do by conductometric titrations of acids of varying strengths in acetone-water mixtures, for as observed by Richardson (61) the strengths of acids appear to be considerably altered in media containing relatively large amounts of acetone.

Hydrochloric acid may be titrated with alcoholic sodium hydroxide solution in solutions containing from 70 to 80% of acetone by volume. A greater proportion of acetone increases the conductance of the sodium chloride and decreases that of the unneutralized hydrochloric acid so much so that the location of the end point then becomes impossible.

Benzenesulfonic acid in 80% acetone yields characteristic strong acid titration graphs.

Picric acid in 80 and 40% acetone mixtures behaves as a strong acid on titration. *Sulfuric acid* in 80% acetone behaves as a strong monobasic acid, but in 40% acetone as a dibasic acid on neutralization with alcoholic soda. With intermediate acetone contents the conductance minimum moves gradually away from 1 equivalent to 2 equivalents of sodium hydroxide.

Sulfurous acid behaves as a monobasic acid in 80% acetone.

Oxalic acid behaves anomalously in high acetone mixtures but in 30–60% acetone its minimum conductance points to its being a monobasic acid.

Tartaric, formic, and acetic acids gave titration curves which had no well-defined minima, such as are obtained with strong acids.

Airs and Balfe conclude that those acids whose dissociation constants are less than 10^{-2} can be exactly titrated to the minimum conductance if the solvent contains 40% or less of acetone. Stronger acids, $K > 10^{-1}$ are exactly neutralized at the minimum conductance if the solvent contains 80% or less of acetone. In place of the usual method of extrapolating the end point, Airs and Balfe regard the point of minimum conductance as indicating the end point in aqueous-acetone media.

To investigate the relative strengths of the acids and the amounts in which they exist in the combined state in vegetable tanning liquors, the bases are removed by percolation through the base-exchange resin or synthetic organolith, described by Cheshire *et al.* (16), under the designation of "Zeo-Karb. H1." To a suitable volume of the resulting acid solution a hundred-fold excess of pyridine was added and then titrated with NaOH (replacement reaction, see section 2.7). The object of using pyridine was to exclude any phenolic acids from the determinations. The amounts of the different groups of acids are then ascertained by a series of titrations: (i) in 80% acetone in which the strong acids, pK < 1, are estimated; (ii) in 40% acetone, (iii) in water. Acids of pK, 1–2, are equivalent to the difference between the titers of (ii) and (i), viz., (ii) − (i). Acids of pK, 2–7, are equivalent to (iii) − (i). The salt content is obtained from the difference between the conductometric titers of the solutions before and after the bases have been removed.

3. Conductometric Titrations Involving Precipitations

3.1. Precipitation Reactions: Theory

In Fig. 20, 1 represents the titration of 100 ml. of 0.0001 N silver nitrate with 0.01 N potassium chloride 2, that of 100 ml. of 0.001 N silver nitrate with 0.1 N potassium chloride; and 3, that of 100 ml. of 0.01 N silver

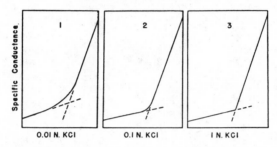

Fig. 20. Conductometric titrations of AgNo₃ with KCl, showing the effect of the concentrations of the reactants on the end-point "break."

nitrate with 1 N potassium chloride. It will be observed in graph 1 that the silver chloride remaining in solution in the region of the end point has a noticeable effect on the conductance, thereby rendering the location of the end point difficult. Using the 10 times more concentrated solutions (2) reduces the rounding of the curve at the end point and the longer straight lines facilitate the detection of the end point, whereas 3 shows that by titrating a centinormal solution of silver nitrate a sharp break is obtained at the end point.

The first section of the titration graph corresponds to the precipitation of silver chloride:

$$AgNO_3 + KCl \rightarrow AgCl\downarrow + KNO_3$$

so that if the solubility of the silver chloride can be ignored the variation in conductance is produced by the gradual replacement of the silver ions by the more mobile potassium ions. After precipitation is complete the marked increase in conductance is caused by the added excess of potassium chloride.

At 25° the specific conductance of an aqueous solution saturated with silver chloride is 1.794×10^{-6} mho. In titrations where the concentration of soluble salts give specific conductances of the order of 10^{-3} mho the conductance of the dissolved silver chloride is negligible.

As shown in Tables IV and V the specific conductances are of this order in titrations 3 and 2.

TABLE IV

Titration 3

100 ml. 0.01 N AgNO$_3$ + x ml. 1 N KCl at 25°

x ml.	$\kappa_{obs.}$ × 10^6	κ × 10^6			
		AgCl	AgNO$_3$	KNO$_3$	KCl
0	1333	—	1330	0	—
0.25	1363	0.003	1000	363	—
0.50	1392	0.005	667	725	—
0.75	1420	0.009	333	1087	—
0.90	1437	0.023	133	1304	—
0.99	1448	0.233	13	1435	—
1.00	1451	1.794	0	1449	—
1.01	1464	0.233	—	1449	15
1.10	1599	0.023	—	1449	150
1.25	1824	0.009	—	1449	375
1.50	2199	0.005	—	1449	750
1.75	2575	0.003	—	1449	1126
2.00	2950	0.002	—	1449	1501

TABLE V

Titration 2

100 ml. 0.001 N AgNO$_3$ + x ml. 0.1 N KCl at 25°

x ml.	$\kappa_{obs.}$ × 10^6	κ × 10^6			
		AgCl	AgNO$_3$	KNO$_3$	KCl
0	133	—	133	0	—
0.25	136	0.03	100	36	—
0.50	139	0.05	67	72	—
0.75	142	0.09	33	109	—
0.90	143	0.23	13	130	—
0.99	146	1.23	1	144	—
1.00	147	1.79	0	145	—
1.01	147	1.23	—	145	1
1.10	160	0.23	—	145	15
1.25	182	0.09	—	145	37
1.50	220	0.05	—	145	75
1.75	258	0.03	—	145	113
2.00	295	0.02	—	145	150

TABLE VI
Titration 1
100 ml. 0.0001 N AgNO$_3$ + ml. 0.01 N KCl at 25°

x ml.	$\kappa_{obs.}$ × 10^6	κ × 10^6			
		AgCl	AgNO$_3$	KNO$_3$	KCl
0	13.3	—	13.3	0	—
0.25	13.9	0.31	10.0	3.6	—
0.50	14.3	0.43	6.7	7.2	—
0.75	15.0	0.76	3.3	10.9	—
0.90	15.5	1.23	1.3	13.0	—
0.99	16.2	1.73	0.1	14.4	—
1.00	16.3	1.79	0	14.5	—
1.01	16.3	1.73	—	14.5	0.1
1.10	17.2	1.23	—	14.5	1.5
1.25	19.0	0.76	—	14.5	3.7
1.50	22.4	0.43	—	14.5	7.5
1.75	26.1	0.31	—	14.5	11.3
2.00	29.7	0.23	—	14.5	15.0

Throughout the titration of the 0.01 N silver nitrate solution, (3), the conductance of the dissolved silver chloride is negligible when compared with the observed specific conductances, whereas in the 0.001 N silver nitrate titration (2) it reaches just over 1% at the equivalence point, but is negligibly small on either side. The conductances of the dissolved silver chloride, however, become quite appreciable in the titration of the extremely dilute solution, (0.0001 N), so much so that the extrapolation of the end point can at best be scarcely more than approximate.

3.2. Selection of Titrant and Angle at Equivalence Point

During the precipitation of AgCl from a silver nitrate solution with potassium chloride, the change in specific conductance is caused by the gradual substitution of the silver ions by the potassium ions. As the mobility of the potassium ion is greater than that of the silver ion, the specific conductance accordingly increases with the consequence that the angle at the end point is large. To facilitate the accurate location of end points it is desirable that the angle should be as acute as possible. A chloride should be chosen which has a cation with a smaller mobility than that of the silver ion so that precipitation will be accompanied by a diminution in specific conductance and thereby reduce the size of the end-point angle. Both sodium and lithium ions have smaller mobilities than the silver ion, and therefore the use of either lithium chloride or sodium chloride gives more satisfactory conductometric titration graphs than potassium chloride. Of the three alkali chlorides, lithium chloride, because of its lowest mobility, is the best titrant for the conductometric titration of silver. Fig. 21 illustrates the superiority of lithium chloride over either sodium chloride or potassium chloride in titrating silver nitrate solutions.

The importance of selecting as titrant a salt, which has (i) an anion of low mobility when its cation is to become a constituent of the precipitate, (ii) a cation of low mobility when the anion is to become part of the precipitate, is again demonstrated in Fig. 22. It illustrates the precipita-

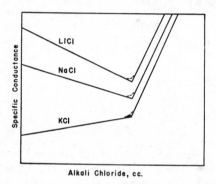

FIG. 21. Conductometric titrations of solutions of $AgNo_3$ with (a) LiCl, (b) NaCl, (c) KCl (the concentrations of the reactants being identical), showing the effect of the mobilities of the Li^+, Na^+ and K^+ ions on the size of the angle at the end point.

tion of barium sulfate from a solution of potassium sulfate by adding a solution of barium chloride, (1A), barium acetate, (1B), i.e.,

$$\text{(1A)} \quad K_2SO_4 + BaCl_2 \rightarrow BaSO_4\downarrow + 2KCl$$

so that during precipitation, the $K^\cdot$ ions remain in solution while the SO_4'' ions are progressively replaced by an equivalent concentration of Cl' ions.

$$\text{(1B)} \quad K_2SO_4 + BaAc_2 \rightarrow BaSO_4\downarrow + 2KAc,$$

$K^\cdot$ ions remaining in solution but the sulfate ions are being substituted by acetate ions.

As $l_{Cl'}$ is less than $l_{SO_4''}$, precipitation in 1A is associated with a decrease in specific conductance, which decrease is proportional to $l_{SO_4''} - l_{Cl'}$. As soon as precipitation is complete, the increasing addition of excess of $BaCl_2$ gives rise to a linear increase in specific conductance if the change in volume of the solution is negligible by the use of a sufficiently concentrated solution of the precipitant.

The mobility of the acetate ion at 18° is 35 and this is very much lower than that of the chloride ion, 65.5, or of the sulfate ion, 68. This fact makes barium acetate an excellent conductometric titrant where the precipitation of barium sulfate is involved. As shown in Fig. 22 (1B), the fall in conductance, which is determined by $l_{SO_4''} - l_{Ac'}$, is much greater than in 2A although the increase in conductance after passing the end point, because of the lower mobility of the acetate ion, is somewhat less.

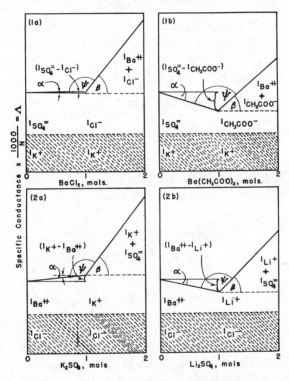

FIG. 22. The precipitation of barium sulfate: dependence of end point angles on ionic mobilities.

Graphs 2A and 2B illustrate precipitations carried out in the reverse manner. Graph 2A refers to the titration of a solution of barium chloride with one of potassium sulfate, whereas 2B refers to the titration of the same solution with a solution of lithium sulfate. In both these titrations the barium-ions are replaced by other cations, so that the initial variation in conductance is due to $l_{Ba''} - l_{cation}$. At 18°, $l_{Ba''} = 55$, $l_{K'} = 64.4$ and $l_{Li'} = 33.3$ and therefore $l_{Ba''} - l_{K'} = 55 - 64.4 = -9.4$ and $l_{Ba''} - l_{Li'} = 55 - 33.3 = 21.7$. Hence 2A shows an increase in conductance, whereas in (2B) there is a much greater decrease.

The conditions requisite for the angle, ψ, at the end point to be as small as possible can be ascertained by considering the tangents of the angles, α and β, which for graphs, 1A and 1B, are related to tan ψ, thus

$$\tan \psi = - \tan (\alpha + \beta);$$

and for graphs 2A and 2B, thus

$$\tan \psi = \tan (\alpha - \beta).$$

The tangents of α and β can readily be expressed in terms of ionic mobilities, e.g., in graph (1B) the "slope of the precipitation curve" is

$$\tan \alpha = \frac{N}{1000\ x} \times (l_{SO_4''} - l_{CH_3COO'}),$$

and the "slope of the excess curve" is

$$\tan \beta = \frac{N}{1000\ x} \times (l_{Ba''} + l_{CH_3COO'}),$$

where x is the number of milliliters of precipitant required for complete precipitation and also the number of milliliters which were added in excess. In this way it can be shown that, in general,

$$\tan \psi = - \frac{\dfrac{N}{1000\ x} \times \left(\begin{array}{c}\text{Sum of mobilities of ion}\\ \text{in precipitate}\end{array}\right)}{1 - \left(\dfrac{N}{1000\ x}\right)^2 \left(\begin{array}{c}\text{Mobility of cation}\\ \text{(anion) in precipitant}\\ - \text{ mobility of cation}\\ \text{(anion) in precipitate}\end{array}\right) \left(\begin{array}{c}\text{Sum of ionic}\\ \text{mobilities of}\\ \text{precipitant}\end{array}\right)}$$

Hence to make ψ as small as possible the denominator must be made as small as possible. This can be effected by making the second term negative by selecting as precipitants those reagents of which the mobility of (i) the cation has the smallest possible value when the cation has to be precipitated, and (ii) the anion has the smallest possible value when the anion has to undergo precipitation. Furthermore, ψ is made smaller by making x very small and this is possible by using the precipitant in concentrated solution.

As Fig. 22 shows, in precipitating a cation (or anion), the anion (or cation) with which it was originally in combination has no effect on the magnitude of ψ. Its only effect is to raise or lower the titration graph with respect to the specific conductance axis. Similarly, the presence in the solution of neutral salts which do not participate in the process of precipitation can have no influence on the shape of the graph, but, by increasing the conductance, they merely raise the conductance graph.

Owing to the exceptionally high mobilities of the hydrogen and hydroxyl ions, strong acids or bases are obviously almost useless as titrimetric precipitants, for tan ψ would become both very small and negative so that ψ would approach $180°$, thereby making the precise location of any "break" exceedingly difficult.

In general, the acuteness of the angle of the end point will be greater, the greater the mobility of the ion of the reactant which is to form part of the precipitate. Thus while it is possible to estimate barium conductometrically by precipitation as either carbonate, chromate, or sulfate, with the respective alkali salt, the use of an alkali sulfate will be the most satisfactory as the sulfate ion has the highest mobility.

3.3. Errors in Precipitation Titrations

Errors in conductometric precipitation titrations sometimes arise through:

(i) adsorption by the precipitates and their consequent entrainment of soluble salts,
(ii) contamination of the electrodes by adhering precipitate, thereby leading to erratic conductance readings,
(iii) slowness of precipitation and variations in the particle size of the precipitate which tend to supersaturate the mother liquor with respect to the insoluble salt.

Errors due to adsorption can be reduced to a minimum by titrating very dilute solutions with effective stirring, whereas errors (ii) and (iii) can largely be avoided by carrying out the titrations at elevated temperatures, which, of course, should be controlled to within $\pm 1°$.

Wherever possible, the concentrations of the solutions being titrated should be about $0.01-0.02\ N$ and the precipitating reagent should be at least 10 times as concentrated. Freak (23) ascertained the limits of dilution at which conductometric estimations of sulfates by titration with barium chloride, and of chlorides by means of silver nitrate, could be performed. Under ordinary conditions, sulfate ion may be accurately estimated in solutions containing 198 mg./l. (i.e., $0.004\ N$) but if a suspension of a fine precipitate of barium sulfate were added to the solution before the titration, then as little as 50 mg./l. (i.e., $0.001\ N$) may be estimated. In the case of chlorides the lowest limit appeared to be 10 mg. chloride/l. (i.e., $0.0003\ N$). Similar observations were made by Duboux and Caciro (18). The adsorption of di- and tervalent cations e.g., calcium, zinc, aluminum by barium sulfate leads to inaccuracies in the conductometric titrations involving its precipitation.

3.4. Precipitants Containing Precipitating Cations

3.4.1. $AgNO_3$. The following silver salts, silver chloride, bromide, iodide, cyanide, cyanate, thiocyanate, chromate, oxalate, ferricyanide, molybdate, tungstate, vanadates, silver tartrate, succinate, citrate, salicylate, are sufficiently insoluble to permit the conductometric estimation of either the silver or the acid radicals in dilute solution.

The titration of a solution of silver nitrate with potassium cyanide is interesting in that two "breaks" are obtained; the first corresponding with the end of the precipitation of silver cyanide with 1 equivalent of potassium cyanide and the second, with 2 equivalents through the formation of the complex anion, $Ag(CN)_2'$, thus

$$AgCN + KCN \rightarrow KAg(CN)_2' \quad (8)$$

Owing to the greater solubility of the silver salts of the above-mentioned organic acids, it is necessary to employ neutral salt solutions of these acids that are not less dilute than 0.1 N.

The conductometric method has been applied successfully to the estimation of the total amounts of the three halide ions, chloride, bromide, iodide, present in solution by titration with silver nitrate, and with some success to the estimation of chloride in the presence of Br' and/or I'. The latter consists of adding a large quantity of ammonia to keep the silver chloride and silver bromide in solution as $Ag(NH_3)_2Cl$ and $Ag(NH_3)_2Br$ respectively and then to titrate the ammoniacal solution with silver nitrate. The AgI alone will be precipitated if the concentration of the added ammonia is high enough to prevent the subsequent precipitation of AgBr on adding an excess of the silver nitrate. A further titration, this time after adding sufficient ammonia to keep the silver chloride in solution, with silver nitrate will give the titer of the iodide plus bromide. A titration of a neutral solution of the three halides with silver nitrate will give an end point corresponding with the titer of the total halides. Difficulties may arise in judging the requisite proportions of ammonia to use in the first two titrations, and attempts have been made to ascertain them (20, 44, 50).

Figure 23 illustrates the conductometric titration of various sodium vanadates with silver nitrate (10).

3.4.2. Lead Nitrate. The sparingly soluble salts of lead, of which use has been made for the purpose of conductometric titration, are: lead iodide, ferrocyanide, sulfate, thiosulfate, oxalate, tartrate, succinate, and malate.

Because of the appreciable solubility of lead iodide, the neutral iodide solution to be titrated must be not less than 0.05 N. On adding lead nitrate solution a small "break" is observed corresponding with $KPbI_3$, and this is followed by a well-defined "break" corresponding with the precipitation of lead iodide.

A solution of potassium ferrocyanide, or even one of a mixture of the ferrocyanide and ferricyanide, can be titrated with lead nitrate. The end point corresponds with the precipitation ,of lead ferrocyanide, $Pb_2Fe(CN)_6$, whilst no precipitate is produced with the ferricyanide, a method which can therefore be employed for the estimation of ferrocyanide in the presence of ferricyanide.

Sulfate may be estimated conductometrically and the addition of alcohol is advantageous.

The conductometric method is especially applicable to the estimation of molybdenum. Dissolve the molybdenum trioxide in alkali, neutralize with acetic acid to phenolphthalein and then titrate conductometrically with lead acetate, the break indicating accurately the titer required to precipitate lead molybdate, $PbMoO_4$.

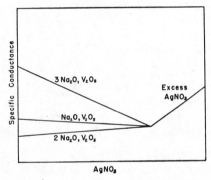

FIG. 23. Conductometric titrations of solutions of sodium vanadate with $AgNO_3$, involving the precipitation of Ag_3VO_4, $AgVO_3$ and $Ag_4V_2O_7$.

In a similar way, sodium tungstate, Na_2WO_4, may be quantitatively titrated with lead nitrate, $PbWO_4$ being precipitated.

3.4.3. Barium Acetate or Barium Chloride. These reagents may be applied to the conductometric titration of sulfates, chromates, carbonates, and, in the presence of alcohol, of oxalates, tartrates, and citrates.

While no strong acid should be present in conductometric titrations which involve the precipitation of barium sulfate owing to its tendency to reduce the angle at the end point, acetic acid may be included in barium acetate solution for use as the titrant. Its presence facilitates the separation of the barium sulfate precipitate, but has little effect on the angle at the "break." The acetic acid also has a solvent action on any metal bases, which, owing to the hydrolysis of their salts, may be carried down with the barium sulfate. Kolthoff and Kameda (47) investigated the conductometric titration of zinc sulfate with barium chloride, but obtained low results.

The use of alcohol in the solution undergoing titration renders the precipitate less soluble but reduces the angle at the end point. If used, the alcohol should not be more than a quarter of the volume of the solution. Contrary to the observations of Kolthoff and Kameda, accurate titers of the sulfate content of zinc sulfate can be obtained at ordinary temperatures. They may also be obtained by carrying out the titrations at 100° without the addition of alcohol. Fig. 24 gives typical titration graphs of solutions of ammonium sulfate, magnesium sulfate and zinc

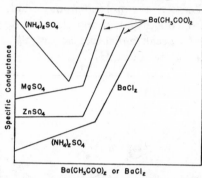

FIG. 24.   Conductometric titrations at 100°C. of solutions of (NH₄)₂SO₄, MgSO₄ and ZnSO₄ with barium acetate, and of (NH₄)₂SO₄ with barium chloride.

sulfate with barium acetate. Comparison of the top graph with that at the bottom shows the marked effect which the mobility of the acetate-ion, compared with that of the chloride-ion, has on the end point angle.

3.5. Estimation of Sulfate in Drinking Water

Decompose the bicarbonate in 50 ml. of tap water by boiling, cool rapidly. Filter off the precipitate of calcium carbonate. To filtrate add 50 ml. of alcohol and titrate conductometrically at room temperature with barium acetate. This must be done as quickly as possible before any calcium sulfate has had time to separate (22). Quite good results may thus be obtained. The chloride in the resulting solution may be estimated with silver nitrate conductometrically. If the total permanent hardness consists of more than 10 parts of calcium to 1 part of magnesium it may be estimated by conductometric titration with 0.1 N lithium oxalate in the presence of 30–40% of alcohol.

3.6. Estimation of Free and Combined Sulfurous Acid in Calcium Bisulfite Solutions

Jander and Jahr (30) have shown that sulfurous acid solutions of calcium bisulfite are oxidized by means of neutral hydrogen peroxide, thus:

$$H_2SO_3 + H_2O_2 \rightarrow H_2SO_4 + H_2O$$
$$Ca(HSO_3)_2 + 2H_2O_2 \rightarrow CaSO_4 + H_2SO_4 + 2H_2O$$

and that the resulting solution can be conductometrically titrated with baryta, ca. 0.16 N barium hydroxide. The titration graph Fig. 25 has two distinct "breaks"; the first, indicating the neutralization of the

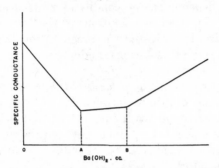

FIG. 25. Conductometric titration of a solution of sulfuric acid and calcium sulfate with barium hydroxide.

sulfuric acid and the simultaneous precipitation of barium sulfate, the second, marking the end of the reaction:

$$CaSO_4 + Ba(OH)_2 \rightarrow Ca(OH)_2 + BaSO_4\downarrow$$

Thus in Fig. 25 the difference in the titers, $OB - OA = AB$, gives the calcium bisulfite, and $OB - AB$ gives the free sulfurous acid in excess of that, equal to AB, required to form calcium bisulfite.

3.7. Precipitants Containing Precipitating Anions

(a) *Lithium sulfate.* Barium and lead salt solutions may be titrated with lithium sulfate. For very dilute solutions the addition of alcohol is advisable.

(b) *Lithium oxalate, ammonium oxalate, and oxalic acid.* Lithium oxalate has been used for the conductometric titration of calcium, strontium, barium, silver, lead, copper, nickel and cobalt salts. Complications may arise through complex oxalate formation, particularly in the case of nickel and cobalt. Alcohol has been of assistance in the titration of nickel salts.

Ammonium oxalate (0.1 N) has proved serviceable in the titration of calcium chloride in solutions as dilute as 0.005 M (23), while Suchtelen and Itano (67) found that 0.05 M calcium chloride could be titrated with 0.5 N oxalic acid.

(c) *Lithium chromate and sodium chromate.* Lithium chromate was used by Mojoiu (50) to titrate barium and strontium solutions, whilst sodium chromate has been used to titrate barium, lead, and thallium salt solutions. To use it to titrate strontium salts the addition of 40–50% of alcohol to the strontium salt solution is advocated (45).

(d) *Potassium ferrocyanide.* Except from solutions of silver and lead salts, potassium ferrocyanide precipitates double salts, the precise composition of which depends on the conditions under which the precipitations are effected (7), from salt solutions of the heavy metals.

Kolthoff (46) has investigated the precipitation of zinc ferrocyanide from ammoniacal zinc salt solutions; under specified conditions accurate results may be obtained.

(e) *Potassium ferricyanide or potassium lithium ferricyanide.* Either potassium ferricyanide or lithium ferricyanide will precipitate the normal ferricyanides of silver, copper, cadmium, cobalt, and nickel, thus enabling these metals to be estimated conductometrically within an accuracy of 1%. As would be expected, the use of potassium lithium ferricyanide leads to more satisfactory "breaks."

(f) *Sodium sulfide.* Solutions of sodium sulfide, Na_2S, and the polysulfide, Na_2S_9, have been used to titrate metallic salt solutions. Accurate determinations are stated to have been obtained of lead in either acetic acid or neutral solution, cadmium in acetic solution, bismuth in nitric acid solution, zinc in either neutral or acetic acid solution, divalent iron in neutral solution, while errors of about 3% are reported in silver and copper estimations. Nickel, cobalt, arsenic, tin and divalent mercury estimations appear to be very inaccurate.

Jander and Schörstein (33) estimated zinc by adding an excess of sodium sulfide to a solution of zinc sulfate to which an excess of carbonate-free sodium hydroxide had previously been added, and titrating the resulting mother liquor, without filtering off the precipitated zinc sulfide, with hydrochloric acid. Two "breaks" are produced, the first of which indicates the neutralization of the excess of alkali and the conversion of the excess of sodium sulfide into sodium hydrosulfide, NaHS,

$$Na_2S + HCl \rightarrow NaCl + NaHS,$$

while the second "break" shows when the zinc sulfide dissolves completely, thereby giving a titer of the hydrochloric acid added between the two "breaks" required to dissolve the precipitated zinc sulfide.

(g) *Sodium hydroxide.* Sodium hydroxide precipitates very few metallic hydroxides, as such, from their salt solutions. Instead, basic salts are nearly always precipitated, the precise composition of which depends on the rate of adding the alkali, the efficiency of the stirring and the temperature.

Magnesium hydroxide and silver oxide are, however, directly precipitated and consequently it is possible to titrate their salt solutions with sodium hydroxide. The basic zinc chloride which is first formed when alkali is added to a zinc chloride solution, unlike the basic sulfate, is readily decomposed by alkali, so much so that if a hydrochloric acid solution of zinc be titrated with a relatively concentrated solution of

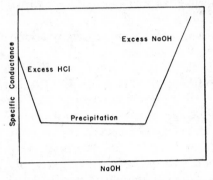

Fig. 26. Conductometric titration of a solution of hydrochloric acid and zinc chloride with sodium hydroxide.

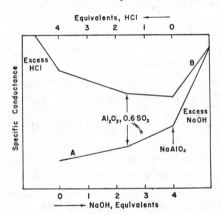

Fig. 27. Conductometric titrations of
A. Al₂(SO₄)₃ with NaOH
B. NaAlO₂ + NaOH with HCl.

sodium hydroxide, the conductometric graph obtained will be the form given in Fig. 26. The titer between the first and second "breaks" gives the correct amount of alkali required to precipitate hydrated zinc oxide.

Aluminium is exceptional in that its hydrous oxide is the only one which can be proved by conductometric titration to be amphoteric. Graph A in Fig. 27 illustrates the action of NaOH on a solution of aluminium sulfate. The first "break" corresponds to the precipitation of basic aluminium sulfate, containing Al_2O_3, $0.6SO_3$, while the second and more clearly defined "break" refers to the formation of the soluble sodium alummate, $NaAlO_2$, when 4 equivalents of sodium hydroxide have been added. The back-titration graph B, with hydrochloric acid of the solution, to which an excess of sodium hydroxide had been added, again shows the $NaAlO_2$ "break" and an additional "break" indicating the complete formation of aluminium chloride and the appearance of free hydrochloric acid in the solution (64).

Britton and Young (12) have shown that hydrochloric acid in excess of that required to form uranyl chloride, UO_2Cl_2, can be estimated conductometrically by titration with alkali. The "break" corresponding with the complete precipitation of uranium hydroxide is slightly delayed owing to some alkali being chemisorbed by the uranium hydroxide.

(h) *Barium hydroxide.* Harned (29) in titrating metallic sulphate solutions with barium hydroxide, found that not only is the base precipitated but also an equivalent amount of $BaSO_4$, e.g.,

$$MgSO_4 + Ba(OH)_2 \rightarrow BaSO_4\downarrow + Mg(OH)_2\downarrow$$

and in so doing, a very much greater angle was obtained at the equivalence point. The method was satisfactory when calcium sulfate was present in the solution and it could therefore be applied to the analysis of dolomite.

To estimate magnesia in dolomite slightly more sulfuric acid is added to the mineral than is necessary to convert it into sulfates, and the carbon dioxide is expelled by boiling under reduced pressure. On cooling, it is neutralized to phenolphthalein with baryta and again boiled to decompose any barium bicarbonate. The mother liquor is titrated conductometrically without removing the insoluble matter.

Conductometric titration with baryta has been successfully performed with solutions of cobalt and nickel sulfates, though owing to the greater stability of basic zinc, cadmium, and copper sulfates, it is inaccurate in the case of these metals. By carrying out the titration of copper sulfate just below 100° the basic sulfate is decomposed and accurate results can be obtained.

4. Conductometric Titrations with Mercuric Perchlorate

Only in very few instances are precipitates formed when mercuric perchlorate reacts with metallic salts, yet mercuric perchlorate is an important conductometric titrant. In the case of a titration involving the separation of a precipitate small changes in conductance occur because one salt in being precipitated leaves the sphere of action. Now certain mercuric salts, e.g., $HgCl_2$, $HgBr_2$, $Hg(CN)_2$, $Hg(CNS)_2$, impart to their aqueous solutions almost no electrical conductance and the little conductance they do supply can be almost entirely accounted for by their slight hydrolysis. In general, the hydrolysis is less than 1% (11). Some idea of lack of ionization of mercuric chloride in solution can be gained from the fact that the specific conductance of its solutions ranging in concentration from $\frac{N}{512}$ to $\frac{N}{32}$ varies from 2.47×10^{-5} to 6.81×10^{-5} mho at 25°C. (49). These values are extremely small and are of the same order as those of aqueous solutions in equilibrium with "insoluble salts."

On the contrary, mercuric nitrate, sulfate and perchlorate in solution are both strongly ionized and hydrolyzed. Their specific conductances compare with those of solutions of ordinary metallic salts. A difficulty, however, may arise, through their appreciable hydrolysis, which, unless suppressed by the presence of free acid, will cause basic salts to separate. Mercuric perchlorate solutions however, despite more than 10% hydrolysis, can be so prepared that they will remain quite clear without the addition of perchloric acid.

Mercuric perchlorate can be prepared by the method described by Chikashigé (17), by grinding a slight excess of red mercuric oxide with $2 N$ perchloric acid filtering through asbestos, and concentrating at 40–50° under reduced pressure until crystals separate. Recrystallization from aqueous solutions under similar conditions is advisable. For conductometric work, it is merely necessary to saturate a solution of perchloric acid with pure mercuric oxide. To ascertain whether any free acid exists in the solution, add an excess of sodium chloride and titrate the free acid with alkali to methyl orange.

The ionic mobility of the perchlorate ion 25° is ca. 72, so that in titrating a solution of potassium chloride with mercuric perchlorate:

$$2KCl + Hg(ClO_4) \rightarrow 2KClO_4 + HgCl_2$$

the conductance during the replacement represented by the above equation will depend on $l_{Cl'} - l_{ClO_4'}$, i.e., $76.6 - 72$, so that there will be a slight diminution. An excess of the titrant will cause an increase in conductance. In a similar manner soluble bromides, thiocyanates, and cyanides may be accurately titrated (43). In titrating a solution of potassium bromide with mercuric perchlorate, a poorly-defined "break" occurs before the final "break." The first "break" shows the formation of K_2HgBr_4, viz.,

$$4KBr + Hg(ClO_4)_2 \rightarrow K_2HgBr_4 + 2KClO_4.$$

and the second "break" refers to the decomposition of K_2HgBr_4, thus

$$K_2HgBr_4 + Hg(ClO_4)_2 \rightarrow 2HgBr_2 + 2KClO_4$$

Soluble iodides may equally well be titrated with mercuric perchlorate, but in such titrations the final "breaks" will coincide with the complete precipitation of mercuric iodide. Before these are reached there will appear smaller "breaks" that indicate the formation of K_2HgI_4 and immediately afterwards mercuric iodide will begin to separate.

Another class of mercuric salts exists which in solution have low conductances. They consist of the salts of the weaker monobasic acids, viz., nitrous, acetic, butyric, valeric, lactic acids. Although they are very poor electrolytes, they ionize slightly in an unknown manner and hydrolysis plays an important role.

Conductometric titration of their respective alkali salts with mercuric perchlorate gives satisfactory end points and accurate titers. For the titration of alkali formates and lactates, the solutions must be more concentrated than 0.01 N in order to obtain good "breaks" at the end points.

Alkali benzoate and salicylate produce white precipitates with mercuric perchlorate. If adequate time be allowed for the attainment of steady conductances, particularly in the vicinity of the end points, correct results may be obtained.

REFERENCES

1. Airs, R. S., and Balfe, M. P., *Trans. Faraday Soc.* **39**, 102 (1943).
2. Bencowitz, I., and Hotckiss, H. T., *J. Phys. Chem.* **29**, 705 (1925).
3. Bengough, G. D., Stuart, J. M., and Lee, A. R., *J. Chem. Soc.* 2156 (1927).
4. Bousfield, W. R., *J. Chem. Soc.* **87**, 740 (1905); **101**, 1443 (1912).
5. Britton, H. T. S., Conductometric Analysis. Chapman and Hall, London 1934.
6. Britton, H. T. S., Hydrogen Ions. 3rd ed., Vol. I, Chapman and Hall, London 1942.
7. Britton, H. T. S., and Dodd, E. N., *J. Chem. Soc.* 1543 (1933).
8. Britton, H. T. S., and Dodd, E. N., *J. Chem. Soc.* 1950 (1932).
9. Britton, H. T. S., and German, W. L., *J. Chem. Soc.* 1250 (1930).
10. Britton, H. T. S., and Robinson, R. A., *J. Chem. Soc.* 2228 (1930).
11. Britton, H. T. S., and Wilson, B. M., *J. Chem. Soc.* 2553 (1932).
12. Britton, H. T. S., and Young, A. E., *J. Chem. Soc.* 2467 (1932).
13. Bruni and coworkers, *Z. Elektrochem.* **14**, 701 (1908); **16**, 223 (1910).
14. Burton, E. F., and Pitt, A., *Phil. Mag.* **5**, 939 (1928).
15. Callan, T., and Horrobin, S., *J. Soc. Chem. Ind.* **47**, 329 (1928).
16. Cheshire, A., Brown, W. B., and Holmes, N. L., *J. Intern. Soc. Leather Trades Chemists* **25**, 254 (1941).
17. Chickashigé, M., *J. Chem. Soc.* **67**, 1013 (1895).
18. Duboux, M., and Caciro, *Arch. sci. phys. et nat.*]5] **1**, 79 (1919).
19. Dutoit, P.; Dutoit P., and Levy, M., *Bull. Soc. chim.* **7**, 1 (1910); *J. chim. phys.* **14**, 353 (1916).

20. Dutoit, P., and Reeb, H., *Chem. Ztg.* **37**, 469.
21. Ehrhardt, U., *Chem. Fabrik* **2**, 443, 455 (1929).
22. Fehn, H., Jander, G., and Pfundt, O., *Z. angew. Chem.* **42**, 158 (1929).
23. Freak, G. A., *J. Chem. Soc.* **115**, 55 (1919).
24. Gehman, S. D., and Weatherby, B. B., *Phil. Mag.* **7**, 567 (1929).
25. Götte, E., and Schramek, W., *Z. Elektrochem.* **37**, 820 (1931).
26. Gollnow, G., *Chem. Ztg.* **55**, 827 (1931).
27. Griffin, C. B., M.Sc. Dissertation, London, 1933.
28. Hall, R. E., and Adams, L. H., *J. Am. Chem. Soc.* **41**, 1515 (1919).
29. Harned, H. S., *J. Am. Chem. Soc.* **39**, 254 (1917).
30. Jander, G., and Jahr, K. F., *Z. angew. Chem.* **44**, 977 (1931).
31. Jander, G., and Manegold, E., *Z. anorg. Chem.* **134**, 283 (1924).
32. Jander, G., and Pfundt, O., Leitfähigkeitstitrationen und Leitfähigkeitsmessungen, Stuttgart, 1934. Also Die Leitfähigkeitstitration, in Physikalische Methoden der analytischen Chemie, Edited by W. Böttger, Teil 2, Akademische Verlagegesellschaft, Leipzig 1936.
33. Jander, G., and Schorstein, H., *Z. angew. Chem.* **48**, 698 (1932).
34. Jones, G., and Bollinger, G. M., *J. Am. Chem. Soc.* **51**, 2407 (1929).
35. Jones, G., and Bradshaw, B. C., *J. Am. Chem. Soc.* **55**, 1780 (1933).
36. Jones, G., and Josephs, R. C., *J. Am. Chem. Soc.* **50**, 1049 (1928).
37. Kano, N., *J. Chem. Soc. Japan* **43**, 556 (1922).
38. Kendall, J., *J. Am. Chem. Soc.* **38**, 1460 (1916).
39. Kohlrausch, F., and Holborn, L., Das Leitvermögen der Elektrolyte, Leipzig, 1916.
40. Kolthoff, I. M., Konduktometrische Titrationen, Steinkopff, Dresden 1923.
41. Kolthoff, I. M., *Z. anorg. Chem.* **111**, 9 (1920).
42. Kolthoff, I. M., *Z. anorg. Chem.* **112**, 156, 196 (1920).
43. Kolthoff, I. M., *Z. anal. Chem.* **61**, 332 (1922).
44. Kolthoff, I. M., *Z. anal. Chem.* **61**, 229 (1922).
45. Kolthoff, I. M., *Z. anal. Chem.* **62**, 161 (1923).
46. Kolthoff, I. M., *Z. anal. Chem.* **62**, 209 (1923).
47. Kolthoff, I. M., and Kameda, T., *Ind. Eng. Chem. Anal. ed.* **3**, 129 (1931).
48. Kraus, C. A., and Dexter, W. B., *J. Am. Chem. Soc.* **44**, 2468 (1932).
49. Ley, H., *Ber.*, **30**, 2192 (1897).
50. Mojoiu, P., Dosage et Séparation par conductibilité electrique des Halogènes et des Metaux Alcalino-Terrenx. Dissertation, Lausanne, 1902.
51. Parker, H. C., *J. Am. Chem. Soc.* **45**, 1370 (1923).
52. Parker, H., and Parker, E., *J. Am. Chem. Soc.* **46**, 33 (1924).
53. Pfundt, O., Dissertation, Göttingen, 1925; *Z. angew. Chem.* **46**, 218 (1933).
54. Pfundt, O., and Junge, C., *Ber.* **69**, 515 (1929).
55. Poetke, W., *Z. anal. Chem.* **86**, 45 (1931).
56. Potts, T. T., *Paper Trade Rev.* **95**, 1037 (1931).
57. Preston, J. M., *J. Chem. Soc.* 1827 (1931).
58. Pritzker, J., and Jungkunz, R., *Mitt. Lebensm. Hyg.* **15**, 54 (1928).
59. Randall, M., and Scott, G. M., *J. Am. Chem. Soc.* **49**, 636 (1927).
60. Randall, M., and Vanselow, A. P., *J. Am. Chem. Soc.* **46**, 2424 (1924).
61. Richardson, G. M., *Proc. Roy. Soc. London* **B115**, 170 (1934).
62. Righellato, E. C., and Davies, C. W., *Trans. Faraday Soc.* **29**, 431 (1933).
63. Robbins, H. E., *J. Am. Chem. Soc.* **39**, 646 (1917).
64. Robinson, R. A., and Britton, H. T. S., *J. Chem. Soc.* 2817 (1931).

104   H. T. S. BRITTON

65. Rother, E., and Jander, G., *Z. angew. Chem.* **43,** 930 (1930).
66. Stuart, J. M., and Wormell, F., *J. Chem. Soc.* 86 (1930).
67. Suchtelen, F. S. H. van, and Itano, A., *J. Am. Chem. Soc.* **36,** 1800 (1914).
68. Treadwell, W. D., and Jannett, S., *Helv. Chim. Acta* **6,** 734 (1923).
69. Treadwell, W. D., and Paoloni, C., *Helv. Chim. Acta* **8,** 89 (1925).
70. Ulich, H., *Z. phys. Chem.* **115,** 377 (1925).
71. Vogel, A. I., *J. Chem. Soc.* 1202 (1931).
72. Walker, J., and Cormack, W., *J. Chem. Soc.* **77,** 5 (1900).
73. Washburn, E. W., *J. Am. Chem. Soc.* **40,** 109 (1918).
74. Weibel, E., Bur. Standards Sci. Paper 297, 23 (1917).
75. Weiland, H. J., *J. Am. Chem. Soc.* **40,** 131 (1918); **44,** 2468 (1922).
76. Whetham, W. C. D., *Phil. Trans. Roy. Soc. London* **194,** 321 (1900).
77. Woodcock, J. W., and Murray-Rust, D. M., *Phil. Mag.* **5,** 1130 (1928).

Potentiometric Analysis

BY

H. A. LAITINEN

Department of Chemistry, University of Illinois, Urbana, Illinois

CONTENTS

1. INTRODUCTION

The term *potentiometric analysis* includes the measurement of concentration (or activity) by a single measurement of cell e.m.f. or electrode potential, as well as the potentiometric titration. The most important type of potentiometric analysis based upon a single measurement is the determination of pH. Other types of measurement, based on membrane potential determinations, concentration cells, and changes of cell e.m.f. by complex formation are also of analytical interest.

In the usual potentiometric titration, the potential of one electrode is kept constant (reference electrode), while the other electrode (the indicator electrode) varies in accordance with the change in concentration or activity of the substance being titrated. The *end point*, taken as the point of maximum slope of the titration curve, may or may not coincide exactly with the *equivalence point*, at which the substance being titrated and reagent are present in equivalent amounts. The difference between the end point and the equivalence point (titration error) may be an inherent property of the titration system or it may be caused by non-stoichiometry due to side reactions, coprecipitation phenomena, slow reaction, etc. or by improper functioning of the electrodes. The cause, the magnitude and the correction of titration errors are of utmost practical importance.

The present discussion is intended to describe the fundamental theory underlying potentiometric methods, and to present examples of their use. An exhaustive treatment of practical applications lies beyond the scope of this work. Likewise, specialized methods of end-point detection, automatic recording of potentials, and special titration cells can be discussed only very briefly. For details, the reader is referred to the monographs listed at the end of the chapter.

2. FUNDAMENTAL PRINCIPLES

2.1. The Relation between Activity and Concentration

Since the potential of an electrode is dependent upon the *activities* of the potential-determining substances involved, while potentiometric measurements are often made for the purpose of determining (at least approximately) *concentrations*, the relationship between these quantities is both of theoretical and practical interest.

The activity, a_i, of a substance is defined by the relation

$$\mu_i = k_i + RT \ln a_i \tag{1}$$

where μ_i is the chemical potential or partial molar free energy of the substance, R is the gas constant, T is the absolute temperature, and k_i is a constant for a given substance at a given temperature. The constant k_i may be interpreted as the value of μ_i when the substance is in an activity state of unity.

But a state of unit activity is purely arbitrary. We may say, as often is done, that a pure substance is in a state of unit activity at a given temperature if it is in the most stable modification of its normal physical state. This definition of a unit activity state is most convenient if we wish to use the mole fraction as the unit of concentration. Then for a pure substance, both mole fraction and activity become unity, and the value of k_i would be the free energy of the pure substance.

However, the absolute value of the free energy of a pure substance is indeterminate (the free energy of a pure element is arbitrarily taken as zero), and the value of k_i is indeterminate. We are only able to determine experimentally the change of chemical potential, which at constant temperature and pressure, from eq. (1) is

$$d\mu_i = RTd \ln a_i = RT \frac{da_i}{a_i} \tag{2}$$

Any quantity proportional to a_i would show the same relative change, $\dfrac{da_i}{a_i}$, and therefore could be used as a measure of activity.

In analytical chemistry, the most convenient choice of a unit activity state in solution is based upon the concept that in all solutions the behavior of the solute approaches ideality at infinite dilution. Thus activity is a quantity which approaches molar concentration at infinite dilution. At finite concentrations the activity and concentration are not equal, but are related by the equation $a = \gamma C$, which serves to define the *activity coefficient*, γ. The activity coefficient approaches unity at infinite dilution, and as a rough approximation the concentration and activity are often considered to be equal in dilute solution.

For a better estimate, it is very convenient to be able to calculate approximate values of the activity coefficient. Strictly speaking, it is impossible to determine the activity coefficient of a single species of ion in a solution of an electrolyte, whereas the activity coefficient of a salt can often be determined accurately. For example, the activity coefficient γ_s for KCl can be experimentally measured, and is equal to

$$\gamma_s = \sqrt{\gamma_{K^+}\gamma_{Cl^-}}$$

but the individual activity coefficients of the ions cannot be evaluated experimentally.

The theory of Debye and Hückel (16), based upon a consideration of electrostatic attraction and repulsion between ions in solution, predicts that in very dilute solutions the activity coefficient of an ionic species depends only on the charge type of the ionic species and the total ionic strength of the solution. Mathematically, the Debye-Hückel limiting law is

$$-\log \gamma_i = AZ_i^2 \sqrt{S} \tag{3}$$

where A is a constant for a given solvent at a given temperature, Z_i is the charge of the ion, and S in the ionic strength, defined by the expression

$$S = \frac{C_1Z_1^2 + C_2Z_2^2 + \cdots}{2} = \frac{1}{2}\sum C_iZ_i^2 \tag{4}$$

Equation (3), while valid only for very dilute solutions, is useful as a first approximation in the calculation of ionic activity coefficients. In any given dilute solution, the activity coefficients of all univalent ions are equal, but closer to unity than those of divalent ions. For example, in 0.0001 M K_2SO_4, the ionic strength $S = 0.0003$. For water at room temperature, A is very nearly 0.5. Then γ is 0.98 for the potassium ions and 0.92 for the sulfate ions.

Uncharged molecules would have activity coefficients of unity according to eq. (3). In actual practice, deviations from ideality can ordinarily be neglected for nonelectrolytes in moderate concentrations.

In potentiometric titrations, the ionic strength usually changes very little in the region of the end point where the electrode potential is changing most rapidly. It is therefore valid in this region to neglect changes in activity coefficients when calculating the equation of the titration curve.

2.2. Electrical Potential

The difference in electrical potential between two points in space is defined as the work required to transport a unit positive electric charge from one point to the other. The point of higher (more positive) potential is that at which a positive charge has a higher potential energy, and from which a positive charge will spontaneously move. The absolute electrical potential of a point has no meaning unless a reference point, say at infinity, is taken arbitrarily as having zero potential.

2.3. Phase Boundary Potential Difference

If two dissimilar phases, for example two metals or a metal and a solution, are brought into contact, a difference of potential in general exists between the two phases. This phase boundary potential difference, frequently called a phase boundary potential, is incapable of exact measurement. The algebraic sum of two or more such potential differences can be measured.

2.4. Electrode Potential. The Nernst Equation

If a metal M is immersed in a solution containing its ions M^{n+}, the metal in general will be at a different electrical potential than the solution. The ions of inactive metals tend to transfer from the solution to the metal, carrying a positive charge to the metal. An active metal has a tendency to undergo oxidation, transferring its ions from the metal to the solution. The valence electrons of the metal cannot be transferred to the solution unless a reaction such as the evolution of hydrogen occurs. Thus as metal ions are transferred to the solution, the metal acquires a negative charge which hinders a further transfer. Eventually a state of equilibrium is reached where metal ions are being transferred at equal rates in the two directions across the boundary. With increasing concentration of metal ions originally in solution, the transfer of metal ions to the solution is hindered or even reversed. Thus the potential of the metal at equilibrium becomes more positive with increasing metal ion concentration in solution.

Even though the absolute potential difference between the metal and the solution is unknown, *changes* in the potential of a single electrode with changes in solution composition can be measured and can often be calculated thermodynamically.

For a metal-metal ion electrode, it may be assumed that a distribution equilibrium of metal ions between the two phases is established.

Let ψ_M be the electrical potential of the metal and ψ_s that of the solution. Then the electrical work per mole necessary for the transfer of metal ions from metal to solution is given by $nF(\psi_s - \psi_M)$, where n is the charge of the ion and F is the faraday of electricity. The chemical work per mole is the difference in partial molar free energies or chemical potentials in the two phases, namely $\mu_s - \mu_M$. At equilibrium, the total free energy change for the transfer is zero, and

$$nF(\psi_s - \psi_M) + \mu_s - \mu_M = 0 \tag{5}$$

or

$$\mu_s + nF\psi_s = \mu_M + nF\psi_M \tag{6}$$

Equation (6) states that the *electrochemical potential* $(\mu + nF\psi)$ of the solute is equal in the two phases at equilibrium. If the solute were uncharged, the chemical potential μ would be equal in the two phases.

Introducing the definition of activity (eq. 1), applying it to the metal ions in both phases and substituting in eq. (6), we have

$$\psi_M - \psi_s = \frac{\mu_s - \mu_M}{nF} = \frac{k_s - k_M}{nF} + \frac{RT}{nF} \ln \frac{(a_{M^{n+}})_s}{(a_{M^{n+}})_M} \tag{7}$$

where $(a_{M^{n+}})_s$ is the activity of metal ions M^{n+} in solution, and $(a_{M^{n+}})_M$ represents their activity in the metal. The quantity $\dfrac{k_s - k_M}{nF}$ is constant at a constant temperature, and for a pure metal at constant temperature the activity $(a_{M^{n+}})_M$ is constant. Therefore for a pure metal in equilibrium with a solution containing its ions, we may write

$$\psi_M - \psi_s = \text{Constant} + \frac{RT}{nF} \ln (a_{M^{n+}})_s \tag{8}$$

The phase boundary potential difference $\psi_M - \psi_s$ cannot be measured, but eq. (8) shows how it varies with the activity of the metal ion in solution.

It is possible to measure the difference in potential between two different metals in contact with the same solution. By assigning a value of zero at every temperature to the potential of the hydrogen electrode in a solution of unit hydrogen ion activity and at a hydrogen gas pressure of one atmosphere, the potential of another electrode may be measured with reference to the hydrogen electrode. The normal potential $E°$ is the potential, referred to hydrogen, at a unit activity of metal ions in solution. From eq. (8), the electrode potential E in general is given by

$$E = E° + \frac{RT}{nF} \ln (a_{M^{n+}})_s \tag{9}$$

Equation (9), commonly called the Nernst equation, may be written in a more general form by considering an oxidation-reduction half reaction

$$Ox + ne^- \rightleftharpoons Red \tag{10}$$

where the oxidant Ox is reduced by n electrons to form its reduced form Red. The reduction of a metal ion to the free metal is a special case of reaction (10).

The electrode potential corresponding to this reaction has the same form as eq. (7), in which the activities of metal ions in the two phases are replaced in general by the activities of the oxidized and reduced forms of the potential-determining substance, or

$$E = E° + \frac{RT}{nF} \ln \frac{a_{Ox}}{a_{Red}} \tag{11}$$

If hydrogen ions or other substances of variable activity are involved in the electrode reaction without being oxidized or reduced, their activities must also be included in the equation. For example, if the electrode reaction is

$$Ox + ne^- + mH^+ \rightleftharpoons Red + \frac{m}{2} H_2O \tag{12}$$

the electrode potential varies with hydrogen ion activity,

$$E = E° + \frac{RT}{nF} \ln \frac{a_{Ox} \cdot a_{H^+}{}^m}{a_{Red}} \tag{13}$$

The activity of water remains essentially constant, and is omitted from the equation. Several important examples of the Nernst equation are given below.

2.5. Cell E.M.F.

The electromotive force of a cell composed of two electrodes without liquid junction is numerically equal to the algebraic difference of the potentials of the two electrodes. To relate the cell e.m.f. to the free energy change of the cell reaction it is necessary to adopt conventions as to the direction of writing the cell reaction, the direction of writing the corresponding cell, and the sign of the e.m.f. In general, if the cell reaction proceeds spontaneously from left to right, the free energy charge is negative, and the cell e.m.f. is given a positive sign. If the cell is to have a positive e.m.f., it is written so that negative electricity flows spontaneously from right to left inside the cell as written. Electrons then spontaneously leave the left hand electrode. The right hand electrode then is positively charged with respect to the left hand electrode. In other words, *the sign of the cell e.m.f. is the same as the charge of the right hand electrode with respect to the left hand electrode regardless of the direction in which the cell was written.* To calculate the cell e.m.f. from the electrode potentials, one simply subtracts (algebraically) the potential of the left hand electrode of the cell as written from that of the right hand electrode, or

$$E_{cell} = E_{right} - E_{left} \tag{14}$$

If the electrode potentials are known, the spontaneous cell reaction can immediately be written in the proper direction, because the *electrode of more positive potential will act as the oxidizing agent.* The free energy change of the cell reaction may be calculated from the cell e.m.f. by the equation

$$\Delta F = -nF E_{cell} \tag{15}$$

It should be stressed that it is unnecessary to adopt a convention as to the direction of the electrode half-reaction if the potential is always given a sign corresponding to its electrostatic charge with respect to the hydrogen electrode. Thus the zinc electrode will always be given a negative electrode potential, since its charge is negative regardless of whether it is right- or left-hand electrode, and regardless of whether zinc is dissolving or zinc ions are plating out during the cell reaction.

2.6. Liquid Junction Potential

If two solutions of different composition are brought into contact, a phase boundary potential difference called the *diffusion potential* or *liquid junction potential* in general exists, owing to the tendency of ions of different mobility to diffuse and migrate at different rates across the boundary. In simple cases the liquid junction potential may be calculated thermodynamically, and included in the expression for the cell e.m.f.

In practical potentiometric analysis the liquid junction potential between two solutions may be minimized by the use of a salt bridge containing an electrolyte composed of ions of nearly equal mobility, e.g., potassium chloride or ammonium nitrate. By this means the liquid junction potential can be lowered to a few millivolts for aqueous salt solutions. If should be remembered, however, that if the acidities of the two solutions to be connected are widely different, an appreciable liquid junction potential exists even with a potassium chloride salt bridge, because of the abnormal mobilities of the hydrogen and hydroxyl ions in water. A junction between an aqueous and nonaqueous solution introduces in general an uncertain liquid junction potential.

2.7. Applications of the Nernst Equation

2.7.1. The Hydrogen Electrode. The reversible electrode reaction

$$2H^+ + 2e^- \rightleftharpoons H_2 \text{ (gas)} \tag{16}$$

occurs at noble metal surfaces of large area, such as platinized platinum, freshly plated palladium, or finely divided gold prepared by decomposing auric chloride on a gold surface. The metal acts as an electronic conductor and as a catalyst for the electrode reaction.

Equation (11) can be directly applied, using for the activity of the reduced form the partial pressure of the hydrogen gas. Since hydrogen is very nearly an ideal gas at room temperature, the pressure and activity are very nearly equal. From eq. (11)

$$E = E^\circ + \frac{RT}{2F} \ln \frac{a_{H^+}^2}{P_{H_2}} \tag{17}$$

but by arbitrary convention, $E°$ is taken as zero and

$$E + \frac{RT}{2F} \ln \frac{a_{H^+}^2}{P_{H_2}} = \frac{RT}{F} \ln \frac{a_{H^+}}{\sqrt{P_{H_2}}} \tag{18}$$

Converting to ordinary logarithms,

$$E = \frac{RT}{F} \cdot 2.303 \log a_{H^+} - \frac{RT}{2F} 2.303 \log P_{H_2}$$

At 25°C., the quantity $2.303\, RT/F$ has the value 0.05912, and at 30°C. it has the value 0.06006.

Defining the quantity pH $= - \log a_{H^+}$, the hydrogen electrode equation at 25°C. becomes

$$E = -0.05913\, \text{pH} - 0.02956 \log P_{H_2}$$

where P_{H_2} represents the partial pressure of hydrogen, corrected for water vapor pressure, expressed in atmospheres.

It is evident that the potential of a hydrogen electrode is a linear function of the pH, changing 59.13 mv. for a pH change of 1 unit at 25°.

2.7.2. The Quinhydrone Electrode. Quinhydrone is an equimolecular compound of benzoquinone, abbreviated Q, and hydroquinone, abbreviated QH_2. The compound is sparingly soluble in water, to yield a solution of equal concentrations of Q and QH_2. At an inert electrode such as platinum or gold the following electrode reaction occurs:

$$Q + 2H^+ + 2e^- \rightleftharpoons QH_2 \tag{19}$$

Applying the generalized Nernst equation (eq. 13) we have

$$E = E° + \frac{RT}{2F} \ln \frac{a_Q}{a_{QH_2}} \cdot a_{H^+}^2 \tag{20}$$

The activities of Q and QH_2 are very nearly equal since the concentrations are equal and the activity coefficients of the uncharged molecules are very nearly unity in salt solutions.

$$E = E° + \frac{RT}{2F} \ln a_{H^+}^2 = E° + \frac{RT}{F} \ln a_{H^+} \tag{21}$$

From eq. (18) and (20) it is apparent that the potential of the quinhydrone electrode varies in the same way as that of the hydrogen electrode with changes in hydrogen-ion activity.

2.7.3. The Calomel Electrode. A calomel electrode consists of a layer of mercury in contact with a saturated solution of calomel in a solution containing chloride ions, usually in the form of potassium chloride. The electrode reaction is

$$Hg_2Cl_2 + 2e^- \rightleftharpoons 2Hg + 2Cl^- \tag{22}$$

and the potential is given by

$$E = E^\circ + \frac{RT}{2F} \ln \frac{a_{Hg_2Cl_2}}{a_{Hg} \cdot a_{Cl^-}^2} = E^\circ + \frac{RT}{F} \ln a_{Cl^-} \qquad (23)$$

since the activities of solid calomel and mercury are unity. The calomel electrode is a mercury-mercurous ion electrode, in which the activity of mercurous ion is determined by the activity of chloride ion in the solution, in accordance with the law of mass action, and therefore it behaves as a chloride ion electrode.

2.7.4. The Metal-Metal Oxide Electrode. The Antimony Electrode. If a metal M forms an insoluble hydroxide $M(OH)_n$, the theoretical electrode reaction of the metal in a solution saturated with its hydroxide is

$$M(OH)_n + ne^- \rightleftharpoons M + nOH^- \qquad (24)$$

and the potential is given by

$$E = E^{\circ\prime} + \frac{RT}{nF} \ln \frac{a_{M(OH)_n}}{a_{OH^-}^n} = E^{\circ\prime} - \frac{RT}{F} \ln a_{OH^-} \qquad (25)$$

or since $a_{H^+} \cdot a_{OH^-} = k_w = $ constant

$$E = E^\circ + \frac{RT}{F} \ln a_{H^+} \qquad (26)$$

Thus a reversible metal-metal hydroxide (or oxide) electrode changes its potential in the same way as the hydrogen electrode does.

The antimony electrode is a common example of an electrode of this type. Practical limitations which govern the applicability of the antimony electrode for pH measurements are discussed below.

2.8. Concentration Cells

Two types of concentration cell could be considered, namely, those with and without liquid junction.

A concentration cell with liquid junction may be made using two metallic electrodes in solutions of the metal salt in different concentrations

$$M|M^{n+}(C_1)\|M^{n+}(C_2)|M \qquad (27)$$

An example of this type of cell is one composed of two hydrogen electrodes in hydrochloric acid solutions of different concentration connected by means of a salt bridge. The e.m.f. of the cell is given by the difference of potential of the two electrodes, if the liquid junction potential is neglected. From the Nernst equation

$$E_{\text{cell}} = E_r - E_l = E^\circ + \frac{RT}{nF} \ln C_2\gamma_2 - \left(E^\circ + \frac{RT}{nF} \ln C_1\gamma_1 \right) \tag{28}$$

$$= \frac{RT}{nF} \ln \frac{C_2\gamma_2}{C_1\gamma_1} = \frac{RT}{nF} \ln \frac{a_2}{a_1} \tag{29}$$

It should not be implied that the activity of a single species of ion can accurately be measured by a concentration cell, because the liquid junction potential cannot be entirely eliminated or accurately estimated in general.

An anion concentration cell with liquid junction can be made in a similar way by using electrodes of the second class. For example, two calomel electrodes of different potassium chloride concentrations connected through a salt bridge comprise a cell with an e.m.f. given by

$$E = \frac{RT}{F} \ln \frac{a_2}{a_1}$$ if the liquid junction potential is neglected.

A concentration cell without liquid junction may be made by a system of two hydrogen electrodes and two calomel electrodes,

$$H_2, Pt|HCl(a_1), Hg_2Cl_2|Hg|Hg_2Cl_2, HCl(a_2)|Pt, H_2 \tag{30}$$

It may be easily shown that the cell e.m.f. is given by

$$E = \frac{RT}{F} \ln \frac{(a_{H^+} a_{Cl^-})_2}{(a_{H^+} a_{Cl^-})_1} = \frac{RT}{F} \ln \frac{(C_{H^+} \cdot C_{Cl^-})_2}{(C_{H^+} \cdot C_{Cl^-})_1} \cdot \frac{(\gamma_{H^+} \cdot \gamma_{Cl^-})_2}{(\gamma_{H^+} \cdot \gamma_{Cl^-})_1} \tag{31}$$

$$= \frac{RT}{F} \ln \frac{(C^2_{HCl})_2}{(C^2_{HCl})_1} \cdot \frac{(\gamma^2_{HCl})_2}{(\gamma^2_{HCl})_1} = \frac{2RT}{F} \ln \frac{(C_{HCl})_2}{(C_{HCl})_1} \cdot \frac{(\gamma_{HCl})_2}{(\gamma_{HCl})_1} \tag{32}$$

since the activity coefficient of HCl is defined by

$$\gamma^2_{HCl} = \gamma_{H^+} \cdot \gamma_{Cl^-} \tag{33}$$

and since the concentrations of chloride and hydrogen ion are equal,

$$C^2_{HCl} = C_{H^+} \cdot C_{Cl^-} \tag{34}$$

A concentration cell without liquid junction may be used to measure accurately the ratio of activities of a given electrolyte in two solutions. Strictly speaking, the mean activity of the ions of the electrolyte is measured. According to the Debye-Hückel theory, the activity coefficient of the hydrogen and chloride ions are equal in dilute solutions, so that to a close approximation, the ratio of activities of the individual ions can also be measured.

2.9. Membrane Potentials

Consider a galvanic cell of the type

$$\begin{array}{c|c|c|c|c} \text{Reference} & M^+A^- & \text{Membrane} & M^+B^- & \text{Reference} \\ \text{electrode} & (a_1) & & (a_2) & \text{electrode} \end{array}$$

in which solutions of two salts of the same metal ion M^+ are separated by a membrane and are connected by means of salt bridges to two identical reference electrodes. If the membrane is impervious to the anions A^- and B^-, but permits the passage of cations M^+ from one solution to the other, the net cell reaction is

$$M^+(a_1) \to M^+(a_2) \tag{35}$$

Neglecting liquid junction potentials, the cell e.m.f. is given by a Nernst expression

$$E = \frac{RT}{F} \ln \frac{a_1}{a_2} \tag{36}$$

In practice, this simple relationship is fulfilled only when the higher activity (a_1) is less than of the order of 0.01 M, the limit being determined by the nature of the membrane and the metal ion. The more complete theoretical relationship is more involved, as a consequence of the fact that a single species of ion cannot freely diffuse through a semipermeable membrane, upsetting the condition of electroneutrality of the solutions. The theory, based upon the Donnan membrane theory and the Henderson equation for liquid junction potentials, was suggested independently by Meyer and Sievers (82) and by Teorell (118).

2.10. The Glass Electrode

It was first shown by Haber and Klemensiewicz (38) that a cell of the type

| Reference electrode | Solution 1 | Glass | Solution 2 | Reference electrode |

consisting of two solutions with reference electrode, separated by a glass membrane, behaves as a hydrogen ion concentration cell. Over a fairly wide pH range, the potential difference between the two surfaces of the membrane is determined by the ratio of hydrogen ion activities on the two sides of the membrane.

To account for the e.m.f. behavior, the glass may be assumed to act as a membrane permeable only to hydrogen ions and not to acid anions. A Nernst behavior similar to that for other membrane systems should then be observed,

$$E = \text{constant} + .0591 \ (\text{pH}_1 - \text{pH}_2) \ (\text{at } 25°C.). \tag{37}$$

Therefore, if the composition of the solution on one side of the glass is kept constant, the e.m.f. of the cell should be a linear function of the pH of the solution on the other side of the glass membrane.

Actually, according to Dole (17), the glass does not act as a semipermeable membrane. Each surface of the glass acts as a separate phase boundary, with a potential difference not dependent on the composition of the solution on the other side. The transfer of ions between glass and solution must be considered at both surfaces with the glass acting as a separate phase. If the current across both phase boundaries is carried entirely by hydrogen ions (transference number equal to unity) the net result is a transfer of hydrogen ions from one solution to the other, and the e.m.f. is the same as that produced by an ideal semipermeable membrane.

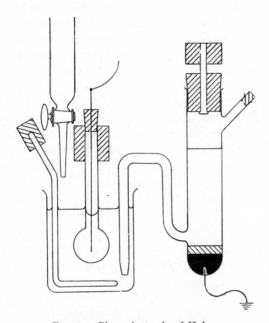

FIG. 1. Glass electrode of Haber.

It has long been recognized that at high pH values the glass electrode potential is no longer linear with pH (17). The magnitude of the error increases with increasing pH, with increasing concentration of alkali metal ions. It depends markedly on the composition of the glass and varies with the temperature. A mathematical theory to account for the alkaline error was developed by Dole (20). It is based upon the concept that in highly alkaline solutions the concentration of hydrogen ion becomes almost vanishingly small compared to the concentration of other cations, with the result that an increasing fraction of the current is carried across the solution-glass boundary by metal ions. However, the nature of the metal ions is very important. The largest effect is noted with the small univalent cations such as lithium and sodium ions, which can readily occupy spaces in the distorted silicate lattice of the glass. With increasing pH, or with increasing alkali metal ion concentration at a constant pH value, the glass assumes in effect an alkali metal membrane function to an increasing extent, and the measured pH value is low by an increasing amount. Electrodes of special composition to minimize the alkaline error are commercially available.

Büchboch (8) and MacInnes and Belcher (75) first showed that the glass electrode is also in error in very acid solutions (pH below 2). Dole (19) pointed out that the same type of error is encountered in very concentrated salt solutions and in alcoholic solutions even at intermediate pH values. He explained the effect by taking into account the transfer of water molecules as well as hydrogen ions (protons) through the glass. In solutions of very low pH the activity of water is appreciably less than in pure water, and in effect the glass electrode behaves as a membrane transferring water from one activity state to another, with a corresponding e.m.f. High concentrations of salt or alcohol likewise act to decrease the activity of water in the solution. Even in 98% ethanol, the effect could be calculated by taking into account the diminished activity of the water. From a theoretical point of view it is apparent that the transfer of solvent imposes a serious limitation on the use of the glass electrode in mixed or nonaqueous solvents.

2.11. The Potentiometric Titration Curve

To develop the theory of the potentiometric curve it is necessary first to consider the manner in which the concentration of the potential-determining substance or substances varies during the titration, next to express the variation of electrode potential with concentration, and finally to find the potentiometric end point and its relationship to the true equivalence point. The method will be illustrated by simple cases which can be extended to more complicated situations without the addition of new principles.

2.11.1. *Precipitation Reactions.* Consider a positive ion M^+ which undergoes a precipitation reaction upon the addition of reagent A^-, the metal ion being the potential-determining substance. Let C be the original concentration of M^+, y the equivalents of A^- added per liter at any point, and x the solubility of MA at any point, in moles per liter. Then neglecting change of activity coefficients, and for simplicity assuming that the volume remains constant,

$$[B^+] = C - y + x \qquad [A^-] = x \qquad (38)$$

and
$$[B^+][A^-] = (C - y + x)(x) = S \qquad (39)$$

where S is the solubility product of MA.

From the Nernst equation

$$E = E° + \frac{RT}{F} \ln [B^+] = E° + \frac{RT}{F} \ln (C - y + x) \tag{40}$$

The slope of the potentiometric titration curve is

$$\frac{dE}{dy} = \frac{RT}{F(C - y + x)} \left(-1 + \frac{dx}{dy} \right) \tag{41}$$

Evaluating dx/dy by differentiating eq. (39) we have

$$\frac{dE}{dy} = \frac{-RT}{F(C - y + 2x)} \tag{42}$$

It is of interest to determine the point at which the slope is a maximum. Here the second derivative is zero.

$$\frac{d^2E}{dy^2} = \frac{-RT(C - y)}{F(C - y + 2x)^3} = 0 \tag{43}$$

From eq. (43), the equivalence point $(C = y)$ is reached when the second derivative is zero, or when the slope of the titration curve is at a maximum. In Fig. 2, titration curves are shown plotted for titration of 0.1 N solutions of iodide, bromide and chloride with silver ion. It is apparent that the magnitude of the potential break at the end point decreases with increasing solubility of the salt. A part of the silver iodide titration curve in the vicinity of the end point is shown on a greatly enlarged scale in Fig. 3. The slope and second derivative, calculated from eqs. (42) and (43) are shown plotted on the same abscissa scale. The calculations are idealized in neglecting adsorption effects which in practice distort the curves in the immediate vicinity of the equivalence point (61).

For more complex precipitation reactions, in which precipitate of the types M_2A, MA_2, etc. are formed the titration curve in general is not symmetrical about the equivalence point. If the end point is taken as the point of maximum slope (second derivative equal to zero) a theoretical titration error exists. The error increases with increasing solubility of the precipitate and with increasing dilution.

Le Blanc and Harnapp (68) have developed the theory for "electrodes of the third class" to be used as indicator electrodes for the ions of metals for which no convenient solid electrodes are available. For example, in the determination of calcium, an electrode system such as

$$Ag|Ag_2C_2O_4, CaC_2O_4, Ca^{++}$$

may be used (128), taking advantage of the easily prepared silver electrode.

In the case of two insoluble salts, B_1A and B_2A, with solubility products S_1 and S_2, LeBlanc and Harnapp (68) have shown that the ideal choice of salts is such that

$$\frac{2S_1 + S_2}{2(S_1 + S_2)} = 0.5$$

to minimize changes in cation concentration by precipitation or dissolution processes.

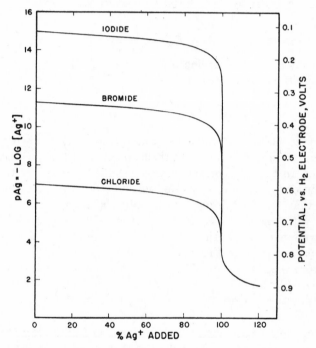

FIG. 2.   Titration curves of titration of 0.1 N iodide, bromide, and chloride with silver.

2.11.2. Neutralization Reactions.   The potentiometric titration curve of a strong acid with a strong base is identical with that of a precipitation reaction in which $S = K_w = 10^{-14}$. The point of maximum slope is that at which the hydrogen and hydroxyl ion concentrations are equal, namely at a pH value of 7.

This situation is no longer true in the titration of weak acids with strong bases or the reverse. Here the hydrolysis of the salt at the equivalence point leads to a pH value greater or less than 7 depending upon whether the acid or base was weak. It is of interest to determine whether the point of maximum slope in these cases coincides with the

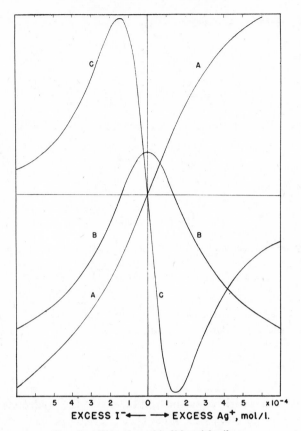

FIG. 3.   Titration of iodide with silver.

Curve A: E vs. amount of reagent
Curve B: dE/dV vs. amount of reagent
Curve C: d^2E/dV^2 vs. amount of reagent

equivalence point.   As a first approximation, activities and concentrations will be considered identical.

Using the same notation as above, for the titration of a weak acid of ionization constant K_a, we have

$$C = [HA] + [A^-] \tag{44}$$
$$y + [H^+] = A^- + [OH^-] \text{ (from electroneutrality)} \tag{45}$$

and

$$K_a = \frac{[H^+][A^-]}{[HA]} \tag{46}$$

For any hydrogen ion indicating electrode we may write the Nernst equation

$$E = E^\circ + \frac{RT}{F} \ln [H^+] \tag{47}$$

which gives the first and second derivative

$$\frac{dE}{dy} = \frac{RT}{F[\text{H}^+]} \frac{d[\text{H}^+]}{dy} \qquad (48)$$

and

$$\frac{d^2E}{dy^2} = \frac{RT}{F[\text{H}^+]} \cdot \frac{d^2[\text{H}^+]}{dy^2} - \frac{RT}{F[\text{H}^+]^2} \frac{(d[\text{H}^+])^2}{(dy)} \qquad (49)$$

At the point of maximum slope, the second derivative is zero, so that

$$\frac{d^2[\text{H}^+]}{dy^2} = \frac{1}{[\text{H}^+]} \frac{(d[\text{H}^+])^2}{(dy)} \qquad (50)$$

Combining eqs. (44), (45), and (46) we have

$$y + [\text{H}^+] = \frac{Ck_a}{k_a + [\text{H}^+]} + \frac{k_w}{[\text{H}^+]} \qquad (51)$$

which may be differentiated twice and substituted into eq. (50) giving

$$([\text{H}^+] + k_a)^3 = Ck_a[\text{H}^+]^2 \frac{[\text{H}^+] - k_a}{[\text{H}^+]^2 - k_w} \qquad (52)$$

If the acid is not extremely weak, we may neglect $[\text{H}^+]$ at the end point in comparison with k_a, and simplify eq. (52) to give, after clearing fractions,

$$[\text{H}^+] = \sqrt{\frac{k_a k_w}{k_a + C}} \cong \frac{k_a k_w}{C} \qquad (53)$$

which is identical with equation obtained for the hydrolysis of a salt solution of concentration C. Thus the inflection point is identical with the equivalence point for moderately weak acids. Titration curves for the titration of 0.1 N solutions of a strong acid and for weak acids of ionization constant $k_a = 10^{-5}$, 10^{-7}, and 10^{-9} respectively, are shown in Fig. 4.

For very weak acids, the inflection point becomes less pronounced and differs somewhat from the end point. Roller (102) has calculated a theoretical titration error of 0.3 % if the product of the ionization constant K_a and the concentration C of the acid is equal to 10^{-11}. If the product is 10^{-10}, the theoretical error is only 0.03 %.

In practice the titration error for very weak acids is of no consequence because the slope of the titration curve becomes so low that the end point cannot be determined with a precision comparable to the titration error. In fact Eastman (22) and Roller (102) have shown that no inflection point occurs at all if $C \cdot K_a$ is of the order of 10^{-12} or 10^{-13}. The limiting factor is the ionization constant of the solvent (K_W for water), which determines the degree of hydrolysis of the salt. This limitation can be overcome in certain instances by titrations in nonaqueous solvent systems (103, 123).

Polybasic acids may be considered as a special case of mixtures of acids in which the concentrations are equal. From the analytical point of view, the first end point cannot be detected with an accuracy of 0.5% unless the first dissociation constant is of the order of 10^4 times the second dissociation constant. The second end point for a dibasic acid simply represents the titration of the weaker acid, and the same limitations hold

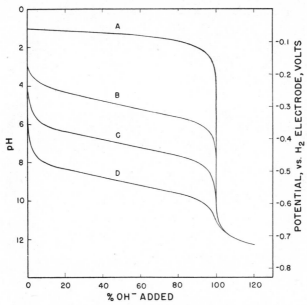

FIG. 4. Titration of 0.1 N acids with sodium hydroxide.

Curve A: Strong acid
Curve B: $K_a = 10^{-5}$
Curve C: $K_a = 10^{-7}$
Curve D: $K_a = 10^{-9}$

as for weak acids in general. Carbonic acid is one of special interest $(K_1 = 3 \times 10^{-7}, K_2 = 6 \times 10^{-11})$ because the ratio of $K_1:K_2$, and the value of K_2 are such that both end points may be determined potentiometrically with an accuracy of the order of 1%.

The titration curves of polybasic acids and of mixtures of weak acids are often of interest from another point of view, even though the end points are not accurate enough to be of analytical value. Michaelis (85) has shown that the ionization constants of a dibasic acid may be evaluated from the titration curve if the first and second ionization constants differ by as much as sixteen fold.

2.11.3. Complex Formation Reactions. The formation of a stable soluble complex of a metal ion can often be made the basis of a potentiometric titration of the metal ion or of the complex forming substance. The simplest situation is one in which a single type of complex stable over a wide range of concentration of complexing anion, for example the formation of $Ag(CN)_2^-$ from the silver ion and the cyanide ion. Even this case is made more complicated by the fact that the silver salt of the complex, $Ag[Ag(CN)_2]$ is slightly soluble.

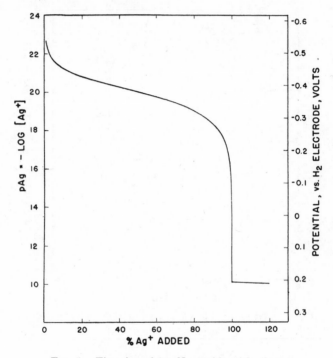

FIG. 5.   Titration of 0.1 N cyanide with silver.

Starting with a solution containing the cyanide ion, the complex ion $Ag(CN)_2^-$ is formed until the solubility product of the salt has been reached, after which the silver ion concentration is practically constant for the points immediately following the end point. The resulting curve (92) shown in Fig. 5, has an increasing slope until the end point, where a discontinuous break occurs upon precipitation. A second end point, corresponding to the complete precipitation of silver argenticyanide, very similar to that obtained with chloride, is then obtained.

More involved situations in which a series of complexes of varying composition are encountered are less important from an analytical point of view, but the titration curves are often extremely useful in the evaluation of equilibrium constants for the stepwise formation of the various complexes. Bjerrum (5) has succeeded in evaluating equilibrium constants and formulating the composition of ammonia complexes of various metal ions by interpreting the potentiometric titration curves using the glass electrode. Similar situations of stepwise formation of complexes are often encountered in the halide ion complexes of various metal ions.

2.11.4. Oxidation-Reduction (Redox) Reactions. Consider the titration of an oxidant Ox, with a reductant Red_2. Suppose that a molecule of the oxidant requires b electrons for its reduction,

$$Ox_1 + b\ e^- \rightleftharpoons Red_1 \tag{54}$$

and a molecule of the reductant loses a electrons upon its oxidation,

$$Red_2 \rightleftharpoons Ox_2 + a\ e^- \tag{55}$$

The reaction then may be written

$$a\ Ox_1 + b\ Red_2 \rightarrow a\ Red_1 + b\ Ox_2 \tag{56}$$

Before the equivalence point, if half-reaction (56) is reversible, the potential varies in accordance with the Nernst equation,

$$E = E_1{}^\circ + \frac{RT}{bF} \ln \frac{[Ox_1]}{[Red_1]} \tag{57}$$

writing concentrations in place of activities for sake of simplicity.

After the equivalence point, the potential is most conveniently calculated from the excess concentration of reductant Red_2 and the concentration of its oxidation product, Ox_2,

$$E = E_2{}^\circ + \frac{RT}{aF} \ln \frac{[Ox_2]}{[Red_2]} \tag{58}$$

A point of special interest is the equivalence point, where the concentrations of oxidant remaining unreduced, Ox_1, and the concentration of reductant remaining unoxidized, Red_2, must be in the stoichiometric ratio $a:b$. Thus

$$\frac{[Ox_1]}{[Red_2]} = \frac{[Red_1]}{[Ox_2]} = \frac{a}{b} \tag{59}$$

from which

$$\frac{[Ox_1]}{[Red_1]} = \frac{[Red_2]}{[Ox_1]} \tag{60}$$

To calculate the potential at the equivalence point (the equivalence potential), we may take advantage of the fact that whenever two oxidation-reduction systems are in equilibrium, the potentials of the two systems are equal. Applying this principle to the equivalence point, we may write

$$E_{Eq} = E_1{}^\circ + \frac{RT}{bF} \ln \frac{[Ox_1]}{[Red_1]} = E_2{}^\circ + \frac{RT}{aF} \ln \frac{[Ox_2]}{[Red_2]} \qquad (61)$$

Using the relationship given in eq. (60), it is readily seen that

$$E_{Eq} = \frac{bE_1{}^\circ + aE_2{}^\circ}{a + b} \qquad (62)$$

From eq. (62) it is evident that in the simple case where $a = b$, the equivalence potential is the arithmetic mean of the two normal potentials. If a and b are not equal, the curve is unsymmetrical about the equivalence point.

An important characteristic of redox titration curves is that the shape is generally independent of the concentration of the substance being titrated, in contrast to precipitation and neutralization reactions. This behavior follows from the fact that the potential is determined by the ratio of concentrations of oxidant to reductant rather than the absolute value of either concentration.

The evaluation of the slope of the titration curves in the vicinity of the equivalence point becomes quite involved for redox titrations (35, 39, 40, 64). In general, there exists a small titration error which has hardly any practical significance because it is negligibly small in those cases where a sufficient difference exists between the oxidation potentials of the two systems to make a titration feasible in practice.

The detailed mathematical analysis of titration curves is of value in evaluating equilibrium constants of reactions (42) and to prove the existence of intermediate oxidation products (83, 85).

An important practical limitation to the exact interpretation of titration curves lies in the irreversibility of electrode behavior. Many electrodes, especially those involving complex oxidation-reduction half reactions do not behave reversibly and therefore the potential does not vary exactly in accordance with the Nernst equation. Often a very exact titration end point is obtained but no data of thermodynamic significance can be calculated from the shape of the curve.

3. APPARATUS AND TECHNIQUE

3.1. Potential Measurements

To measure accurately the e.m.f. of a cell, it is necessary to avoid the passage of an appreciable current through the cell, because the passage of current would cause polarization effects due to chemical reactions at the electrodes, with a consequent change in the e.m.f. Two general techniques of e.m.f. measurement may be recognized: the potentiometric compensation technique, and vacuum-tube techniques.

3.1.1. The Potentiometer.   The most commonly used method of e.m.f. measurement is based upon the compensation technique, in which the unknown cell e.m.f. is opposed by a variable e.m.f. from a potentiometer, adjusted until no current flows in the unknown cell circuit.   The cell e.m.f. is then equal to the e.m.f. impressed by the potentiometer.   To calibrate the potentiometer reading, a standard cell of known e.m.f. is used.

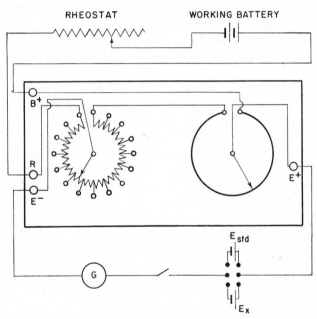

FIG. 6.   Student potentiometer with accessories.

A simplified circuit diagram of the Leeds and Northrup student potentiometer is shown in Fig. 6.   The circuit inside the box consists of a series of 15 coils of equal resistance to represent 0.1-volt settings, and a continuous slide-wire of resistance equal to that of one coil to represent 0–0.1 volt.   The total voltage through the coils and slide-wire is made exactly equal to 1.6 volts by adjusting the rheostat in series with the working battery.   This is done by setting the dial readings exactly equal to the e.m.f. of a standard cell, and balancing to zero current as indicated by the galvanometer.   To measure the e.m.f. of an unknown cell, the rheostat is left unaltered, and the potentiometer dials then read the e.m.f. directly in volts when a state of balance is indicated by a zero deflection of the galvanometer. It is advisable to balance against the standard cell at the beginning and end of each set of readings, to guard against any change in the voltage of the working battery.

The working battery may consist of two dry cells in series, a single lead storage cell, or a lead storage battery. Some of the older student potentiometers were made with a range of 0–2.3 volts, in which case a single lead storage cell could not be used. A freshly charged lead storage cell shows a decreasing voltage during the first portion of its discharge, and for that reason it should be connected into the potentiometer circuit and allowed to operate until a constant reading is observed.

The usual standard cell which is commercially available is the "unsaturated" Weston cell consisting of a mercury-mercurous sulfate electrode in a solution of cadmium sulfate saturated at 4°C. and a cadmium amalgam electrode in contact with the same solution. The standard cell must never be short-circuited, and only a very small current should be drawn from the cell during the instantaneous depression of the tapping key in the potentiometer circuit.

The sensitivity of the galvanometer to be chosen depends upon the internal resistance of the unknown cell and the desired sensitivity of the measurement. For most practical work, a current sensitivity of 0.01–0.05 microampere/mm. is entirely adequate. This range of sensitivity is available in small enclosed and scale type galvanometers. A galvanometer of short period with a shunt circuit of proper resistance to provide critical damping is ideal.

Several commercial types of portable potentiometers are available. The principle is identical with that outlined above, but the galvanometer, tapping key, standard cell, working battery and rheostat are built into a compact unit.

3.1.2. Vacuum Tube Voltmeters and Amplifiers. Vacuum tube techniques have proved to be of especial value in the measurement of pH with the glass electrode, which has an extremely high electrical resistance if the thickness of the glass wall is great enough to afford mechanical ruggedness. Several types of commercial pH meters have reached an advanced state of development, using circuits which are simple, sturdy and stable. Both battery and A.C. line-operated instruments of various makes are available. A discussion of various types of amplifier circuits suitable for use with the glass electrode has been presented by Dole (18).

For potentiometric titrations, direct-reading vacuum tube voltmeters are becoming increasingly popular. The circuit diagram of a simple battery-operated instrument, designed by Garman and Droz (34) and introduced commercially as the Leitz "Electrotitrator," is shown in Fig. 7. The resistors R_2 and R_3 are two arms of a Wheatstone bridge, the other two arms being the effective resistance from the cathode to the plate and from the cathode to grid-2. The microammeter M indicates the degree of unbalance of the bridge, in such a way that the meter reading is directly proportional to the unknown e.m.f. at the terminals 1 and 2. The sensitivity of the instrument may be adjusted by resistor R_4. In this way the meter may be made to show a full-range deflection over the course of a titration.

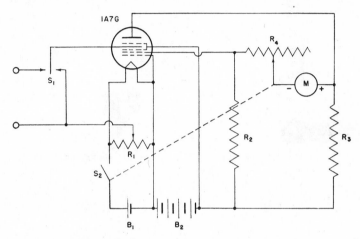

FIG. 7.   Electronic circuit of Garmon and Iroz.

Titrimeters using a visual tuning tube instead of a microammeter or galvanometer have been introduced by Smith and Sullivan (109) and later in a somewhat simplified circuit by Serfass (104).

3.2. Reference Electrodes and Salt Bridges

Calomel half-cells are very widely used as reference electrodes, both for pH measurements and for potentiometric titrations. A potassium chloride solution of definite concentration, saturated with calomel, is placed in contact with mercury and solid calomel. Generally the calomel is added in the form of a paste made by grinding mercury and calomel together in a mortar and washing several times by decantation with the potassium chloride solution to be used.

Several types of calomel electrodes are recognized, according to the concentration of potassium chloride solution used. The most common are the 0.1 N, the 1 N, and the saturated calomel electrode, corresponding to a 0.1 N, 1 N, or saturated solution of potassium chloride.

The type of electrode vessel and salt bridge varies widely according to the particular use and preference of the investigator. A common

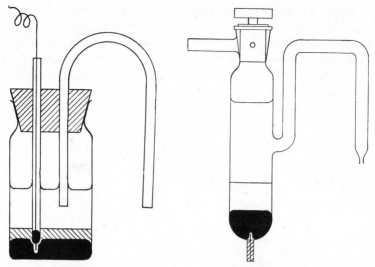

FIG. 8. Bottle type calomel
cell.

FIG. 9. Calomel half cell.

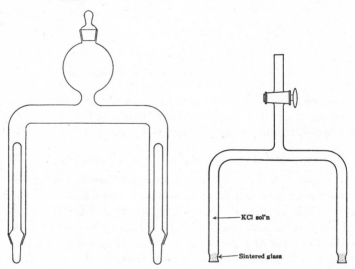

FIG. 10. Salt bridge with ground
glass plugs.

FIG. 11. Sintered glass salt
bridge.

type of calomel half cell is shown in Fig. 8. The bottle type (Fig. 9)
is convenient for potentiometric titrations. An inverted U-tube filled
with saturated potassium chloride-agar gel serves as a salt bridge. Hume
and Harris (57) suggested using a long rubber tube with saturated potassium chloride, ending in an agar plug, as a convenient salt bridge.

Salt bridges which avoid the use of agar, and therefore are recommended for titrations at elevated temperatures have been described by Irving and Smith (58) (Fig. 10) and Laitinen (66) (Fig. 11). The former uses ground glass plugs at both ends, while the latter uses sintered glass ends.

Commercially available calomel electrodes which have been developed for pH measurements and use either ground glass plugs or fiber salt bridges are convenient reference electrodes, particularly when using vacuum tube voltmeters or titrimeters where the cell resistance is unimportant.

Other types of reference electrodes which should be mentioned are the silver-silver chloride electrode electrode (126) and the glass electrode (52, 74).

3.3. Methods of End Point Detection

3.3.1. The Classical Method. The classical method of detecting a potentiometric end point is based upon the fact that a potentiometric titration curve of the symmetrical type theoretically shows a point of inflection at the equivalence point. The end point may be determined by plotting the titration data and finding the point of inflection, by calculating the slope (dE/dv) of the titration curve as a function of volume and finding the volume corresponding to the maximum slope, or by calculating the second derivative (d^2E/dv^2) and determining the volume corresponding to a zero value. For asymmetrical curves the end point is likewise taken as the point of maximum slope, the titration error being neglected. An examination of Fig. 3 shows clearly that for a given titration the second derivative curve shows an abrupt change in sign at the end point and therefore lends itself best to an interpolation between experimentally determined points. For the most accurate results and convenient calculations, the increments of reagent should be made small and equal in the immediate vicinity of the end point (23, 43, 44, 64). Such equal additions of reagent can readily be made by a dropwise addition of reagent near the end point, with a calibration of the drop size for the particular buret and reagent being used.

To illustrate the application of the classical method, the following experimental results are presented in Table I for the titration of potassium iodide with 0.01 N potassium permanganate in sulfuric acid solution. In this experiment, the buret reading was taken at an arbitrary location near the end point (volume 1.67 ml.) and then dropwise increments of reagent were added. Another buret reading after 4 drops served to determine the drop volume and to establish another reference point very near the end point. In this way, an end point as precise as the buret reading can readily be calculated by a linear interpolation of the second increments of potential (Δ^2E) without the necessity of plotting a graph. A plot of the first increment (ΔE) would yield the same result, but with no convenient means of interpolation to values closer than $\pm\frac{1}{2}$ drop of reagent.

TABLE I

Titration of 120 ml. 0.05 N KI (approx.) with 0.4 N KMnO$_4$, Starting with Weight Buret, Finishing with 0.01 N KMnO$_4$

Vol. KMnO$_4$	E	ΔE	Δ^2E	
1.67 ml.	0.590			
1.67 + 1 drop	0.597	0.007	0.001	
2 drops	0.605	0.008	0.004	
3 drops	0.617	0.012	0.009	
(1.87 ml.) 4 drops	0.638	0.021	0.027	E.P. 1.89[a]
5 drops	0.686	0.048	−0.016	
6 drops	0.719	0.033	−0.017	
7 drops	0.735	0.016	−0.016	
8 drops	0.745	0.010		

[a] E.P. $= 1.87 + \dfrac{0.027}{0.027 + 0.016} = 1.89$ ml.

Special methods of determining the end point based upon the mathematical behavior of the titration curve have been suggested by Cavanagh (11) who has described a method for the calculation of the end point from two or more readings of the e.m.f. corresponding to suitable volumes of reagent, and Hahn and Weiler (45) who describe an involved graphical analysis of the titration curve. The method of Cavanagh has been shown to give good results in the titration of very dilute solutions of halides with silver.

3.3.2. Titration to Equivalence Potential. It is apparent that once a given titration has been performed with a given electrode system, the e.m.f. of the titration cell at the end point can be used as a reference point for titrations run under the same conditions. Considerable saving in time may be achieved in routine work by setting the potentiometer to indicate the value of the e.m.f. expected at the end point, and titrating to a zero deflection of the galvanometer. In practice, however, it should always be borne in mind that the equilibrium value of the e.m.f. is rarely reached instantaneously in the immediate vicinity of the end point, and care must be taken to approach the end point slowly enough to insure stable e.m.f. readings.

Ideally, the "equivalence potential" could be calculated from the composition of the solution at the equivalence point, but as Kolthoff

(62) has pointed out, the equilibrium constant of the reaction is rarely known accurately under the exact experimental conditions used. Therefore he suggests the calculation of the "practical" equilibrium constant from the data of the titration, and from this value the equivalence potential. For curves of very slight slope, this procedure is of special advantage.

In certain cases, the equivalence potential may be determined empirically by making up a solution of a composition corresponding to the equivalence point, and measuring the cell e.m.f. However, this method should be used with caution, because the equivalence potential is often very poorly defined (irreversible oxidation-reduction reactions), sensitive to variation in acidity, or affected by adsorption phenomena (precipitation reactions).

A special case of titration to an equivalence potential, and historically the earliest titration of this type, is the method of Pinkhof (98) and Treadwell and Weiss (124) in which a special reference electrode is prepared so that its potential is equal to that of the indicator electrode at the end point. Since the titration is run to zero potential difference, no potentiometer is needed, but simply a galvanometer, a resistance, and a tapping key. Treadwell (121) also used a cell continuously short-circuited through a high resistance and galvanometer in a cell of this type. An obvious disadvantage is the necessity of constructing a special reference electrode of the proper potential for each reaction.

Müller (91) impressed an e.m.f. equal to that developed by the titration cell at the end point, and titrated to a zero deflection of a galvanometer. While Müller used a battery and rheostat to impress the desired e.m.f., the method in principle is exactly the same as that described in the first paragraph of this section, in which a potentiometer is used for the purpose. Data on practical equivalence potentials are listed in Müller's book (91).

Cavanagh (11) has described cells without liquid junction made in such a way that the e.m.f. is zero or some finite value at the equivalence point. For example, a cell composed of a silver chloride electrode and a hydrogen electrode will have a zero e.m.f. at the end point of an acid-base titration if the chloride ion concentration is kept within a certain range. Conversely, if the hydrogen ion concentration is kept in the proper range, the e.m.f. of the cell will be zero at the end point of a titration of chloride ion with silver ion. The method of Cavanagh has the advantage of using a cell without liquid junction, but suffers from the disadvantage that the "reference ion" concentration must be known at least approximately and of course would vary for a given determination with ionic strength, because the activity coefficients of the ions would vary.

In general, the methods of titration to the equivalence potential are advantageous in routine work to gain speed, but in each case the method should be devised only after a careful study of the titration by the classical method, to avoid the possibility of unexpected errors.

3.3.3. Differential Titrations. If two identical indicator electrodes are used during a titration, and if a small portion of the solution being titrated can be temporarily isolated in the vicinity of one electrode and

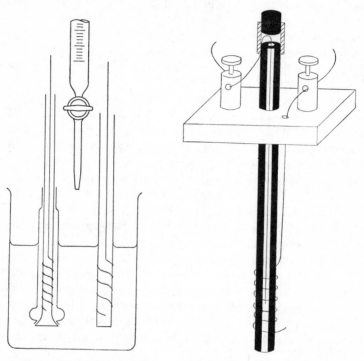

Fig. 12. Differential titration apparatus of Mac-Innes and Jones.

Fig. 13. Differential electrode of Müller.

kept from mixing with the bulk of the solution, then a difference of potential will be set up for each increment of reagent. By using equal increments of reagent, and mixing the entire solution between additions, the titration curve resembles a plot of the slope of an ordinary titration curve against volume of reagent. The end point is taken as the point of maximum e.m.f.

The differential method, originally proposed by Cox (14), has been developed in a more practical form by MacInnes and Jones (76). The apparatus, shown in Fig. 12, consists of an electrode with a cap to isolate a small portion of the solution before each addition of reagent. Between increments, the entire solution can readily be mixed.

Another form of differential titration apparatus, described by Müller (90) is shown in Fig. 13. A capillary tube, containing an electrode within it and another electrode wound around it, serves to isolate a minute volume of solution. This device does not give differential readings unless the liquid inside the capillary is forced out periodically. A simple modification is that of Hall, Jensen, and Baeckström (48), who used a medicine dropper with a platinum electrode sealed inside and another wound around the outside. By squeezing the bulb between readings a fresh portion of solution is conveniently brought in contact with the inner electrode but isolated from the bulk of the solution.

3.3.4. *Bimetallic Electrodes.* The bimetallic electrode consists of two dissimilar metals, used without a reference electrode, in the solution to be titrated. If the two electrodes do not respond to give the same potential in the same solution owing to irreversibility of one or both electrodes, or if the rate of attainment of the final potential is different for the two metals, a difference of potential will exist at least temporarily during the titration. Since the potential of both electrodes changes most rapidly in the vicinity of the end point, the difference of potential between the two electrodes changes abruptly at the end point, followed by a constant or slowly changing e.m.f. depending upon the particular titration and electrode system.

Willard and Fenwick (131) and Van Name and Fenwick (127) carried out the first systematic investigations of bimetallic systems, and concluded that accurate results can be obtained for many titrations, especially those involving oxidation-reduction reactions. The early work was mainly done with platinum or platinum-rhodium coupled with tungsten. Later investigations have been carried out with many metallic couples and metal-nonmetal electrode systems.

Many acid-base titrations with bimetallic electrodes have been performed. Fuoss (27) described the use of antimony-copper amalgam, antimony, antimony-lead, bismuth-silver, and copper-copper oxide systems. Many later investigations have extended the variety of such electrode systems in use. A list, together with literature references, is given by Furman (31).

Furman and Wilson (33) devised a simple, continuous-reading titration system, using platinum and tungsten electrodes short-circuited through a high resistance and galvanometer (Fig. 14).

3.3.5. *Polarized Electrode Systems.* Willard and Fenwick (131), using two identical platinum electrodes, impressed a polarizing potential difference through a high resistance, as shown in Fig. 15, and measured the e.m.f. by means of the usual potentiometric method. An abrupt potential change marked the end point. The investigation of Van Name and Fenwick (127) showed that the sharpness of the potential break is determined by the difference in degree of reversibility of the electrode reactions before and after the end point. This type of end point, as Furman (30) has pointed out, is similar in principle to a bimetallic system, or "chemically polarized" system.

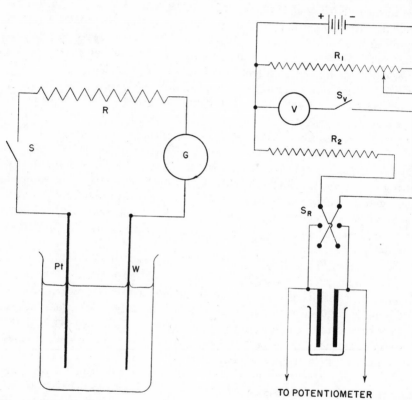

FIG. 14.   Bimetallic system of Furman and Wilson.

FIG. 15.   Polarized electrode system of Willard and Fenwick.

The "dead-stop" end point of Foulk and Bawden (26) is similar in using an external source of polarizing e.m.f., but differs from the Willard and Fenwick circuit in using a small difference of potential between the electrode (10–15 mv.) and measuring the current in a low-resistance circuit connecting the two electrodes (Fig. 16). The method of Furman and Wilson (33) while superficially similar, is based on a high resistance external circuit. The resistance is so large that the measurement of current is almost equivalent to the measurement of the potential difference between the electrodes. The Willard and Fenwick circuit corresponds to the use of an infinitely large external resistance and is truly a potentiometric method. The dead-stop end point is based on a different principle, in the sense that an electrolytic current can flow with a small polarizing e.m.f. only if electrolysis reactions can occur at both electrodes with essentially zero back e.m.f. (depolarized anode and cathode). If one or both electrodes are polarized before the end point because of irreversibility of electrode reaction or high back e.m.f., and the excess of reagent causes both electrodes to become depolarized, then the end

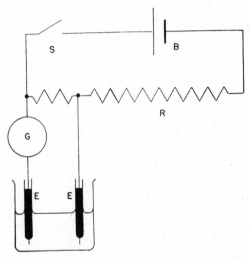

FIG. 16. Foulk and Bawden dead stop apparatus.

point appears as a sudden surge of current at the end point, and continuing beyond it.

An example is the titration of thiosulfate with iodine. No cathode reaction can occur until an excess of iodine is present, while the anodic oxidation of iodide can occur before and after the end point. The reverse titration of iodine with thiosulfate likewise shows a dead-stop end point, because the cathode suddenly becomes polarized as the last trace of free iodine is consumed.

The dead-stop end point actually resembles more closely the amperometric (65) end point than the potentiometric, but differs in the sense that no diffusion current is observed at a depolarized electrode. Thus, the amperometric current is proportional to the concentration of depolarizer, while the dead-stop end point is a qualitative indicator for the presence of depolarizer.

4. Practical Applications

4.1. pH Measurements

4.1.1. The Hydrogen Electrode. The hydrogen electrode is of great theoretical importance because it is the standard of reference for electrode potentials. All other pH measurements are indirectly calibrated against the hydrogen electrode, but in practice the hydrogen electrode is seldom used if another electrode will serve equally well, because of the technical difficulties involved in its use.

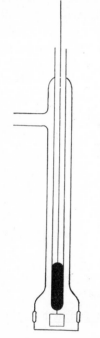

A noble metal such as platinum, gold, or palladium will act as an electrode of elementary hydrogen if the surface is properly prepared by deposition of a layer of finely divided noble metal. The most common type is prepared by thoroughly cleaning a platinum wire or plate with a dichromate cleaning mixture, washing with water, and electrolyzing in a solution of 1–3 % chloroplatinic acid using a platinum anode. After the electrolysis, the electrode is washed thoroughly with water and polarized cathodically in a dilute (0.5 N) sulfuric acid solution to reduce any adsorbed chlorine from the platinizing bath. A thin layer of platinum black is generally preferable to a thick layer, in reaching equilibrium more rapidly. The electrode should be kept under water when not in use.

According to Hamer and Acree (50), a palladium electrode is more reliable than a platinized electrode for pH measurements in phthalate buffers.

Fig. 17. Hydrogen electrode of Hildebrand.

Several types of hydrogen electrode vessels are used. Two of the simplest and most common are the Hildebrand electrode (53) (Fig. 17) and the Kolthoff (64) titration cell (Fig. 18) in which a straight piece of platinized wire is used.

The hydrogen gas, most conveniently withdrawn from a commercial cylinder, must be purified before use. The removal of the last traces of oxygen is especially important. The gas may be passed over heated copper turnings at 450–550°, then through successive washing bottles of 0.2 N potassium permanganate, and water. For accurate results, both the reference electrode and unknown solution should be immersed in a thermostat bath.

To calculate the pH from the measurement it is first necessary to correct the hydrogen electrode potential to a pressure of 760 mm. The correction involves the vapor pressure of water at the temperature of the measurement because the gas is saturated with water vapor. If the

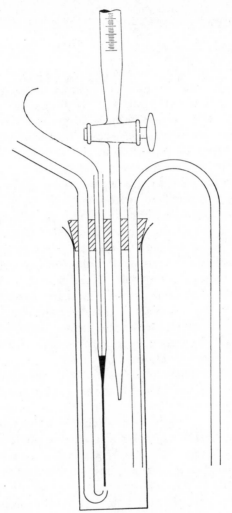

Fig. 18. Kolthoff titration cell.

hydrogen electrode is the negative electrode of the cell, and the partial pressure of hydrogen is less than 760 mm., as is generally the case, the correction will make the hydrogen electrode potential more negative and will increase the absolute value of the cell e.m.f.

Depending upon the type of calomel reference electrode used, the pH is calculated from the following equations:

$$pH = \frac{E_{0.1N} - 0.3365 + 0.00006(t - 25)}{0.0591 + 0.0002(t - 25)} \quad 0.1 \; N \text{ Calomel electrode}$$

$$= \frac{E_{1N} - 0.2828 + 0.00024(t - 25)}{0.0591 + 0.0002(t - 25)} \quad 1 \; N \text{ Calomel electrode}$$

$$= \frac{E_{sat} - 0.2438 + 0.00065(t - 25)}{0.0591 + 0.0002(t - 25)} \quad \text{Saturated calomel electrode}$$

The accuracy of pH measurements is limited by the liquid junction potential, which depends upon the composition of the unknown solution and the type of reference electrode and salt bridge used.

The hydrogen electrode is subject to several interferences which seriously limits its practical application. In the presence of traces of oxygen it is slow to reach equilibrium, and with large amounts an erroneous reading is obtained. The interfering effect of oxygen is particularly noticeable when working with alkaline solutions. The catalytic surface is easily poisoned by traces of materials such as hydrogen sulfide or arsine. Easily hydrogenated organic compounds are prone to interfere, as are oxidizing agents or salts of inactive metals. With oxidizing agents such as dichromate, permanganate, etc., or with strong reducing agents such as stannous ion or chromous ion the electrode acts partly as an oxidation-reduction electrode of the system in solution. With solutions of salts of inactive metals such as silver, mercury, bismuth, or copper the electrode assumes the behavior of the corresponding metal, because hydrogen reduces the metal ions to the metal. Even with these limitations, the hydrogen electrode is important as the ultimate standard against which the behavior of other pH electrodes is checked.

4.1.2. The Quinhydrone Electrode. The quinhydrone electrode, introduced by Biilman and Lund (4) is very simple and convenient in its application. A piece of bright platinum wire or gauze, freshly ignited in a flame, is used as the electrode in a solution which has been saturated with quinhydrone by shaking with a small amount of the solid. According to Morgan, Lammert, and Campbell (88) it is very important to avoid cracks in the glass where the platinum is sealed into the soft glass tube, or large errors may result.

It was seen on p. 113 that the potential of the quinhydrone electrode varies with pH in the same way as that of the hydrogen electrode. The constant difference $E°$ is equal to 0.6994 volt at 25° at an ionic strength of zero.

At higher salt concentrations, the quinhydrone electrode is subject to a salt error. This error is caused by an unequal salting-out effect of the hydroquinone and quinone, with a corresponding change in the activity ratio of the two substances in solution. The salt effect may be prevented by the saturation of the solution not only with quinhydrone but also with either quinone or hydroquinone (3, 112), the activity of the third component remaining constant in solution. Obviously, a different value for the normal potential must then be used.

The most serious limitation of the quinhydrone electrode is that it cannot be used in alkaline solutions, with a pH value above about 8. Hydroquinone is a weak acid, and therefore reacts with hydroxyl ions to affect the pH, especially in poorly buffered solutions. Also, it undergoes air oxidation very readily in alkaline solutions forming brown oxidation products which are distinctly acidic (63). In potentiometric titrations, it is important not only to titrate the acid with the base, but to avoid a local excess of alkali before the end point by thorough stirring. Detailed studies of the behavior of the quinhydrone electrode have been made by Morgan, Lammert, and Campbell (87–89) and by Harned and Wright (51).

4.1.3. The Glass Electrode. The limitations of the glass electrode as a pH electrode in strongly acidic, strongly alkaline, and nonaqueous or mixed solvents have already been mentioned. Gemant (36), however, has recently made measurements in solvents of low dielectric constant, such as dioxane, xylene, and hydrocarbon oils.

For the measurement of the pH of aqueous solutions in an intermediate acidity range, the glass electrode is accurate, rapid and convenient. The particular electrode is calibrated by means of a buffer solution of known pH value immediately before reading the pH of the unknown solution. In this manner, it is possible to compensate for the "asymmetry potential" of the glass electrode, which is the difference in potential of the two surfaces of the glass membrane when in contact with solutions of equal pH.

For most accurate measurements it is advisable to calibrate against a standard buffer of roughly the same pH as the unknown. Recommended standard buffer solutions of known pH values are listed by Bates *et al.* (2). The most commonly used reference solution is 0.05 M potassium biphthalate, pH = 4.01 at 25°C., a saturated solution of potassium hydrogen tartrate, pH = 3.57, is recommended by Lingane (70) as a more conivenient and equally accurate standard. For an alkaline standard, 0.05 M borax is recommended (55, 67).

Among the advantages of the glass electrode may be mentioned the following: (1) pH measurements may be made in the presence of strong oxidizing or reducing agents; (2) the electrode surface is not sensitive to surface active materials, hence measurements may be made in colloidal and turbid solutions; (3) reliable results may be obtained even in unbuffered solutions; (4) the sample may be recovered unchanged, since no addition of reagents need be made; (5) the electrode equilibrium is reached rapidly, an important consideration in potentiometric titrations or in automatic recording of pH; (6) the glass electrode is easily adapted to micromeasurements.

4.1.4. The Antimony Electrode. It was seen on p. 114 that a metal-metal oxide electrode should change its potential with pH in the same way as the hydrogen electrode. Of the several possible electrodes of this type, the antimony-antimony oxide electrode is the only one that has been widely used with much success.

The method of preparation of the electrode affects both the normal potential and the slope of the potential-pH curve. Roberts and Fenwick (101), using antimony prepared by electrolysis of antimony fluoride together with the stable cubic modification of antimonious oxide, found that the potential varied with pH in accordance with the Nernst equation. Hovorka and Chapman (56), working with pure antimony plated from hydrofluoric acid solution, observed that the potential referred to the normal hydrogen electrode varied in accordance with the equation

$$E = 0.2552 - 0.05893 \text{ pH}$$

at 25° from pH 2 to 8. This behavior is in fair agreement with the observations of Parks and Beard (94) and Perley (95) who, however, report slightly different values for the normal potential.

Above a pH value of 8, the slope of the curve changes somewhat, perhaps because of the amphoteric character of the oxide.

For pH work, the particular antimony electrode being used must be standardized against a known buffer solution in the pH range being studied. Perley (95) reported a reproducibility of 0.15 pH unit. The exact experimental conditions, such as the absence or presence of air and stirring, should be duplicated in the standardization and the measurements.

Strong oxidizing agents interfere badly, and organic compounds such as hydroxy acids which form complexes with trivalent antimony cause erroneous results.

4.2. Concentration Cells

Concentration cells may be used both for potentiometric determination with a single measurement, or for titration procedures. If, for example, a concentration cell is titrated to zero e.m.f. then the concentrations in the two halves of the cell become equal.

Johnson and Low (60) used a silver, silver chloride, potassium chloride concentration cell in the determination of the atomic weight of potassium, for estimating the excess or deficiency of silver very near the end point of the silver nitrate-potassium chloride titration. A concentration cell procedure was used by Furman and Low (32) for the determination of traces of chlorides in various salts. Hahn (41) proposed that the effect of bromide on the potential of the calomel electrode might be used for the determination of traces of bromide in chlorides.

Low and Pryde (72) devised a concentration cell method for fluoride based upon the effect of fluoride on the potential of the ferric-ferrous electrode. Fluoride forms a stable complex with ferric iron but not with ferrous iron, and therefore has a marked effect upon the potential. Drewski (21) used a concentration cell method for excess halogen in the determination of iodine numbers.

A hydrogen-ion concentration cell composed of two antimony electrodes in buffer solutions has been proposed by Sergeev and Yavorskii (105) for pH determinations. By trying various known buffers in conjunction with the unknown until no galvanometer deflection was observed, the pH of the unknown could be determined.

Potentiometric neutralization titrations have been carried out in selenium oxychloride using a concentration cell technique (96), because neither salt bridge and reference electrode systems nor bimetallic electrodes have been successfully developed in aprotic solvents.

4.3. Membrane Potential Measurements

The early work of Willbrandt (132) and Michaelis (84) using collodion membranes showed that membrane potentials dependent on the activity of monovalent cations but independent of the nature of the anion could be observed with collodian membranes.

Marshall and coworkers carried out extensive investigations of zeolite and clay membranes. With montmorillonite membranes (78), the observed and calculated membrane potentials agreed well for various potassium salts in 0.0005–0.08 N solutions, independent of the nature of the anion. Divalent electrolytes, such as calcium chloride or magnesium sulfate did not interfere, affecting only the activity coefficient. Sodium ions, or hydrogen ions (pH less than 4) interfered. Such membranes have been applied to the determination of potassium ion activity in clays (79), and the estimation of ammonium ion activities (80). Colloidal beidellite membranes were shown to act as general cationic membranes (81), responding to sodium ion activities below 0.03 N to within 1 mv. of the potentials calculated from the Nernst equation.

Sollner (110) has prepared collodion membranes of two types, the "electronegative" (cation permeable) and the "electropositive" (anion permeable). The latter were made by the adsorption of protamines on collodion. Again, in very dilute solutions, an essentially reversible Nernst behavior was observed (111). Many interesting analytical applications of treated collodion membranes should be possible. For example Kolthoff (10) studied ionic activities of soap solutions by such a method.

Membrane electrodes of silver halides have been used as indicator electrodes in silver halide titrations (107) and similarly a calcium fluoride membrane has been studied for the estimation of calcium (117).

4.4. Potentiometric Titrations

4.4.1. Acid-Base Titrations. Any of the indicator electrodes suitable for pH determination may be successfully used for potentiometric acid-base titrations, subject to the limitations of the particular electrode. Since all the indicator electrodes change in the same way with pH, the theoretical limitations are the same for all electrodes. The practical choice is determined by the presence or absence of oxidizing or reducing agents, the applicability of the electrode in the pH range of most interest, the nature of the solvent, the rate of attainment of electrode equilibrium, and the simplicity of the equipment.

The indicator electrode need not change in potential in the theoretical way with pH to be useful in potentiometric titrations. The oxygen or air electrode, consisting simply of a bright or platinized platinum electrode in a solution saturated with air or oxygen, responds approximately to hydrogen ion concentration in accordance with the electrode reaction

$$O_2 + 4H^+ + 4e^- \rightleftharpoons 2H_2O$$

The potential shows a pronounced tendency to drift, especially in alkaline solution (9, 28) but satisfactory titration curves of strong acids or bases even in the presence of strong oxidizing agents (29, 99) are obtained.

The hydrogen electrode was extensively studied for the titration of weak and strong acids as early as 1897 (6), and a great many applications have been made. However, in recent years, the spectacular developments in glass electrode techniques have overshadowed the use of the hydrogen electrode. The possibilities of the hydrogen electrode in certain nonaqueous solvent systems where the glass electrode may not be suitable should be borne in mind.

The quinhydrone electrode represents a simple and convenient indicator electrode for the titration of weak or strong acids, or salts of weak acids with strong acids. Since the potential very rapidly becomes constant, the differential end point system (12, 13) and the Pinkhof equivalence potential method (98) may be used to advantage. The limitations of the quinhydrone electrode in alkaline solution and in the presence of strong oxidizing and reducing agents must be kept in mind.

The antimony electrode responds relatively slowly to pH changes, but has been applied to many cases applicable to the hydrogen electrode, as well as to titrations for which the hydrogen electrode is unsuitable, for example, the titration of alkaloids, or titrations in the presence of strong oxidizing agents. While the potential does not correspond to pH in the presence of permanganate for example, the end point indicates the amount of acid present.

The glass electrode has found wide application in acid-base titrations. The advantages over other electrodes for pH measurements are also important in potentiometric titrations. The usefulness of the glass electrode in solutions of strong oxidizing and reducing agents, in colored and turbid mixtures, in solutions containing high molecular weight materials such as proteins, and in heterogeneous systems such as suspensions and sludges is noteworthy.

Numerous bimetallic electrode systems for acid-base titrations have been suggested. A list is given by Furman (31) who emphasizes the need for cautious application when working with weak acids, especially in dilute solutions. He recommends the use of a system consisting of one electrode which is known to be a good indicator electrode, e.g., antimony, and the other a good reference electrode, e.g., silver in the presence of chloride.

Acid-base titrations may also be carried out in nonaqueous and mixed solvents. Seltz and McKinney (103) used amyl alcohol and Treadwell and Schwarzenbach (123) used ethyl alcohol as a solvent for very weak acids such as phenols. Hall and Conant (47) used the chloranil electrode (tetrachlorohydroquinone and the corresponding quinone) in glacial acetic acid for the titration of acids. Hall and Werner (49) used the same electrode and solvent system for the titration of weak bases. Lykken et al. (73) have carried out extensive work using the glass electrode in a solvent consisting of equal parts of benzene and methanol, with 1% water. The work of Peterson, Heimerzheim, and Smith (96) in selenium oxychloride has already been mentioned.

4.4.2. Precipitation Reactions. Many applications have been made of acid-base titrations to precipitation reactions. Any reaction in which the pH of the solution suddenly changes after a precipitation reaction has been completed may be followed by a hydrogen-ion indicating electrode. These reactions include the precipitation of hydroxides or of basic salts of metals by titration with alkali, and the precipitation of salts of weak acids. An example of the latter titration in the precipitation of a metallic soap, the pH change after the end point being due to the hydrolysis of the soap anion. Indirect changes of pH brought about by adsorption of hydrogen and hydroxyl ion have been suggested for detecting the end point for the precipitation of oxalates and sulfates of lead and the alkaline earth metals (113, 114).

The silver electrode has found application for many titrations. Silver nitrate has been used as a reagent for halides alone and in mixtures, for thiocyanate, sulfide, mercaptans, arsenate, phosphate, hypophosphite, oxalate, cyanate, selenocyanate, ferrocyanide, selenite, etc.

Ferrocyanide is a popular precipitating reagent because the platinum electrode serves as an oxidation-reduction indicator electrode for ferrocyanide. Among the metals precipitated in this way are zinc, cadmium, copper, cobalt, nickel, lead, cerium, and thorium. Cobalticyanide has been found applicable to the titration of silver, cupric, and mercurous ions (15).

Lead nitrate has been used for the titration of iodate, sulfate, carbonate, chromate, tungstate, and molybdate. Barium salts have been made for sulfate, tungstate, and chromate.

Several bimetallic electrode systems have been suggested for precipitation reactions. For example Jerkovsky (59) studied fourteen electrode pairs as well as eight monometallic electrodes for the titration of chloride with silver. Brintzinger and Jahn (7) found chromium, tungsten, and molybdenum electrodes useful for the determination of these metals.

Miscellaneous precipitation titrations include the titration of fluoride with calcium (125) or cerous ion (1, 93) phosphate with uranyl acetate, copper with thiocyanate or sulfide, lead with sulfide or phosphate, mercurous salts with iodide, rare earths and thorium as oxalates. Sulfide precipitation titrations have been attempted for numerous metals, but without accurate results (64).

4.4.3. Complex Formation Reactions. Cyanide complexes have been studied extensively. The formation of the silver complex has already been discussed. Many papers have appeared on the determination of nickel by the cyanide method. Generally a silver or silver salt electrode is used. Copper (97, 129) and more recently cobalt (46) and cadmium (69) have been studied in a similar way.

Aluminum (115) and beryllium (116) have been titrated with fluoride with the formation of the complexes $AlF_6^{\equiv}$ and $BeF_4^{\equiv}$ respectively. The uranium complex UF_5^- has been utilized in the titration of fluoride with uranous salt (24).

Mercury may be determined by titration with iodide to form HgI_4^- (54).

4.4.4. Oxidation Reduction Reactions. So many oxidation-reduction reactions have been made the basis of potentiometric titrations that a complete discussion would be far beyond the scope of this discussion. For details the reader is referred to the monographs (64, 91), review papers (30, 31) and to the original literature. A few of the more recent references are included here.

Potassium permanganate undergoes stoichiometric reactions with many reducing agents, and having a high oxidation potential it is favorable in producing potentiometric curves with large breaks at the end point. The reaction with iodide to give iodine in acid solutions is very exact, and has been applied for the standardization of the reagent, and for the indirect determination of silver, of bromate, and of nitrite. In hydrochloric acid medium, iodide can be titrated to an ICl end point. Bromide, nitrite, oxalate, and hydrogen peroxide can all be determined by permanganate titration. Ferrocyanide can be accurately titrated to ferricyanide, a reaction suitable for standardization and for the indirect determination of zinc. Various metal ion titrations are very useful, notably ferrous to ferric iron, vanadium (II) successively to vanadium (III) (IV) and (V), uranium (IV) to (VI), molybdenum (III) successively to molybdenum (IV) and (V), arsenic (III) to (V), tin (II) to (IV), titanium (III) to (IV), and manganese (II) to (III) taking advantage of the formation of complexes with pyrophosphate (71) or, less conveniently, fluoride. Manganese (II) can also be titrated to manganese dioxide in neutral solution. Columbium (III) can be oxidized to the pentavalent state after electro reduction (122).

In alkaline medium permanganate has been suggested for the determination of sulfite, arsenite, tellurite, antimony (III), and cerium (III).

Cerium (IV) has proved to be one of the most important oxidants in potentiometric titrations. Depending on the nature and concentration of the anion present and the acid concentration, the oxidation potential may be varied over a rather wide range. Thus in nitrate or perchlorate media the potentials are higher than in sulfate or chloride solutions (106, 108). The applications are similar to those of permanganate, with the advantage of greater stability of reagent. Often iodine chloride or osmium tetroxide is used as a catalyst. Among the important titrations may be listed the following: arsenious acid to arsenic acid (convenient for standardization), oxalate (also for indirect determination of calcium and rare earths (100)), ferrocyanide, iodide to iodine or to ICN in the presence of hydrogen cyanide, hydrogen peroxide, hydroquinone, hydrazoic acid. Uranium (III) to (IV), and (IV) to (VI), vanadium (IV) to (V), molybdenum (III) to (IV) and (IV) to (V), iron (II) to (III), and antimony (III) to (V) represent important determinations of metals. Sometimes an excess of cerium must be added, with a back-titration, as in the oxidation of chromium (III) to (VI) and mercury (I) to (II).

Dichromate has been very widely used for the titration of ferrous iron, or the reverse. The fact that potassium dichromate is a primary standard substance and can be used to prepare very stable solutions is of importance. Often as in the determination of tellurous acid, an excess of dichromate is added and the excess is determined by ferrous titration. This titration is useful in indirect determinations of barium after chromate precipitation, or in indirect determinations of organic compounds which can be quantitatively oxidized with dichromate. Other titrations with dichromate include those of ferrocyanide, iodide, hydroquinone, tin (II), and antimony (III).

Bromate is an important oxidant because a stable solution of known concentration can be prepared directly from the potassium salt. In acid solution, in the presence of bromide, it releases bromine, which is an oxidizing agent and a halogenating agent. Useful titrations include those of iodide, thiocyanate, arsenic (III), antimony (III), copper (I), thallium (I), tin (II), iron (II), titanium (III), and ferrocyanide. It is useful for the oxidation of mercaptans, and the determination of many aromatic compounds through substitution reactions. For example, the determination of 8-hydroxyquinoline may be used for the indirect analysis of metals.

Iodate, while less generally applicable than the bromate, is useful for the titration of tin (II), iron (II), arsenic (III), antimony (III), thiocyanate (in strong HCl to give ICl), copper (I), and iodide.

Chlorate has been applied to the determination of arsenic (III), antimony (III), thallium (I), tin (II), iron (II), iodide, and hydroquinone.

Chloramine-T is a strong oxidant which has been used for arsenic (III), antimony (III), tin (II), iron (II), ferrocyanide, iodide, thallium (I), hydrazine, hydroquinone, and bisulfite. It can be used for the indirect determination of oxidants.

Hypochlorite has been used as an alkaline oxidizing agent for various reducing agents, including sulfite, cyanide, selenite, and tellurite. In acid solution, iodide and bromide have been titrated respectively to iodine chloride and bromine chloride. Hypobromite is less stable than hypochlorite but undergoes many reactions more rapidly. It has been suggested for the oxidation of thiosulfate, sulfite, and thiocyanate, but the results are not accurate.

Bromine has been used for phosphite, hypophosphite and thiosulfate. Iodine, through the thiosulfate reaction, is useful for the indirect estimation of arsenic, antimony, iodate, thallium, and oxygen. The Karl Fischer reagent, employing a solution of iodine and sulfur dioxide in pyridine can be used potentiometrically for the determination of water (77, 130) and the indirect determination of many organic compounds.

Ferricyanide in alkaline medium is an interesting oxidizing agent. It will oxidize chromium (III) to chromate, in the presence of a trace of thallium salt as catalyst, vanadium (IV), arsenic (III), antimony (III), and tin (II). In ammoniacal medium, cobalt (II) is oxidized to cobalt (III) (119). In strongly alkaline medium, manganese (II) is oxidized to manganese (III) in the presence of tartrate and to manganese (IV) in the presence of glycerol or glycol (120). In concentrated potassium carbonate, which acts as a complexing agent, cerium (III) can be oxidized to cerium (IV). In acid solution, titanium (III) can be titrated to titanium (IV), and iodide to iodine (in presence of zinc and potassium ions to remove ferrocyanide as insoluble $K_2Zn_3Fe(CN)_6$).

Titanium (III) is one of the most popular reducing agents. Being a strong reducing agent, it undergoes many important reactions. A disadvantage is that titanous solutions must be stored in an inert atmosphere and the titration must be carried out in an air-free system. Among the determinations which have been reported are the following: iron (III), copper (II), antimony (V), uranium (VI) to (IV), Hg (II), Tl (III), molybdenum (VI) to (V), ferricyanide, permanganate, dichromate, vanadium (V) to (IV) and (III), iodate, bromate, chloride, selenite, selenate, tellurite, tellurate.

Chromium (II) salts are even more powerful reducing agents than titanous salts. An apparatus suitable for titrations in an air-free environment with chromous solutions has been described by Flatt and Sommer (25). It will reduce antimony (V) to (III), leaving pentavalent arsenic unreduced. Silver, gold, mercury, and copper salts are reduced to the metals. Iron (III), tin (IV), and titanium (IV) are reduced to the lower valence states. Chromium (VI) is reduced to chromium (III), vanadium (V) to (IV) to (III), molybdenum (VI) to (V) to (III), tungsten (VI) to (V).

Ferrous salts are weaker reducing agents, and correspondingly are more stable in air, especially in acid solutions. The titrations of dichromate, permanganate, cerium (IV), gold (III), and vanadium (V) to (IV) are especially noteworthy.

Arsenite is a stable reducing agent if stored in neutral or weakly acidic solution. It is useful in the determination of hypochlorite, hypobromite and bromate. Chromium (VI) undergoes reduction in sulfuric acid medium whereas vanadium (V) does not. Peroxymonosulfuric acid (Caro's acid, H_2SO_5) may be determined in the presence of hydrogen peroxide after the addition of bicarbonate. Hydrogen peroxide reacts in alkaline solution with an excess of arsenite, which can be determined after acidification by bromate titration. Peroxydisulfuric acid ($H_2S_2O_8$) can be determined by its reaction at 100° in acid solution with excess arsenite.

Stannous solution has been suggested as a reagent for chromium, vanadium, molybdenum, iron, and rhenium. Vanadyl sulfate has been proposed for the determination of chromate, ferricyanide, gold, copper, silver, mercury, permanganate, selenite, and tellurite.

It is beyond the scope of this discussion to mention several other reagents of minor or specialized importance (31, 69). Enough examples have been mentioned to emphasize the ever-growing variety of titrations which have won a place in systematic and routine applications.

REFERENCES

1. Allen, N., and Furman, N. H., *J. Am. Chem. Soc.* **55**, 90 (1933).
2. Bates, R. G., Hamer, W. J., Manov, G. C., and Acree, S. J., *J. Research Nat. Bur. Standards* **29**, 183 (1942).
3. Biilmann, E., *Bull. soc. chim., Mem.* [4] **41**, 213 (1927).
4. Biilmann, E., and Lund, H., *Ann. chim.* **16**, 321 (1921); **19**, 137 (1923).
5. Bjerrum, J., Metal Ammine Formation in Aqueous Solution. P. Haase and Son, Copenhagen, 1941.
6. Böttger, Dissertation, Leipzig (1897), *Z. physik. Chem.* **24**, 253 (1899).
7. Brintzinger, H., and Jahn, E., *Z. anal. Chem.* **94**, 396 (1933).
8. Buchböck, G., *Z. physik. Chem.* **156A**, 232 (1931).
9. Butler, J. A. V., and Armstrong, G., *Trans. Faraday Soc.* **29**, 862 (1933).
10. Carr, C. W., Johnson, W. F., and Kolthoff, I. M., *J. Phys. Chem.* **51**, 636 (1947).
11. Cavanagh, B., *J. Chem. Soc.* **1927**, 2207; **1928**, 843.
12. Clarke, B. L., and Wooten, L. A., *J. Phys. Chem.* **33**, 1468 (1929).
13. Clarke, B. L., and Wooten, L. A., *Ind. Eng. Chem., Anal. Ed.* **2**, 385 (1930).
14. Cox, D. C., *J. Am. Chem. Soc.* **47**, 2138 (1925).
15. Czaporowski, L., and Wiercinski, J., *Roczniki Chem.* **11**, 95 (1931).
16. Debye, P., and Hückel, E., *Physik. Z.* **24**, 185, 305 (1923).
17. Dole, M., *J. Am. Chem. Soc.* **53**, 4260 (1931).
18. Dole, M., The Glass Electrode. Wiley, New York, 1931.
19. Dole, M., *J. Am. Chem. Soc.* **54**, 2120, 3095 (1932).
20. Dole, M., *J. Chem. Phys.* **2**, 862 (1934).
21. Drewski, K., *Przemysl Chem.* **19**, 63 (1935).
22. Eastman, E. D., *J. Am. Chem. Soc.* **47**, 333 (1925).
23. Fenwick, F., *Ind. Eng. Chem., Anal. Ed.* **4**, 144 (1932).
24. Flatt, R., *Helv. Chim. Acta* **20**, 894 (1937).
25. Flatt, R., and Sommer, F., *Helv. Chim. Acta* **25**, 684 (1942).
26. Foulk, C. W., and Bawden, A. T., *J. Am. Chem. Soc.* **48**, 2044 (1926).
27. Fuoss, R. M., *Ind. Eng. Chem., Anal. Ed.* **1**, 125 (1929).
28. Furman, N. H., *J. Am. Chem. Soc.* **44**, 2685 (1922).
29. Furman, N. H., *Trans. Am. Electrochem. Soc.* **43**, 79 (1923).
30. Furman, N. H., *Ind. Eng. Chem., Anal. Ed.* **2**, 213 (1930).
31. Furman, N. H., *Ind. Eng. Chem., Anal. Ed.* **14**, 367 (1942).
32. Furman, N. H., and Low, G. W., *J. Am. Chem. Soc.* **57**, 1585, 1588 (1935).
33. Furman, N. H., and Wilson, E. B., Jr., *J. Am. Chem. Soc.* **50**, 277 (1928).
34. Garman, R. L., and Droz, M. E., *Ind. Eng. Chem., Anal. Ed.* **11**, 398 (1939).
35. Geake, A., *Trans. Faraday Soc.* **34**, 1395 (1938).
36. Gemant, A., *J. Chem. Phys.* **12**, 79 (1944); **13**, 146 (1945).

37. Gueron, J., *Bull. soc. chim. Mem.* [5] **1**, 425 (1934).
38. Haber, F. and Klemensiewics, Z., *Z. physik. Chem.* **67**, 385 (1909).
39. Hahn, F. L., *Angew. Chem.* **43**, 712 (1930).
40. Hahn, F. L., *Z. physik. Chem.* **146**, 363 (1930).
41. Hahn, F. L., *J. Am. Chem. Soc.* **57**, 2537 (1935).
42. Hahn, F. L., and Klockmann, R., *Z. physik. Chem.* **146**, 373 (1930).
43. Hahn, F. L., and Klockmann, R., *Z. physik. Chem.* **157A**, 203 (1931).
44. Hahn, F. L., and Klockmann, R., *Z. physik. Chem.* **157A**, 206 (1931).
45. Hahn, F. L., and Weiler, G., *Z. anal. Chem.* **69**, 417 (1926).
46. Hall, A. J., and Young, R. S., *Chemistry and Industry* **1946**, 394.
47. Hall, N. F., and Conant, J. B., *J. Am. Chem. Soc.* **49**, 3047 (1927).
48. Hall, N. F., Jensen, M. A., and Baeckström, S. A., *J. Am. Chem. Soc.* **50**, 2217 (1928).
49. Hall, N. F., and Werner, T. H., *J. Am. Chem. Soc.* **50**, 2367 (1928).
50. Hamer, W. J., and Acree, S. F., *J. Research Nat. Bur. Standards* **33**, 87 (1944).
51. Harned, H. S., and Wright, D. D., *J. Am. Chem. Soc.* **55**, 4849 (1933).
52. Heintze, S. G., *J. Agr. Sci.* **24**, 28 (1934).
53. Hildebrand, J. H., *J. Am. Chem. Soc.* **35**, 847 (1913).
54. Hiltner, W., and Gietel, W., *Z. anal. Chem.* **101**, 28 (1935).
55. Hitchcock, D. I., and Taylor, A. C., *J. Am. Chem. Soc.* **59**, 1812 (1937).
56. Hovorka, F., and Chapman, G. H., *J. Am. Chem. Soc.* **63**, 955 (1941).
57. Hume, D. N., and Harris, W. E., *Ind. Eng. Chem., Anal. Ed.* **15**, 465 (1943).
58. Irving, G. W., and Smith, N. R., *Ind. Eng. Chem., Anal. Ed.* **6**, 480 (1934).
59. Jerkovsky, R., *Chem. Listy* **34**, 159 (1940).
60. Johnson, C. R., and Low, G. W., *J. Phys. Chem.* **36**, 2390 (1932)
61. Kolthoff, I. M., *Rec. trav. chim.* **41**, 176 (1922).
62. Kolthoff, I. M., *Rec. trav. chim.* **47**, 397 (1928).
63. Kolthoff, I. M., and Bosch, W., *Biochem. Z.* **183**, 434 (1927).
64. Kolthoff, I. M., and Furman, N. H., Potentiometric Titrations. Wiley, New York, 1931.
65. Kolthoff, I. M., and Pan, Y. D., *J. Am. Chem. Soc.* **61**, 3402 (1939).
66. Laitinen, H. A., *Ind. Eng. Chem., Anal. Ed.* **13**, 393 (1941).
67. Lauchlan, A. D. E., *Nature* **154**, 577 (1944).
68. LeBlanc, M. and Harnapp, O., *Z. physik. Chem.* **A166**, 321 (1933).
69. Leden, I., *Svensk. Kem. Tid.* **56**, 31 (1944).
70. Lingane, J. J., *Ind. Eng. Chem., Anal. Ed.* **19**, 810 (1947).
71. Lingane, J. J., and Karplus, R., *Ind. Eng. Chem., Anal. Ed.* **18**, 191 (1946).
72. Low, G. W., and Pryde, E. H., *J. Am. Chem. Soc.* **61**, 2237 (1939).
73. Lykken, L., Porter, P., Ruliffson, H. D., and Tuemmler, F. D., *Ind. Eng. Chem., Anal. Ed.* **16**, 219 (1941).
74. Lykken, L., and Tuemmler, F. D., *Ind. Eng. Chem., Anal. Ed.* **14**, 67 (1942).
75. MacInnes, D. A., and Belcher, D., *J. Am. Chem. Soc.* **53**, 3315 (1931).
76. MacInnes, D. A., and Jones, P. T., *J. Am. Chem. Soc.* **48**, 2831 (1926).
77. McKinney, C. D., and Hall, R. T., *Ind. Eng. Chem., Anal. Ed.* **15**, 460 (1943).
78. Marshall, C. E., and Bergman, W. E., *J. Am. Chem. Soc.* **63**, 1911 (1941).
79. Marshall, C. E., and Bergman, W. E., *J. Phys. Chem.* **46**, 52 (1942).
80. Marshall, C. E., and Bergman, W. E., *J. Phys. Chem.* **46**, 325, 327 (1942).
81. Marshall, C. E., and Krinbill, C. A., *J. Am. Chem. Soc.* **64**, 1814 (1942).
82. Meyer, K. H., and Sievers, J. F., *Helv. Chim. Acta* **19**, 649, 665, 987 (1936).
83. Michaelis, L., *Chem. Rev.* **16**, 243 (1935).

84. Michaelis, L., *Colloid Symposium Monograph* **5**, 135 (1937).
85. Michaelis, L., Physical Methods of Organic Chemistry. Vol. II, Edited by Weisberger, A., Interscience, New York, 1946, Chapter XXII.
86. Michaelis, L., and Schubert, M. D., *Chem. Rev.* **22**, 437 (1938).
87. Morgan, J. L. R., and Lammert, O. M., *J. Am. Chem. Soc.* **53**, 2154 (1931).
88. Morgan, J. L. R., Lammert, O. M., and Campbell, M. A., *J. Am. Chem. Soc.* **53**, 454, 597 (1931); **54**, 910 (1932).
89. Morgan, J. L. R., Lammert, O. M., and Campbell, M. A., *Trans. Electrochem. Soc.* **61**, 405 (1932).
90. Müller, E., *Z. physik. Chem.* **135**, 102 (1928).
91. Müller, E., Electrometrische Mass analyse. Steinkopf, Dresden and Leipzig, 1932.
92. Müller, E., and Lauterbach, H., *Z. anorg. u. Allgem. Chem.* **121**, 178 (1922).
93. Nichols, M. L., and Olsen, J. S., *Ind. Eng. Chem., Anal. Ed.* **15**, 342 (1943).
94. Parks, L. R., and Beard, H. C., *J. Am. Chem. Soc.* **54**, 856 (1932).
95. Perley, G. A., *Ind. Eng. Chem., Anal. Ed.* **11**, 240, 316 (1939).
96. Peterson, W. S., Heimerzheim, C. J., and Smith, G. B. L., *J. Am. Chem. Soc.* **65**, 2403 (1943).
97. Piccinini, C., *Met. ital.* **27**, 707 (1935).
98. Pinkhof, J., Dissertation, Amsterdam, 1919.
99. Popoff, S., and McHenry, J. H., *Ind. Eng. Chem.* **20**, 534 (1928).
100. Rasin-Streden, R., and Müller-Gamillscheg, M., *Z. anal Chem.* **127**, 81 (1944).
101. Roberts, E. J., and Fenwick, F., *J. Am. Chem. Soc.* **50**, 2143 (1928).
102. Roller, P. S., *J. Am. Chem. Soc.* **50**, 1 (1928).
103. Seltz, H., and McKinney, D. S., *Ind. Eng. Chem.* **20**, 542 (1928).
104. Serfass, E. J., *Ind. Eng. Chem., Anal. Ed.* **12**, 536 (1940).
105. Sergeev, A. P., and Yavorskii, A. N., *J. Applied Chem. U.S.S.R.* **11**, 113, 117 (1938).
106. Sherrill, M. S., King, C. B., and Spooner, R. C., *J. Am. Chem. Soc.* **65**, 170 (1943).
107. Skobets, E. M., and Kleibs, G. A., *J. Gen. Chem. U.S.S.R.* **10**, 1612 (1940).
108. Smith, G. F., and Getz, C. A., *Ind. Eng. Chem., Anal. Ed.* **10**, 191, 204 (1938); **12**, 339 (1940).
109. Smith, G. F., and Sullivan, V. R., Electron Beam Sectometer. G. Frederick Smith Chemical Company, 1936.
110. Sollner, K., *J. Phys. Chem.* **49**, 47, 171, 265 (1945).
111. Sollner, K., and Gregor, H. P., *J. Phys. Chem.* **50**, 53, 88, 470 (1946); **51**, 299 (1947).
112. Stonehill, H. I., *Trans. Faraday Soc.* **39**, 67 (1943).
113. Tannaev, I., *J. Applied Chem. U.S.S.R.* **5**, 86 (1932).
114. Tannaev, I., and Mirianashvili, N. I., *J. Applied Chem. U.S.S.R.* **10**, 2082 (1937).
115. Tarayan, V. M., *Zavodskaya Lab.* **8**, 273 (1939).
116. Tarayan, V. M., *Zavodskaya Lab.* **12**, 543 (1946).
117. Tendeloo, H. J. C., *J. Biol. Chem.* **113**, 333 (1936).
118. Teorell, T., *Trans. Faraday Soc.* **33**, 1054 (1937).
119. Tomicek, O., and Freiberger, F., *J. Am. Chem. Soc.* **57**, 1209 (1935).
120. Tomicek, O., and Kalny, J., *J. Am. Chem. Soc.* **57**, 801 (1935).
121. Treadwell, W. D., *Z. anorg. u. allgem. Chem.* **4**, 398 (1921).
122. Treadwell, W. D., and Nieriker, R., *Helv. Chim. Acta* **25**, 474 (1942).
123. Treadwell, W. D., and Schwarzenbach, G., *Helv. Chim. Acta* **11**, 386 (1928).

124. Treadwell, W. D., and Weiss, L., *Helv. Chim. Acta* **2,** 680 (1919).
125. Uri, N., *Ind. Eng. Chem., Anal. Ed.* **19,** 192 (1947).
126. Vance, J. E., *Ind. Eng. Chem., Anal. Ed.* **13,** 68 (1941).
127. Van Name, G., and Fenwick, F., *J. Am. Chem. Soc.* **47,** 19 (1925).
128. Velisek, J., *Chem. Listy* **27,** 3 (1933).
129. Weihreich, R., *Arch. Eisenhüttenw.* **14,** 55 (1940).
130. Wernimont, G., and Hopkinson, F. J., *Ind. Eng. Chem., Anal. Ed.* **15,** 272 (1943).
131. Willard, H. H., and Fenwick, F., *J. Am. Chem. Soc.* **44,** 2504 (1922); **44,** 2516 (1922).
132. Willbrandt, J., *J. Gen. Physiol.* **18,** 933 (1935).

REFERENCE BOOKS

Böttger, W., Physikalische Methoden der Analytischen Chemie. Vol. III, Akademische Verlagsgesellschaft, Leipsig, 1939.

Hiltner, W., Ausführung potentiometrischer Analyse. Julius Springer, Berlin, 1935.

Kolthoff, I. M., and Furman, N. H., Potentiometric Titrations. 2nd ed., Wiley, New York, 1931.

Müller, E., Elektrometrische Massanalyse. 5th ed., Steinkopf, Dresden, 1932.

Electrography and Electro-Spot Testing

By

H. W. HERMANCE AND H. V. WADLOW

Bell Telephone Laboratories, Inc., New York, New York

CONTENTS

1. INTRODUCTION

1.1. Surface Analysis

Ordinarily, chemical analysis is employed to obtain information concerning the mass composition of a specimen. A sample is so selected as to be completely representative, even though the specimen be heterogeneous in character. This composite sample is then rendered uniform by appropriate treatment, for example, by solution, and the analytical operations are carried out on the resulting product.

Such an approach purposely avoids differentiation of the nonuniformities in the structure of the specimen. Numerous occasions arise, however, when knowledge is required of both the composition and the distribution of materials present on a surface. Surfaces often receive special treatment that changes their character from that of the body as a whole. Thus protective coatings, organic or inorganic, may be applied. Mechanical processing such as rolling, grinding, polishing or any frictional operation against another substance may change surface structure and introduce foreign substances. The deterioration of surfaces by atmospheric agents (dusts and gases) produces films, the examination of which may lead to corrective measures.

It is a fundamental requirement in the examination of such surfaces that a very thin film must suffice for sample. Moreover, simple identification is not always enough. Often a diagnosis is possible only when the exact distribution and form of the surface components can be charted. The composition of a metal plating may be known but its continuity may be in question. The shape, size, and orientation of inclusions in rolled stock may be as important as their composition.

Another kind of surface purposely created to give information concerning the structure of a body is made by cutting through the mass in a specified direction and polishing and examining the resultant surface. This examination particularly requires methods of distinguishing the structural units as they appear in the exposed surface. Upon this differentiation are based the techniques of metallography.

Thus, the second requirement of surface analytical methods is the localization of the identified products to permit recognition of significant distributive patterns. Recognition of this need was undoubtedly a factor in the early development of microchemistry, especially in its relation to petrography and mineralogy.

The classical approach to differential surface analysis involves exploration of the surface under the microscope and the isolation of questioned areas by micromanipulative means. Samples so obtained are then analyzed by microanalytical, spectrochemical or other sensitive techniques. In certain cases, the identifying reactions may be carried out directly on the surface under examination as in the etching of metallographic specimens and the staining of minerals. Generally speaking, this technique has rather limited applicability. Color reactions suffer reduction of sensitivity against the poor background usually afforded. It is generally difficult to confine the colored products over the area of reaction so as to define that area. On the other hand, it is very often possible to transfer an extremely thin layer from a surface to an inert absorptive material without serious loss of distributive patterns, if the chemically prepared medium is pressed into intimate contact with the specimen. Paper is the most common example of such a material. It is moistened with a suitable dissolving agent which attacks the surface. The soluble products transfer by diffusion to the cell-like interstices of the fibrous mat. These, aided by the adsorptive character of cellulose, limit lateral diffusion, preserving the local patterns. Color reactions, used in conjunction with such a transfer are provided with a very favorable background and once the reaction products are precipitated (fixed), various treatments can be applied to increase both selectivity and sensitivity.

1.2. Chemical Contact Printing

The first application of such a method was made by Baumann to determine the location of sulfides in steel alloys. It was termed "The Chemical Contact Print Method (3). The polished metal specimen containing sulfide segregations is pressed against a sheet of photographic paper previously soaked in dilute sulfuric acid. The liberated sulfide ion then reacts with the silver halides in the paper to produce a black stain over the area of the original inclusion. Thus a print of the shape and distribution of the sulfide inclusion is obtained. An extension of this method was made by Neissner (42) to detect phosphorous segregations in iron alloys and copper and nickel in their alloys. Gutzeit,

Gysin, and Galopin (27) employed both hardened filter paper and gelatin coated paper more generally to obtain prints of other alloys and of polished mineral specimens.

In most uses of contact printing the surface must be brought into solution chemically. Control of this process is the most difficult part of the method. Sometimes buffered solutions having moderate acidity or alkalinity, or complex-forming salts which exert selective dissolving action may be used. Thus sulfide tarnish films on silver or copper are not readily attacked, even by relatively strong acids. Potassium cyanide however, forms stable silver and copper complexes, liberating the sulfide ion for reaction with lead carbonate treated paper. Excess cyanide does not interfere. In a great many cases, however, solution of the surface is obtainable only by the use of drastic agents such as strong acids or alkalies. This is particularly true of metal surfaces. Such agents prevent the immediate fixation by precipitation of the transferred material, hence favor lateral diffusion and loss of print detail. They are not readily removable after completion of the transfer and may interfere with the application of subsequent color reactions. The course of the solution is difficult to control so as to obtain uniform removal of a definite thin layer. Quantitative comparisons are rarely possible.

However, when a favorable combination of reagents can be found, the contact printing method is extremely useful. The method does have serious limitations, among which are: a, restrictions in the choice and use of dissolving agents; b, difficulty of controlling the process of solution; c, since the transfer depends entirely on the diffusion of the dissolved material into the printing medium, printing is necessarily slow, and some lateral diffusion cannot be avoided.

1.3. Electrolytic Transfer

Where the surface to be printed is conducting and ionizable, a method of transfer can be used which is far superior to the simple contact method. This method is based on the electrolytic solution of the surface and acceleration of the dissolved ions to provide controlled transfer into the printing medium. Such a transfer process is rapid, under instant quantitative control, utilizes neutral, noninterfering electrolytes for dissolving the surface and the electrical field acts to prevent lateral diffusion of ionic material.

In 1929, H. Fritz (8) and A. Glazunov (19), working independently, both published methods employing electrolytic solution of a metal specimen to drive its ions into a paper reaction medium. Each of these workers had rather specialized and, at the same time, quite different objectives. Fritz used a very carefully controlled anodic solution of the metal to transfer known quantities to paper. The resulting standards were used to study the sensitivity of various identification reactions such as those used by Feigl in his spot-test methods. For this reason, Fritz termed his technique the "Elektro-Tüpfel-Methode." His arrangement consisted of a clock-driven metal drum cathode, around which was wrapped the paper, moistened with the color-producing reagent, and when necessary, a suitable electrolyte. The anode, furnishing ions of the metal under study, was in the form of stylus resting lightly on the rotating drum. When a potential is applied, solution of the anode and the reaction of its ions produces a uniform streak on the moving paper. The density of this streak, expressed, for example, in micrograms per centimeter of length, could be controlled quite precisely by controlling the applied current. This was done by use of a vacuum tube, coarse adjustment being obtained by stepwise control of grid potential, fine adjustment by control of the filament heating current. A milliammeter in the circuit and the known speed of drum travel permitted calculation of dissolved metal by applying the Faraday law.

Glazunov first applied anodic solution to the reproduction of macrostructure details in metal specimens, particularly ferrous metals. This he did by pressing the polished specimen surface against paper moistened with an electrolyte capable of producing colored reaction products with the metal ions. The paper rested on a cathode plate of aluminum or stainless steel. A typical electrolyte was potassium ferrocyanide. When a relatively small potential was applied for a few seconds, a differentiation of macrostructure was obtained in the resulting print whenever the structural parts and crystal orientations were not equally anodic and therefore dissolved at different rates. Because this technique had as its primary objective the reproduction of surface features in the form of a print, Glazunov called it the "Electrographic" method.

1.4. Historical Review

In later papers, Fritz (9–16) continued to develop the idea of the "Electro-Tüpfel" technique, preferring this term to the "Electrographic" designation of Glazunov. Fritz broadened the coverage of "Electro-Tüpfel" methods to include all tests based on electrolytic solution or precipitation of ions. In this he departed considerably from the original concept of transfer and fixation of surface material and much of his work falls outside the scope of this chapter.

Fritz recognized two methods of obtaining electrolytic solution. One was to apply an outside source of potential to the plate and specimen. The other was to utilize internal electrolysis by directly connecting the plate and the specimen with the electrolyte-soaked paper between them, forming a galvanic cell in which solution of the anode specimen or a portion of it would depend on the electromotive relation between the two metals. Selective solution in a multiphase alloy thus is obtainable, according to Fritz. Two general transfer methods were also described. In one, a print is obtained by pressing the specimen against the paper spread on a plate. In the other, either the specimen or the paper is moved so that a streak is obtained, thus avoiding polarization by a continual supply of fresh electrolyte and providing a means of controlling the time factor by the speed of movement between paper and specimen.

In later papers, Glazunov (20, 21, 22) proposed the qualitative analysis of alloys by the electrographic method. He extended the method to include the detection of iron, silver, nickel, cobalt, copper, bismuth, zinc, lead, cadium, tin, antimony. Jirkovsky (36, 37, 38) used the electrographic method for detecting nickel and cobalt in steel and for the identification of conducting minerals, as did also Galopin (17) Hiller (30, 31, 32) and Yushko (48, 49).

E. Arnold (2) combined the spot test methods of Feigl and the electrographic method of Glazunov by transferring the sample electrolytically into paper, then testing for the metal ions by dropwise addition of reagents. Yagoda (46, 47) has made new use of the electrographic method in an interesting application for the localization of inorganic ions in plant and animal tissue. This application is different in that the material is not brought into solution, but rather, its migration into the printing medium is promoted by electrolysis.

The quantitative applications of electrography have received some attention but considerable exploratory work is still indicated before its full possibilities are known. Glazunov and Krivohlavy (25) published a detailed report of work done on the estimation of nickel in nickel steel. M. Garino and R. Catto (18) have estimated small quantities of bismuth in copper from the intensity of the cinchonine iodide print. Glazunov and Drescher (23) have determined the quantity of lead in lead-tin alloys, where the lead is present in concentrations above 0.25%.

2. Equipment, Materials, and Manipulative Techniques

2.1. Basic Technique of Electro-Transfer

Basically, the electrographic arrangement is quite simple. It consists of two metal surfaces between which is sandwiched a layer of absorbent paper or other porous material, moistened with electrolyte. Pressure is applied to the surface to insure intimate contact. When connected to a potential source, the metal surfaces form the anode and cathode of an electrolytic cell.   When, as is most common, the specimen is the anode, its ions move into the paper where they react with either the ions of the electrolyte or with an added reagent to produce an identifiable colored product.   Occasionally anions in thin conducting films such as sulfide or chloride need to be identified.   Then the specimen is made the cathode.   In either case, the electrode opposite the specimen is an inert metal or one chosen to avoid interfering reactions.   In very special applications, the outside source of potential may be eliminated and the metals joined by a low resistance conductor.   Assuming sufficient electromotive dissimilarity between the metals, a galvanic cell is then formed in which the internally generated potential is the driving force for the electrolytic transfer of the specimen material.   As Fritz points out, the chief advantage of this method lies in the automatic control of the cell voltage when critical electrolytic separations are desired.

If the anode and cathode surfaces are both flat and parallel and pressed evenly against the paper, a uniform electrical field is obtained with the shortest path normal to the metal surfaces.   Ions move into the paper, therefore, with practically no lateral diffusion.   If they are precipitated ("fixed") immediately, the distribution pattern formed by the ions leaving the metal surface can be preserved with great fidelity, even though several successive chemical treatments may be needed to obtain the final identification product.   This control of lateral diffusion by the electrical field makes the electrographic print of Glazunov much superior in its rendition of detail to the chemical contact print.

Elaboration of the apparatus may vary in practice, depending on whether the objective be simple spot testing, surface printing, or a more quantitative result.   Factors over which control may be necessary are current, voltage, time, and pressure.   Manipulative considerations such as shape, size, and accessibility of the test specimen may also influence the form of the equipment to be used.   There appears to be no single unit capable of serving all purposes equally well.   For this reason, several types of equipment will be described and their applicability discussed.

2.2. Cell Arrangements and Accessories

The simplest apparatus for electro-transfer operations consists of a flat metal plate, suitably mounted and provided with connection to the current source.   This is shown schematically in Fig. 1a.   Such a base plate of aluminum or stainless steel may form one electrode or it may be used simply as a convenient contacting surface on which to rest flat specimens to be explored by the electro-spot testing technique.   These inexpensive metals rarely interfere when used as cathodes if the impregnated paper is not left too long in contact without potential. A plan which makes for flexibility is to provide an assortment of auxiliary plates of different metals. These may be placed interchangeably on the base plate, thus providing any type of electrode surface needed, including the specific metals required for the galvanic couple in internal electrolysis as well as small plates faced with gold or platinum, or plates of graphite when inert electrodes are essential.

In special cases, the possibility of interfering reactions makes it undesirable to have the opposite electrode surface directly in contact with the area of paper which receives the specimen ions. This may be avoided by the use of an outer ring electrode placed around the specimen on the paper which is held on a glass plate (Fig. 1b). The electrical

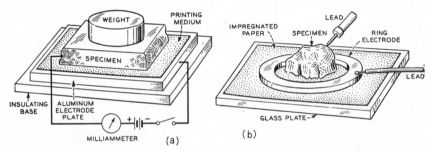

FIG. 1

field in this case is no longer through the thickness of the paper, but rather in the plane of the paper, radiating from the point of specimen contact. The relatively long path taken by the outwardly moving ions raises the effective resistance of the paper, increasing printing time. It also creates possibilities for electrocapillary separations which have been little explored.

The simple base plate is ordinarily used when small, easily manipulated specimens are to be spot tested or roughly printed and critical pressure control is not necessary. A 3 by 4-inch plate is convenient. On a reagent paper of this size, a number of small objects can be tested on the same sheet and compared. Division of the sheet into numbered squares facilitates recording the results. A surface of this size also provides ample area for streak tests made by drawing some particular point on the specimen over the paper.

Electrical connection to the specimen is established by flexible cords terminating in a variety of clips and probes. Where the specimen has a flat area and can be rested on the paper, a test probe can be used to make contact and to transmit pressure. Where the irregular shape of the

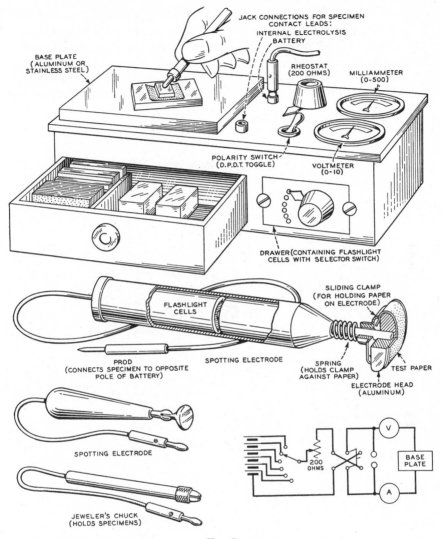

JACK CONNECTIONS FOR SPECIMEN
CONTACT LEADS:
INTERNAL ELECTROLYSIS
BATTERY

BASE PLATE
(ALUMINUM OR
STAINLESS STEEL)

RHEOSTAT
(200 OHMS)

MILLIAMMETER
(0-500)

POLARITY SWITCH
(D.P.D.T. TOGGLE)

VOLTMETER
(0-10)

DRAWER (CONTAINING FLASHLIGHT
CELLS WITH SELECTOR SWITCH)

SLIDING CLAMP
(FOR HOLDING PAPER
ON ELECTRODE)

FLASHLIGHT
CELLS

PROD
(CONNECTS SPECIMEN TO OPPOSITE
POLE OF BATTERY)

SPOTTING ELECTRODE

SPRING
(HOLDS CLAMP
AGAINST PAPER)

TEST PAPER

ELECTRODE HEAD
(ALUMINUM)

SPOTTING ELECTRODE

JEWELER'S CHUCK
(HOLDS SPECIMENS)

V

200
OHMS

BASE
PLATE

A

Fig. 2

specimen makes it necessary to hold it in the hand and orient it on the
paper, an "alligator" clip may be used. Fine instrument parts, wire,
pins, etc., too small for convenient manipulation in the hand may be held
in jewelers' pin vises. These should have flexible leads connecting to the
jaws through the handle.

Large, immovable specimens such as castings, tanks, structural
members, etc., require a somewhat different procedure. The plate is

replaced by a small "spotting" electrode, held against the paper-covered test area.   A type used by the authors consists of an aluminum button with rounded edges, about 1 cm. in diameter.   It is provided with a flexible ball joint at the connection to the handle so as to be self aligning. An elaboration of such an electrode has a spring clamp for holding the impregnated paper on the electrode surface and carries a battery of

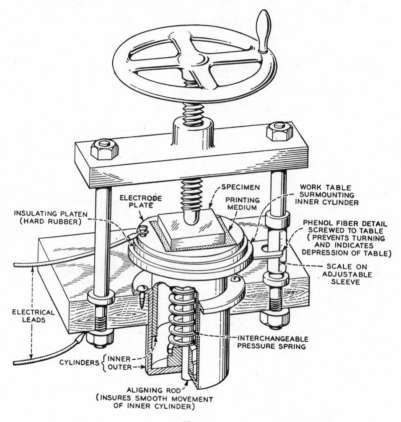

FIG. 3

flashlight cells in the handle.   Spotting thus is made a simple manipulative operation and the testing of difficultly accessible areas is facilitated. Figure 2 shows the base plate, control circuit, and battery supply assembled as a convenient, portable unit, together with spotting electrodes and other accessories.

When emphasis is placed on the reproduction of surface patterns, placement of the specimen and regulation of pressure to provide intimate contact become important.   Some form of clamping arrangement is needed to hold the cell elements together at a fixed unit pressure. Several devices are described in published methods (18, 28, 41, 47) but the importance of maintaining a constant and reproducible pressure seems not to have received the attention it deserves. Glazunov devotes very little discussion to the actual apparatus used to obtain electrographs.

Where apparatus has been described, it usually consists of a base on which is mounted an insulated electrode platen. An arm or yoke, supported over this platen, carries a spring, screw, or a weighted rod which applies pressure to the specimen.

Fig. 4

To be of universal use, however, the electrographic printing device should provide a wide range of pressure adjustments so as to furnish the desired unit pressure on areas varying from that of a screw head to several square inches. Placement and removal of the specimen should involve a minimum of manipulation to avoid blurring of the image.

An apparatus which fills most electrographic needs where extreme pressures are not necessary is shown in Fig. 3. It consists of a screw press in the base of which is mounted a depressible table, supported on a coil spring. This table holds the electrographic setup, which is suitably insulated from the screw frame at the base. It is removable and interchangeable springs provide several ranges of pressure. For most purposes, a spread of from 10 to 300 pounds suffices. An adjustable sleeve on one post of the screw carries a scale which measures the depression of the table as pressure is applied. The indicating member attached to

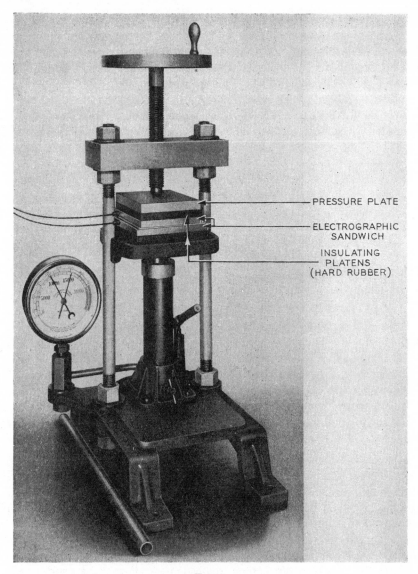

FIG. 5

the table is notched around the sleeve and thus it serves the additional purpose of preventing the table from turning.   The sleeve is first adjusted to bring the zero point to the indicator level for the particular loading of the table.   Pressure applied by the screw is then measurable from the scale reading by applying calibration data for the spring used.   Connection to the top electrographic member is made through the screw frame so that the circuit is closed only when the pressure is applied.

Figure 4 shows a commercial electrographic press (Fisher Scientific Co., Pittsburgh, Pa.) in which the pressure is adjusted by means of a compression spring and the values indicated on an engraved scale. The accompanying control unit has a battery selector switch, a current-polarity switch and a rheostat for current adjustment. This press has been used by the authors and found very satisfactory for general purposes.

Work done by the authors has indicated several advantages in the use of high pressure in electrography where extreme detail is desired, as in the study of the minute porosity of plated surfaces and organic finishes. A Carver laboratory hydraulic press, capable of pressures up to 20,000 pounds was employed for the purpose and it performed very satisfactorily. The press platens were covered with bakelite plates, $\frac{1}{2}$-inch thick, for insulation and the electrographic sandwich was placed between them. To facilitate operation of the press, the top member was provided with a heavy screw and hand wheel. The hydraulic pump was used only to build up the desired pressure. The modified pressure is shown in Fig. 5.

2.3. Current Supply and Control

Choice of current supply for electrographic tests will be governed by the frequency of use and by the size of the areas tested, since the latter will determine the volume of current needed. Also the choice will depend on whether the tests are to be made in the laboratory or with portable field equipment. For relatively small test areas, primary cells are entirely satisfactory, the No. 6 size dry cell being suitable for laboratory uses, while pocket flashlight cells can be used for portable units, where the object is spot testing rather than electrographs of large areas. Where a considerable amount of routine laboratory testing is done, storage batteries are more reliable. Current from A.C. mains can be stepped down with a suitable transformer and converted to D.C. with a copper oxide rectifier, providing a power source requiring no attention. An especially attractive feature of this source of power is the very excellent voltage regulation afforded by the use of variable transformers such as the Variac. There appears to be no objection to a slight pulsation in any practical uses of electrography and an elaborate filter is not needed to smooth out the D.C. output. For a discussion of the use of rectified A.C. in electroanalysis, the reader is referred to a note by A. J. Lindsey (40).

Circuit details will vary with the degree of regulation needed. For qualitative spot testing, the circuit may be very simple, consisting of the battery, a push-button switch, and possibly an inexpensive milliammeter.

In comparing a series of tests reproducibility becomes more important. Some control of time, current, and voltage then may be necessary. Successful electrographic printing often depends on reproducing experimentally determined conditions. The need for precise control in quantitative work is obvious.

A general laboratory circuit, capable of adaptation to all types of electro-transfer is shown in Fig. 6. For use with batteries, the circuit contains the following equipment:

1. A battery selector switch which cuts in one cell at a time, thus affording stepwise control of the applied voltage.

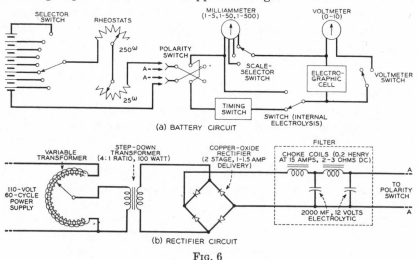

(a) BATTERY CIRCUIT

(b) RECTIFIER CIRCUIT

Fig. 6

2. Two rheostats in series, one about 25 ohms, the other, about 250 ohms. These should be capable of carrying about 50 watts without overheating. The 25 ohm rheostat is used for a low external resistance circuit, which is best for maintaining a nearly constant voltage at the printing cell. For constant current conditions, a high external resistance is needed and is obtained with the 250 ohm rheostat

3. A polarity switch for changing the direction of the current through the printing cell.

4. A milliammeter, preferably one with two or three scale ranges, covering 1 to 500 milliamp., with a selector switch for these ranges.

5. A voltmeter, 0 to 10 volts range, 1000 ohms/volt. Both of these meters should be of the zero-center type. An optional addition to the circuit is a timing switch. Accurate timing becomes important when it is desired to calculate the quantity of ion dissolved, or at least to dissolve the same quantity in successive tests. A switch of the type used

in photographic timing, capable of any setting from 1 to 60 seconds is very satisfactory. It will be noted in the circuit diagram that provision has been made for closing the circuit between the electrodes through the milliammeter, without the external power. This permits the use of internal electrolysis with the milliammeter in the circuit to indicate the progress of the reaction.

For use with rectified A.C., the circuit is the same as for battery operation except that the variable transformer, rectifier and filter replace the battery and selector switch.

2.4. Transfer Media

The porous or permeable medium used in the transfer process acts as a reservoir for the electrolyte, determines the spacing between the electrode surfaces and controls the electrolytic paths. It receives the ions from the specimen surface and limits their diffusion and the diffusion of their reaction products so that distributive patterns are preserved and a satisfactory print is obtained. Often a succession of treatments with reagents and washes must be made before the print is rendered specific. Rendition of detail is successful in such cases only if the transferred material remains fixed sufficiently well to withstand these treatments.

The choice of the transfer medium will be determined by the purposes of the test and by the subsequent processing operations. In electro-spot testing, the primary objective is rapid and specific identification tests with a reasonably accurate localization of identifiable products. The printing of fine detail does not fall within its scope. Identification of a single component in an alloy or other mixture may require the removal of interferences by immersion of the spot print in various dissolving and masking reagents with washing and drying as intermediate steps. Such operations are facilitated when the printing medium has a relatively open capillary structure but at the same time possesses sufficient wet strength to permit handling without the risk of disintegration. An open structure also introduces little electrical resistance above that of the electrolyte, thus reducing the printing time. This is desirable in spot testing.

The material which appears best to meet the general requirements of electro-spot testing is a hardened filter paper such as Schleicher and Schüll #576 or Whatman #50. These papers are of sufficiently fine texture to permit reproduction of distributive patterns down to a fraction of a millimeter and are at the same time sufficiently open in structure to insure fairly rapid printing and processing. They are hardened enough to have the desired wet strength, but not to the point where the fibers have become fused and the porosity lost as in the case of the so-called "parchment" paper.

It is generally advantageous to employ a thick, soft paper beneath the printing paper. This provides a cushion, improving the contact, particularly if the specimen surface is slightly rough. The printing paper then is in contact only with the specimen and any interference caused by contact with the opposite electrode is minimized. This thicker backing paper also increases the capacity for electrolyte, lessening the likelihood of drying out when long printing times are required or when several specimens are to be printed successively on the same paper. A thick, soft filter paper such as that used in spot testing (Schleicher and Schüll #601) or photographic blotting paper are satisfactory materials.

For electrographic prints, in which delicate patterns are to be recorded, absorbent paper is less satisfactory. The fine detail is largely lost against the relatively coarse fibrous structure of unsized paper. A material must be used which has a structure· finer than the finest detail to be recorded. In this respect, there is a similarity in the requirements of the electrographic, and the photographic image. This at once suggests the use of gelatin or gelatin coatings as a medium for electrography. The idea of employing such a base for chemical contact prints is not new. M. Neissner (42) used gelatin coated paper, impregnated with various reagents to print inclusions and segregations in metal specimens.

To obtain suitably coated papers, earlier workers dissolved the silver halides out of photographic papers. However, a gelatin coated paper is now supplied by the Eastman Kodak Co. as "Imbibition Paper." The paper base is heavily filled and is supplied in two weights. The "single weight" material is better for electrographic purposes, since it offers less resistance to the passage of ions.

Since gelatin is microscopically structureless, coated papers place no lower limit on the detail recordable. Such limits will still exist, but the controlling factors will be the sensitivity of the color reaction and the diffusibility of the ions or reaction products in the gelatin. Hunter, Churchill, and Mears (33) have pointed out that the diffusion of ions in the gelatin medium is very slow. Because of this slow diffusion, the transfer of ions from the specimen to the gelatin surface is more rapid than movement through the gelatin toward the opposite electrode and a concentration occurs about the point of entry. This concentration of transferred material at the gelatin surface results in sharper and more delicate electrographic prints for two reasons. First, the threshold concentration for a given color reaction is reached quickly and with relatively little solution of the specimen surface. Consequently, a trace of material can be recorded which might escape detection on filter paper where rapid diffusion would prevent attainment of the reaction threshold. Second, slow diffusion limits the spread of transferred material around the point of entry, rendering the image of that point more perfect. It is even possible to employ soluble reaction products in gelatin and to obtain good detail. The electrolyte may be chosen so that no colored, insoluble or nondissociating products are formed with the ions under test. A "latent" print results which contains the transferred ions in reactive form. This print can be explored and spotted with various reagents, including those which, because of their instability, could not be employed in direct printing.

The combination of dense filling and gelatin coating raises the resistance of the imbibition paper considerably above that of filter paper for a given electrolyte. Allowance must be made for this in determining the printing conditions. The diffusion of fluids is naturally much slower in this medium, and processing operations therefore require more time. Before using imbibition paper for printing, it should be soaked for at least 10 minutes to allow complete penetration of the electrolyte.

Although the gelatin coated paper undoubtedly produces the best quality prints, commercial sized and filled papers are often capable of rendering considerable detail and are very much cheaper. Thus a heavy grade of hectograph copying paper has been used with considerable success. Such papers are not pure chemically and often contain enough iron to give a distinct blue background color when ferrocyanide is used as the reagent, consequently it would be unwise to use them on a completely unknown specimen. For many purposes, however, the impurities are not bothersome. This is especially true of routine tests, where cost is a factor and the effects of the paper, once they are known, can usually be discounted.

Occasionally it is desired to prepare prints on a transparent base to facilitate projection and microscopic study. Several interesting attempts have been made, but there is still need for a transparent permeable medium which is easy to prepare and handle. Unplasticized cellophane has been proposed, but it has very little capacity for electrolyte and shrinks badly on drying. Yagoda (47) minimizes this tendency by preshrinking prior to impregnation with the electrolyte. He points out that this material is especially adapted to the printing of iron patterns with ferrocyanide, since the blue product does not bleed when washed as it does in most other media. Yagoda (46) has also recommended the use of plates of plaster of Paris about 1-mm. thick formed from a water slurry in a special mold. These plates are sufficiently translucent to permit examination of the image in transmitted light and the structure is fine enough to allow microscopic examination of the print detail. This medium possesses some special properties worthy of mention. The low solubility of calcium sulfate provides a constant and controlled source of sulfate and calcium ions and moistening is all that is necessary. The controlled sulfate ion makes this medium suitable for lead fixation. Difficultly soluble reagents such as zinc sulfide may be incorporated readily by adding them to the slurry at the time of casting. The chief drawbacks are the fragility of the medium and the time and special technique required for its preparation.

. Frequently, electrographic prints of curved or irregular surfaces are required. When the irregularities are slight, tin or aluminum foil may be used as the opposite electrode and cushioned with rubber or felt. When the surface curves sharply, but is of such shape that the paper can be formed to it successfully, the other electrode can be cast of a low melting alloy such as Wood's metal. The specimen surface is first covered with tightly drawn paper and the alloy is cast around it. An aluminum foil liner can then be used to avoid interferences.

The greatest difficulty is encountered when the specimen surface is such that the printing paper cannot be made to conform to it without bursting. One answer to this problem is suggested by Yagoda's use of plaster of Paris (46). A plaster cast is made by filling the space between the irregular specimen surface and the nonconforming plane or curved opposite electrode. The cast is dried, impregnated with the electrolyte-reagent solution and refitted to the surfaces. Electrographic printing then proceeds in the normal manner, the print being obtained on the plaster cast instead of paper.

2.5. Preparation of the Specimen

The treatment of the specimen surface will depend on the information desired of the electro-transfer. If a print is to be made of inclusions, films, and other impurities which may be hardly more than surface deep, little should be done to the specimen beyond washing with an inert solvent to remove loose dusts and any oily films. On the other hand, when a surface is used to sample the composition and structure of the specimen, every precaution should be taken to insure that it is representative and free from contamination. For electro-spot testing, a fresh surface obtained by abrasion ordinarily suffices. Abrasive cloth or paper may be used, or better, a water suspension of emery or carborundum. Small specimens may be ground on a glass plate, to which a few drops of wet abrasive have been added. The wet abrasive may be applied to large specimens on cotton or felt. Before printing, the specimen should be washed or wiped free of abrasion products.

When structural features are to be electrographed, preparation of the specimen follows closely the procedures used in petrography and metallography. The surface is ground and polished to a smoothness determined by the fineness of the structure under study. Irregularly shaped specimens may be mounted in plastic materials before final polishing, with provision made for electrical connection to the back of the specimen. The following adaptation of a method proposed by Yagoda (47) provides electrical continuity and avoids the use of a special moulding press. A collar is first prepared of nonconducting material of a depth and diameter sufficient to enclose the specimen. Yagoda uses plastic bottle caps with the tops ground off. Bakelite, vulcanized fiber, and other types of tubing are obtainable commercially in diameters from 1 to 6 inches, however, and can be used for larger specimens. The collar is placed on a metal plate which is covered with a sheet of glazed paper. The specimen with the test surface rough-ground, is placed inside the collar with the ground surface resting on the glazed paper. This assembly is placed in an oven at 110°C. for 5–10 minutes, removed, and a sealing wax containing an inert filler (silica flour, diatomaceous earth, etc.) is poured in to fill the space between the specimen and the collar, but not completely covering the specimen. When cool, the space above the wax is filled with a low melting alloy such as Wood's metal to provide electrical contact for the specimen. Wet polishing of the mounted specimen is then completed. Usually the polishing of specimens for electrographic printing need not be carried as far as in conventional metallography. So long as the surface is smooth enough to contain the structural elements in a fairly plane section and intimate contact secured with the printing medium, good prints may be made.

The electrode surface used opposite the specimen should be cleaned frequently, otherwise tarnish and electrolysis products may accumulate and cause contamination of the print as well as false distributive patterns due to uneven current distribution. Aluminum and stainless steel both tend to acquire invisible passivating films. A few strokes with fine emery or carborundum paper followed by wiping with a damp cloth after each printing will prevent trouble.

2.6. Standard Specimen Block

The effective use of the electrographic method as a tool in general analysis and research requires a continuing development of methods to meet particular problems. The behavior of metal combinations with given electrolytes, reagents, conditions of printing and aftertreatment must be determined by testing specimens of known composition. When these are handled one at a time, the task becomes unnecessarily laborious and the advantages of immediate comparison are lost. A better plan is to print all the specimens simultaneously on the same paper. Conditions then are identical and the results can be compared readily at any point in the processing.

Simultaneous printing of a number of specimens may be accomplished with the mounting block shown in Fig. 7. The standard specimen consists of a cylindrical pellet, 18-mm. long and 12 mm. in diameter. These cylinders slide freely in holes drilled through a block of bakelite, hard rubber, lucite, or other impervious insulating material. The block is 30-mm. high and the bottom is faced with a plate of copper about 3-mm.

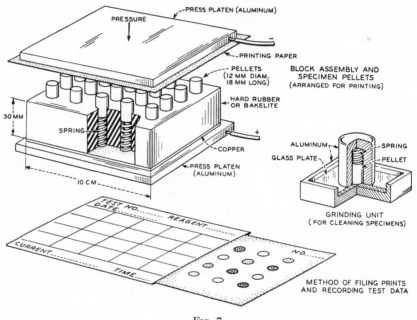

Fig. 7

thick, to provide electrical contact in the press. Phosphor bronze coil springs support the pellets in the holes and make contact between them and the copper plate. These springs are so adjusted that when the pellets are depressed flush with the block face, a pressure of about 200 g. is exerted on each. Thus any desired combination or configuration of these interchangeable specimens can be arranged in the block which is then placed in the electrographic press, made anodic, and the print obtained in the usual manner.

The specimens are cleaned by grinding individually on a glass plate with fine emery or carborundum suspension. A special holder is used to keep the grinding plane normal to the pellet axis. The metal contact plate is removable from the bottom of the block by loosening four screws.

This facilitates cleaning of the block, plate, and springs.   A square block of 10 cm. side will easily accommodate twenty holes, which is sufficient for most purposes.

Assume the problem to be the identification of one component of an alloy containing a number of metals.   Pellets of the alloy and of all the metals likely to be present are placed in the block.   Prints are made with the electrolyte, electrolysis conditions, and color producing reagents best suited to the metal to be identified.   Interferences by other metals are noted and masking treatments tried until a development sequence is found which eliminates all spots on the print except those of the pure specimen of the metal under test and the alloy containing it.   For example, a test is desired to distinguish leaded brass from plain brass.   The block contains copper, zinc, tin, lead, iron, plain and leaded brass specimens.   Developed with sodium sulfide, the print gives colors with copper, lead, iron and both brasses.   However, treatment with potassium cyanide, then with acetic acid and water clears all spots but those of lead and leaded brass.

The specimen block technique also may be used quantitatively.   A series of standard brass pellets containing known concentrations of lead are placed in the block, printed, and developed.   The unknown, printed under identical conditions, is compared with the known series and the lead content estimated from the densities of the prints.

2.7. The Technique of the Electro-transfer

The physical operations of the transfer are quite simple and should be fairly evident from the descriptions of the apparatus in the earlier part of this chapter.   In assembling the sandwich, the larger, more tabular member is normally placed at the bottom.   Usually this will be the base plate or press platen, but occasionally the specimen may be of such shape and dimensions as to reverse the order.   The pad, consisting of the printing material and the soft backing paper, is immersed in the appropriate electrolyte, drained, blotted, and placed on the electrode with the printing surface toward the specimen.   The sandwich is completed by the bringing of the other electrode member down on the paper.   The latter may be held with the hand for simple spot testing and rough printing or the sandwich may be clamped in the electrographic press for longer and more precise operations.   The paper should not be too wet, and before the circuit is closed care should be taken to blot up any excess electrolyte squeezed from the sandwich when pressure is applied.

For flawless electrographic reproduction, films or bubbles of air at the specimen surface must be avoided.   Bubbles in the matrix of the printing medium block the movement of ions and may produce concentration changes which would affect the final pattern. Somewhat greater care is therefore indicated in the impregnation of the medium and in the manner of bringing the surfaces together. Unsized paper should be slowly lowered edgewise into the electrolyte so that air is driven out by the capillary climb of the fluid. After immersion for a minute or longer, it should be agitated in the bath to remove any accumulated bubbles before withdrawing. Gelatin or sized papers require soaking for 10 minutes or longer to permit full penetration of the electrolyte. A trace of Aerosol or similar wetting agent often may be added without interference to improve wetting, both of the paper and the metal surfaces.

When manipulative details can be so arranged, it is advantageous to apply the printing medium to the specimen surface first, using a rubber roller to work out any bubbles unavoidably trapped. Even irregular specimens which have to be mounted face downward can be so handled if the printing paper is cut to the exact contour of the specimen surface. The backing paper is laid over the base plate or platen and is kept fairly moist. The specimen, with the printing paper rolled on, is then inverted on the backing paper, and pressure is applied. The excess electrolyte squeezed out is thoroughly removed by blotting.

In making electrographic prints, the pressure to be applied will vary with the condition of the specimen and the nature of the printing medium and is best determined for the individual case. It should be sufficient to insure intimate contact at all points. Thus, if pinholes in a plated surface are to be reproduced, the printing medium, or at least the electrolyte, must be forced into contact with the base metal at the bottom of such discontinuities. Pressures of 1000 lb./sq. in. or more have been found desirable in such cases and the use of the hydraulic press for obtaining them has already been indicated. For most purposes, pressures of 25–100 lb./sq. in. will be found satisfactory.

The current and time required for printing will be determined by the area of the specimen and by the quantity of the ion which must be transferred to produce a satisfactory print density. Assuming that a low enough voltage is used so that practically all of the energy is applied to the solution of the specimen, Faraday's second law establishes the relation quantitatively:

$$I \cdot t = \frac{96,500 \cdot K \cdot A}{Q}, \tag{1}$$

where I is the current in amperes,

  t, the time in seconds,

  A, the area of the specimen surface in cm.^{2}

  Q, the equivalent weight of the dissolved metal in g.

K is a specific factor based on the sensitivity and color producing power of the reaction used. It is expressed in g./sq. cm.[2] of the ion needed to produce a print of the desired density.

The units in the above equation are large for electrographic purposes and it is convenient to express area and current together as current density. The following equation is therefore suggested:

$$i_d \cdot t = \frac{96.5 \cdot k}{Q},\tag{2}$$

where i_d is the current density in $Ma./sq.\ cm.$
t, the time in seconds,
k, the specific factor, expressed in *micrograms per sq. cm.*
Q is the equivalent weight as in the first equation.

The factor k is not precise, its value depending on the print density best suited to the purposes of the test. A greater print density is needed, for example, in the detection of pinholes than in the reproduction of larger details. In general, it may be said that a satisfactory color intensity is obtained with most reactions when the quantity of the ion electrolyzed is between 20 and 70 μg./cm[2]. Yagoda suggests an average figure of 50.

Example: A copper print, using zinc sulfide paper, requires 20 micrograms/cm.[2] for good recognition of detail. The current density used is 15 milliamp./cm.[2] The time required is obtained from the equation:

$$15t = \frac{96.5 \times 20}{31.5}, \text{ from which } t \text{ is 4.1 seconds.}$$

The value of the current through the electrographic cell determines the potential across it and this in turn, influences the phenomena occurring at the electrodes. The voltage measured across the electrographic cell is the algebraic sum of the IR drop through the pad and the internal e.m.f. generated by the two electrodes when they function as a primary cell. The internal e.m.f. is determined by the potential difference between the two electrodes in the electrolyte used. It may oppose the applied current or it may aid it, depending on whether the material serving as the cathode of the electrographic sandwich is anodic or cathodic relative to the specimen. Thus, if an aluminum cathode were used and the specimen being dissolved anodically were a copper alloy, the e.m.f. of the sandwich would oppose the applied potential. No printing would then occur until the applied voltage is made to exceed that of the cell. On the other hand, if conditions were reversed, and an aluminum alloy were being dissolved against a cathode of copper, theoretically no outside potential would be needed. Its application would simply speed up the process, reducing the time and providing a better rendition of detail.

In the printing of metallic specimens, the current density, in general, should be so controlled that the anodic voltage does not greatly exceed the solution potential of the metal to be detected. Then practically all of the electrical energy is used for the solution of the metal and Faraday's law holds. Very high current densities may raise the voltage to the decomposition potential of the electrolyte, when gassing will occur, driving the electrolyte out of the sandwich and producing poor prints.

When the specimen is not homogeneous but is made up of materials having different potentials, anodic and cathodic areas will exist on its surface. Then, in addition to the potential required to balance the back-e.m.f. of the cell as a whole, a further potential will be that which is necessary to render all areas of the specimen surface anodic. An excellent discussion of the conditions on such a surface has been provided by Hunter, Churchill, and Mears (33). A slightly condensed version is here given:

"Let us assume that a specimen A contains an inclusion of a more cathodic material C. The open circuit potentials of the two are denoted by the points A and C respectively in Fig. 8. These two materials, being in physical contact are short circuited and a liquid circuit is furnished by the electrolyte-filled paper of the cell. The anodic material will polarize along the curve A-B, while the cathodic material will polarize along the curve C-B, until the point B is reached. At this point the potential of the entire specimen will be that corresponding to the point B (neglecting the small IR drops which exist in the electrolyte) and a self-generated current will be flowing in such direction that only the anodic material will be dissolved. Thus, without an applied current, the more cathodic inclusion would not be dissolved and hence would not be detected.

"However, as current is applied to the specimen, it will polarize along the curve B-D-E. Until point D, which corresponds to the open-circuit potential of C, is reached, only the anodic material A will be dissolved. Beyond point D, both A and C will dissolve. Thus practically all elements may be forced from the surface of the specimen into the printing medium regardless of their open-circuit solution potentials.'

These voltage requirements thus set a minimum value for the current density. The latter must be such that the potential across the cell is sufficient to render the specimen completely anodic. Suppose, for example, a copper inclusion in a zinc surface is to be printed. The difference of potential between these two metals in the electromotive series amounts to 1.23 volts. The potential in the electrographic cell will be somewhat different because of the difference in the electrolyte, but it will be of the same order. In a sandwich using filter paper soaked in 2% sodium nitrate, the initial resistance measures about 90 ohms/cm.^{2} The current density necessary to print the copper, therefore, should be 1.23/90, or 14 milliamp./cm.^{2}; which corresponds to point B in Fig. 8. Experimentally, it was found that a copper print in a zinc specimen could not be obtained until applied voltage reached 1.6 when an aluminum cathode was used. The current density under these conditions measured 17 milliamp./cm.² at the start of the printing, corresponding to point D in Fig. 8.

When a printing pad of higher resistance is used, the necessary potential can be obtained with a lower current. Thus, in the example just given, if gelatin paper is used, the resistance measures about 200 ohms per cm.² A copper print is obtained with a current density of only 8 milliamp./cm.², instead of 17.

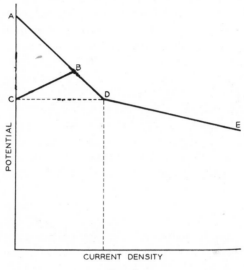

FIG. 8

The foregoing discussion has dealt in some detail with heterogeneous surfaces in which the components display their individual solution tendencies. When the specimen is a single phase alloy, however, a different behavior is observed. From such solid solutions, the component metals go into electrolytic solution in the same proportion as their concentration in the alloy. Glazunov discusses this behavior as it is illustrated in iron-nickel alloys and has made use of it in a quantitative application of electrography. This subject will receive further attention later in the chapter.

The resistance of the electrographic cell will increase as the transfer progresses and polarization effects increase. Ions concentrate at the electrodes and are depleted in the intermediate layers. Precipitation of reaction products removes further ions and tends to seal off and isolate the anode surface. The resistance increase in the electrographic cell will be accompanied by a simultaneous decrease in the current. If the resistance in the external circuit were negligible, the product IR then would remain constant and the cell voltage would not change. In practice, some external resistance will always exist. The decrease in current therefore will not exactly compensate the increase in the cell resistance since the current will fall in proportion to the increase in the total resistance of the circuit. Hence, the voltage will slowly rise and the greater the external resistance relative to the sandwich resistance, the more pronounced will be the voltage increase. From this, it should be clear that if it is desired to hold the voltage constant, or nearly so, its adjustment should be made at the battery selector switch rather than by adding resistance. The control resistance should be used only to obtain regulation between the steps of the battery selector, and should be as low as possible. Under these conditions, the slight rise in voltage during printing can be compensated by manipulation of the resistance. Regulation to within 0.1 volt is usually easy this way when the ion dissolved does not exceed 100 micrograms/cm.[2]

If, on the other hand, the current is to be held constant to facilitate calculation of the dissolved ion, this is best accomplished by employing a high external resistance relative to the resistance of the cell and a sufficiently high circuit voltage to obtain the desired drop at the printing cell. Since the current is relatively constant in this arrangement, the cell voltage will rise almost as its resistance rises. It is therefore desirable for quantitative work, to employ transfer conditions which involve the least possible polarization effects. For this purpose, sensitive reactions requiring only small quantities of transferred material are the most suitable.

3. Electrolytes, Reagents, and Developing Processes

3.1. Production of the Image

The simplest production of the electrographic image is exemplified by the printing of iron inclusions and alloyed copper in duralumin. Prints are obtained directly with paper moistened with 2% potassium ferrocyanide in which the iron particles are reproduced as blue ferric ferrocyanide against a reddish background of cupric ferrocyanide. The ferrocyanide serves both as electrolyte and color-producing reagent. It gives strongly contrasting colors with copper and iron and none with aluminum and thus is ideally suited to the particular problem.

On the other hand, if we wish to test a bronze specimen electrographically for alloyed manganese, we are not favored with so convenient a reagent. The manganese print is not obtainable directly, but rather as the product of a series of transforming operations. First, a "latent" print is produced electrographically, in which the transferred metals are obtained as basic sulfates. This print is next treated with ammonia and hydrogen peroxide and thoroughly washed. This step removes the copper and converts the manganese to the hydrated dioxide. Finally, treatment of the print with benzidine acetate develops the manganese image as the fugitive blue oxidation product of benzidine.

These examples illustrate the two general approaches used in the development of the electrographic image. Direct printing results when the color producing reagent is present at the time of the transfer. The alternative method is to employ the transfer as a separate operation with appropriate precautions to prevent diffusion of the products. This is followed by one or more developmental operations, the final product being a selective colored print. Naturally, where the conditions of the problem permit, direct printing is to be desired. Such a procedure is limited, however, to cases where (a) the electrolyte contains a reacting ion or group which is stable and capable of giving a colored product with the metal to be detected under the conditions of the electrolysis and (b) where the specimen surface yields no interfering ions. A fundamental limitation to the direct printing procedure derives from the fact that few of the so-called specific reagents possess the property of reacting with a single metal out of a group of possible metals without the introduction of special treatments and "masking" reagents to overcome interferences. Specificity in the spot testing techniques of Feigl is obtained largely by combining the use of group selective color-producing reagents with preparatory treatments designed to suppress or to remove interfering substances. Another limitation to direct printing is illustrated in the case of the manganese bronze where no suitable color reaction existed for the manganous ions. When given a separate treatment, however, to oxidize the manganese and remove the interfering copper, the print is capable of development with benzidine and the test is fairly specific for manganese.

Some organic reagents, for example, diphenylcarbazide or benzidine, undergo oxidation at the anode with the formation of interfering colored products, hence could not be used in the direct printing process although they are entirely satisfactory for use in outside development.

Aside from overcoming the limitations of direct printing, the use of the "latent" or undeveloped print has certain advantages. For example, if one is dealing with an unknown specimen, identification of its components requires the stepwise application of group and specific reagents. A single undeveloped transfer can be given many tests with such reagents by spotting or brush-streaking. It can be conditioned by heating, fuming, exposure to gases, etc. before development. By using a simple universal printing electrolyte, uncomplicated by the presence of special reagents or masking agents, a better control is maintained over the transfer process and more reproducible results are obtained.

3.2. The Electrolyte

The oxidation or reduction attending the electrographic solution is brought about entirely by the potential differences maintained at the specimen surface and not by the chemical activity of the impregnating solution. This solution, therefore, functions primarily to provide ionic conduction through the printing medium and to establish anodic or cathodic conditions conducive to the smooth, efficient transfer of specimen material. With these requirements fairly easily satisfied, the choice of impregnant is determined largely by the secondary effects desired, such as the precipitation of the transferred ions as colored insoluble salts or their fixation as colorless, temporarily insoluble products to be transformed and developed subsequent to printing.

The salt concentration in the electrolyte should not be too high. Then the desired voltage drop may be established without excessive current. Heating and gassing are also avoided and better control of the whole process is obtained. Two tenths to five tenths molar solutions produce good prints. It is convenient to use equivalent concentrations of the various electrolytes. These may be interchanged without large changes in resistance and the circuit will require a minimum of adjustment.

The number of electrolytes containing color-forming ions suitable for direct electrographic printing is rather limited. Table I lists those

TABLE I

Reagent	Ag	Cu	Cd	Zn	Pb	Bi	Fe	Ni	Co	Mn
Iodide	Lt. yel.	—	—	—	Yel.	Yel.	—	—	—	—
Sulfide	Blk.	Blk.	Yel.	Wh.	Blk.	Blk.	Blk.	Blk.	Blk.	Flesh
Chromate	Red	—	Yel.	Yel.	Yel.	Yel.	—	—	—	—
Ferrocyanide	Wh.	Red	Wh.	Wh.	Wh.	—	Blue	Apple green	—	—
Ferricyanide	—	—	—	—	—	—	Blue	—	—	—
Nitrite	—	—	—	—	—	—	—	—	Yel.	—

which have been used, together with the colored products formed with commonly encountered metals. The greater number of electrographic procedures employ organic and special reagents in conjunction with a general electrolyte.

In certain cases, when electrolysis is accompanied by formation of an insoluble product, precipitation may be so rapid and the product so impervious that the specimen surface is quickly coated with a barrier film and little or no transfer can occur. Such films may be so thin as to be invisible. Lead, for example, is quickly rendered inactive in a sulfate electrolyte and practically no transfer to the paper occurs. Passivation sometimes may be employed to advantage where it is desired to repress the solution of one component of a surface to the enhancement of the solution of another. Thus pinholes in chromium plate on brass may be studied advantageously with a phosphoric acid electrolyte which passivates the chromium and favors the solution of the copper.

When indirect print development is used, it is important that diffusion be prevented during the interim operations. With gelatin paper, this diffusion is very slow, and for most purposes, it can be neglected. Prints made on open textured paper, however, suffer much loss of detail unless the transferred materials are converted immediately to a nondiffusible product. Although relatively insoluble, such products must be capable of reaction with developing reagents. It is important also that the precipitated product be formed within the body of the paper rather than on the specimen surface, where it would quickly block further solution. For metals, these requirements are generally met by fixation as basic salts, carbonates, or other insoluble salts of weak acids. With such products, precipitation is an easily reversible process, controlled by pH adjustment, and no special problem is created in the subsequent development. The dependence of precipitation on pH also provides a mechanism by which it can be deferred until the ions have reached the desired depth in the printing medium. This is understandable when it is recalled that the region about the anode becomes increasingly acidic during electrolysis, while the cathodic region grows alkaline. The acidic and alkaline zones tend to spread respectively from the anode and cathode, so that when a neutral salt is used, the pH will vary continuously through the printing pad from acidic low values at the anode to alkaline high values at the cathode. Basic or weak acid salts cannot be precipitated in the strongly acid anode region, but as the metal ions move into the paper, they will reach a zone where the pH is high enough to permit this precipitation. The pH gradient through the printing pad will not be uniform, mainly because of the difference in the migration rates of hydrogen and hydroxyl ions. The pH distribution will depend also on the electrolyte and on the amount of electrolysis. For neutral salts such as sodium nitrate, with the average transfer, using #576 and #601 papers, the acid zone extends two-thirds to three-quarters of the way through the pad. Thus it is likely that no fixation at all will take place in the thin printing paper which is used on a thick backing sheet.

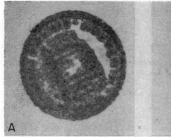
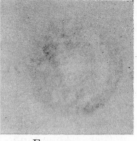

PAPER   ELECTROLYTE

C.S. & S. #575   0.2M NaNO$_3$
C.S. & S. #601

UNBUFFERED ELECTROLYTE ON UNSIZED PAPER

Excessive diffusion resulting in bad blurring
Diffusion extends into backing paper

PAPER   ELECTROLYTE

C.S. & S. #575   0.2M NaNO$_3$
C.S. & S. #601   0.5M Na$_2$CO$_3$

BUFFERED ELECTROLYTE ON UNSIZED PAPER

Fixation of copper by precipitation as basic salt results in clear print detail

PAPER   ELECTROLYTE

E. K. Co. Imbibition (gela-   0.2M NaNO$_3$
tin) paper

UNBUFFERED ELECTROLYTE ON GELATIN COATED PAPER

This print shows marked retarding of diffusion by gelatin medium.

FIG. 9. Developed ferrocyanide electrographs of bronze coin showing control of diffusion by buffering the electrolyte and using gelatin printing medium. Prints developed in 5% potassium ferrocyanide solution.

Metal ions will pass through the pad until they reach the deep alkaline layers of the backing paper, close to the cathode, and some lateral diffusion may take place on the way. There they will precipitate as basic nitrates or hydroxides. If, on the other hand, the electrolyte is buffered with sodium carbonate, extension of the acid zone into the paper can occur only as the buffer is used up. By experimental adjustment of the concentration of the buffer, the precipitation can be made to occur at the desired depth in the printing paper. For a C.S. & S. #576 and #601 paper pad and a 30-second printing, 0.5 M sodium carbonate with 0.1 M sodium nitrate or chloride provides satisfactory solution and fixation for most metals. Fig. 9 shows prints made with buffered and unbuffered electrolytes as well as in gelatin paper.

Solution of silver, copper, and lead is best obtained with the nitrate ion, while iron, aluminum, and nickel sometimes show passive tendencies with nitrate and dissolve better in the presence of the chloride ion. Amphoteric metals such as bismuth, antimony, and tin, whose salts hydrolyze readily, require a strongly acid condition at the anode. They react best to chloride ion with little or no buffer.

3.3. Recognition of Transferred Products

A full discussion of the many reactions and treatment sequences which can be employed to establish the identity of transferred products is beyond the scope of this chapter. General approaches will be indicated and these will be enlarged upon in the specific examples given in a later section. The problem may be simple, involving only a color rendition of one or more unalloyed metals in a known surface. On the other hand, recognition of a minor component in the print of a complex alloy, or the systematic investigation of a completely unknown surface may require operations as involved as any encountered in conventional qualitative analysis, with the additional restriction that the treatments must neither damage the printing medium nor cause disturbance of the patterns.

3.3.1. Examination of the Undeveloped Print. The colors of the metal ions or precipitates often are useful by themselves for identification purposes. Preliminary examination may be furthered by simple treatments such as fuming with ammonia, heating, exposure to strong light etc., which will not interfere with later development. Thus the blue green of copper changing to strong blue on fuming with ammonia, the intense blue of strongly dried cobalt, the yellow of ferric iron and the yellow of the chromate ion, formed when chromium dissolves, all provide valuable clues and often are sufficient identification. Table II contains a summary of the colors of transferred materials and the effects of simple treatments.

TABLE II

Metal	Electrolyte 0.5 M Na₂CO₃, with 0.1 M NaCl or NaNO₃	Fuming		Heat-light
		NH₃	HCl	
Cu	Greenish blue	Deep blue	Green-yellow	Green-blue
Ag	Colorless			Brown to black
Fe	Brown	Brown	Orange-yellow	Brown
Ni	Light green	Light violet	Green	Light green
Co	Dirty brown	Brown	Bright blue	HCl Blue deepens
Mo	Deep blue-violet	Gray	Gray	Gray
Cr	Yellow (chromate)	Yellow	Yellow	Yellow

3.3.2. Color Producing Reagents. Generally speaking, any color reactions which are nondestructive to the medium are applicable to the electrotransfer. Those used by Feigl and coworkers in spot and drop tests are particularly well suited. When identification is the sole objective, treatment of the transfer by spotting with the reagent is convenient and the colored product need not be insoluble. Chromate, from a chromium-bearing surface, for example, may be confirmed with diphenylcarbazide, or iron with thiocyanate. When print detail is to be developed, however, the colored product must be insoluble or a medium such as gelatin in which diffusion is negligible must be used. Reagents such as dimethylglyoxime or a-benzoinoxime give nondiffusing colors in unsized paper under proper conditions of use and they may be employed in direct printing or in development of the "latent" print, after its processing to eliminate interferences.

In direct printing, incorporation of reagents in the impregnating electrolyte is not always possible. Many organic reagents such as those just mentioned are insoluble or only slightly soluble in aqueous salt solutions. Even when the reagents are soluble, their use in that form is not always advisable for the reason that many colloidal reaction products, when formed in the free liquid tend to diffuse, or "bleed," causing poor prints. Thus sodium diethyldithiocarbamate or sodium sulfide in unsized paper both give badly running prints with copper specimens. These difficulties are largely overcome through use of prepared papers, in which a difficultly soluble reagent has been incorporated prior to moistening with the electrolyte (6). Water "insoluble" organic reagents are introduced in alcohol, acetone or other suitable solvents, after which the medium is completely dried before use. In this way, the reagent is deposited on the fibers of the paper matrix, becoming a part of the medium structure. When moistened with the electrolyte, a saturated solution is maintained around the reagent-coated fibers and, under conditions of electrography, precipitation will be largely confined to their immediate vicinity. Attachment of the colored product to the fiber surfaces thus is greatly facilitated and very little colloidal diffusion occurs. The troublesome coating of the specimen surface with the precipitated product is entirely avoided. In the case of gelatin coated papers, impregnation with reagents in organic solvents is not very satisfactory because the gelatin does not swell in such liquids and very little reagent can be introduced. Sometimes this difficulty can be avoided by using an alkaline aqueous solution of the reagent such as an ammoniacal solution of dimethylglyoxime, but it is generally better practice to use such reagents as developers of "latent" prints. Nothing is lost by this approach because of the greatly retarded diffusion in gelatin.

The arguments advanced for "fixed" organic reagents apply equally to color producing anions which are ordinarily employed in the form of water soluble salts. Often these may be used in paper in a less soluble form to obtain the advantages discussed. Thus, instead of using a sodium sulfide solution, colorless zinc sulfide may be incorporated on the fibers of the paper by direct precipitation. Diffusion is eliminated and an automatic control of the sulfide ion concentration is obtained, making the paper more selective in its reactions. Cadmium and antimony sulfide papers provide lower sulfide concentrations and, although colored, they are capable of giving excellent prints with copper and silver. Cadmium diethyldithiocarbamate is soluble in acetone and other organic solvents and can be so introduced into the paper. It is a far better electrographic reagent for copper traces than the soluble sodium salt. Zinc ferrocyanide paper gives prints for copper and iron with improved fixation of the colloidal reaction products.

"Fixed" reagent papers are best prepared with hardened paper possessing good wet strength. First, an impregnation is made with one of the two stoichiometrically equivalent reacting solutions, followed by complete drying. The paper is then immersed in the other solution rapidly and uniformly, to avoid irregular precipitation due to capillary effects. It is withdrawn, spread on a glass plate, and washed thoroughly in running water to remove any unreacted salts. After drying, the paper is best preserved in convenient cut sizes under compression to exclude air. Reagents precipitated from aqueous solutions can be incorporated successfully in gelatin papers, but longer periods of immersion in the reacting solutions and longer washing must be allowed because of the slow rate of diffusion in the medium.

Table III lists a number of typical "fixed" reagent papers, organic and inorganic, with their preparation and reactions.

TABLE III

Reagent	Preparation	Paper color	Cu	Ag	Pb	Bi	Cd	Zn	Ni	Co	Fe	Mo	Al	Sn	Cl	S	Remarks
Zinc sulfide	1. Zn Acetate } 0.25 M 2. Na Sulfide	White	Bk	Bk								*					Electrolyte 0.3 M Na₂CO₃, 0.1 M NaNO₃
Cadmium sulfide	1. Cd Acetate } 0.25 M 2. Na Sulfide	Yellow	Bk	Bk	Bn	Bn						*					Same
Antimony sulfide	1. Na Sulfantimoniate, 2-5% 2. HCl, Dilute	Orange	Bk	Bk	Bn	Bn						*					Same
Zinc ferrocyanide	1. Zn Acetate } 0.25 M 2. K Ferrocyanide	White	Brick Rd						Lt Gn		Bl	Bn					Same
Lead carbonate	1. Pb Acetate } 0.1 M 2. Na Carbonate	White														Bk	Cathodic redn. for sulfide
Silver chromate	1. Ag Nitrate } 0.1 M 2. Na Chromate	Red													Wh		Cathodic redn. for chloride
Zinc xanthate	1. Zn Acetate } 0.1 M 2. K Xanthate	White	Yl	*					Or	Gy Gn	Bn	Vi					Above electrolyte
Cadmium diethyldithiocarbamate	1% Soln. in acetone or chloroform	White	Lt Bn	*								*					0.25 M Am. citrate
Dimethyl-glyoxime	1% Alcoholic soln.	White		*					Rd			*					Wash-NH₄OH-am. citrate, above (1st) electrolyte
α-Benzoinoxime	1% Alcoholic soln.	White	Gn	*								*					After washing dil. acetic acid, above electrolyte
Cinchonine	1% Alcoholic soln.	White	Bn	Yl	Yl	Or			Or	Or		*					KI Electrolyte bleach-H₂SO₃
Morin	0.5% Alcoholic soln.	Yellow white	Lt Yl	*	Wk Fl	Wk Fl	Wk Fl	Br Fl		Bn	Bn	*	Br Fl	Wk Fl			Fluorescent reagent examine-U.V.
Salicylic acid	2% Alcoholic soln.	White	Gn Yl					Fl	Gn		Vi		Fl				0.3 M Na₂CO₃, 0.1 M NaCl
Barium rhodizonate	1. 0.5% Na rhodizonate 2. 0.25 M Ba acetate	Orange-red														(SO₄) Wh	Cathodic redn. of sulfates

Yellow, Yl; Red, Rd; Blue, Bl; Orange, Or; Green, Gn; Violet, Vi; White, Wh; Gray, Gy; Brown, Bn; Black, Bk; Fluorescence, Fl; Weak, Wk; Bright, Br; Light, Lt.
* = Reduction (of Ag or Mo).

3.3.3. Elimination of Interferences.   In practical electrography, two types of surface are encountered.   One consists either of a pure metal or of macroscopically distinct units, each of which is a pure metal.   Thus tin plate may present a pure tin surface, or, if the coating is poor, the surface may be largely pure tin with tiny areas of exposed iron.   Reagents used in the printing of such surfaces are not necessarily specific for the metal under investigation.   All that is necessary is that contrasting colors be produced with the different metal species in the surface.   Iron inclusions in a copper surface, printed with ferrocyanide, for example, are rendered blue against the red copper ferrocyanide.

The other type of surface is presented by alloys.   From the electrographic standpoint, it differs essentially in that transfers made from it contain no areas where there is a single ionic species.   The usual problem is that of detecting, and sometimes roughly estimating, a component of the alloy, often a minor component.   Here a higher degree of specificity is required of the color reaction than in simple mapping of heterogeneous surfaces.   Interferences by the other components of the alloy must be eliminated.   Even when the reaction products with these components are light colored, they may hide the colored product of the metal under test, particularly if its concentration in the alloy is low.   Few color reactions are specific enough by themselves to identify one metal in the presence of those ordinarily associated in alloys.   Specificity is usually attained by preliminary treatments which remove the unwanted metals or by the inclusion of "masking" agents which tie up their ions, making them nonreactive.   Thus both copper and lead give black sulfides, but a small quantity of lead in brass may be printed on zinc sulfide paper if cyanide is added to the electrolyte to tie up the copper ions as the stable cuprocyanide complex.   A variation which avoids cyanide in the printing electrolyte employs a "latent" print, which is developed with a mixture of sodium sulfide and sodium cyanide.   "Masking" procedures become increasingly important when the color development depends on the formation of lakes as in the case of the reactions for aluminum, magnesium, and beryllium, with quinalizarine and other alizarine derivatives. Such reactions are not very specific, colored lakes being produced with Cu, Ni, Co, Fe, Zn, Pb, etc.

"Masking" agents function by forming stable complex ions or precipitates which lower the ion concentrations of the interfering metals below the threshold value required by the color reagent.   Often such agents may be used as the printing electrolyte or they may be added to the regular electrolyte, particularly in direct printing.   The high concentrations required, however, may render control of current density and voltage difficult, and undesirable anodic reactions may result.   Whenever possible, therefore, it is better to employ developed printing with masking applied before or at the time of color development. A full discussion of masking agents and their use will be found in Feigl's book "Specific and Special Reactions." Application of the principle of spot testing to the development of prints follows logically, with only minor changes in technique.

Sometimes interfering substances can be removed by rendering them soluble and washing the undeveloped print while the metal under test remains fixed. Even when masking agents are used, their continued presence in the print may hamper subsequent development and it is better to remove them by washing. Thus, there are many alloys of copper in which it may be required to identify such elements as aluminum, tin, lead, manganese, beryllium, zinc, and cadmium present in minor amounts. From sodium carbonate-nitrate prints, the copper may be washed out with cyanide leaving aluminum, tin, lead, manganese, and beryllium in the print as hydroxides, basic carbonates, or hydrated oxides, which can be developed readily. Zinc and cadmium can be fixed as sulfides by inclusion of sodium sulfide in the wash solution. Nickel can be revealed in iron specimens by printing with dimethylglyoxime paper in a sodium acetate electrolyte, then washing the iron out with dilute acetic acid.

The technique of developing and washing prints warrants some comment. Gelatin coated and sized papers must be handled much the same as in photography, with prolonged agitation in the reagent bath and washing in running water. The process is necessarily slow, since it depends entirely on diffusion to get the reagents in and out of the medium. However, the more complex development treatments are usually employed where emphasis is on identification and the use of unsized paper is permissible. Such prints can be developed and washed rapidly by drawing the reagents through the paper. A simple and effective washing arrangement consists of a large Büchner funnel, the perforated bottom of which is covered with one or two discs of blotting paper to distribute the suction evenly. The funnel delivers into a standard suction flask. The print is spread evenly on the moistened blotter pad, suction is applied, and the washing agent is added dropwise to the print surface without flooding it. If the blotter pad is kept moist by adding a few drops of water occasionally about its periphery, the suction through the print will be maintained very satisfactorily and treatment with reagents and washing can be completed in a matter of seconds. The method has the advantage of providing support for the print so that even relatively weak paper can be handled, and the flow of the fluids *through* the paper assures complete penetration and reaction without lateral diffusion.

4. APPLICATIONS

The remainder of this chapter will be devoted to brief descriptions of specific applications of the electrotransfer technique, chosen for their illustrative value. It is hoped that these examples may point the way to further applications to be found in everyday laboratory problems. The general principles already discussed should help to guide the analyst in his manipulative approach, while the selection of reagents and the elimination of interferences must necessarily be based on text books such as those of Feigl, and confirmed in the laboratory with known specimens.

The localized solution and transfer of surface materials from a specimen to an inert reaction medium without loss of distributive detail is undoubtedly the signal achievement of the electro-transfer process. On the other hand, the convenience of electrolytic solution should not be overlooked even when pattern reproduction is not an objective. In simple spot testing, the electro-transfer eliminates the tedious manipulations attending the use of acids and other dissolving agents. It provides perfectly controlled solution and concentration of the dissolved product in the spot-testing medium in a single manipulative operation, thus affording a means for carrying out very rapid identification tests. It may be desired to supplement such identification with approximate knowledge of distribution, particularly where spotty contamination of a surface is suspected. Such information can usually be obtained with sufficient accuracy from the simpler prints used for spot testing. Only where fine detail is to be recorded accurately does it become necessary to resort to more elaborate methods employing sized or gelatin papers and careful control of printing conditions. When emphasis is on identification, with printing an incidental objective, the term "Electro-Spot Testing" would seem more appropriate than "Electrography" which focuses attention on the pattern reproductive aspect of the electro-transfer process.

4.1. Electro-Spot Testing

4.1.1. Identification of Pure Metal Surfaces. Electro-spot testing has its simplest application to pure metal surfaces, where it is unnecessary to take into account the mutual interferences of alloy components. Various metallic coatings, electrodeposited or otherwise applied, provide practical examples of pure surfaces which frequently need to be identified. The electro-spot method is particularly useful in such testing because often the coating is so thin that only by carefully controlled solution can attack of the base metal be avoided.

The use of electro-spot testing is exemplified by the identification scheme in outline in Table IV. A single print of the unknown surface is prepared under the stated conditions. After preliminary examination, the print is divided into three parts, two of which are used for treatment with group reagents, while the third is used for final confirmatory tests. A box, $\boxed{\text{Me}}$ is placed around the metal at that point in the scheme where a colored product is sufficiently distinctive to justify conclusion of the presence of the metal (29).

4.1.2. Identification of Alloys. The identification of alloy components usually requires a more complex treatment of the print to avoid interferences. Occasionally single-step tests can be devised which are specific enough to permit direct printing. In the majority of cases, however, the masking treatments and indirect color reactions necessitate stepwise development. In the tables which follow (Tables V,A and V,B) an attempt has been made to list and to describe briefly, selected tests for alloy components of copper, iron, and aluminum base alloys. These examples should illustrate sufficiently the elimination of interferences and the application of the spot-testing principles of Feigl to the electro-transfer. The approach to other alloys would follow a similar plan.

Table V,A lists the alloys, their composition ranges, and the conditions for the electro-transfer. The details of the print development are given in Table V,B and are found by reference to the procedure index number given in the last column of Table V,A. In Table V,A, "Std. pad" is understood to consist of a top (printing) sheet of hardened paper, C.S. & S. #576, Wh #50, or C.S. & S. #507, with a soft thick backing paper such as C.S. & S. #601. Whenever an impregnated paper is listed, it is understood that it is used in conjunction with the backing paper. To avoid unnecessary repetition, the more frequently used electrolytes are numbered and their compositions are listed in Table V,C.

4.1.3. Identification of Anions. Analogous to the electro-transfer of metal surfaces by anodic oxidation is the cathodic reduction of certain *anions* of "insoluble" tarnish or corrosion films coating a metal surface. Sulfide films, for example, on silver or copper can be reduced and recorded as the brown-black lead sulfide on lead carbonate paper (see Table III). Such prints have been very useful in studying electrical contact performance in telephone circuits, where contamination may cause noise or signal failure. (See Fig. 10.)

Corrosion films may contain chloride or sulfate which are not detectable in a simple contact print because they are tied up as basic, insoluble

TABLE IV

Systematic Examination of a Single Print of a Pure Metal Surface for Cr, Fe, Cu, Ni, Ag, Pb, Sn, Cd and Zn.

PRINTING CONDITIONS

Electrolyte	Pad	Current density—25 ma./cm.[2]
0.5 M Na$_2$CO$_3$ 3 parts	C.S. & S. 575 (printing)	
0.5 M NaNO$_3$ 1 part	C.S. & S. 601 (backing)	Time—10 seconds

PRELIMINARY EXAMINATION OF THE PRINT
Hold print over concentrated ammonia until thoroughly permeated

STRONGLY COLORED PRINT		WEAKLY COLORED PRINT		COLORLESS PRINT
YELLOW	LIGHT BROWN	BLUE-GREEN	GRAY	
Cr	Fe	Cu Ni	Ag	Pb Sn Cd Zn
Clear yellow indicates CrO$_4$	Indicates Fe(OH)$_3$		(After exposure to light)	
Confirm, Diphenyl-carbazide	Confirm, Ferro-cyanide	If neither iron nor chromium are found, cut the print into three parts for further testing. Use parts I and II for group treatments, part III for confirmatory tests.		

P A R T I

a. Immerse in warm photographic developer such as Eastman D76. Wash well in 1% sodium carbonate, then water.
If result is negative, proceed with treatment b.

GRAY TO BLACK Ag
Confirm, dichromate

b. Immerse blotted print in 1% potassium ethylxanthate, 60 sec. Wash thoroughly and note color.
If results are negative, proceed with treatment, part II.

BRIGHT YELLOW   Cu
Confirm, a-benzoinoxime
ORANGE   Ni
Confirm, dimethylglyoxime

P A R T II

a. Immerse in soln. containing:
Na$_2$S 1 g.
NH$_4$ Acetate 2g. } in 100 ml. water.
Wash with 1% acetic acid and water (suction apparatus) until all sulfide is removed.

COLORLESS Zn Spot the print as directed in footnote.
YELLOW   Cd
BROWN   Sn } Apply treatment b.
BROWN-BLACK Pb

b. Immerse print suspected of containing Pb or Sn in soln.:
NaOH 5 g.
Na$_2$S 5 g. } water, 25 ml.
S 1 g.
Wash in suction apparatus with several small portions of above reagent, then with water.

BROWN COLOR HAS DISAPPEARED Sn
BROWN-BLACK REMAINS   Pb
Confirm, Iodide or chromate

Note: Zinc forms the only insoluble white sulfide. Hence if all soluble sulfide is removed by thorough washing with 1% acetic acid and then the print is spotted with 5% lead nitrate or 2% silver nitrate, the black sulfides of these metals will form at the expense of the more reactive zinc sulfide.

TABLE V,A

Electro-Spot Tests for Alloy Components. Composition and Printing Conditions

No.	Metal under test	Copper alloy composition ranges										Alloy class	Printing conditions				Proc. No. (Table V,B)
		Cu	Zn	Sn	Al	Pb	Mn	Ni	Fe	Bi	Be		Medium	Electrolyte	$I/\text{cm.}^{2a}$	t^b	
1	Al	90		*c	10	*c			*c	*c	*c	Aluminum Bronzes, Ampco Metal	Std. pad	"A"	20–25	60	1
2	Fe	88/96			8/10				1/10				Std. pad	"A"	20–30	60–120	2
3	Mn	70/95				□d	4/25	0/12				Manganese Bronzes, Manganin	Std. pad	"B"	20–25	60	3
4	Ni	..						..					Dimethylglyoxime paper	"A"	20–25	30–60	4
5	Al	..	0/27	*c	0/3	*c	0/1.5	18/40	*c	*c	*c	Nickel Coinage, Nickel-Silver, Constantan, Typewriter Metal, etc.	Std. pad	"A"	20–25	30–60	5
6	Mn	..	..	..	..	□d	..	..					Std. Pad	"B"	20–25	60	3
7	Ni	..	..	..	..		..	..					Dimethylglyoxime paper	"A"	20–25	60	4
8	Zn	..	..	..	..	*c				*			Std. pad	"A"	15–20	30	6
9	Zn	50/96	1/40	1/33	..	1/3			tr 0.2			Brasses and Bronzes	Std. pad	"A"	15–20	30	6
10	Sn	..	..	..	..	..			..				1) C.S. & S. #576 veil 2) Phosphomolybdate paper	0.5 M NaNO₃	15–20	60	7
11	Pb	..	..	..	..	..			..				Std. pad	"A"	15–20	60	8
12	Fe	..	..	..	..	..			..				Std. pad	"A"	20–30	60–120	2
13	Be	90/95		*c	*c	*c				*c	5/10	Copper Beryllium	Std. pad	"A"	20–25	60	9

TABLE V,A.—(Continued)

Iron alloy composition ranges (rows 14–16)

No.	Metal under test	Fe	Ni	Cr	Mn	Cu	Mo	Alloy class	Medium	Electrolyte	I/cm.²ᵃ	tᵇ	Proc. No. (Table V,B)
14	Cr	60/89	0.5/25	10/30	0/1	0/1	0/1	Alloy Steels	Std. pad	"C"	15	30–60	10
15	Ni	"	"	"	"	"	"		1) C.S. & S. #576 top 2) Dimethylglyoxime paper	"C"	15	60	10A
16	Cu	"	"	"	"	"	"		Cadmium diethyldithio- carbamate paper	"D"	20	60–120	11

Aluminum alloy composition ranges (rows 17–20)

No.	Metal under test	Al	Cu	Fe	Mn	Zn	Mg	Si	Alloy class	Medium	Electrolyte	I/cm.²ᵃ	tᵇ	Proc. No. (Table V,B)
17	Cu	97/70	0/14	0/1.5	0/1.5	0/30	0/30	0/5	Aluminum Alloys	Cadmium diethyldithio- carbamate paper	"D"	20	60	11
18	Fe	"	"	"	"	"	"	"		Std. pad	"A"	20–30	60–120	2
19	Mn	"	"	"	"	"	"	"		"	"A"	15	60	3
20	Zn	"	"	"	"	"	"	"		"	"A"	15–20	60	6

ᵃ I/cm.², Current density, in ma./sq. cm.
ᵇ t, Time, in seconds.
ᶜ * Indicates interfering metals not normally present.
ᵈ □ Indicates interfering metals removed by "masking" procedure.

TABLE V,B
Development Procedure

Proc. No.		Print development steps	Interpretation
1	A.	*Immerse* 1 M KCN + 1% aq. NH_3	*Aluminum* indicated by bright red color with alizarine or brilliant yellow-green fluorescence under U.V. with morin.
	B.	*Wash* (suction apparatus) water.	
	C.	Suck dry and add dropwise to print on pad with suction continued: 1) Alizarine, sat. soln. in 50% alcohol, 5% aq. NH_3 or 2) Morin sat. soln. in 50% alcohol, 5% aq. NH_3.	
	D.	*Wash,* 50% alcohol and dilute NH_3	
2	A.	*Wash* (suction apparatus) with 5% NH_3 + 5% KNO_3, until blue color of cupric ion has *entirely* disappeared from print. Follow by water wash.	*Iron* is indicated by the blue color of ferric ferrocyanide (Prussian blue).
	B.	Continue suction and add dropwise to the print $K_4Fe(CN)_6$ + 5% acetic acid. Wash with water.	
	Note	A pinkish color indicates incomplete removal of copper by the above washing procedure. If iron is 1% or more, this may usually be discounted, particularly if a red filter is used to view the print. If the results are doubtful, the printing should be repeated and a more complete washing made.	
3	A.	*Immerse* 1 M KCN + 1% aq. NH_3.	*Manganese* is indicated by green-blue benzidine oxidation product changing slowly to yellow-brown. *Lead* reaction is suppressed by the formation of sulfate.
	B.	*Wash* 1% ammonia (suction apparatus).	
	C.	Add, dropwise to print on suction pad, 5% H_2O_2 (dilute superoxol). Draw several additions through, finally wash with water and suck dry.	
	D.	*Immerse* 1% benzidine acetate aq soln.	
4	A.	*Wash* dimethylglyoxime print with 0.2 M NH_4Cl + 10% aq. NH_3 to remove Cu and Mn.	*Nickel* is indicated by the red dimethylglyoxime complex.

TABLE V,B.—(Continued)

Proc. No.		Print development steps	Interpretation
5	A.	*Wash* undeveloped print in suction apparatus with 0.5 M NH$_4$Cl-0.5 M KCN solution with 10% aq. NH$_3$ added. Finish with water. Suck dry.	*Aluminum* is indicated by bright red color with alizarine or yellow-green fluorescence under U.V. with morin.
	B.	Immerse in alizarine or morin as in procedure No. 1.	
6	A.	*Immerse* 1 M KCN + 1 M. Na$_2$S (freshly prepared) agitate 2–3 minutes.	If no interfering elements such as *lead* or *bismuth* are present and the washings are properly made the print should bleach to a white. Small amounts of lead will give an off-white to yellowish brown. *Tin* is still detectable if spotting is used so that the increase in color can be noticed. *Zinc* is indicated by brown spot or increased color developing on the bleached original print area.
	B.	*Wash* in suction apparatus with the following, in order 1) 0.25 M KCN + 0.25 M NH$_4$Cl + 5% aq. NH$_3$. 2) Na$_2$Sx, 5% (to remove Sn) 3) Water 4) Acetic acid, 2%. Suck dry.	
	C.	*Blot and immerse* in 0.5 M Pb(C$_2$H$_3$O$_2$)$_2$ (or use spotting or streaking technique if a residual color is obtained.	
7	Note	A top veiling sheet of plain #576 paper is used to prevent contact of the phosphomolybdate paper with the metal surface. (All metals above Ag in the electromotive series will reduce this paper to the blue.) In this way only *stannous* ions can effect the reduction. The paper is light sensitive and should be freshly prepared and preserved away from light and metal contact.	*Stannous tin* is indicated by the blue color formed by the reduction of the phosphomolybdate, the veil protecting against contact reduction. The excess phosphomolybdate is removed by dissolving in dilute alkali giving a light-stable print.
	A.	Preparation of paper Soln. No. 1: Dissolve 5 g. ammonium phosphomolybdate in 100 cc. water with the aid of ammonia. Impregnate paper with soln. No. 1; dry. Soln. No. 2: 5% HNO$_3$. Immerse paper in soln. No. 2 in dark room. Wash thoroughly with water. Dry in darkness. Preserve under compression out of light.	
	B.	*Immerse* print in 2% KOH until yellow background color is bleached. Wash with water.	

TABLE V,B.—(*Continued*)

Proc. No.		Print development steps	Interpretation
8	A.	*Immerse* the print in 0.2 M $K_2Cr_2O_7$ + 5% acetic acid, with agitation, 2–3 minutes.	*Lead* is indicated by the yellow color of lead chromate not removed by the acetic acid washing.
	B.	*Wash* on suction pad, 5% acetic acid, until all color of dichromate is gone from area outside print.	
9	A.	*Immerse* the undeveloped print in 1 M KCN until the blue-green copper color has disappeared.	*Beryllium* is indicated by the lavender color of its alizarine lake which persists on washing print with ammonia.
	B.	*Wash* with water in suction apparatus. Follow by dropwise treatment with sat. alizarine soln. in 50% alcohol on suction pad, sucking through paper each time.	
	C.	*Wash* with dilute NH_3 until background color is reduced sufficiently to permit recognition of beryllium lake.	
10	A.	*Wash* the direct print with water in suction apparatus to remove reddish-colored ferric acetate.	*Chromium* is indicated by a yellow color of $BaCrO_4$
10A	Note	The simultaneous detection of chromium and nickel can be effected by the use of two papers in the sandwich. The one in contact with the specimen removes the chromate ion as the yellow $BaCrO_4$, proc. No. 10, but allows Fe + Ni to pass through to the next paper which is impregnated with dimethylgloxime. Here Ni is precipitated as the red complex.	*Chromium* is indicated as in No. 10, by a yellow color on the top print. *Nickel* is indicated by a red color on the second print.
	A.	Prepare the printing pad as follows: Immerse the dimethylglyoxime paper and the backing paper in the barium acetate and blot fairly dry. Place on the cathode plate. Then immerse and blot the top printing paper and place on the pad. Print immediately. This sequence prevents excessive solution and diffusion of the dimethylglyoxime into the top sheet.	
	B.	Separate the printing sheets and wash with water in suction apparatus.	

TABLE V,B.—(*Continued*)

Proc. No.		Print development steps	Interpretation
11	A.	*Wash* on suction apparatus alternately with water and 0.25 M NaK tartrate until color is no longer lost.	Light-brown color indicates *copper*.
	N o t e	Copper down to 0.3–0.1 % detectable by above. For lower concentrations, etch the metal in 10% HCl 15–30 minutes, wash, and blot dry without rubbing. This concentrates alloyed copper on the surface, increasing the sensitivity. 0.05% Cu can then be detected.	

TABLE V,C

Electrolyte Compositions

Designation	Components	Parts	Principal uses
"A"	0.5 M Sodium carbonate 0.5 M Sodium nitrate	3 1	General "fixing" electrolyte for "latent" prints.
"B"	0.5 M Sodium carbonate 0.5 M Sodium sulfate	2 1	General "fixing" electrolyte when lead interference is to be eliminated.
"C"	0.5 M Barium acetate		Solution of ferrous alloys and fixation of chromate ion
"D"	0.5 M Sodium potassium tartrate		Solution of ferrous alloys where iron reactions are to be masked.

products.   Electrolytic reduction may be employed to free such ions, permitting them to be recorded as prints on silver chromate and barium rhodizonate papers respectively.   In this technique, a protective "veiling" sheet between the specimen surface and the reagent paper avoids undesirable reactions and other effects which may follow direct physical contact with the cathode.

For successful cathodic reduction, films must be thin enough to permit the passage of ions.   Some sulfides, particularly the sulfide of silver, are sufficiently conducting to permit electrography of mass specimens such

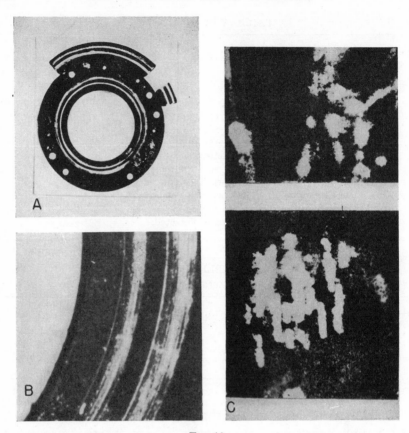

Fig. 10

A. Electrograph of sulfide on silver contact cam by cathodic reduction on lead carbonate paper.

    E. K. Co. imbibition paper, soaked 10 minutes in 0.5 M lead acetate, dried and soaked 10 minutes in 1 M sodium carbonate.

    4.5 volts, 120 seconds, 200 lb./sq. in.

B. Magnified section of print A, showing detail in brush track. (×10)

C. Electrographs of sulfate corrosion on bronze plate.

    Pad: 1. C.S. & S. #575 veiling sheet

        2. Barium rhodizonate paper (C.S. & S. #575)

        3. C.S. & S. #601 backing sheet

    Electrolyte: 0.2 M NaCl

        60 seconds, 10 ma./cm.^{2}, aluminum anode

    Photographed with green filter to give greater contrast.

TABLE VI

Anions

Anion	Printing conditions				Interpretation
	Printing pad	Electrolyte	$I/cm.^2$	t	
Sulfide	1) Lead carbonate paper 2) Backing sheet (601)	$0.5\ M\ Na_2CO_3$	15 to 25	10 to 60	*Sulfide* is registered as PbS, brown to black, according to density of film.
	— or — E. K. imbibition paper	$0.5\ M\ Pb(C_2H_3O_2)_2 +$ $1\ M\ Na_2CO_3$	5	30 to 120	See Note 1, below.
Chloride (halogens)	1) Veiling sheet (575) 2) Silver chromate paper 3) Backing sheet	$0.5\ M\ Mg(C_2H_3O_2)_2$	5 to 10	10 to 60	*Chloride* (or halogens) is indicated by a bleaching of red silver chromate paper. See Note 2, below.
Sulfate	1) Veiling sheet (575) 2) Barium rhodozonate paper 3) Backing sheet	$0.5\ M\ NH_4C_2H_3O_2$	10 to 20	60 to 120	*Sulfate* is indicated by bleaching of red barium rhodozonate paper. See Note 3, below.

Note 1: Sulfide. Gelatin papers should be soaked 10 minutes in the lead acetate, blotted, and completely dried and then immersed in the sodium carbonate for the same length of time. Use of a carbonate solution of twice the lead molarity insures complete precipitation of the latter and provides the necessary free salt for the electrolyte. Good prints are obtained in 30 seconds with the current-density given. If estimates of film density are desired, it must be reduced completely and sufficient time must be allowed for this.

Note 2: Chloride. A "veiling" sheet of paper is placed between the specimen surface and the silver chromate paper to prevent cathodic reduction of the silver chromate to metallic silver. Magnesium acetate is used as electrolyte to buffer the hydroxyl ion at the cathode. High alkalinity would decompose the silver chromate.

Note 3: Sulfate. A "veiling" sheet protects the print against the adhesion of sponge metal, dust, etc., which might mask the bleaching of the barium rhodozonate. Ammonium acetate as electrolyte prevents excess alkalinity at the cathode, which tends to bleach the barium rhodozonate.

as ore minerals. Table VI summarizes the conditions for anion printing (29).

4.2. Electrography—The Recording of Distributive Patterns

Whenever an electrolytically soluble surface contains areas which differ either in the kind or quantity of ions yielded under a given impressed potential, it would seem reasonable to expect that prints may be obtained reproducing such areas. An alloy may consist of a solid solution, but more commonly it contains two or more distinct phases comprising units whose size, separation, and arrangement determines the structure of the specimen. On anodic dissolution, these structural units may each yield a different cation, producing contrasting colors in the final reaction products in the print. On the other hand, a common cation might be yielded by all of the phases but, because of composition differences, the quantity of that cation might vary, producing varying densities of a single color in the final print, corresponding to the different surface units. The yield of a cation may be further influenced by differences in the solution potential of the structural units. Often small changes in composition produce significant differences of potential. This is typified by the components of steel. With low current densities, when the over-all potential drop between the specimen surface and the electrolyte does not greatly exceed that between the individual phases, these phase potential differences will exert a controlling influence over the yield of the common ion, the greater part of the electrical energy being then used to drive this ion from the more anodic areas. Even in a single phase alloy, a section may show potential differences between its crystal units because of the different orientations of their lattices. Here the close relationship between electrography and metallographic etching should be apparent. Both depend on a nonuniform rate of solution governed by differences in composition, solution potential, and crystal orientation of the structural units.

In electrography there are, of course, practical limitations which may not be present in differential etching of the original specimen. The fineness of printable detail is limited by control of lateral diffusion and the background structure of the printing medium. Suitable color reactions must be available for the cations involved.

4.3. Special Applications

4.3.1. Structure of Steel. In 1929, Glazunov (19) published the first account of the electrographic method as applied to the study of the macrostructure of iron and steel. He used potassium ferrocyanide as electrolyte and color reagent and obtained prints which recorded macrostructural features in varying densities of the blue iron ferrocyanide. In these prints, the behavior of a ferrous specimen parallels generally that observed in its metallography. Areas which are most readily affected by etching reagents also dissolve most readily when made anodic to a ferrocyanide electrolyte, yielding the deepest colors. This is illustrated in Fig. 11. Magnetic iron, largely ferrite, and a pearlitic steel were clamped together to form a single electrographic specimen, polished and printed with an impressed potential of 1.4 volts. The pearlitic area, which normally etches rapidly, printed a deep blue, while the ferrite, which etches slowly gave only a spotty pattern, due largely to impurities. Nonmetallic inclusions such as slag or separated graphite naturally would yield no color. Ammermann (1), as well as Jimeno, Bernal, and Ibarz (35) call attention to the fact that the solution potential is also influenced by conditions of strain. Thus a cold worked surface is rendered more electropositive and will render as a deeper blue in the electrograph.

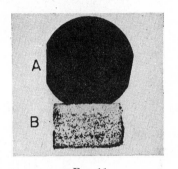

Fig. 11
(Enlarged 2 ×)
A. Pearlitic steel.
B. Magnetic iron.
Specimens are bolted together, mounted, and polished. Printed with 0.1 M potassium ferrocyanide at 1.4 volts.
Pearlitic surface shows more rapid solution with correspondingly denser print.
The specimen was prepared by Mr. F. G. Foster of Bell Telephone Laboratories.

With specimens of cast iron and processed steels, Glazunov (19–21, 22, 25, 26), Ammermann (1), Hruska (34), and Jimeno, Bernal, and Ibarz (35) have obtained electrographs which give clear tracing of such gross structural irregularities as slag inclusions, blow holes, piped conditions, fibrosity, and flow structure, and in general, all the features observed in macrographic examinations. Jimeno, Bernal, and Ibarz also report the successful application of electrography to alloy steels, especially to chrome-nickel steels which are otherwise difficult to study because of their resistance to chemical etching agents. For an excellent account of the method and a series of reproductions of electrographs, the reader is referred to the original paper (35).

Glazunov's prints were made on unsized paper, moistened in the ferrocyanide and applied to the specimen surface with a rubber roller to exclude air bubbles. The cathode was an aluminum or a stainless steel plate and a potential between 1 and 2 volts was impressed for from 15 seconds to several minutes. Ammermann as well as Jimeno, Bernal, and

FIG. 12.   Ferrous electrograph (enlarged 5×).
Steel specimen, etched with iodine-potassium iodide, 30 seconds; printed E. K. Co.
imbibition paper, 0.1 M potassium ferrocyanide; developed H_2O_2.
1.5 volts, 15 millicoulombs/sq. cm.
Shows dendrite structure.

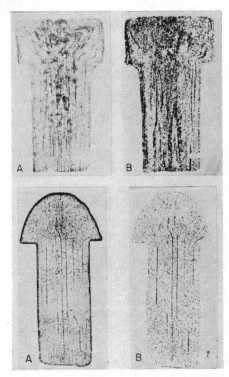

FIG. 13.   Ferrous electrographs.
Upper.   Bolt, longitudinal section, 2×
Lower.   Rivet, longitudinal section

A. No etching
B. Etched 20 seconds, iodine-potassium iodide
    E. K. Co. imbibition paper (gelatin), 0.1 M potassium ferrocyanide; developed,
    H_2O_2
    1.5 volts, 15 millicoulombs/sq. cm., aluminum cathode

Ibarz point out that detail is necessarily limited to gross structures in Glazunov's prints because of the coarse background structure of filter paper and the excessive diffusion attending its use. Ammermann favored a lightly sized, fine grained drawing paper while Jimeno, Bernal, and Ibarz preferred a sized visiting card material. The latter workers also make mention of a gelatin coated paper, then supplied by the German firm of Bayer.

Glazunov does not mention the strength of the electrolyte but states that an "aged" ferrocyanide solution, or one to which a few drops of peroxide have been added gives more satisfactory results. Thus he indicates a need for ferricyanide ions in addition to the ferrocyanide. Ammermann (1), commenting on Glazunov's work, noted that prints made with ferrocyanide are initially weak and develop their color largely after printing, through oxidation in the wash water. He states that equally good prints are obtainable with ferricyanide alone. On the other hand, Hruska (34), and Jimeno, Bernal, and Ibarz (35) use potassium ferrocyanide containing no ferricyanide. The latter workers maintain that this is superior to ferricyanide-containing electrolytes because the more electropositive areas are likely to yield ferric ions which would not print with ferricyanide. It should be noted, however, that they used higher voltages than Glazunov (2V–4V), a condition favorable to the production of ferric ions.

These conflicting views indicate the need for further study of the iron printing reactions. The writers have observed that prints made with ferrocyanide electrolyte at low current densities are likely to be quite faint but are oxidizable to full intensity with peroxide, dichromate, or more slowly, by exposure to air. Immersion in ferricyanide also brings up the blue color. This would indicate that the bulk of the iron dissolves as the ferrous ion and is probably fixed as the nearly colorless ferrous ferrocyanide, oxidizable to blue ferric ferrocyanide or reactive to ferricyanide to form blue ferrous ferrocyanide. On this basis, one might be inclined to use ferricyanide in the electrolyte to provide immediate conversion of the ferrous ions to the blue ferrous ferrocyanide, but when this was tried, it was found that the patterns were not always reproducible and differentiation between unlike areas was less pronounced than with ferrocyanide alone. This was traced to the fact that ferricyanide reacts fairly rapidly with iron *without* the aid of anodic solution, oxidizing it to ferrous ions which precipitate as ferrous ferrocyanide. Part of the ferricyanide is reduced to ferrocyanide in this reaction. Thus it is possible to make simple contact prints with ferricyanide, capable of yielding considerable structural detail in which differentiation follows from the varying oxidizibility of the surface components. For electrographic purposes, however, the oxidizing action of ferricyanide is undesirable in that it superposes a chemical attack on the anodic process, thus interfering with the purely electrical control of solution. The best results were obtained using pure ferrocyanide at low current densities and developing the resulting pale print in very weak peroxide.

For macrography, it is generally agreed that it is unnecessary to give the specimen a high polish. Finishing on #400 aloxite paper followed by crocus cloth or the equivalent is usually sufficient. It should be pointed out that polishing tends to leave a thin amorphous layer on the surface of a specimen which usually masks its structure and must be removed by etching before macrographic examination can be made. In electrography, such layers would constitute an equipotential surface and, if sufficiently thick, might easily mask the potential differences of the underlying grains, thus yielding a structureless, solid color print. It is well, therefore, to compare prints made on the polished surface with those made on the same surface after etching. The amount of etching required to give the best electrograph of its macrostructure must be determined experimentally for each material. Some steels electrograph best after an extremely light etch, the prints becoming contrasty and losing detail rapidly as the etching becomes deeper. Others yield structure patterns only after intense treatment with etchants. Etching agents which tend to leave a patina should be avoided and in any case, the surface of the specimen should be thoroughly swabbed with cotton in running water before printing. Iodine-potassium iodide, 5% nitric acid in alcoholic solution, or electrolytic etching are suggested.

Summary of Conditions for Electrographs of Ferrous Macrostructure

Preparation of specimen: Finish on #400 Aloxite paper, followed with crocus cloth. Etch, if desired, with iodine-potassium iodide or 5% alcoholic nitric acid. Swab surface with cotton in running water and print immediately.

Printing medium: Eastman Kodak imbibition paper, immersed at least 10 minutes in the electrolyte.

Electrolyte: 0.1 M Potassium ferrocyanide.

Cathode: Aluminum.

Pressure: 25–50 lb./sq. in.

Current density: 0.5–1.0 ma./cm.² $\Big\}$ To pass 10 to 15 millicoulombs/cm.²
Time: 10–30 seconds

Development: Immerse print for 1 minute in 1 ml. superoxol/100 ml. water wash.

General: Place paper without blotting on the cathode surface so that a pool of the electrolyte remains on its surface. Wet the specimen with the electrolyte and lower onto the paper by pivoting about one edge so as to squeeze out air bubbles. Apply pressure immediately and take up the excess electrolyte around the specimen with blotting paper. Print, develop, and wash in running water for 10 minutes.

4.3.2. Structure of Nonferrous Metals. Ferrous metals have received by far the greatest attention in the applications of electrography to structure printing. However, Glazunov states he has prepared macrographs of zinc structure with potassium ferrocyanide and crystal violet. Precipitation of the white zinc ferrocyanide in the unsized printing paper is accompanied by fixation of the dye in that area so that on washing a print is obtained (26). Glazunov also records silver structure by printing with dichromate, and nickel with dimethylglyoxime. He prepared copper macrographs with ferrocyanide, but Ammermann (1) claims difficulty with the method when used to print copper oxide inclusions.

The writers have used ferrocyanide prints to record the distribution of copper and iron in aluminum base die castings. The specimen is first given an etching for several minutes in a 10% caustic bath and then scrubbed in running water to remove the dark, spongey metal which collects on its surface. It is printed on gelatin paper soaked in 1 part of 0.5 M sodium nitrate to three parts of 0.1 M potassium ferrocyanide. The print is intensified by development in 0.1 M potassium ferricyanide and finally washed. Printing is done at 4 volts (aluminum cathode), 15–30 seconds.

Preliminary work has shown some promise in the printing of macrostructures in brasses and other copper alloys with antimony, cadmium, or zinc sulfide impregnated gelatin papers. 0.5 M Ammonium acetate is used with 1.5–3.0 volts, against a carbon cathode.

4.3.3. Surfaces. Quite aside from heterogeneities of the mass structure, the surfaces of metal specimens may exhibit composition irregularities, acquired as a result of initial processing or exposure to operational conditions. Often the surface purity of a material will determine its suitability for a given use. Thus an aluminum foil to be used in an electrical condenser is affected adversely by traces of iron or other metals rolled into its surface during manufacture. The corrodibility of many metal surfaces is markedly increased by accidental inclusion of particles of more negative metals. On the other hand, contamination need not necessarily occur during manufacture. Mechanical failure, particularly where sliding surfaces are concerned, may result from the introduction of traces of foreign metals as dusts or filings which cause seizure and "freezing." Electrographic methods are especially useful in the identification and mapping of such contaminants, where the extreme superficiality of a transferred film or particle precludes application of mechanical sampling.

For corrosion protection or to provide desirable mechanical properties, surfaces may receive thin coatings of other metals, applied by electroplating, hot-dipping, or by other methods. Organic protective coatings likewise may be applied. The initial continuity of such coatings as well as their stability toward corrosive agents, their resistance to wear, etc., can often be evaluated quickly and conveniently by electrographic methods.

A complete discussion of the application of electrography to surface studies here is impossible, but it is hoped that the inclusion of several selected examples will suffice to illustrate the general approach.

Inclusions: Iron and copper inclusions in aluminum, magnesium, zinc, or nickel surfaces are registered readily by printing with a 0.5 M ammonium acetate electrolyte on gelatin paper and developing in ferrocyanide. A current density should be employed which is sufficient to polarize the specimen surface above the couple potential of the more negative inclusion (see p. 178, also Hunter, Churchill, and Mears, 33). With aluminum or zinc, a faint blue background may be obtained due to alloyed iron. Against this, particulate iron or copper will appear as the deep blue or red ferrocyanides. A nickel surface will give the apple green color of its ferrocyanide but iron and copper will contrast sufficiently against this unless they are present in only the faintest traces. When the quantity of copper is extremely minute, a more sensitive developing reagent is diethyldithiocarbamate, used in 1% solution of the sodium or ammonium salt. For copper on an iron surface, 1% diethyldithiocarbamate in 0.5 M sodium potassium tartrate, made ammoniacal with 2% concentrated ammonium hydroxide is used.

Iron on a copper surface is not registered by direct printing because the red copper ferrocyanide would mask any faint blue iron patterns. In this case, a print is made on unsized paper with a basic nonreactive electrolyte, (Table V,C, electrolyte "A"), the copper being washed out with ammonia before developing for iron with ferrocyanide. (See Tables V,A, Test No. 2, and V,B, Proc. No. 2.) For a further discussion of inclusions in electrography, see Hunter, Churchill, and Mears, (33).

Frictional transfer: Through frictional contact or impact, metal may be transferred from one surface to another. Development of the resulting pattern may reveal the nature of the action involved. Such information often has diagnostic, and possibly criminological value. Thus it might be important to learn whether or not a certain axe was used to sever a cable. An electrographic print made on the steel blade reproduced the pattern of the frictionally transferred copper, providing strong circumstantial evidence. (See Fig. 14.)

Mechanical transfer also may occur between sliding surfaces. The study of such transfer may yield valuable information concerning wear and the type of lubrication required. The authors have used prints to demonstrate transfer from a wiping silver contact to a fixed brass surface when both are protected from atmospheric tarnish by a lubricant.

Prints were made with 0.5 M NaNO₃, then developed for silver with photographic developer. Bowden (4), in his studies of sliding friction has used electrography to record transfer from a copper slider to a steel plate under dry and lubricated operation. He employed a gelatin coated

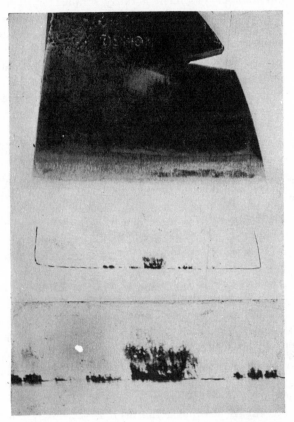

FIG. 14. Hatchet blade used to cut copper cable, with electrograph of transferred copper.
Printing: 0.5 M sodium potassium tartrate with 1% sodium diethyldithiocarbamate
20 seconds, 3 volts, aluminum cathode

paper (electrolyte not stated) and developed the print for copper with dithioxamide.

The porosity and discontinuities of protective coatings: The detection and mapping of discontinuities in metallic or organic coatings can be accomplished electrographically whenever the base metal is electrolytically soluble and capable of entering into suitable color reactions. The precise control of the solution rate and the reduction of diffusion gives the electrographic method definite superiority over chemical printing in this field.

When the coating is an organic finish or a noble metal, selection of the electrolyte and color development is fairly simple, for then no problem is presented by solution of the coating itself during electrolysis. When the protective coating is soluble, however, the choice becomes more critical. If possible, the electrolyte should exert a selective action, favoring the solution of the base metal while retarding solution of the coating. Solution of the coating sometimes may be retarded by employing an electrolyte which forms an insoluble, protective film or induces a passive condition. When this is not possible, the total metal taken into solution may be reduced to a negligible quantity through employment of sensitive color reactions requiring a minimum of the base metal. With indicators such as ferrocyanide for iron or diethyldithiocarbamate for copper, the quantity needed is so small that the danger of creating further pores is practically eliminated for all but the thinnest coatings. As an example, it was found by the authors that 0.5 μg. iron/sq. mm. is the minimum quantity needed to give a deep blue color discernible with certainty when viewed on pin-point areas. This would be about 0.3 mg./sq. in. of iron, or about .35 mg. zinc. On a zinc coated steel specimen, because of the 0.3 volt potential difference between Zn and Fe, solution of the two metals will not proceed at the same rate. In practice, two to three times the zinc equivalent of the iron may be removed, yet a porosity print could be obtained with solution of about 1 mg./sq. in. Commercial coatings range from 10 to 200 mg./sq. in., hence the metal dissolved would amount to 0.5–10% of the coating thickness.

Since the discontinuities of the coating usually consist of pinholes or fine scratches, the importance of securing intimate contact with the printing medium cannot be overemphasized. Lateral diffusion must be prevented as far as possible if the print is to convey information as to the size and shape of the breaks in the coating. The writers have found that these conditions are best met by using high contact pressures obtained with a hydraulic press, (see p. 167) and a relatively dry printing medium. After soaking in the electrolyte, the printing pad is sandwiched between larger pieces of blotting material and pressed for a few seconds at about half the printing pressure. For gelatin papers, 500–1000 lb./sq. in. is a satisfactory pressure, while for unsized papers it can be made considerably higher, up to 2500 lb./sq. in. Some caution is necessary in using these high pressures lest the pores be closed when the coating is a paint film or other organic material subject to plastic flow, and in such cases, experimentation is advisable. In general, however, the high pressure technique is desirable. since then the electrolyte and even the printing substance is forced into the smallest pores and the reaction product is so confined that lateral diffusion is greatly retarded.

The use of gelatin paper has been generally recommended to obtain the least diffusion of reaction product and hence the most detailed reproduction. In porosity testing, however, there may be instances where the use of unsized paper with the attending diffusion has merit. Pinholes may be so small that their recognition on gelatin paper requires magnification. For research purposes, this may be advantageous but in practical testing it may be desirable to obtain enough amplification of the original pore by diffusion on the print to make its recognition easy to the unaided eye. In such cases, the use of a hardened, unsized paper such as C.S. & S. #575 will provide the desired "bleeding." They are, of course, easier and cheaper to prepare than the gelatin prints.

Tin on iron: For the porosity of tin plate, a mixture of equal parts of 0.1 M potassium ferro- and ferricyanides and 0.5 M sodium acetate is a suitable electrolyte reagent (29). Without the acetate, the iron ferrocyanide reaction products tend to precipitate in the pores, clogging them and giving faint or blank prints. At about 3 volts, a flow of about 50 millicoulombs/sq. in. gives a satisfactory density of the blue iron color with negligible diffusion. This would correspond to the solution of about .03 mg./sq. in. of tin, or about .0004 mils thickness.

Tin on copper base alloys: Tin develops considerable passivity toward an electrolyte composed of 1% sodium diethyldithiocarbamate plus 2% concentrated ammonium hydroxide. At the same time, solution of copper is facilitated and its detection by this reagent is among the most sensitive tests known. Gelatin coated paper must be used, however, because of the tendency for the colored product to "bleed." At 3 volts, printing for 20 seconds produces ample density. The current, in a series of experiments, averaged about 100 millicoulombs/sq. in., corresponding to solution of about .06 mg. tin/sq. in. (29).

Chromium plating: Chromium plating is usually quite thin and it therefore becomes the more desirable to dissolve as little as possible in the production of porosity prints. When the impressed voltage is over 2, chromium dissolves rapidly with oxidation to the chromate ion. If the voltage does not exceed 1.5, however, in an electrolyte such as ammonium acetate, oxidation apparently does not proceed beyond the trivalent stage and is accompanied by the rapid formation of a passive oxide film which effectively blocks any transfer of the coating to the printing medium. Iron, nickel, and copper exposed through pores or scratches in the chromium may be printed successfully at 1.5 volts if sufficient time is allowed. Passivity is so complete that current measurements under these conditions will have little significance since the flow is determined largely by the number and size of the breaks in the coating rather than the total printed specimen area. The printing time is best determined experimentally on specimens of the pure base metals at 1.5 volts with the same printing pad and pressure as used on the specimen. Gelatin paper works well with 0.5 M ammonium acetate, followed by development with ferrocyanide, diethyldithiocarbamate or dimethylglyoxime for iron, copper, or nickel respectively (29).

Lead coatings: The porosity printing of lead-clad steel affords a good example of retarded solution of the coating through the selection of an electrolyte which forms a thin, insoluble layer on it. At low voltages lead is oxidized only to the divalent ion. When the electrolyte contains sulfate ions, a protective layer of lead sulfate quickly forms and further solution becomes negligible. Solution of iron, copper, and most other base metals through imperfections and pores remains unhampered. Above 3.5 volts, (aluminum cathode) however, lead is oxidized to the tetravalent state with formation of nonprotective peroxide. Figure 15A shows the behavior of pure lead and iron specimens toward sulfate and nitrate electrolytes. Curve I illustrates the almost uniform high rate of solution of lead in nitrate while curve II shows the very rapid sealing off of the surface, with very little current flow after 5 seconds. Curve III, on the other hand shows the uninhibited solution of lead in the sulphate electrolyte when the voltage is raised to 4. Curves IV and V depict the behavior of iron toward these same electrolytes. It is quite evident that the sulfate, while facilitating the solution of the iron, protects the lead from being dissolved.

For direct printing, the authors have used an electrolyte composed of 0.5 M sodium sulfate, 1 part; 0.1 M potassium ferricyanide, $\frac{1}{2}$ part; 0.1 M potassium ferrocyanide, $\frac{1}{2}$ part. This solution works well for both copper and iron bases. The voltage is held at 3 or below and the time ranges from 10 to 60 seconds, depending on the pad used. Gelatin paper at 500 lb./sq. in. gives excellent detail. Figure 15B shows the behavior of lead and iron toward the mixed electrolyte, which is essentially the same as toward sulfate alone.

Further applications of electrography to porosity testing of metallic coatings are given in the tabular summary (p. 214). In the opinion of the authors, several of the published methods fail to take full advantage of the employment of sensitive reagents as well as controlled and selective solution in minimizing attack of the coating.

Organic finishes: Since organic coatings are nonconducting and chemically inert, the recording of pores and breaks can be accomplished with almost any electrographic printing technique suited to the base

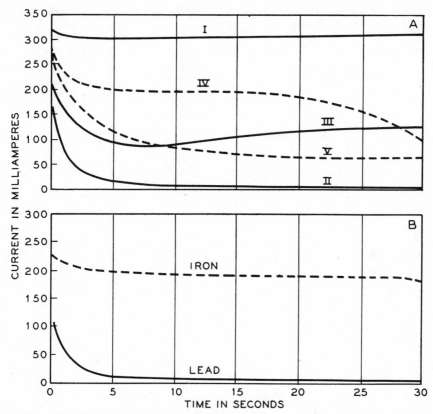

Fig. 15.   The behavior of lead and iron specimens toward various electrolytes. Pure metals, 1-inch square, aluminum cathode plate, printing pad C.S. & S. #575 and #601.

A: I—Lead, 3 volts, 0.5 M sodium nitrate
    II—Lead 3 volts, 0.5 M sodium sulfate
    III—Lead 4 volts, 0.5 M sodium sulfate
    IV—Iron, 3 volts, 0.5 M sodium sulfate
    V—Iron 3 volts, 0.5 M sodium nitrate
B: Iron, 3 volts, ferro- ferricyanide-sulfate
   Lead, 3 volts, ferro- ferricyanide-sulfate

metal.   Glazunov (24) used printing with ferrocyanide to detect faults in varnish films on iron.   He compared chemical contact printing with the electrographic method and points out the greater sensitivity and sharpness obtained by the latter technique.   Shaw and Moore (43) have described the application of electrography to the testing of paint and other protective coatings on an iron base.   They use E.K. Imbibition paper soaked in 5% KNO_3 and pressures of 600 lb./sq. in.   The print is developed in a mixture of potassium ferro- and ferricyanides.

Coat-ing	Base metal	Electrolyte reagent	Medium	Color	Time sec.	I_d or volts	Ref.
Au	Cu	Potassium ferro-cyanide		Red-brown			26
	Sn	Ammonium phos-phomolybdate (electrolyte not stated)		Blue			26
Zn	Cu	Potassium ferro-cyanide	"Filter paper"	Red-brown	30	12V	26
Sn	Fe	Potassium ferro-cyanide	"Filter paper"	Blue		4V	26
Zn	Fe	Potassium ferro-cyanide	"Filter paper"	Blue	30	3V	26
Zn	Fe	3% NaCl 0.3% $K_3Fe(CN)_6$ 0.3% $K_4Fe(CN)_6$	Gelatin-coated baryta paper	Blue		3V	39
Ni	Cu	5% $NaNO_3$. Develop in 5% $K_4Fe(CN)_6$ + 3% acetic acid	"Filter paper"	Red-brown	180	30 ma./cm.^{2}	5
Ag	Cu	0.5 M $NaNO_3$ Sb_2S_3 or CdS paper	C.S. & S. $\begin{cases} 575 \\ 601 \end{cases}$	Ag-Black Cu-Brown	2–5	3V	29
Au, Pt, Ir	Mo	0.5 M $KHSO_4$ 5% $K_4Fe(CN)_6$	C.S. & S. $\begin{cases} 575 \\ 601 \end{cases}$	Brown	1–5	4V	29

4.3.4. Minerals. Certain minerals such as the sulfides, arsenides, and antimonides of heavy metals are fairly good conductors and may be printed electrographically, yielding either anions or cations, depending on the polarity of the specimen. The electrographic method was first applied to minerals by Jirkovsky (37) and later elaborated on by Wenger, Gutzeit, and Hiller (44). Hiller (32) has published a detailed summary of the techniques and reactions applicable to polished mineral sections. Table VII, taken from Hiller's article, lists the minerals and the elements detectable electrographically, together with the conditions for obtaining

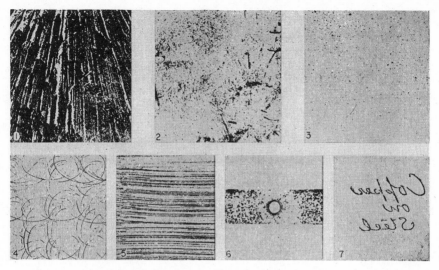

Fig. 16.   Electrographs of surface conditions.
1. Lead on steel, applied by centrifugation.
2. Lead, .075 mils, on .01 mil copper, on steel, electrodeposited.
3. Lead, 0.5 mils, on steel, electrodeposited.
   0.5 M sodium sulfate, 1 part ⎫
   0.1 M potassium ferrocyanide, ½ part ⎬ electrolyte
   0.1 M potassium ferricyanide, ½ part ⎭
   C.S. & S. 575 paper, 601 backing sheet, 2500 lb./sq. in.
   3 volts, 10 seconds, aluminum cathode
4. Tin on copper, scratched with #1 emery cloth.
   1% sodium diethyldithiocarbamate, 2% ammonia
   E. K. imbibition paper, 601 backing sheet, 50 lb./sq. in.
   3 volts, 30 seconds, aluminum cathode
5. Tin on iron, scratched with #1 emery cloth.
   0.1 M potassium ferrocyanide, 1 part ⎫
   0.1 M potassium ferricyanide, 1 part ⎬ electrolyte
   0.5 M sodium acetate, 1 part ⎭
   E. K. imbibition paper, 601 backing sheet, 50 lb./sq. in.
   3 volts, 20 seconds, aluminum cathode
6. Chromium on brass specimen.
   0.5 M ammonium acetate, 1% sodium diethyldithiocarbamate
   E. K. imbibition paper, 601 backing sheet, 50 lb./sq. in.
   1.5 volts, 30 seconds, aluminum cathode
7. Writing on steel plate with copper stylus to illustrate mechanical transfer.
   0.5 M sodium potassium tartrate, 1% sodium diethyldithiocarbamate, 2% ammonia
   E. K. imbibition paper, 601 backing sheet, 50 lb./sq. in.
   4.5 volts, 20 seconds, aluminum cathode

TABLE VII
Reactions of Minerals

Conducting minerals	Elements sought	Electrolyte	Volts	T, sec.	Specific reagent	Color of print
Bismuth (Native)	Bi	HCl (1:20)	4	30	KI—Cinchonine	Orange
Galena	Pb	Acetic acid	4	30	KI—Sn Cl$_2$	Yellow-orange
	S	5% NaOH (cathodic reduction)	4	15	SbCl$_3$ + HCl	Orange
Pyrites, Marcasite Pyrrhotine	Fe	HCl or HNO$_3$, (1:20)	4	20	K$_4$Fe(CN)$_6$	Blue
	S	5% NaOH (cathodic reduction)	4	15	SbCl$_3$ + HCl	Orange
Millerite	Ni	NH$_4$OH	4	10	Dimethylglyoxime	Red
	S	5% NaOH (cathodic reduction)	4	15	SbCl$_3$ + HCl	Orange
Pentlandite	Fe	HCl or HNO$_3$, (1:20)	4	30	K$_4$Fe(CN)$_6$	Blue
	Ni	NH$_4$OH	4	15	Dimethylglyoxime	Red
	S	5% NaOH (cathodic reduction)	4	14	SbCl$_3$ + HCl	Orange
Linnaeites	Co	5% KCN	8	30	(Direct print)	Yellow-orange
	Ni	NH$_4$OH	8	15	Dimethylglyoxime	Red
	Fe	HCl(1:20)	8	30	Chromotropic acid	Green
	Cu	NH$_4$OH	8	30	α–Benzoinoxime	Green
	S	5% NaOH (cathodic reduction)	8	15	SbCl$_3$ + HCl	Orange
Chalcosine	Cu	NH$_4$OH (dilute)	4	5	Rubeanic acid	Dark green
Covellite	S	5% NaOH (cathodic reduction)	4	15	SbCl$_3$ + HCl	Orange
Bornite	Cu	NH$_4$OH	4	15	Rubeanic acid	Dark green
Chalcopyrite	Fe	HCl (1:20)	4–8	30	Chromotropic acid	Green
	S	5% NaOH (cathodic reduction)	4	30	SbCl$_3$ + HCl	Orange
Gray Copper	Cu	NH$_4$OH	4–8	15	Rubeanic acid	Dark green

Mineral		Treatment			Reducing agent	
	Ag	HNO₃ (1:4)	8-12	60-180	Methyltrioxyfluorone	Black
	Sb	10% Tartaric acid + H₃PO₄	8-12	60	SnCl₂ + HCl	Red
	As	HCl (1:1)	8-12	60	SbCl₃ + HCl	Brown
	S	5% NaOH (cathodic reduction)	8-12	30		Orange
Mispickel Danaite	Fe	HCl or HNO₃ (1:20)	4-8	30	K₄Fe(CN)₆	Blue
	Co	NH₄OH	8-12	60	Rubeanic acid	Yellow-brown
	As	NH₄OH + H₂O₂ (5:1)	4-8	30	AgNO₃	Brown
	S	—	—	—	NaN₃ + I₂	—
Cobaltite	Co	NH₄OH	4-8	30	α-Nitroso-β-Naphthol	Brown
	As	NH₄OH + H₂O₂ (5:1)	8	30	AgNO₃	Brown
	S	—	—	—	NaN₃ + I₂	—
Gersdorffite Ullmannite	Ni	NH₄OH	4	15	Dimethylglyoxime	Red
	As	HCl (1:1)	4-8	30	SnCl₂ + HCl	Brown
	Sb	Tartaric acid + HNO₃	8	60	Methyltrioxyfluorone	Red
	S	5% NaOH (cathodic reduction)	8	30	SbCl₃ + HCl	Orange
Löllingite	Fe	HCl or HNO₃ (1:20)	4	30	K₄Fe(CN)₆	Blue
	As	HCl (1:1)	4	30	SnCl₃ + HCl	Brown
Smaltite-Chloanthite-Safflorite-Rammelsbergite	Co	NH₄OH (dilute)	8	30	α-Nitroso-β-Naphthol	Brown
	Ni	NH₄OH	8	15	Dimethylglyoxime	Red
	Fe	HCl or HNO₃ (1:20)	8	60	K₄Fe(CN)₆	Blue
	As	NH₄OH + H₂O₂ (5:1)	4	30	AgNO₃	Brown
Nickeline Breithauptite	Ni	NH₄OH	4	10	Dimethylglyoxime	Red
	As	HCl (1:1)	4	30	SnCl₂ + HCl	Brown
	Sb	Tartaric acid + H₃PO₄	4	30	Methyltrioxyfluorone	Red
Magnetite	Fe	HCl or HNO₃ (1:10)	4-8	30	K₄Fe(CN)₆	Blue
Ilmenite	Fe	HCl or HNO₃ (1:10)	12-16	60	K₄Fe(CN)₆	Blue
	Ti	25% H₂SO₄ + H₃PO₄	16	180	Chromotropic acid	Red-brown

the print.   In general, Hiller has used low voltages, short printing periods and sensitive reagents.   The printing was done largely on gelatin coated papers.

The mineral specimen is provided with a ground face, from which the print is made.   When there is sufficient electrical continuity through the mineral, contact may be made by mounting, face up, in a bed of crumpled aluminum foil or in a low melting alloy such as Wood's metal (see p. 173).   Hiller discusses several manipulative techniques which may be used when the conducting mineral is more or less isolated in a nonconducting mass.   The mineral may exist as a vein which emerges at an unknown point on the unground surface of the specimen.   In such case the electrographic assembly is completed, but the surface is explored with a probing needle contact until the milliammeter indicates establishment of a circuit, when the print is completed.

In the case of mineral grains which are completely isolated, the printing operation must be localized so as to permit electrical connection to the grain to be made with a small probe.   Hiller uses a small spatula-shaped electrode with which he holds the printing medium against a portion of the grain with one hand, while the probing contact is manipulated with the other.   Where the mineral inclusions are very small, Hiller has devised a micro electro-spot testing technique in which a tiny square of #575 paper, held under a needle electrode, is brought in contact with the grain under a binocular microscope.

When the specimen contains both highly and poorly conducting minerals, it may be difficult to maintain sufficient current density through the poorly conducting mineral to produce a print.   In such cases Hiller covers the good conductor with a film of lacquer.

4.3.5. Quantitative Applications.   The quantity of metal dissolved in the electro-transfer can be brought under fairly close regulation.   It is only natural, therefore, that the colorimetric possibilities of the method should have received some exploration.   The rotating drum method of Fritz (8), while applied primarily to the study of color-reaction sensitivities, involved the application of Faraday's law to the solution and transfer of metal ions and the relation of the quantities thus estimated to the intensity of the line traced on the reagent paper.   The conventional electro-transfer method was given quantitative study by Glazunov and Krivohlavy in a special application to iron-nickel alloys (25).   The original article contains a rather thorough discussion of the theoretical basis for the method but leaves much unsaid concerning experimental details, particularly the technique of comparing print densities and the precision obtained.   It would appear to the present authors that much work remains before a generalized quantitative technique can be realized.

It is hoped that the equipment, circuits, and techniques described in this chapter may facilitate the controlled operations necessary to systematic quantitative investigations. The usefulness of semiquantitative methods for routine control inspections should easily justify such effort.

The quantitative approach involves: (a) estimation, from the color density of the print, of the quantity of an alloy component dissolved, and (b) estimation, through application of Faraday's laws of electrolytic solution, of the quantity of the alloy dissolved.

Approximate determination of certain metals by comparison of spot densities on reagent-impregnated papers has been described by Yagoda (45) and by Clarke and Hermance (7), using independent techniques. In each case, it was concluded that differences of about 10% could be distinguished within the favorable range of concentration of the metal ion. Unless more sensitive methods of spot comparison are developed, therefore, it would appear doubtful that anything beyond a semiquantitative order of accuracy is possible from direct examination of electrotransfer prints. Greater accuracy may be obtainable by ashing the transfer and determining the metal by conventional micromethods (see ref. 7), using the electro-transfer solely as a means of obtaining a "weighed" microsample. However, much of the rapidity of the method would be sacrificed in such a procedure. On the whole, it would appear that the chief value of semiquantitative electro-transfer methods would be in their use for classifying alloys and for estimating minor components rather than for obtaining precise information.

Assuming that a given metal ion may be estimated satisfactorily from the print density, its quantity in the print can be related to the alloy composition only if the components go into solution in the proportions in which they occur in the alloy. Glazunov points out that this condition is rigorously met only when the alloy is a solid solution, presenting an equipotential surface to the transfer medium. If more than one phase is present, each phase will have its own solution potential and the yield of the ion under test will be governed by the individual compositions and relative rates of solution of the separate phases. As the potential impressed on a polyphase specimen is raised, however, the phase potential differences exert diminishing control over the solution rates of the components. By employing experimentally established conditions for the electro-transfer, it is often possible to approximate the composition of such alloys on an empirical basis. Glazunov and Drescher (23) have reported such a semiquantitative method for lead in lead-tin alloys that are mechanical mixtures. They use an electrolyte consisting of 1.85 g. KNO_3 and 1.35 g. KI in 100 ml., applying 6 volts (aluminum cathode) for 20 seconds. An empirical lead iodide color scale was prepared from known specimens which, they report, permits the estimation of lead contents ranging from 0.25 to 10%.

Estimation of the dissolved alloy: Assume a binary alloy to consist of a solid solution of y in z and the proportion of y is to be determined. A print is obtained with a suitable color reagent for y, the density of which will depend on the quantity of alloy dissolved and the proportion of y contained in it.

$$D = \frac{xW_a}{A},$$

where D, the print density is expressed in terms of the color produced per microgram of y/sq. cm., x is the fractional content of y in the alloy, W_a is the weight, in micrograms, of the alloy dissolved, and A is the print area in square centimeters. Then, applying the Faraday law,

$$D = \frac{xItE_a}{A},$$

where I is the current, in milliamperes, t, the time, and E_a is the electrochemical equivalent of the alloy in micrograms per millicoulomb. Since in this type of alloy, the metals y and z dissolve proportionately, E_a is the sum of the electrochemical equivalents of y and z, each multiplied by its fractional content in the alloy, hence,

$$D = \frac{Itx(xE_y + (1 - x)E_z)}{A}, \quad \text{or} \quad \frac{DA}{It} = x^2E_y - x^2E_z + xE_z \quad (3)$$

Equation (3) is general for binary alloys. The quantities E_y and E_z are constants. D, A, I, and t are measurable experimentally. x, The fractional content of component y, then is obtained by solving the resulting quadratic equation. The equation applies to single phase alloys, dissolved at current densities low enough to permit all of the electrical energy to be utilized in the solution of the metals. With two phase binary alloys, the results will depart more or less from the theoretical, depending on the magnitude of the phase potential differences and the loss of electrolytic efficiency attending the increased current density necessary to minimize such differences.

Measurement of I · t: The current is never entirely constant during the transfer, the electrolysis being attended by changes in the concentration and composition of the electrolyte with precipitation of products in the paper that may block the electrolytic paths and increase the resistance. Changes in the pH at anode and cathode also may exert considerable influence on the current. However, by careful choice of electrolyte and the use of sensitive reagents requiring only a light attack of the alloy, these changes may be held to a minimum. Passivation of the specimen surface or its coating by precipitated films must be avoided. Unsized papers containing "fixed" reagents (see Table III), combined with a thick backing pad are helpful in holding the current constant. Precipitated products then show less tendency to clog the paper and the augmented reservoir of electrolyte is less affected by concentration changes. Buffered electrolytes hold a constant pH at the specimen surface and facilitate a uniform rate of solution. With many organic reagents this is necessary, for excessive anodic acidity would prevent complete reaction. If the printing pad extends beyond the specimen edges, some of the current will flow outward through the surrounding uncompressed pad. This produces an increased density at the periphery of the print and a corresponding increase in the measured current. Appreciable errors may result. The simplest remedy is to employ a pad cut to conform to the specimen.

Fig. 17 shows a current-time curve under conditions suited to quantitative printing. After the first 5 seconds, the current remains practically unchanged for the 60 second observation period. Measurement of $I \cdot t$ for very short periods would involve some error due to the very rapid initial drop. However, it is probable that even then the error would not exceed 10%. For printing periods of 15 seconds and over, the error would be insignificant for semiquantitative work. Under less favorable conditions, the current may continue to fall, but after the initial sharp drop, the rate is usually almost linear and it is possible to effect a compensation by manipulation of the circuit rheostat or potentiometer. In general it is advisable to employ a current density as low as is consistent with satisfactory solution of the specimen surface. In this way the extremely short printing periods may be avoided. Because of the difficulty of following simultaneously both stop watch and milliammeter, it will be found convenient to time the printing by means of a metronome adjusted to a 1 second beat. The eye is then free to give full attention to the milliammeter and readings can be made at regular intervals.

Measurement of D: The density of the unknown print is estimated by comparison with a series of standards, similarly prepared from the pure metal or from known alloys. Quantitative printing is best done on a relatively thick, fine-textured paper, such as C.S. & S. #598 and the reagent impregnation should be fairly light. Then the colored reaction product will tend to coat the fibers in a uniform, thin layer which will extend progressively deeper into the paper as more metal is dissolved. In this way, the ratio of the surface to the weight of colored product is held more constant and the paper interstices remain open. Under these conditions, the print density is most nearly proportional to the quantity of metal dissolved.   For each reaction, there will exist a favorable density range, within which differentiation can be made most accurately.   For example, copper on cadmium or zinc sulfide-impregnated #598 paper is best estimated in the range from 1 to 50 μg./sq. cm.   When the print

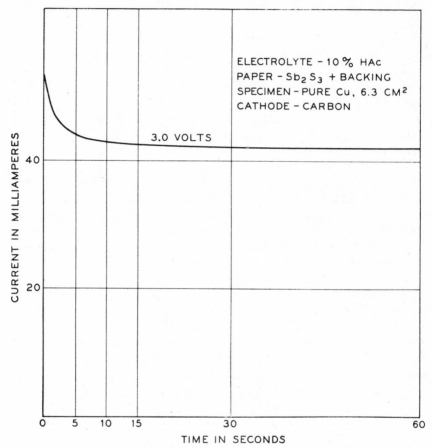

ELECTROLYTE – 10 % HAc
PAPER – $Sb_2 S_3$ + BACKING
SPECIMEN – PURE Cu, 6.3 CM²
CATHODE – CARBON

3.0 VOLTS

FIG. 17.   Current-time curve for typical quantitative print.
Electrolyte: 10% acetic acid
Paper: Sb_2S_3 + backing
Specimen: pure copper, 6.3 cm.²
Cathode: carbon

density is light and the precipitation of colored product is largely confined to the upper layers of the paper, comparison is made best in incident light, with the print illuminated from above and viewed at an angle of 30–45 degrees.   Dense prints, in which the colored product has penetrated deeply, are best compared in transmitted light.   Immersion in clarifying agents such as cyclohexanol improves the light transmission and facilitates comparison. A special illuminator for viewing spots in both incident and transmitted light has been described by Clarke and Hermance (7).

Area of print: For comparison purposes, color and current intensities must be expressed in terms of print area. When this is of irregular outline, its measurement may become troublesome. If, regardless of the size of the specimen, the printing is confined to a definite, reproducible area, one variable is eliminated and the operations, in general, are made more convenient. The writers have used circular cathodes, 2–3 cm. in diameter, with the printing and backing papers cut to discs of exactly the same size. In this way the area is precisely defined, both for printing and for the current flow. The discs are laid on the specimen without blotting. The cathode is then carefully aligned over them, pressure applied, and the excess electrolyte is absorbed from the edges of the sandwich with blotting paper. The quantity of electrolyte remaining in the paper, and hence the conductivity, will depend on the pressure applied. Reproducibility of printing conditions therefore requires control of the pressure. This can be accomplished with the calibrated spring press described earlier in the chapter.

Comparison techniques: Experimentally, the relation between the quantity of the dissolved alloy and the print density may be established in various ways. In their analysis of nickel-iron alloys,* Glazunov and Krivohlavy (25) prepare dimethylglyoxime prints on "filter paper" with an acetic acid electrolyte.† The iron interference is eliminated by washing the print with dilute acetic acid, leaving the pure nickel color. Their procedure involves essentially the following steps:

1. A series of nickel prints are made from a known alloy, with conditions held identical except for the time, which is varied in regular steps.
2. Prints of the unknown alloy are likewise prepared with varying time intervals but other conditions the same as for the known alloy.
3. The prints of the known and the unknown alloys are compared to obtain the times for which identical color intensity is obtained.
4. New prints are now made for both alloys, using the times which give equal color intensity. Now, however, the current is read at regular intervals to obtain the product $I \cdot t$ for each alloy.

* Alloys having nickel contents from 0 to 6.5%, and from 51 to 100% nickel are solid solutions, to which eq. (3) may be applied accurately.

† The electrolyte used was:

Acetic acid, 5%,   2 parts
Dimethylglyoxime, 1% alcoholic, 1 part.

5. Steps 1 to 4 give the time and current conditions necessary to produce prints of equal density from the two alloys. Since $D = D'$, applying eq. (3),

$$\frac{It}{A} (x^2E_y - x^2E_z + xE_z) = \frac{I't'}{A'} (a^2E_y - a^2E_z + aE_z)$$

or

$$x^2E_y - x^2E_z + xE_z = \frac{I't'A}{ItA'} (a^2E_y - a^2E_z + aE_z)$$

where I', t', and A' are current, time, and area respectively for the known alloy and a is the fractional content of component y in it.

The electrochemical equivalents for nickel and iron are so nearly alike that for approximate analyses, they may be considered equal. If $E_y = E_z$, the above equation reduces to

$$x = \frac{I't'A}{ItA'} \cdot a$$

In a somewhat different technique employed by the writers, the values for I, t, and A are held constant for the two alloys to be compared, and the common component, y, is estimated from the relative densities of the prints obtained. The density ratio is arrived at by comparing the prints with a series of permanent standard prints, suitably mounted and protected.

The method involves placing the printing cells in series in the same press and printing the two specimens simultaneously. Figure 18 shows the arrangement. In this way, the same current flows through each cell for the same period and the pressure must be the same on both. If cathodes and printing papers of uniform area are used, A, I, and t will be identical for the two prints. From eq. (3),

$$\frac{A}{I \cdot t} = \frac{x^2E_y - x^2E_z + xE_z}{D}.$$

Since the left hand member of the above equation is identical for both alloys, the relation between the print density and the composition in binary alloys may be expressed by the following equation:

$$x^2E_y - x^2E_z + xE_z = \frac{D}{D'} (a^2E_y - a^2E_z + aE_z)$$

where x and a are the fraction contents of y in the two alloys and D and D' are the print densities, respectively. As pointed out in the discussion of the method of Glazunov and Krivohlavy, when E_z and E_y are nearly the same, the equation may be simplified for approximate work. The above equation then becomes:

$$x = \frac{D}{D'} a$$

When there is available a series of known alloy specimens in which the y content increases regularly, the simultaneous printing method is particularly helpful, for then the unknown may be compared directly until a color match is obtained in the prints.   Its composition will then approximate that of the matching known, without further calculation.

The estimation of minute quantities of bismuth in copper by the electro-transfer method was reported by Garino and Catto (18).   The electrolyte reagent was cinchonine iodide, and the print was made on

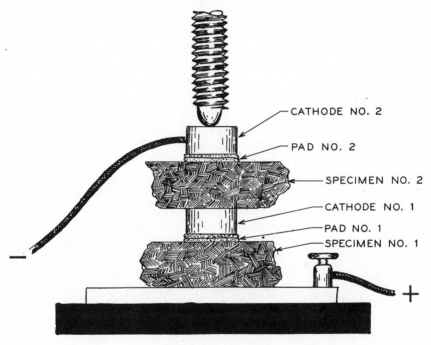

CATHODE NO. 2

PAD NO. 2

SPECIMEN NO. 2

CATHODE NO. 1

PAD NO. 1

SPECIMEN NO. 1

FIG. 18.   Series electro-transfer.

cotton fabric, with a veiling sheet containing 10% HNO_3 between it and the specimen.   For quantities of bismuth of the order of .01%, differences of .002% could be distinguished.

An advantageous application of the quantitative electro-transfer might be found in the controlled stripping and analysis of surface layers to determine the concentration gradient when one metal penetrates another by diffusion.   For example, protective metal coatings may alloy with the base metal through mutual solution.   This process is accelerated when heat is involved, as in hot-dip applications.   Sometimes heat treatments are purposely applied to bring about such alloy formation. Successive prints may be made, the quantity of surface dissolved in each case being determined by application of Faraday's law. From this and the print density, the concentration of the metal in question may be estimated.

Related to this application is the estimation of the weight of thin metal coatings. Successive prints for the base metal are made with measurement of the quantity of coating stripped each time. When the print indicates exposure of the base metal, the individual strippings are totaled, giving the weight of coating over the print area. In addition to the quantitative information, this method would also reveal any variations in the coating thickness in the area printed.

4.3.6. Electrography of Salt and Structural Patterns. There is one special application of electrography which, while not directly related to metallurgical problems, deserves brief mention. This is the reproduction of patterns derived from conductivity differences in a material. Such conductivity patterns may result from localized salt concentrations or from specific electrolytic paths afforded by the structure of the material.

Yagoda (46) has obtained remarkably detailed electrographs of fresh sections of plant and animal tissues, using the potential gradient between anode and cathode platens to drive the naturally occurring chloride ions into a silver chromate-impregnated gelatin paper. The printing cell is built up as follows: On the anode plate is placed a thick absorbent pad, then the printing paper, both soaked in saturated calcium sulfate. On the printing paper is laid the specimen section, 1–3 mm. in thickness, then the cathode plate is lowered to form the sandwich. 45 Volts are applied through a 500 ohm variable resistance until 200 millicoulombs/sq. cm. have passed. The yield of the chloride ion is controlled both by the local salt concentration and by the electrolytic paths in the specimen. Since the speed of ionic migration differs in the various tissue elements, prints are often obtained which show considerable amount of cellular structure.

Electrolytic paths through wax or resin impregnated fibrous products may reduce their value as electrical insulators. Yagoda's work suggests a method of testing for such paths electrographically. A material such as phenol fiber would be dried first, then soaked in a suitable electrolyte for several hours. At the end of this time, it would be placed on a gelatin printing paper containing the same electrolyte and a copper sensitive reagent. The printing paper, with the usual backing sheet, rests on an aluminum cathode platen. A copper anode platen is placed over the specimen, and the sandwich is placed under considerable pressure. A fairly high voltage is applied for sufficient time to drive the dissolved copper ions through the paths in the specimen to the printing paper, where it is registered as the colored product, revealing the number and location of the paths.

REFERENCES

1. Ammerman, E., *Stahl u. Eisen* **51**, 207 (1931).
2. Arnold, E., *Chem. Listy* **27**, 73 (1933) (*Brit. Chem. Abstracts* **B393**, 1933).
3. Bauman, R., *Metallurgie* **3**, 416 (1906).
4. Bowden, E. P., and Moore, A. J. W., *Nature* **155**, 451 (1945).
5. Brenner, A., Plating and Finishing Guide Book. 14th ed., Edited by Hall, N., and Hogaboom, G. B., Jr., Metal Industry Publishing Co., New York, 1945, p. 173.
6. Clarke, B. L., and Hermance, H. W., *Ind. Eng. Chem., Anal. Ed.* **9**, 292 (1937).
7. Clarke, B. L., and Hermance, H. W., *Ind. Eng. Chem., Anal. Ed.* **10**, 591 (1938).
8. Fritz, H., *Z. anal. Chem.* **78**, 418 (1929).
9. Fritz, H., *Mikrochemie* **19**, 6 (1935).
10. Fritz, H., *Mikrochemie* **21**, 47 (1936).
11. Fritz, H., *Mikrochemie, Molisch Festschrift* 125 (1936).
12. Fritz, H., *Mikrochemie* **22**, 34 (1937).
13. Fritz, H., *Mikrochemie* **22**, 168 (1937).
14. Fritz, H., *Mikrochemie* **23**, 61 (1937).
15. Fritz, H., *Mikrochemie* **24**, 22 (1938).
16. Fritz, H., *Mikrochemie* **24**, 171 (1938).
17. Galopin, R., *Schweitz. mineralog. petrog. Mitt.* **16**, 1 (1936).
18. Garino, M., and Catto, R., *Chimica e industria Milan* **17**, No. 4, 218 (1935).
19. Glazunov, A., *Chimie & industrie* Spec. No., 425 (1929).
20. Glazunov, A., *Chimie & industrie* Spec. No., 247 (1930).
21. Glazunov, A., *Chimie & industrie* Spec. No., 332 (1932).
22. Glazunov, A., *Oesterr. Chem. Ztg.* **41**, 217 (1938).
23. Glazunov, A., and Drescher, E., *Congr. chim. ind. Compt. rend.* 17ème *Congr.* pt. 2 (1937).
24. Glazunov, A., and Jenicek, L., *Korrosion u. Metallschutz* **16**, No. 10, 341 (1935).
25. Glazunov, A., and Krivohlavy, J., *Z. physik. Chem.* **A161**, 373 (1932). (Ref. *Metal Progress* **24**, 58 (1933).)
26. Glazunov, A., and Teindl, J. *Metallwaren-Ind. u. Galvano-Tech.* **33**, 371 (1935).
27. Gutzeit, G., Gysin, M., and Galopin, R., *Compt. rend. soc. phys. hist. nat. Genève* **51**, 53 (1934).
28. Hermance, H. W., *Bell Labs. Record* **18**, No. 9, 269 (1940).
29. Hermance, H. W., Wadlow, H. V., and Egan, T. F.   Bell Telephone Laboratories, unpublished work.
30. Hiller, Th., *Compt. rend. soc. phys. hist. nat. Genève* **52**, 119 (1935).
31. Hiller, Th., *Compt. rend. soc. phys. hist. nat. Genève* **53**, 54 (1936).
32. Hiller, Th., *Schweitz. mineralog. petrog. Mitt.* **17**, 88 (1937).
33. Hunter, M., Churchill, J., and Mears, R., *Metal Progress* **42**, 1070 (1942).
34. Hruska, J. H., *Heat Treating and Forging* 1034 (Nov. 1931).
35. Jimeno, E., Bernal, J., and Ibarz, J., *Anales soc. españ. fís. y quím.* **30**, 655 (1932).
36. Jirkovsky, R., *Chem. Listy* **25**, 254 (1931).
37. Jirkovsky, R., *Bansky Svet* Bd. **XI**, Heft 2–3 (1932).
38. Jirkovsky, R., *Mikrochemie* **15**, 331 (1934).
39. Koehler, W. A., and Burford, R. O., *Trans. Electrochem. Soc.* **70**, 397 (1936).
40. Lindsey, A. J., *Analyst* **63**, 425 (1938).
41. Masters, D. L., *Metallurgia* **29**, 101 (1943).

228   H. W. HERMANCE AND H. V. WADLOW

42. Niessner, M., *Mikrochemie* **12**, 1 (1932).
43. Shaw, W. E., and Moore, E. T., *Anal. Chem.* **19**, 777 (1947).
44. Wenger, P., Gutzeit, G., and Hiller, T. G., *Compt. rend. soc. phys. hist. nat. Genève* **51**, 63 (1934).
45. Yagoda, H., *Mikrochemie* **24**, 117 (1938).
46. Yagoda, H., *Ind. Eng. Chem., Anal. Ed.* **12**, 698 (1940).
47. Yagoda, H., *Ind. Eng. Chem., Anal. Ed.* **15**, 135 (1943).
48. Yushko, S. A., *Bull. acad. sci. U.R.S.S. Ser. geol.* No. 3, 137 (1939).
49. Yushko, S. A., *Khim. Referat. Zhur.* No. 2, 64 (1940).

Magnetic Methods of Analysis

By

A. R. KAUFMANN

Department of Metallurgy, Massachusetts Institute of Technology, Cambridge, Massachusetts

CONTENTS

Page

1. Introduction

The magnetic properties of matter have been studied for many years by numerous investigators. A large number of research methods adapted to this work have been developed, with almost every worker incorporating variations of design in his own apparatus. This situation exists because the large range of phenomena and experiments covered by magnetic studies have precluded the construction of a standard piece of test equipment. The following article will cover the broad field of magnetic test methods insofar as they may be of use to the analyst, without mentioning certain techniques used either in the realm of pure physics or in connection with the detailed applications of ferromagnetic materials in commercial equipment.

2. Definitions and Units

Magnetized bodies will exert forces on each other which may be described in terms of magnetic poles located on the surface of the bodies. There are two types of poles, north and south; like poles repel each other and unlike poles attract. A north pole is one that would move in a northerly direction in the earth's field. The force, F, between two poles of strength p_1 and p_2, separated by a distance, r, acts along a line drawn between them and is given by the equation $F = \dfrac{p_1 p_2}{\mu r^2}$, where μ is the permeability (to be discussed below) of the medium surrounding the poles. Two poles of unit strength will exert a force of 1 dyne on each other when $\mu = 1$ (as in a vacuum) and $r = 1$ cm.

2.1. Magnetic Field

A magnetized body produces a magnetic field, H, whose strength at any point is given by the force it exerts on a unit pole placed in a vacuum at that point (the unit is the oersted). The direction of the field is that in which it causes a north pole to move. A unit field exerts a force of 1 dyne on a unit pole. It follows from this that a unit pole produces a unit field at a distance of 1 cm.

2.2. Intensity of Magnetization and Susceptibility

Two magnetic poles of equal strength and of opposite kind, when separated by a distance l, form a magnetic moment (dipole) of strength $m = pl$. The intensity of magnetization, I, of a body is defined as its magnetic moment per cubic centimeter. When I is produced through the action of a magnetic field, the volume susceptibility, K, of the material is defined as $I/H = K$. The magnetic moment per gram, σ, and the mass susceptibility, χ, are obtained by dividing I or K by the density, respectively. The corresponding quantities for a gram molecular weight of material are obtained by multiplying σ or χ by the gram molecular weight.

2.3. Flux

A magnetic field may be represented by drawing lines through space indicating the direction in which a unit pole would move at any point and with the strength of the field being indicated by the density of lines (the unit is the gauss). A unit field corresponds (by convention) to a density of one line per square centimeter of area perpendicular to the line. From this it follows that 4π lines originate from each unit pole since such a pole produces unit field strength over the surface of a sphere of 1 cm. radius. A cube of material 1 cm. on a side, magnetized to an intensity I, has a magnetic moment equivalent to that of the same cube with magnetic poles of strength $p = I$ located on two opposite faces. In other words, I has the dimensions of magnetic moment per cubic centimeter or pole strength per square centimeter.

If a disclike cavity (see Fig. 1) is created inside a body uniformly magnetized to an intensity I, with the plane of the disc normal to the direction of I, north poles of strength I per centimeter squared will be formed on one face of the cavity with south poles of the same strength on the other face. Thus, these poles will produce a field of strength $4\pi I$ across the cavity that is due to the magnetization of the material. In addition there will be a field due to the magnetizing field, H, which exists within the body at that point. This field is not necessarily the same in strength as the field that would exist at that point if the specimen were removed since there may be a demagnetizing field (see discussion below). The true value of H at a point within a body could be determined by measuring the field in the middle of a long, needlelike cavity, as shown in Fig. 1.

The sum $H + 4\pi I = B$ is known as the magnetic flux in a body. It is apparent that B, H, and I have the same dimensions, but in spite of this the units of the first two are gauss and oersted, respectively, while I

has no commonly used unit. It is customary for engineers to use the quantity B since this measures the useful flux produced in magnetic equipment, while scientists prefer the quantity I or σ, since these refer directly to a property of the material.

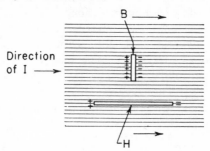

Fig. 1. B and H inside an inductively magnetized specimen.

2.4. Permeability

The ratio $B/H = \mu = 1 + 4\pi K$ is known as the permeability. This quantity is used by engineers in preference to K for the same reasons that they prefer B to I. It is apparent that both μ and K, as defined in this article have no dimensions. The μ defined here is assumed to be the same as in the introductory paragraph of section 2 but apparently there is no way of proving this experimentally (2).

3. Magnetic Energy and Force

The mutual energy of a dipole and the field producing apparatus is determined by the orientation of the dipole with respect to the field, that is, $E = -mH \cos \theta$ where θ is the angle between the axis of the dipole and the field direction. This follows from the fact that the work required to bring the north pole of the dipole into the field is equal and opposite to that required to bring the south pole into the field, except for the small difference determined by the orientation with respect to the field. The mutual energy of a magnetized body and the field apparatus is $-IHV \cos \theta$, where V is the volume in cubic centimeters. The torque acting on the body is $\dfrac{\partial E}{\partial \theta} = IHV \sin \theta$. The force on the body in the x-direction is $\dfrac{\partial E}{\partial x} = F_x = \left(I_x \dfrac{\partial H_x}{\partial x} + I_y \dfrac{\partial H_y}{\partial x} + I_z \dfrac{\partial H_z}{\partial x} \right) V$. If the specimen is isotropic, that is, if K is the same in all directions, then $F_x = KV \left(H_x \dfrac{\partial H_x}{\partial x} + H_y \dfrac{\partial H_y}{\partial x} + H_z \dfrac{\partial H_z}{\partial x} \right)$. For nonisotropic specimens the energy and force relationships are more complicated (3).

When magnetization is induced by a field, the internal energy change of the specimen is $V \int_0^H I dH$ (6), which is the area between the magnetization curve and the I-axis. From this result, it is easy to show that for cyclic magnetization the area within the hysteresis loop equals the loss of energy per cycle.

4. MAGNETIC MATERIALS

There are three types of magnetic behavior: diamagnetic, paramagnetic and ferromagnetic. No attempt will be made to give a discussion of these phenomena from an atomic standpoint since the subject is very extensive and is covered in standard works on magnetism. A brief reference to the atomic theory is given in Section 9.6.

4.1. Diamagnetism

For a diamagnetic material, K is negative and hence the magnetization is antiparallel to the applied field, H. The value of K will be of the order of 10^{-6} as shown by a few examples listed in Table I. K is strictly independent of H and varies only slightly with the temperature (40). Appreciable temperature dependence of K for diamagnetic materials indicates that there is a paramagnetic component of the magnetization which is not great enough, however, to make the resultant magnetization paramagnetic.

4.2. Paramagnetism

A paramagnetic material has a positive K of the magnitude 10^{-6} to 10^{-4} at room temperature (Table I) and likewise is independent of H at room temperature. The magnetization will be parallel to H. Many paramagnetic susceptibilities, particularly of nonmetals, vary roughly as the reciprocal of the absolute temperature and hence may become very large at low temperatures. At such temperatures K may become dependent on H, but the magnetization will always be reversible.

4.3. Ferromagnetism

Ferromagnetism is a special case of paramagnetism in the sense that K is positive (for virgin magnetization) and I is parallel to H when H is large. However, K will vary tremendously with H and can have large values as shown in Table I. This means that I can have large values at relatively small values of H. The magnetization, I, at low field strengths can be at any angle to H depending on numerous factors such as shape and orientation of the specimen, structure and orientation of the crystals comprising the specimen, and previous magnetic history. Most ferromagnetic materials can retain some magnetization in zero field and this distinguishes them fundamentally from paramagnetic substances.

The magnetization of a ferromagnetic will substantially reach a limiting value, known as the saturation value, I_s, in fields of several thousand oersted. It is found that I_s decreases with increasing temperature and goes rather abruptly to almost zero at a critical temperature, T_c, known as the Curie temperature. At still higher temperatures the magnetization is essentially paramagnetic in nature.

Typical magnetization curves for the three types of magnetic behavior are shown schematically in Fig. 2. The virgin curve for the ferro-

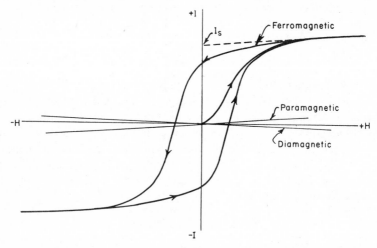

FIG. 2.   Magnetization curves for diamagnetic, paramagnetic and ferromagnetic materials.

magnetic case is seen to be greatly different from the curve obtained on succeeding reversals of the field. This phenomenon is known as hysteresis and is of great consequence both in practical applications and to the analyst. It is obvious that previous magnetic history would need to be considered in making analytical deductions from measurements on a ferromagnetic material.

After a ferromagnetic material reaches its saturation value, there will be a further almost linear increase in magnetization with field. This effect is small at temperatures considerably below the Curie temperature but may be quite appreciable in the neighborhood of T_c. The true value of I_s can be found by extrapolating the linear behavior in very high fields (above 20,000 oersted) back to the zero field axis and obtaining the intercept as shown in Fig. 2. At a given temperature I_s is a characteristic of the material and could be used as an aid in identification.

TABLE I

Volume Susceptibility of Various Substances

Substance	Tempera- ture °C.	$K \times 10^6$	Remarks
Sodium chloride	18	-1.08	
Copper	20	$-.76$	
Water	20	$-.720$	
Ethyl alcohol		$-.58$	
Air	20	$+.029$	760 mm.
Oxygen	20	$+.143$	760 mm.
Aluminum	18	$+1.75$	
Manganese	20	$+73$	
Ferric chloride	20	$+240$	
Iron	20	5×10^8 to 10^{10}	Ferromagnetic

The magnetization curve and hysteresis loop of a ferromagnetic material are of such great technical importance that many features of the curves have received specific names and symbols as shown in Fig. 3, where $B = H + 4\pi I$ is plotted against H. The slope of a line drawn from the

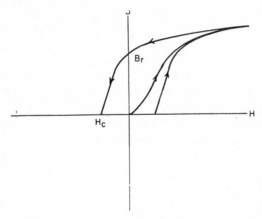

Fig. 3.   Illustration of remanence, B_r, and coercive force H_c.

origin to any point on the virgin curve gives the permeability at that point. The slope of the curve at the origin is known as the initial permeability, while the slope of the virgin curve at any other point is known as the differential permeability. If, at any value of H a small variation of field, ΔH, is carried out many times, the quantity $\Delta B/\Delta H$, known as the reversible permeability, may be obtained and this will be greatly different from the differential permeability. The intercept of the demagnetization curve with the B-axis is known as the remanence, B_r, while the intercept on the H-axis is the coercive force, H_c. The remanence and coercive force have definite values only if the magnetization is carried to saturation.

5. DEMAGNETIZING FIELD

A magnetized body will have free poles on its surface at the places where the flux either enters or leaves the body. These poles will create a magnetic field, as discussed above, which will extend in all directions through space. Within the body itself this field, known as the demagnetizing field, will act in a direction more or less opposite to that of the magnetization and to the field producing the magnetization. In a specimen of irregular shape the direction and magnitude of the demagnetizing field, H', will obviously be hard to specify. In the case of an oblate or prolate spheroid, however, which is uniformly magnetized parallel to one of the axes, it can be shown that H' not only is uniform throughout the body but also is proportional to I and is antiparallel to it. Thus, the true field inside such a body is $H - H' = H - DI$. The constant D can be computed from equations given in books on magnetism (36). The value of D is $\frac{4}{3}\pi$ for a sphere and 4π for magnetization perpendicular to the plane of a thin disc, showing that the demagnetizing field can be very important when I is large as in a ferromagnetic material. The coefficient of demagnetization along the axis of long thin ellipsoids becomes small as the ratio of length to diameter is increased, as shown in the second column of Table II. The quantity, m, in this table is the ratio of length to diameter for the ellipsoids or cylinders. Measurements are often made on specimens in the form of cylinders and for this case empirical values of D, which presumably apply only to the middle region of the rod, have been determined and are given in the third column of Table II (31).

TABLE II

Demagnetization Factors

m	D Ellipsoid	D Cylinder
1	4.188	
5	.701	
10	.255	
20	.085	.067
30	.043	.034
50	.018	.014
100	.0054	.0045
500	.0003	.00018

6. Production of Magnetic Fields

6.1. Electromagnets

Electromagnets are familiar to most people and have been discussed in many places (4). A maximum of about 21,000 oersted may be obtained using an iron core and flat pole pieces, while with tapered poles and special steels about 35,000 oersted from the iron alone may be obtained. By placing the magnetizing coils in line with and close to the pole pieces a further increase in field is possible depending on how much current is used. In this way about 45,000 oersted may be obtained with a moderate size of installation, while 70,000 oersted has been reached in extreme cases.

The distribution of field between the pole pieces may be quite complex and ordinarily will be uniform only over a small region. Special shapes of pole pieces can be used to obtain specific field distributions, but the shaping is difficult to determine except by trial and error. Circular poles with slightly concave faces have been used to give uniform fields and poles of unequal size to produce uniform field gradients (9). When placing a strongly magnetic specimen in the gap of a magnet it is important to remember that the specimen may react on the magnet and alter the strength and distribution of the field.

6.2. Solenoids

The magnetic field produced by a known distribution of electric currents can be accurately calculated in most cases (24). By this means standard fields for the calibration of magnetic equipment can be produced and also fields with accurately known uniformity or gradients. A very long helix of wire with n turns per centimeter, which carries a current of i amperes will produce a uniform field at its center of strength of $H = .4\pi n i$. Formulas giving the strength and distribution of field for shorter coils may be found in many references (13).

A uniformly wound multiple-layer solenoid is very convenient for producing fields up to about 500 oersted. For greater field strengths in continuous service it becomes necessary to provide cooling. Through the use of enough power and enough ingenuity in removing heat, it is possible to produce continuous fields up to 100,000 oersted (5) or fields up to 300,000 for a fraction of a second (37).

Fields of great uniformity over a large space may be produced through the use of Helmholtz coils. These consist of two circular coils spaced and dimensioned as shown in Fig. 4 with equal currents flowing in the same sense in the two coils. The field so produced is given closely by the equation $H = \dfrac{.286\pi N i}{R}$ where i is the current in amperes, N is the number of turns in each coil, and R is the radius of the coil in centimeters. This is an inefficient way of producing a field and, hence, the coils are used mostly to produce relatively weak fields such as are needed to balance out the earth's field. According to McKeehan a uniform

$$\frac{a^2}{b^2} = \frac{36}{31}$$

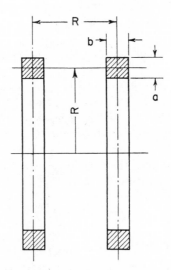

Fig. 4.   Helmholtz coils for producing uniform field.

gradient, dH/dx (23) may be produced by spacing the coils a distance $\sqrt{3}\ R$ apart and running the currents in opposite directions.

6.3. Permanent Magnets

Permanent magnets have found only a limited use as a field source for magnetic testing owing to the inability to vary the field (except with a winding) and to the expense of the material required for a sizable magnet. In general, the maximum attainable field would be of the order of 5000 to 10,000 oersted, depending on the magnet material and the size of the gap. A properly designed and stabilized permanent magnet should give a much more constant field than is obtainable when electric currents are required to produce the field (due to fluctuations in current) and this feature may be highly desirable in special cases.

6.4. Earth's Field

The magnetic field of the earth is uniform over large regions (unless distorted by local magnetized material) and is quite constant from day to day. For this reason it is sometimes used as a reference field, particularly in the magnetometer apparatus to be described below. The strength of the horizontal component of the earth's field in the northeastern United States is about 0.2 oersted, while the vertical component is about 0.5. Observations which are made in fields of this order of magnitude would obviously need to be corrected for the effect of the earth's field.

7. MEASUREMENT OF MAGNETIC FIELDS

7.1. Search Coil

A search coil coupled to a ballistic galvanometer through the secondary of a mutual inductance, as shown in Fig. 5, is probably the most

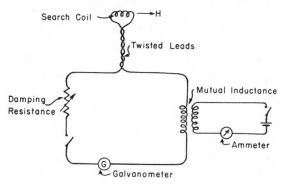

Fig. 5. Wiring diagram for search coil and ballistic galvanometer circuit.

widely used means of measuring H. If the component of H perpendicular to the plane of the coil is varied rapidly, a voltage is induced in the coil and this causes a current i_1 to flow through the galvanometer. If all of the current flows before the galvanometer has moved appreciably, the amplitude of swing of the galvanometer coil will be strictly proportional to the angular impulse imparted by the current to the galvanometer coil. The instantaneous voltage at the search coil is $E = 10^{-8} \dfrac{d\phi}{dt}$ $= 10^{-8} NA \dfrac{dH}{dt}$ where ϕ is the flux through the coil, N equals the number of turns in the search coil and A is the cross-sectional area of the coil in square centimeters. The angular impulse is proportional to $\int i \, dt$

$$= \int \frac{E}{Z} dt = 10^{-8} \frac{NA\Delta H}{Z} = c\theta_1$$ where Z is the total impedance of the circuit, ΔH is the change of field, θ is the deflection of the galvanometer, and c is a constant. The mutual inductance is used to calibrate the galvanometer by breaking a current i' in the primary. This will cause a galvanometer deflection θ_2 where $c\theta_2 = \frac{M}{Z} i'$. Hence, $\Delta H = \frac{10^8 M i' \theta_1}{NA\theta_2}$ where M is in henries and i' is in amperes.

The flux through the search coil may be varied by reducing H to zero, by pulling the coil from the field, or by rotating the coil till its plane is parallel to the field. If the area of a coil is difficult to fix, it may be determined by making the above measurements in an accurately known field. There are many details on the operation of a ballistic galvanometer which may be found in text books on electrical measurements (34).

7.2. Flux Meter

A galvanometer that has practically no restoring force or that is heavily overdamped can be used to measure flux changes through a search coil without the necessity of making all of the flux change before the instrument moves (25). Such instruments in portable form can be bought commercially and are quite convenient for rough work. They are not suitable for precise work, however, since it is difficult to obtain accurate readings owing to the small scale and the slow drift of the pointer.

7.3. Standard Substances

The field in apparatus used for measuring the susceptibility of paramagnetic or diamagnetic materials may be calibrated by using substances of known susceptibility. Pure water with $K = -0.720 \times 10^{-6}$ at 16°C. has been used for this purpose. The susceptibility of paramagnetic salts varies rapidly with temperature, hence the temperature must be fixed when making a calibration with such materials. Some of these methods, as will be described later, give H directly and others give $H \frac{dH}{dx}$ at a point. The technique is useful mostly for determining large fields.

7.4. Bismuth Wire

The electrical resistance of a bismuth wire varies roughly as the square of the magnetic field in which it is placed, with a 40% increase being observed at 10,000 oersted. Such wires can be made quite small and hence are useful for field determination in a small region. It is necessary to maintain a constant temperature since the effect varies with temperature.

7.5. Current Methods

A field can be measured by determining the force which it exerts on a known electric current. The force, F, in dynes on an element, ds, of current is $F = \dfrac{Hids}{10} \sin \theta$, where θ is the angle between ds and H, and i is the current in amperes. The force will be at right angles to the plane defined by the directions of ds and of H. The Cotton balance (38) has been used in several investigations. Another very simple arrangement consists of a uniformly wound single layer solenoid suspended from the arm of a balance (19). In each case the difference of the field at the two ends of the current carrying structure is determined. These methods can be used where absolute accuracy is required.

8. Apparatus for Magnetic Measurements

8.1. Force Measurements

8.1.1. Curie Method. The magnetization of a body can be determined by measuring the translation force exerted on the specimen by an inhomogeneous magnetic field of known strength and gradient. This method is particularly adapted to observations on diamagnetic and paramagnetic substances since the induction methods used on ferromagnetic materials are not sufficiently sensitive for this purpose. Let the x-axis coincide with the direction in which the force is to be measured: For a magnetically isotropic substance the force on a small volume, dV, is $f_x = K \left[H_x \dfrac{\partial H_x}{\partial x} + H_y \dfrac{\partial H_y}{\partial x} + H_z \dfrac{\partial H_z}{\partial x} \right] dV$. If the specimen is suspended from a balance along the axis of a solenoid, as shown in Fig. 6, H_y and H_z will be zero and the force (in dynes) is $F_x = \displaystyle\int K H_x \dfrac{\partial H_x}{\partial x} dV$ $= KVH_x \dfrac{dH_x}{dx} = \chi w H_x \dfrac{dH_x}{dx}$ (w = weight of specimen), if $H_x \dfrac{\partial H_x}{\partial x}$ is uniform over the specimen. If the specimen is suspended near the gap of an electromagnet, as shown in Fig. 7, the force is $F = \chi w H_y \dfrac{dH_y}{dx}$. If the specimen is surrounded by a gaseous or liquid medium of susceptibility K_0, the force will be $F_x = (K - K_0) V H_x \dfrac{dH_x}{dx}$.

This procedure, known as the Curie method, has the advantage that only a small sample is required and that the specimen can be of irregular shape. The disadvantage is that $H \dfrac{dH}{dx}$ cannot be determined very accurately at a point and, hence, the precision is usually not better than a few per cent. The method is capable of great sensitivity if the specimen is held on a horizontal arm which is suspended from a torsion fiber.

8.1.2. Gouy Method. If the specimen consists of a long cylinder of uniform cross section, A (sq. cm.), the force exerted on it by a field (Fig. 8) can be found by integration of the above expression over the

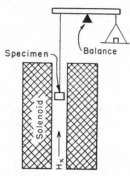

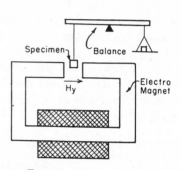

FIG. 6. Curie method for measuring susceptibility using a solenoid.

FIG. 7. Curie method for determining susceptibility using an electromagnet.

length of the specimen. The result is $F_x = \dfrac{(K - K_0)A}{2}(H_1{}^2 - H_0{}^2)$. The advantage of the Gouy method is that it is not necessary to know $\dfrac{dH}{dx}$, and, if H_0 is small compared with H_1, then H_0 usually can be neglected. The disadvantage is that a large specimen of uniform cross

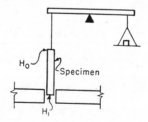

FIG. 8. Gouy method for determining susceptibility using an electromagnet.

section is required. A long specimen is particularly disadvantageous when the specimen is to be either heated or cooled.

8.1.3. Quincke Method. Susceptibility measurements on liquids can be made by the Curie or Gouy methods but, in either case, a correction would need to be made for the sample container. This is avoided in the Quincke method where the liquid is contained in a stationary U tube with one arm of the U in the magnetic field and the other in zero field as shown in Fig. 9. The level of the liquid will move when the field is turned on and an observation of this change, h, or of the motion of a reservoir which will restore the original liquid level is a measure of the susceptibility. The mass susceptibility is given by $\chi = \dfrac{2hG}{H^2} + \dfrac{\rho_0 \chi_0}{\rho}$ when the outer arm of the U has a large enough reservoir so that its level does not change appreciably and when the density, ρ_0, of the medium above the sample can be neglected. In this expression, G is the gravitational constant, ρ is the density of the sample, and χ_0 is the susceptibility of the upper medium. This method has the advantages of the Gouy system with the further feature that the cross-sectional area need not be known.

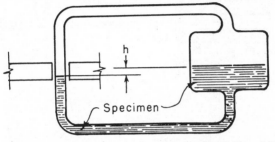

Fig. 9. Quincke method for measuring the susceptibility of liquids.

8.1.4. General Precautions. The presence of ferromagnetic impurities in a sample can produce serious error in susceptibility measurements. To avoid this it is necessary to measure K at a series of field strengths above about 7000 oersted and then to plot K against $1/H$ to get the extrapolated value at infinite field. If I' is the saturation value of the impurities, then $K_H = \dfrac{I'}{H} + K_\infty$ for the Curie method, and $K_H = \dfrac{2I'}{H} + K_\infty$ for the Gouy method.

When using the Curie method, it is necessary to make corrections for the force exerted by the field on the specimen holder and suspension thread. This can best be done by correcting the observed force at each field strength rather than calculating a susceptibility for the holder.

With the Curie or Gouy methods where the specimen is freely suspended in the field, the forces perpendicular to the direction of measurement may be great enough, when K is large, to deflect the specimen against the sides of the apparatus. The only cure for this is to use weaker fields or more homogeneous fields. When K is very large (as at low temperatures), the equilibrium in the direction of measurement may become unstable. The remedy for this is to decrease the sensitivity of the balance or to use weaker fields.

There are many variations of the methods given above, particularly with regard to the means of measuring the force. The reader is referred to standard works on magnetism for a more extensive discussion (39).

8.2. Magnetometer Methods

8.2.1. Pendulum. The magnetization of strongly paramagnetic or ferromagnetic materials can be determined by measuring the translational force on specimens attached to a horizontal rod suspended from

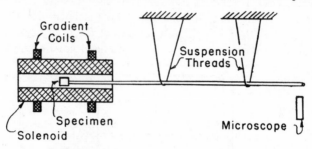

FIG. 10.   Pendulum magnetometer.

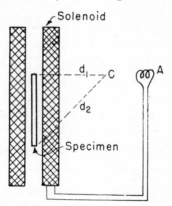

FIG. 11.   Compass magnetometer.

four threads as shown in Fig. 10 (14, 23). The specimen can be quite small but must be shaped into an ellipsoid in order to have a known demagnetizing factor. The field gradient need only be small and, hence, can be supplied with modified Helmoltz coils. If the weight and suspension length of the pendulum are known, the force on the specimen can be calculated from the observed deflection.

8.2.2. Compass. Magnetization may be measured in a long thin rod of ferromagnetic material by observing the deflection it produces in a nearby compass. One arrangement is as shown in Fig. 11 with the compass at C on a level with the upper end of the specimen and the specimen in a vertical position. The earth's field, H_e, will counterbalance the effect of the specimen on the compass (the effect of the solenoid is cancelled out with another coil, A), and it may be shown that $H_e \tan \theta = IAd_1 \left(\dfrac{1}{d_1{}^3} - \dfrac{1}{d_2{}^3} \right)$, where H_e is the horizontal component of the earth's field, θ is the angle of deflection of the compass, and I and A are the intensity of magnetization and cross-sectional area of the specimen. This is one of the older methods for measuring a ferromagnetic material, but it might still find use today.

8.3. Torque Methods

If I is at an angle θ to H, then a torque of magnitude $VIH \sin \theta$ (dyne-cm.), where V is the volume, will act on the body. Thus, if the torque is measured, either I or H may be determined if the other is known. For permanent magnets and with small values of H, this result is quite accurate. With induced magnetization, I will be parallel to H unless a demagnetizing field or a "crystalline field" within the body prevents this. The former situation exists when an elongated specimen is held with the long axis at an angle ϕ to the field. Because of the large demagnetizing factor, N_2, perpendicular to the specimen and the smaller factor, N_1, parallel to the axis, I will tend to lie along the axis. Using small values of ϕ, it is possible to determine the magnetization curve from the measured torque (42). In high fields, I will coincide closely with H in direction and the torque will then be $T = (N_2 - N_1)VI_s{}^2 \sin \phi \cos \phi$ where I_s is the saturation value (44); thus, I_s can be determined without knowing H.

Single crystals of Fe, Ni, and Co can be magnetized more readily in some directions than in others, and this effect is attributed to a "crystalline field" (7). If H is applied in an arbitrary direction, the crystal will first magnetize in that easy direction that makes the smallest angle with H. As a result of this, a torque will act on the specimen. As H is increased, I will be rotated until it is almost parallel to H. Under these conditions, the torque will approach a limiting value which is independent of H and depends only on crystallographic direction. By measuring this limiting torque, the crystal orientation may be determined and data on preferred orientation in rolled sheets can be found.

8.4. Induction Methods

A search coil and ballistic galvanometer (or fluxmeter) may be used to measure ferromagnetic magnetization in the same manner as was described for field measurements. The specimen is placed inside the coil and the flux is varied by suddenly changing the field or by withdrawing the specimen. A mutual inductance is again used for calibration. If the search coil fits the specimen closely, the flux through the coil will be $BA = (H + 4\pi I)A$ where A is the cross-sectional area of the specimen and H is the field inside the specimen. If there is no demagnetizing field, then H is equal to the applied field. A second coil may be placed in the galvanometer circuit and located in such a way that it picks up flux from the magnetizing solenoid which is equal and opposite to the field pick up of the search coil. Then when the field is varied, the search coil will measure only the change in $4\pi I$.

Ballistic galvanometers may be purchased from a number of manufacturers in a wide range of sensitivities. The sensitivities usually are specified in microcoulombs per millimeter of deflection on a scale 100 cm. from the galvanometer. The flux sensitivity of an apparatus may be defined as millimeter deflection per line of flux change through the search coil, and this is given approximately by $\dfrac{NA}{10^2 RM}$ where N is the number of turns and A is the cross-sectional area of the search coil (in square centimeters), R is the resistance of the circuit, and M is the microcoulomb sensitivity. The coulomb sensitivity varies with circuit resistance, becoming very poor for low resistance (overdamping) (22). The flux sensitivity becomes greater as NA is increased, but only if R can be kept from increasing at the same time. A high sensitivity galvanometer with suitable search coil should easily give 10 mm. deflection for a change of one line per square centimeter of search coil area.

For measurements of ferromagnetic materials in weak fields, it is extremely important either to know or to eliminate the demagnetizing field. The demagnetizing field is known only for ellipsoids in a uniform field, but empirical values for cylinders have been used (Table II). If the specimen is made part of a complete magnetic circuit, as by clamping it between the poles of an electromagnet, the free poles at the ends of the specimen and, hence, the demagnetizing fields are eliminated. Many devices of this kind, known as permeameters, have been built (32). The Burrows and the Fahy-Simplex permeameters are used extensively with the latter being preferred for commercial testing. The means of obtaining uniform magnetization and H in these devices is not entirely satisfactory but, apparently, is good enough for routine testing.

8.5. Alternating Current Methods

The testing of commercial magnetic materials at 60-cycle frequency is discussed in a number of places (33) and will not be covered here.

It is possible to measure paramagnetic or diamagnetic susceptibilities in high frequency fields using an oscillating circuit of frequency, $F = \dfrac{1}{2\pi \sqrt{LC}}$ where L and C are the inductance and capacity of the circuit. If a nonconducting sample is placed within the coil in the circuit, there will be a change ΔL in inductance and ΔC in capacity with the result that $\Delta F = -\dfrac{F}{2\pi}\left[\dfrac{\Delta L}{L} + \dfrac{\Delta C}{C}\right]$. If F is large, then a small change in L will produce a large enough change in ΔF to be detected by the beat method. The ΔL is equal to $4\pi K$ when the sample fills the coil and, hence, will be of the order 10^{-3} to 10^{-5}. The difficulty with this method is that the specimen will also change the capacity with this effect becoming larger as the frequency increases. A way of overcoming this by the use of a large D.C. field in addition to the A.C. field appears to be satisfactory (35).

A.C. measurements on conducting materials are complicated by the induced eddy currents in the specimen and, hence, such methods are not readily adopted to metals. Also, the effect of any ferromagnetic impurities cannot be readily eliminated since the A.C. fields are small in magnitude.

9. Applications of Magnetic Analysis

A few examples of the technical information which may be obtained by magnetic methods will be listed. It is hoped that this information, together with that presented above, will enable the reader to see applications to his own problems.

9.1. Oxygen in Air

As an example of quantitative analysis in the chemical sense, the determination of oxygen in gases will be described. The method is based on the fact that the volume susceptibility of oxygen is greater by a factor of 100 to 1000 than the susceptibility of all other gases except nitric oxide, nitrogen dioxide, and chlorine dioxide. Hence, if these three gases are absent, it is easy to determine oxygen in amounts greater than a few per cent. A convenient apparatus (26) consists of a small glass dumbbell attached at its midpoint to a quartz fiber as shown in Fig. 12. The dumbbell is located symmetrically about the axis of the poles of a permanent magnet. The force on the two spheres will be equal and opposite in direction and will lead to a rotation about the axis of the suspension. As described in Section 8.1, the force on each sphere at any position will be proportional to the difference of the susceptibility of the glass and of the surrounding gas. A small chamber is placed around the dumbbell and this is filled with the gas to be measured. The rotation of the dumbbell is observed using the mirror shown in Fig. 12. Using the calibration curve for the apparatus, the oxygen content of the sample can be determined in a few seconds to a precision of 1%. A similar technique could be used for determining the concentration of a known paramagnetic salt in water.

Other applications of this type are the determination of the amount of ferromagnetic material in a nonmagnetic sample. This has been done

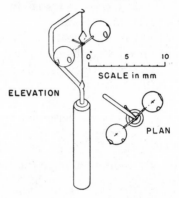

Fig. 12.   Test body for determination of oxygen in gases.

for minute impurities (11) using sensitive methods and for large amounts with induction techniques or force methods (10).

9.2. Carbon in Steel

Rapid methods of analysis for certain elements such as carbon in iron have been developed by a number of people (29). These methods are indirect in that the effect of the element on some magnetic property of the iron such as hysteresis loss, coercive force, or reversible permeability are determined. Once the device has been calibrated, the results are quite accurate provided, of course, that only the same general type of material is tested.

The rapid identification of batches of steel or other magnetic metal can be carried out using a differential induction method with a known sample in one coil and the unknown specimen in the other.

9.3. Phase Transformations

Another application of magnetic techniques is in the determination of phase diagrams or for detecting and following transformations in materials. An extensive work on an alloy system (16) is shown in Fig. 13 which gives the susceptibility data and Fig. 14 which presents the phase diagram obtained from it. A similar application to the system Fe-S

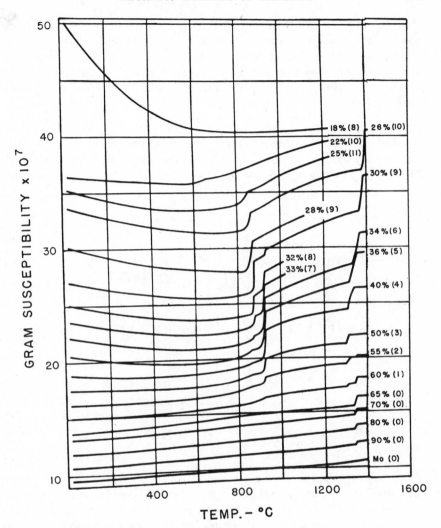

FIG. 13. Susceptibility vs. temperature in the Ni-Mo system.

(17), Fig. 15, shows how nicely solid solution in the compound FeS may be detected. The progress of a reaction at temperature is illustrated in Fig. 16 where the susceptibility changes which occur during the precipitation of copper from aluminum are plotted (1).

9.4. Geological Applications

Magnetic measurements have been used in a number of geological studies. In one case, similar strata below ground in adjacent areas, as in a region of oil wells, are located by susceptibility measurements on samples collected from various depths (30). Data on the orientation of the earth's field in past ages have been obtained by measuring the orientation of magnetized impurities at various depths in the mud of the ocean (18). Similar information has been obtained from sedimentary rocks (21).

9.5. Single Crystals

The orientation of single crystals of iron in the form of discs has been determined with an accuracy of a few degrees by measuring the torque exerted by a strong field whose direction lies in the plane of the specimen

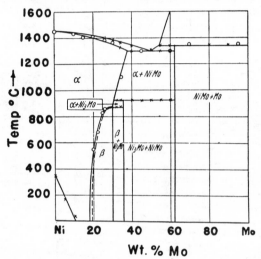

FIG. 14. Ni-Mo phase diagram as determined from susceptibility measurements.

(43). The method is much more rapid than the standard x-ray technique and presumably can be applied to other ferromagnetic single crystals.

Much information on the preferred orientation of crystals in a rolled sheet of ferromagnetic metal can be obtained by the magnetic torque method. The spread of orientation about the fiber axis can be studied in this way (8).

9.6. Molecular Structure

Magnetic measurements provide a powerful method for studying the electronic configuration of atoms, the degree of ionization of atoms in compounds and the structure of complex molecules and compounds. This is based on the fact that all magnetic phenomena (other than nuclear effects) are due to the electrons of atoms. An isolated electron has a definite magnetic moment (one Bohr magneton) and, in addition, electrons moving in closed orbits in an atom produce magnetic effects just as does a microscopic electric current.   The various electrons in an atom interact in a complicated way such that the magnetic effects of the individual electrons cancel each other out whenever a shell of electrons is

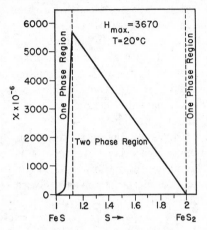

FIG. 15.   Susceptibility in the iron-sulfur system.

completed.   For this reason only the outer most electrons in incomplete shells contribute to the permanent magnetic moment of an atom.

When atoms interact with each other as they are brought together either in the pure elements or in compounds, the state of the outermost electrons will be altered and this shows up as a change in magnetic

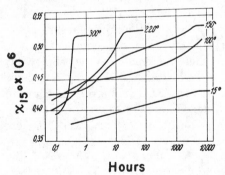

Hours

FIG. 16.   Susceptibility vs. aging time at various temperatures for quenched aluminum containing 5 % copper.

properties.   A large variety of effects are possible ranging from normal paramagnetism through the temperature independent paramagnetism of most metals to the ferromagnetic state.   In compound formation the exchange of electrons often leads to completed electron shells for the ions with a resultant loss of magnetic moment, thus leaving only a diamagnetic behavior. The magnetic moment of almost all atoms, both neutral and ionized, can be calculated from known electronic configurations and a comparison of these various calculated values with the experimental quantities often leads to definite information on the degree of ionization of atoms in various states (41).

All types of atoms experience a diamagnetic magnetization which, however, is often masked by a stronger paramagnetic or ferromagnetic behavior. Diamagnetism is due to a small change in the motion of the electrons moving around in an atom, which occurs as a result of the applied field. The change in motion is such that a magnetization opposing the applied field is produced. Since all the electrons contribute to this behavior, changes in the outer electrons produce only small changes in diamagnetic materials. Hence, it is possible to approximately compute the susceptibility of a diamagnetic compound just by adding up the known diamagnetic susceptibilities of the various atoms comprising the compound. Small correction quantities, known as Pascal's constants, need to be added to get complete agreement with experiment. It is found that for organic compounds the Pascal's constants have characteristic values for various molecular structures and, hence, susceptibility measurements on new substances can be used for determining the structure (27). The changes in bonding during polymerization, for example, can be determined in this way.

By means of magnetic measurements much information has been obtained in recent years on the grouping of atoms into radicals in complex compounds, chiefly organic (28). These research methods should be of use not simply for scientific information but also for the chemical analyst who is trying to develop new compounds.

In recent years measurements of susceptibility have been carried out at radio and microwave frequencies using a weak microwave field at right angles to a strong D.C. field which produces the magnetization. Under these conditions it is found that the specimen absorbs energy at certain resonance frequencies (15) and that this phenomenon may be understood theoretically (20). The results are of interest in connection with physical theory but also could be of use to the analyst since the energy absorption is determined by the coupling between the magnetic moment and the other degrees of vibrational freedom of the atoms, and hence could yield information on the structure of liquids and solids.

9.7. Magnetic Titrations

A chemical reaction in which the magnetic moment of certain of the atoms or ions changes appreciably, may be followed by means of magnetic measurements.   In this way it is possible in many cases to tell when the reaction has gone to completion and thus to conclude, in the case of a known reaction, what quantity of one of the reacting substances was initially present.   Conversely, if the amounts of reacting material are known, it is possible to conclude what the reaction has been through knowing the point at which the reaction is complete.   An illustration of the latter procedure is shown in Fig. 17, where the change in susceptibility

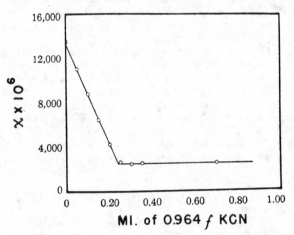

FIG. 17.   The magnetic titration of ferrihemoglobin with potassium cyanide at pH 6.75.

of a solution of ferrihemoglobin after various additons of KCN is plotted. From these data it was concluded that the reaction involved one cyanide per heme (12).

REFERENCES

1. Auer, H., *Z. Elektrochem.* **45,** 608 (1939).
2. Bates, L. F., Modern Magnetism, Cambridge, London, 1939, p. 6.
3. Bates, L. F., Modern Magnetism, Cambridge, London, 1939, p. 133.
4. Bates, L. F., Modern Magnetism, Cambridge, London, 1939, p. 70; Stoner, E. C., Magnetism and Matter, Methuen, London, 1934, p. 53.
5. Bitter, F., *Rev. Sci. Instruments* **7,** 482 (1936).
6. Bitter, F., Introduction to Ferromagnetism, McGraw-Hill, New York, 17 (1937).
7. Bitter, F., Introduction to Ferromagnetism, McGraw-Hill, New York, 194 (1937).
8. Bitter, F., Introduction to Ferromagnetism, McGraw-Hill, New York, 213 (1937).
9. Buehl, R., and Wulff, J., *Rev. Sci. Instruments* **9,** 224 (1938).
10. Buehl, R., Holloman, H., Wulff, J., *Trans. Am., Inst. Mining Met. Engrs.* **140,** 368 (1940).
11. Constant, F. W., *Rev. Modern Phys.* **17,** 81 (1945); Bitter, F., and Kaufmann, A. R., *Phys. Rev.* **56,** 1044 (1939).
12. Coryell, C., Stitt, F., Pauling, L., *J. Am. Chem. Soc.* **59,** 633 (1937).
13. Dwight, H. B., *Am. Inst. Elec. Engrs.*, Technical Paper #42–27, Nov. 1941.

14. Foex, G., and Forrer, R., *J. phys. radium* **7**, 180 (1926).
15. Griffiths, J. H. E., *Nature* **158**, 670 (1946).
16. Grube, G., and Winkler, O., *Z. Elektrochem.* **44**, 423 (1938).
17. Haraldson, H., and Neuber, A., *Naturwissenschaften* **24**, 280 (1936).
18. Johnson, E. A., and McNish, A. G., *Terr. Magn.* **43**, 401 (1938).
19. Kaufmann, A. R., *Rev. Sci. Instruments* **9**, 369 (1938).
20. Kittel, C., *Phys. Rev.* **71**, 270 (1947).
21. Koenigsberger, J. G., *Terr. Magn.* **43**, 119 and 299 (1938).
22. Leeds and Northrup Co. Notebook #2, Philadelphia, 1930, p. 32.
23. McKeehan, L. W., *Rev. Sci. Instruments* **5**, 265 (1934).
24. Page, L., and Adams, N., Principles of Electricity, Van Nostrand, New York, 1934, p. 234.
25. Page, L., and Adams, N., Principles of Electricity, Van Nostrand, New York, 1934, p. 407; Bates, L. F., Modern Magnetism, Cambridge, London, 1939, p. 82.
26. Pauling, L., Wood, R. E., and Sturdivant, J. H., *J. Am. Chem. Soc.* **68**, 795 (1946).
27. Selwood, P. W., Magnetochemistry, Interscience, New York, 1943, p. 51.
28. Selwood, P. W., Magnetochemistry, Interscience, New York, 1943, p. 116. Weissberger, A., Physical Methods of Organic Chemistry II, Interscience, New York, 1233 (1946).
29. Selwood, P. W., Magnetochemistry, Interscience, New York, 236 (1943).
30. Selwood, P. W., Magnetochemistry, Interscience, New York, 1943, p. 264.
31. Shuddemagen, C., *Phys. Rev.* **31**, 165 (1910); Wurschmidt, J., *Z. Physik* **19**, 388 (1923).
32. Spooner, T., Properties and Testing of Magnetic Materials, McGraw-Hill, New York, 1927, p. 231.
33. Spooner, T., Properties and Testing of Magnetic Materials, McGraw-Hill, New York, 1927, p. 302.
34. Starling, S. G., Electricity and Magnetism, Longman-Green, London, 1930, pp. 256 and 273.
35. Starr, C., *Phys. Rev.* **60**, 245 (1941).
36. Stoner, E. C., Magnetism and Matter, Methuen, London, 1934, p. 39; Ewing, J. A., Magnetic Induction in Iron and Other Metals, London, 1900, p. 24.
37. Stoner, E. C., Magnetism and Matter, Methuen, London, 1934, p. 57.
38. Stoner, E. C., Magnetism and Matter, Methuen, London, 1934, p. 60.
39. Stoner, E. C., Magnetism and Matter, Methuen, London, 1934, p. 70; Bates, L. F., Modern Magnetism, Cambridge, London, 1939, p. 91.
40. Stoner, E. C., Magnetism and Matter, Methuen, London, 1934, p. 251.
41. Stoner, E. C., Magnetism and Matter, Methuen, London, 1934, p. 310.
42. Sucksmith, W. Potter, H. and Broadway, L. *Proc. Roy. Soc. London* **A117**, 481 (1928).
43. Tarasov, L. P., and Bitter, F., *Phys. Rev.* **52**, 353 (1937).
44. Weiss, P., and Onnes, K., *J. phys. radium* **9**, 555 (1910).

The Determination of the Area of the Surfaces of Solids

GEORGE JURA

Department of Chemistry, University of California, Berkeley, California

CONTENTS

1. INTRODUCTION

In many respects the surfaces of solids exhibit the same general behavior as those of liquids. There is a tremendous amount of detailed knowledge of the surfaces of liquids and the interaction of these surfaces with other molecules. On the other hand there is very little such knowledge of the surfaces of solids. This discrepancy in available information is largely due to the fact that until recently no reliable methods have been available for the estimation of the surface areas of solids. Fundamentally, the area of the surface is essential for the comprehension of any surface phenomena, since the gross effect or interaction studied is directly proportional to the area.

A simple illustration for the necessity of an area figure follows. If any solid is cleaned, i.e., foreign molecules removed from its surface, and then is immersed in a liquid, heat is usually evolved which can be measured in a sensitive calorimeter. The measurement is called the heat of immersion or wetting. Four samples of titanium dioxide, I, II, III, and IV, all in the form of anatase, were immersed in water at 25°C. Samples III and IV are known to have been treated with aluminum oxide. It was found that 1.15, 1.69, 1.42, and 2.21 cal. g.$^{-1}$ were evolved. These figures are useless for comparative purposes and are of value only for the samples in their respective bottles or barrels. If the areas of these samples are determined it is found that the heats of immersion are 520, 510, 650, and 1200 ergs cm.$^{-2}$ respectively. These figures show that the degree of subdivision of the untreated samples has no effect on the surface properties for the range of particle sizes involved. They also show that treatment with aluminum oxide seriously affects the surface properties, and that the treatments involved in samples III and IV were sufficiently different to alter their interaction radically. The knowledge of the area permits not only this comparison but also comparisons with solids other than titanium dioxide. It has been found that in water the heats evolved for "pure" solids ranged from 165 ergs cm.$^{-2}$ for graphite to 850 ergs cm.$^{-2}$ for zirconium silicate (36).

Many methods have been proposed for the determination of the area of solids. Unfortunately, none has such a strong theoretical basis that the results obtained by its application can be considered as certain. The experimental evidence available at the present time does indicate strongly that the relative areas of various solids can be determined to within 10%. For any comparative purpose it is only the relative areas that are essential. The evidence for the absolute areas of solids rests on the "absolute" method of Harkins and Jura (39) or the values of the effective cross-sectional areas of adsorbed molecules to be used in the theory of Brunauer, Emmett, and Teller (18). Both of these are discussed in detail in later sections.

The methods for area determination may be classified in three groups: (1) Those that depend on the determination of particle size, (2) those that depend on the determination of the adsorption isotherm, and (3) those that depend upon some special property other than particle size and adsorption, which must depend in some known manner on the available area. Most of the proposed methods fall into the first two groups, and since the adsorption methods are the simplest experimentally, most of the attention has been given to this class. Thus, the majoi portion of this chapter deals with the methods based on adsorption.

The methods of particle size determination are numerous. From the known density of the solid, the geometry of the particles, and the average particle size or size distribution it is relatively simple to calculate an area. Particle size determinations in general are not satisfactory for obtaining the area. One uncertainty arises with every such method. If the solid is porous, i.e., possesses an internal area, the particle size measurement cannot account for this area. Thus, the area obtained is the lowest that the solid may have. Many particle size determinations have one other further difficulty. Small particles tend to aggregate in many solids. In determinations such as sedimentation or microscopic examination, either visual or electron, an aggregate will appear as a single particle. Since a large particle has a lower area than the same weight of smaller particles the area again will be low. This difficulty is not encountered when the particle size is determined by the broadening of x-ray diffraction lines or the low angle scattering of x-rays. Because of these inherent difficulties, the determination of areas from particle size will not be considered in this chapter. Many methods of particle size determinations are given in other chapters of this volume.

2. "Absolute" Method of Area Determination

2.1. General Considerations

The "absolute" method is a calorimetric method and was first proposed by Harkins and Jura (39). This method is experimentally slow and difficult, and its theory restricts its use to nonporous solids. In spite of its difficulties and limitations, it is considered first because (1) the theory is simple and sound, (2) it is the only known method that gives an area directly, and (3) it indicates that the answers obtained by adsorption methods are absolute as well as relative.

In general outline, the method is based on the fact that when the solid has adsorbed the vapor of a liquid on its surface, and the fugacity or chemical potential of the adsorbed molecules is equal to that of the liquid at the same temperature, then the heat content per unit area of the surface can be related to the heat content of the liquid. In any system for which the method can be used, the surface of the solid with respect to this property is changed to that of a liquid if the contact angle of the liquid against the solid is zero.

2.2. Theory of "Absolute" Method

With every surface, whether solid or liquid, there is associated a free surface energy, γ, a surface heat content, h, a surface entropy, s, etc. If the surface is that of a liquid, the free surface energy is more commonly called the surface tension. The heat content and surface tension are simply related. The relationship is given by eq. (1)

$$h = \gamma - T \left(\frac{\partial \gamma}{\partial T}\right)_p \tag{1}$$

where T is the absolute temperature and p is the external pressure. A simple derivation is given by Lewis and Randall (57). If a clean solid is immersed in a liquid, its free surface energy is changed from γ_S to γ_{SL}, and its heat content from h_S to h_{SL}. Thus, the heat evolved, Δh_E in the immersion process per unit area is

$$\Delta h_E = h_S - h_{SL} = \gamma_S - \gamma_{SL} - T \left(\frac{\partial \gamma_S}{\partial T} - \frac{\partial \gamma_{SL}}{\partial T}\right)_p \tag{2}$$

Equation (2) has been extensively discussed by Harkins and Boyd (36). If the solid is saturated with the vapor of the liquid, then its free surface energy is changed from γ_s to γ_{se} and the heat evolved on immersion from Δh_E to Δh_{Ee}, and

$$\Delta h_{Ee} = \gamma_{se} - \gamma_{sl} - T \left(\frac{\partial \gamma_{se}}{\partial T} - \frac{\partial \gamma_{sl}}{\partial T}\right)_p \tag{3}$$

Equation (3) can be simplified by use of the Dupree equation

$$\gamma_{Se} = \gamma_{SL} + \gamma_L \cos \theta \tag{4}$$

where γ_L is the free surface energy of the liquid and θ is the contact angle, measured through the liquid, of the liquid against the solid. If eq. 4 is substituted in eq. 3 it is found that

$$\Delta h_{Ee} = \left\{ \gamma_L - T \left(\frac{\partial \gamma_L}{\partial T}\right) \right\} \cos \theta + T \gamma_L \sin \theta \frac{\partial \theta}{\partial T} \tag{5}$$

If the contact angle is zero, which is usually true, eq. (5) reduces to

$$\Delta h_{Ee} = \gamma_L - T \left(\frac{\partial \gamma_L}{\partial T}\right) = h_L \tag{6}$$

Equation 6 simply states that when a drop of liquid with unit area is immersed in a larger body of the liquid the heat evolved is exactly the same as that obtained if a unit area of the solid saturated with the liquid is immersed, provided the contact angle is zero. Thus, if Σ' is the area per gram of the solid covered with its film and H_{Ee} is the heat evolved, when one gram of the solid is immersed in the liquid the area g.$^{-1}$ of the film covered solid is

$$\sum{}' = \frac{H_{Ee}}{h_L} \tag{7}$$

The total surface energies of most liquids are available in the literature.

The *International Critical Tables*, Vol. IV, McGraw-Hill, New York, for example, contains the necessary data for nearly any liquid which might be used for this purpose.

If the solid is porous, the pores will be filled in as the solid absorbs the vapor and the area will be decreased. Since there is no independent method of determining the area of the porous part of the sample, the area of the film covered solid cannot be related to the area of the clean solid. This is a limitation which restricts the use of the method.

Even if the solid is nonporous one further correction must be made before the area of the solid is known. Fortunately, this correction is not large. This correction is made necessary by the fact that the adsorbed film is polymolecular, which increases the size of the particle and consequently the area. The relation between the area of the solid and the film covered solid depends upon the geometry of the individual particle, the film thickness, and the size distribution of the particle. Since the entire correction for all of the factors is not large, ca. 5%, none of these need be known with great accuracy.

The film thickness can be obtained with sufficient accuracy from the area of the film covered solid, the amount of gas adsorbed at saturation, and the assumption that the density of the adsorbed material is the same as that of the liquid. None of the above is strictly correct but no serious error is introduced by these assumptions. For example, if the particles are cubes of titanium dioxide 1200 A. on edge and the film thickness is assumed to be 20 A. the final result is changed by only 2% if the film thickness is changed from 20 to 40 A. The adsorption work indicates that at saturation the film thickness is on the order of 25 A. for water (38). The film thickness depends upon the vapor as well as the solid. Films of *n*-heptane average about 200 A. at 25°C. Thus, there is a distinct advantage in the use of water. The above figures probably could be used for any solid without introducing too great an error. For liquids other than water and *n*-heptane it would be necessary to determine the amount adsorbed at saturation. Since the area of the solid covered with the film is not much different from that of the clean solid, the film thickness is essential only if the highest accuracy is desired.

The geometry of the individual particle also affects the magnitude of the correction. For example, consider the rectangular parallelopipeds whose dimensions in the three normal directions have the ratios 1:1:1, 1:10:10, and 1:100:100. For a sample of graphite whose area is 4.2 m.^{2}g.$^{-1}$, when *n*-heptane is the liquid, the necessary correction for each of these shapes would be 10, 5, and 0%, respectively. This variation in the correction factor arises from the ratio of the area to the volume for a given geometry.

A small variation in the correction factors arises depending on the assumptions made concerning the particle size distribution. It is readily seen that the smaller the particle, the greater the correction. The assumption of an average size, as determined from the density of the solid and area of the film covered solid leads to the largest difference in area between the film-covered and clean solid. If the particle is a cube, the relation between the area g.$^{-1}$ Σ of the clean solid and Σ' is

$$\sum = \frac{\Sigma'}{1 + \alpha \frac{\tau}{d}} \tag{8}$$

where τ is the film thickness, d the edge of the cube, and α depends upon the assumed shape of the film-covered particle. If it is assumed that the film forms a cube, α has the value of 4. On the basis that the film will be cylindrical about the edges the value of α is π. On physical grounds, the cylindrical shape about the edges is more probable, since the surface area is lower. The assumption of the formation of the cubical shape, yields the largest correction factor, and consequently the minimum area for the clean solid. If any reasonable, continuous size distribution is assumed, then the value for α is even less than π. The smallest value of α thus far obtained is $\frac{\pi}{2}$, on the assumption that the distribution is of the form

$$N = Ce^{-bd2}$$

Thus, for a nonporous solid, the minimum correction is zero, and the maximum possible correction is given by the use of eq. (8) when α is 4.

Equation (8) shows that the most accurate result is obtained by making the ratio $\frac{\tau}{d}$ as small as possible. The smallest values for τ have been obtained with water. Water also has one further advantage, the ratio of its surface energy to specific heat is the highest. It is also evident that better results can be obtained by the use of large rather than small particles since τ is dependent only upon the crystalline face, and chemical composition.

2.3. Experimental Method

Figure 1 shows the calorimeter that has been used for measuring the heats. This calorimeter is essentially the same as that described by Harkins and Dahlstrom (37) and has a sensitivity of 2×10^{-5} °C. The technique of making the measurements is that described by Boyd and Harkins (12). Figure 2 shows the apparatus used for the preparation of the samples.

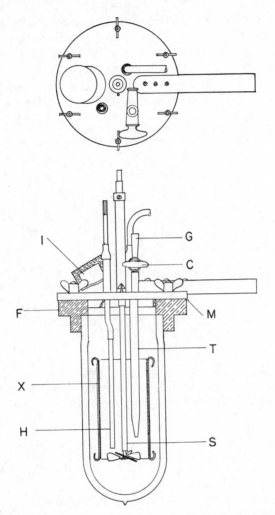

Fig. 1.   Calorimeter.   *T*, 36 junction thermal; *H*, heating element; *G*, inlet for liquid; *C*, stopcock; *X*, chimney to give better circulation for powder; *I*, opening for introduction of powder; *S*, stirrer driven by synchronous motor; *F* and *M* brass collar and cap.

Between 10 and 15 g. of the powder is placed in each of the sample bulbs B, of which there are usually six, and 5 to 10 cm.³ of liquid is placed in C.   The water is degassed by boiling away about one-half of the original volume and then sealing the bottom of the bulb.   The tubes that contain the powder are heated in an electrically heated furnace at 500° for 24 hours, after which they are allowed to cool to room tem-

perature.   The pumps are in continuous operation during this period.
After the samples have cooled, the manifold is sealed off at C, and the
whole apparatus is submerged in a thermostat at 25.00°.   After 4 hours
in the thermostat, the tip of C is broken with an iron rod and a magnet.
This allows the water vapor to penetrate the entire system.   After
about 24 hours, which is more than sufficient time for the system to

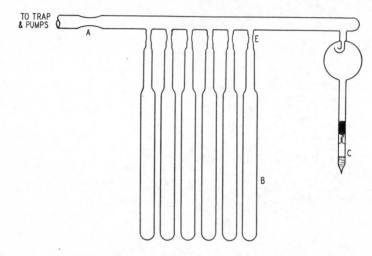

Fig. 2.   Apparatus for the adsorption of an equilibrium film on a powder.   C is
the liquid, and the powder is in the tubes, B.   After the degassing of the surface the
system is sealed off from the pumps at A and the tubes and liquid are immersed in a
thermostat.   After equilibrium is reached the tubes are sealed off at E.

reach equilibrium, the manifold is raised and the sample tubes are
sealed off at E.

2.4. Results

Only three areas have been determined by this method: two samples
of titanium dioxide in the form of anatase, one of which had been treated
with aluminum oxide and a sample of graphite (8) containing less than
0.004% ash and presumably free from any oxygen complexes.   Water
was used with the two samples of anatase and n-heptane with the graphite.
In each case, the temperature was 25°C.   Water could not be used with
graphite since the contact angle is not zero (30).   Table I lists the areas
for these three solids.   The values given in Table I were obtained by
using 118.5 and 50 ergs cm.$^{-2}$ as the heat contents of the surfaces of water
(34) and n-heptane (2), respectively.

Experimentally the best value is that for the untreated titanium
dioxide.   Much weight can not be given to the treated sample, since

the evolution of heat was too slow for the type of calorimeter used. With this slow evolution of heat, low results are generally obtained. The results with graphite are the best that could be hoped for with the low area and low heat evolved per unit area.

The agreement between the results obtained by adsorption measurements and the absolute method is excellent.

Before the values obtained by this method can be considered as certain, it is essential to show that these solids are nonporous. There is no known method for showing this. The only direct evidence that the powders are nonporous is that none obviously appear to be so in

TABLE I

Areas of Powders Obtained by the "Absolute" Method

Solid	Σ'	Σ	
	m.^{2}g.$^{-1}$	m.^{2}g.$^{-1}$	Obtained from adsorption measurements m.^{2}g.$^{-1}$
TiO$_2$ (untreated)	14.4 $\pm$ 0.4	13.8	13.8[a]
TiO$_2$(Al$_2$O$_3$ treated)	9.1 $\pm$ 0.4	8.9	9.6[b]
Graphite	4.6 $\pm$ 0.6	4.4	4.1–4.3[c]

[a] This sample was used to standardize the adsorption measurements.
[b] Nitrogen adsorption at −195.8°C.
[c] These values were obtained with nitrogen at −195.8°C., *n*-hexane at 0°C. and *n*-heptane at 25°C.

electron microscope photographs. From the nature of the instrument, this evidence cannot be considered satisfactory. The general theory of solids indicates that cracks would not appear in individual crystals of the size used, ca. 1200 A. This is the point upon which the validity of the area of the clean solid rests. Until some method can be devised which will show that these powders are nonporous, there will be some doubt as to whether or not the area of the clean solid can be related to that of the solid covered with a film.

The absolute method gives directly the area of the solid which has adsorbed the vapor of a liquid to saturation. Because contact angles and the temperature coefficients of contact angles cannot be accurately measured, the method is restricted to the use of liquids that exhibit a zero contact·angle against the solid. If the solid is nonporous, the area of the clean solid can be related to that of the film covered surface. This relation is not accurate, but since it is small, equal to or less than 5% for the solids and liquids thus far used, this source of error is not serious. The entire difficulty with the application of the method lies in demonstrating that the solid is nonporous. There is no direct experimental evidence to demonstrate this point.   The theory of the structure of solids does indicate that crystals as small as those used in these experiments would not exhibit any cracks that contribute to the area.

3. ADSORPTION OF GASES

3.1. Introduction

The most general and reliable methods for the determination of the areas of solids are based on the determination of the adsorption isotherms of gases on the surfaces of solids.   The isotherm is the determination of the quantity of gas adsorbed as a function of the equilibrium pressure of the adsorbed gas at constant pressure.

The adsorption of gases is one of the oldest known phenomena. Scheele (65) is credited with the discovery in 1773.   Since this time thousands of papers have appeared in the literature with reports of experimental results, and many theories have been proposed in explanation.   The complexity of the phenomena that may occur has been such that it is only in the last half century that there has been any real progress in the elucidation of the observed facts.

When a gas is adsorbed a number of possibilities exist.   The gas may dissolve in the solid.   This solution may or may not lead to compound formation.   For example, hydrogen is soluble in iron at high temperatures (67).   Here, there is no evidence of compound formation. If paladium is substituted for iron, solution occurs with the formation of the interstital compound, paladium hydride (68).   Alternately the gas molecules may form a compound with molecules on the surface of the solid.   The nature of many of their compounds is unknown.   For example, if carbon monoxide is adsorbed on iron at temperatures as low as 77°K., the amount of gas adsorbed which is sufficient to form a monomolecular layer is apparently bound differently from the remainder of the adsorbed gas (27).   This first layer cannot be desorbed at low temperatures as can the remainder of the gas.   This gas can be removed at high temperatures, not as carbon monoxide, but as iron carbonyl.   The experiments indicate that there is one such carbon monoxide molecule adsorbed for each iron atom in the surface.   It is true that no iron carbonyl is known that has the formula Fe(CO), but it is evident that there is some sort of chemical binding between the gas and solid.   When a reaction occurs between the gas molecules and the surface of the solid, the name used to describe the process is chemisorption.   The process of surface compound formation may be irreversible as in the example cited, or reversible.

The molecule may undergo any number of chemical reactions on the surface, and the products may be described.   The solid itself apparently is unchanged.   This is, of course, the well-known process of hetergeneous catalysis.   The role of the surface is not thoroughly understood at present.

Finally, the adsorption may occur, due to the intermolecular forces between the molecules of the solid in the surface region and the molecules of gas.   The nature of these forces depends of course on the nature of the molecules in both the gas and the solid.   This process occurs because there is a decrease in free energy of the system, particularly that of the surface of the solid.

Of all the various possibilities, the one that will always occur is the last.   Therefore, any general method of area determination must be based on the intermolecular interaction.   Since Van der Waals' forces are always present, the theory should be founded on this type of interaction.   Another requirement, of course, is that all other effects be absent.   The adsorption methods of area determination are based upon the above assumptions.

Only a few theories of adsorption that involve area determination are discussed.   Other theories and proposals are excellently reviewed in a recent book by Brunauer (14).   A survey of the earlier literature is to be found in McBain (59).

3.2. Experimental Methods

The determination of the adsorption isotherm involves the measurement of the amount of gas adsorbed as a function of the pressure.   A large number of methods and techniques have been devised.   Many of these have been built for obtaining information concerning a specific system.   In this review, the factors that affect the final results are discussed and a detailed description is given for a volumetric method that gives results of the highest precision.   It is hoped that this is sufficient so that changes can be made to fit individual needs.

One of the most important factors in a successful area determination is the choice of the gas and temperature at which the determination is to be made.   The gas should have the following characteristics: it must not react with the solid, it must not dissolve in the solid, the solid should not catalyze a change in the chemical nature of the gas, the gas should be pure, or readily purified, and a gas molecule without a permanent electric moment is preferable.

There are two factors that dictate the choice of temperature.   A temperature should be chosen such that the bath can be maintained at constant temperature.   This is essential since the effect of temperature on the equilibrium pressure of the adsorbed gas is marked.   Convenient temperatures are the melting and boiling temperature of pure compounds. Those in most general use are liquid nitrogen at 77.3°K. for use with nitrogen, oxygen, argon, carbon monoxide, etc. Ice is generally used at 0°C. for determinations with n-butane. At room temperatures simple water thermostats can be used.

The other important factor determining the choice of temperature is the area of the solid. The temperature is used to control the vapor pressure of the stable three-dimensional phase of the gas. For materials of small area, it is necessary that the vapor pressure be low so that the amount of gas adsorbed is a reasonable fraction of the amount of gas measured if a volumetric method is used, and that the change in bouyancy correction does not overshadow the increased weight of the sample if gravimetric methods are used. For economy of time, it is essential that as high a temperature as possible for a given gas be used, because the time required to obtain equilibrium between the adsorbed and unadsorbed gas is materially reduced for many solids as the temperature is increased.

3.3. Preparation of Solids

One of the important features in the determination of the area of a solid is the "degassing." Degassing consists in the removal of all gases from the surface preparatory to the actual determinations. The general method is to heat the sample in a vacuum until these gases are removed. No specific rules can be given to cover all possible solids. Frequently, the exact conditions are determined by the solid. In general, as high a temperature and vacuum as possible should be used.

The temperature chosen should be such that the structure of the solid is undisturbed. These disturbances are of several kinds. If the solid has more than one crystalline form, the temperature should not exceed the transformation temperature. An example of this type of behavior is tin, which changes its crystalline form at 185°C. (44). A second factor which may determine the maximum temperature is sintering. Most crystallites have a minimum temperature below which crystal growth will not occur, regardless of the time maintained at a given temperature. Above this temperature crystal growth can occur. Many noncrystalline materials exhibit a similar effect, a decrease in area with an increase of temperature. Table II exhibits the effect of temperature on the area of a silica-alumina cracking catalyst. The maximum temperature used in degassing should be below the sintering temperature for crystals, and below the maximum temperature to which a noncrystallite has been previously heated.

Frequently these conditions cannot be met, and a compromise must be made. If this is done, it should be borne in mind that the observed result may not be the correct result, and may depend on the actual time and temperature used.

One other factor determining the degree of degassing is the range of pressures of the adsorbed gas. The lower the gas pressures the more drastic are the conditions needed for degassing. For example, assume that the solid can be heated to 500°C. for any desired time. If the vapor

TABLE II

The Change of Area of a Cracking Catalyst as a Function of Activation Temperature

T°C.	Area (m.^{2}g.$^{-1}$)
100	455
500	434
600	409
700	395
800	321

pressure of the liquid or solid is 760 mm. the error is not greater than 3 to 5% if the vacuum maintained is 10^{-3} mm. Hg for a period of 12 hours. By the time the vapor pressure is 100 mm., a vacuum of 10^{-5} mm. Hg must be used. When the vapor pressure is below 1 mm. the above conditions are no longer satisfactory. Three to four days at 500°C., and a vacuum of 10^{-6} mm. is absolutely essential. Also, it is necessary to bake out the entire system.

3.4. Apparatus Design

There are numerous methods that can be used for pressure determination. The exact method chosen will depend upon the pressures to be measured. The device used should be such, if possible, that each pressure measured is determined to within 1%. For pressures between 35 and several hundred millimeters of mercury, an ordinary mercury in glass manometer is suitable. For pressures ranging from .2 to several millimeters, a wide bore mercury manometer may still be used if the difference in height is measured with a traveling microscope sensitive to .001 mm. (46). For intermediate pressures mercury manometers of suitable bore, used in conjunction with cathetometers of sufficient accuracy, are suitable. The factor that determines the bore of the tubing for the manometer is that the change in capillary depression due to variations in the internal diameter be less than the precision desired in the measurement of height. For pressures below 0.2 mm., recourse must be had to other devices, the McLeod and Pirani gauges, etc. For descriptions of these and other gauges used for these low pressures see Strong (69), Hoag (43), or Ostwald-Luther (61).

The methods for the determination of the amount of gas adsorbed are of two kinds, gravimetric and volumetric. In the gravimetric methods the gas adsorbed is determined by the change in weight of the sample of solid. Two general methods are available, the extension of a spring and a beam balance.

The extension-spring method was used by McBain and Bakr (60). One end of a quartz spiral spring is attached to the top of a long tube. The solid, in a platinum bucket, is suspended at the other end of the spring, and its extension is determined with a cathetometer, or traveling microscope. The spring is calibrated by placing weights in the bucket and measuring the extension. For sufficiently high pressures it is also essential to make a buoyancy correction, which depends on the actual pressure and molecular weight of the gas surrounding the system.

This method is useful for high area materials but does not possess sufficient sensitivity for determination of solids of low specific area. Boyd and Livingston (13) applied the method to low area materials but the precision of the amount adsorbed is not as high as desirable. The area of these solids can be conveniently determined with much higher precision by a volumetric method.

The quartz beam balance on the other hand can be made as sensitive as desired. With sufficient care the balance can be made sensitive to 10^{-11} to 10^{-12} g. This method is useful for determinations of the lowest areas. In theory an isotherm could be determined on a few square centimeters of solid. The calibration of the quartz beam is essentially the same as that for the quartz spiral. A satisfactory apparatus is described by Barrett et al. (7).

In the volumetric methods, the volume and pressure of the gas is determined before and after exposure to solid. From the thermodynamic behavior of the gas, the amount of gas that is adsorbed is calculated from the measured initial and final pressures. This method is rapid, and capable of high precision. By the judicious choice of gas, temperature, and apparatus design, it is possible to determine areas of any extent. The method can be made as precise as desired by an increase in the accuracy of the determinations of both volume and pressure.

There are two characteristics of gas behavior which must be considered. Many gases cannot be considered ideal and corrections must be made for the deviation of the gas from the perfect state. Since extensive fugacity data are not available for most gases, approximations must be made. The method for making these corrections recommended by Giauque (33) is to use the Berthelot equation,

$$pV = RT\left[1 + \frac{9}{128}\frac{pT_c}{p_cT}\left(1 - 6\frac{T_c^2}{T^2}\right)\right]$$

where the critical temperature and pressure, T_c and p_c, are the constants in the equation.

The other property of gases creates a problem only if the pressure measuring device and the pressure to be measured are at widely different temperatures. The possible effect of the thermal transpiration (51) brought on by these conditions must be considered. If the pressures are such that the mean free path is small compared to the diameter of the tubing the effect can be neglected. If the mean free path of the gas is long compared to the diameter of the tubing, the correction is simple, since the pressure desired, p_1, is related to the measured pressure p_2 by the formula

$$\frac{p_1}{p_2} = \left(\frac{T_1}{T_2}\right)^{\frac{1}{2}} \tag{9}$$

where T_1 and T_2 are the corresponding absolute temperatures. If the mean free path is of the order of the diameter of the tubing, tedious measurements are necessary to obtain the correct pressure. Thus, the temperature should be chosen so that all of the necessary measurements are made when the mean free path is small or large compared to the diameter of the tubing.

Apparatus design for volumetric methods depends on the area to be determined. For the very smallest areas, the apparatus described by Wooten and Brown (71) or Armbruster and Austin (3) is satisfactory. For areas on the order of one square meter, the method of Beebe and co-workers (9) is satisfactory. For several square meters to about 40 m.², the apparatus described by Jura and Harkins (46) is suitable, while for the largest areas, the apparatus described by Emmett and Brunauer (24) is usable. A modification of the latter is described in detail. Needless to say many special variations and modifications are possible which are useful for special needs. For example, if all of the solids have approximately the same area, then the apparatus suggested by Krieger (53) is economical of both space and time.

In the following paragraphs a variation of the design of Brunauer and Emmett is illustrated in Fig. 3. The apparatus has been designed primarily for determinations with nitrogen at −195.8°C., its normal boiling point. The gas reservoirs and purification trains are not shown.

The temperature is determined by means of a vapor pressure thermometer which is composed of the compression chamber C, the manometer M, and the tube T, which is next to the adsorption bulb B. After the bath is placed around the adsorption bulb, the gas is admitted into the evacuated compression chamber to the approximate vapor pressure of the gas at the bath temperature. The gas is then condensed by filling, or partially filling the compression chamber with mercury. The vapor pressure is read off the manometer M.

Any gas which has an easily measurable pressure at the bath temperature may be used. In the event that the gas used in the ther-

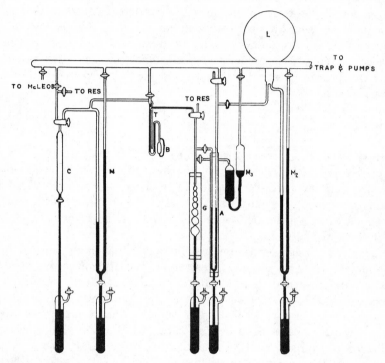

FIG. 3. Apparatus for the determination of adsorption isotherms. This system is designed for work over two ranges: to 100 mm. and to 760 mm. For the low pressure range the manometer M_3 is used. The U tube A and the manometer M_2 are removed from the working system by stopcocks. For the higher pressure range manometer M_3 is closed out of the system and the U tube A and manometer M_2 used as indicated in the text.

mometer is different from that used in the adsorption the measured vapor pressure of the thermometer gas is used to calculate the temperature, from which the vapor pressure of the adsorbent is calculated. Since for the purpose of area determinations, the vapor pressure determination is more important than the temperature, it is preferable to use the adsorbent in the thermometer and measure its vapor pressure directly.

The burette is the series of glass bulbs marked G. Calibration marks are either cut or etched. The volume of each bulb is determined by the weight of mercury it holds.   Duplicate determinations agree to within 0.005 cc.

The pressure in the burette system is read on manometer M_2.   The pressure read on manometer M_2 is that of the air in the 5-liter flask marked L.   The pressure in L is made equal to that in the burette in the following manner.

The mercury in the cut-off A is pulled down and the cut-off is evacuated.   After this the mercury is allowed to rise.   On the left side the meniscus of the mercury is brought exactly to one of the graduation marks.   The amount of mercury in the cut-off is maintained constant by closing stopcock 1.   As long as the temperature remains constant, the pressures on the right and left hand sides are equal when the mercury is at the chosen graduation mark.   When this method is used it is possible to reproduce pressures to 0.05 mm. with a maximum deviation of 0.10 mm.

This method of determining pressures is chosen because the small internal diameter of the burette means that small variations in diameter have a marked effect on the level due to capillary depression.   In a given system the difference in height of the mercury in the two arms with a vacuum on both sides is -3 to about $+3$ mm. as the mercury is moved up.   Thus, if it were assumed that the pressure on both sides is the same when the arms are level, an error of as much as 3 mm. might be made.   The per cent error would of course depend on the absolute value of the pressure.   Working with nitrogen at $-195.8°$ at a relative pressure of 0.2, the error in the pressure reading could be as high as 4%. This error would obviously also be reflected in the calculation of the adsorbed volume of gas.

4. LANGMUIR ISOTHERM

4.1. Theory

One of the earliest attempts to obtain a theoretical relationship between the area of a solid and the adsorption of a gas on the surface is that of Langmuir (55).   The application of the results of this theory have met with restricted success.   The fundamental lack of generality of this treatment lies in one of the assumptions of the theory, namely, that the adsorption of gases on the surfaces of solids is monomolecular. Actually, if the structure of the solid does not restrict the adsorption to the thickness of a single layer, polymolecular films are formed.   In a later section, it is shown that the Langmuir theory is a special case of the theory of Brunauer, Emmett, and Teller.   Although several derivations of the Langmuir equation have been formulated, the original treatment of Langmuir is followed in this chapter.

The treatment of Langmuir represents a simple application of the kinetic theory of gases. If μ molecules impinge per second on a surface, some are adsorbed while others are elastically reflected. If α is the absorbed fraction of molecules that strike the surface, then the total number of molecules adsorbed in unit time on unit area is $\alpha\mu$. However, a certain number of molecules per unit area, ν, will obtain sufficient energy to leave the surface and re-enter the gas phase. When equilibrium is reached, the number of molecules leaving the surface is the same as that being adsorbed. Thus

$$\alpha\mu = \nu \tag{10}$$

The result expressed by eq. 10 is completely general, and no assumptions that limit the validity of the equation have as yet been made. The assumptions that limit the usefulness of the final result are made in the evaluation of the quantities in eq. 10 in terms of pressure, p, and the fraction of the surface, θ, covered by adsorbed molecules.

Both sides of eq. 10 can be evaluated with the aid of certain assumptions. Only those molecules on the surface that have an energy equal to or greater than the heat of adsorption, q, can evaporate. If it is assumed that there is no interaction between the adsorbed molecules, then the only energy change in the process is that due to the interaction between the atoms, ions, and/or molecules of the solid and the gas. q is then a constant and is independent of the surface concentration of the adsorbed molecules. Thus if ν_1 is the rate of evaporation where the surface is completely covered, then

$$\nu = \nu_1\theta \tag{11}$$

where θ is the fraction of the surface covered by the adsorbed molecules. Also the number of molecules on the surface that have an energy equal to a greater than q is proportional to $\nu_1 e^{-q/kT}$. Thus the rate of evaporation is

$$\nu_1 = k_0 e^{-q/kT} \tag{12}$$

where k_0 is a proportionality constant, k the Boltzmann constant, and T the absolute temperature. The complete expression for ν is,

$$k_0\nu_1\theta_1 e^{-q/kT} \tag{13}$$

In the evaluation of μ, the rate at which molecules are adsorbed, another assumption is made: the adsorption is monomolecular, those molecules which strike the surface where molecules are present are elastically reflected, and only those which come into contact with the bare surface can be adsorbed. From this assumption it follows that,

$$\alpha\mu = \alpha_0(1 - \theta)\mu \tag{14}$$

From the kinetic theory of gases

$$\mu = \frac{p}{\sqrt{2\pi mkT}} \tag{15}$$

where p is the gas pressure and m the molecular mass. Thus

$$\alpha = \frac{\alpha_0(1 - \theta)p}{\sqrt{2\pi mkT}} \tag{16}$$

Equating eqs. (16) and (13) and solving for θ, the result is

$$\theta = \frac{ap}{1 + ap} \tag{17}$$

where

$$a = \frac{\alpha_0 1^{/kT}}{k_0 \sqrt{2\pi mkT}}$$

If v_m is the number of molecules required to completely cover the surface and v cm.^{3} of gas have been adsorbed, then

$$\theta = \frac{v}{v_m} \tag{18}$$

The substitution of $\dfrac{v}{v_m}$ for θ in eq. (17) gives the final result

$$\frac{v}{v_m} = \frac{ap}{1 + ap} \tag{19}$$

For the purposes of calculation eq. (19) is written

$$\frac{p}{v} = \frac{1}{av_m} + \frac{p}{v_m} \tag{20}$$

Equation (20) is now in a linear form with respect to the variables p/v and p. If the Langmuir equation is valid, a plot of p vs. p/v results in a straight line whose slope is $1/v_m$ and whose intercept is $1/av_m$. Assumptions other than the kinetic approach of Langmuir, can be used to derive equations which possess the same form as that of eq. (19). The most important of these is that of Fowler, who used the methods of statistical mechanics (31).

The statistical method does have the advantage in that the assumptions underlying the derivations are clearly defined. In the treatment of Fowler and Guggenheim (32), the following assumptions are essential: (1) the adsorption is monomolecular, (2) there is no interaction between the adsorbed molecules, and (3) the adsorbed molecules have a fixed position on the surface, that is, there is no motion of the adsorbed molecules in the plane of the surface. The third assumption required in the statistical treatment does not appear in the kinetic derivation. The equation derived by Fowler is

$$\theta = \frac{a(T)p}{1 + a(T)p} \tag{21}$$

where

$$a(T) = \frac{h^3}{(2m)^{\frac{3}{2}}(kT)^{\frac{5}{2}}} \frac{f_a(T)}{f_g(T)} e^{\epsilon/kT}$$

In the definition of $a(T)$, h is Planck's constant, $f_a(T)$ is the partition function of the molecule in the adsorbed state, f_g the partition function in the gas state, and ϵ is the energy difference of the lowest energy states in the adsorbed and gaseous phases.

Other derivations are those of Volmer (70) and Laidler *et al.* (54). Volmer obtained his result by a thermodynamic treatment applied to an assumption of a Van der Waals type equation of state for the adsorbed molecules. Laidler *et al.* obtained the equation from a consideration of the absolute reaction rate theory of Eyring (29).

For the purpose of area determination, the theory of Langmuir, if applicable, yields v_m, the number of molecules required to cover the surface with a monomolecular layer of gas. Before the area can be obtained it is essential to determine in some manner the effective cross sectional area, σ, of the molecules in the adsorbed state. The specific area, Σ, then is,

$$\sum = \frac{v_m N_0 \sigma}{V_m} \tag{22}$$

where N_0 is Avogadro's number and V_m is the gaseous molar volume. Any number of methods can be used to approximate σ. None of these are really satisfactory. This problem is discussed in detail in a later section.

The assumptions made in the derivation are rather sweeping, and the consequences are a serious limitation on the applicability of the theory. The assumptions discussed in the following paragraphs are those made in the statistical treatment of Fowler. The most important assumption made is that the adsorption is monomolecular. It is true that Langmuir in later discussions of the theory (56) does make allowance for the fact that in special cases the adsorbed layer may become more than monomolecular, but this does not occur in the treatment until high relative pressures are reached, i.e., for values of p/p_0 near unity. Since in general the adsorbed films are polymolecular, it is apparent that the equation will not be generally valid. The only systems known to the author for which the Langmuir equation holds for solids in which the structure does not limit the adsorption to a thickness of a unimolecular layer is for the adsorption of n-propyl alcohol on barium sulfate and titanium dioxide in the form of anatase. These systems were investigated by Boyd and Livingstone (13). Since, in general, the adsorption of gases is polymolecular, the Langmuir isotherm does not possess general utility. Brunauer, Emmett, and Teller, have succeeded in removing this restriction. This theory is discussed in the following section.

The second assumption made is that the energy of adsorption is independent of the concentration of molecules on the surface, i.e., there is no contribution to the energy of adsorption due to the interaction of the adsorbed molecules. For low surface concentrations the measured energies of adsorption vary greatly with the number of molecules adsorbed per square centimeter, while at high surface concentrations there is usually only a small variation in the energy of adsorption. Thus, from the consideration of the energy relations, the equation should be valid only at high surface concentrations. Actually this is found to be true. When the Langmuir equation is valid over an extended region, it is always at high surface concentrations that agreement is obtained between the observed pressure-volume relations and those demanded by theory.

One other consequence of the assumption that the adsorbed molecules do not interact with each other is that the theory demands that the volume adsorbed is a continuous function of the pressure, and also that all of the derivatives of the volume with respect to the pressure are continuous. The physical consequence of this assumption is that the adsorbed phase must be in a single two dimensional phase for any value of the pressure. Recent experiments by the author and co-workers show that two dimensional phase changes do exist in films adsorbed on the surfaces of solids (49, 50). Theoretically, the interaction between the adsorbed molecules has been considered by Fowler and Guggenheim for films of non mobile molecules (32). These isotherms exhibit discontinuities that are changes of phase. The equations, however, are two complicated for ordinary use. This restriction can be removed from the theory; the results are such, however, that nothing is gained for the purpose of area determination.

The final assumption, concerning the mobility of the adsorbed molecules also can be removed. This has been accomplished by Hill (42). On the basis of a simple model Hill has come to the conclusion that in the absence of ionic or dipole intermolecular forces the molecules are mobile at temperatures above 250°K. and are partially mobile and partially localized at 77°K., the lowest temperature normally used in adsorption work. The consideration of this effect also has a negligible effect on the determination of the area.

Of all the assumptions made in the theory the one that seriously affects the utility of the theory is that which restricts the adsorption to a thickness of a single layer. The other assumptions, though unsound, do not cause a serious error.

4.2. Applications of Langmuir Theory

Since the Langmuir theory assumes that adsorption is monomolecular, it is evident that the theory is applicable only if the adsorption is indeed

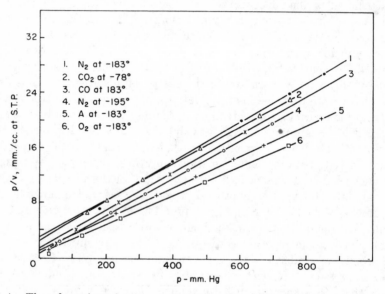

FIG. 4. The adsorption of gases on charcoal. The data are represented by the linear form of the Langmuir equation.

monomolecular or if the adsorbed film remains monomolecular to high pressures. The first class contains charcoals and gels whose pore diameters are small. In general, the structure of these solids is such that only monomolecular adsorption can occur. At the present time knowledge of the second class is limited to the adsorption of n-propyl alcohol on titanium dioxide and barium sulfate at room temperatures.

As an example of the application of the Langmuir equation to porous solids, Fig. 4 exhibits the data for the adsorption of several gases on charcoal in the linear form of the equation. The data are those of Brunauer and Emmett (17). It is readily seen that the points fall on

TABLE III
Area of a Charcoal as Determined with Several Gases

Gas	T°C.	v_m cm.^{3} STP g.$^{-1}$	m.^{2}g.$^{-1}$
N_2	−195.8	181.5	795
N_2	−183	173.0	795
A	−195.8	215.5	804
A	−183	215.5	839
CO_2	−183	234.6	894
CO_2	−183	179.5	820
CO_2	−78	185.5	853

good straight lines except at low pressures. Table III gives the values for v_m calculated for each isotherm and the area obtained from v_m.

The average area from all these determinations is 829 m.^{2}g.$^{-1}$, the average deviation 29 m.^{2}g.$^{-1}$ (3.5%), and the maximum deviation

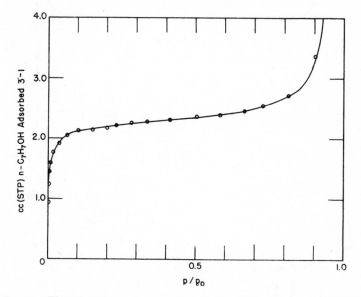

Fig. 5. The adsorption of *n*-propyl alcohol on TiO_2 (anatase) at 25°C.

65 m.^{2}g.$^{-1}$ (7.8%). The agreement is excellent. There are many charcoals for which such good agreement is not obtained; for many charcoals the Langmuir equation does not give agreement over any region of pressures. In these cases, it is not possible to calculate an "area."

Figure 5 exhibits the adsorption isotherm of *n*-propyl alcohol on a sample of titanium dioxide in the form of anatase at 25°C. Figure 6 shows the linear form of the Langmuir equation. If 25°A.^{2} is used as the effective cross-sectional area of the n-propyl alcohol molecule the area is found to be 13.6 m.^{2}g.$^{-1}$, which is in good agreement with the 13.8 m.^{2}g.$^{-1}$ obtained by other methods for this sample. For the com-

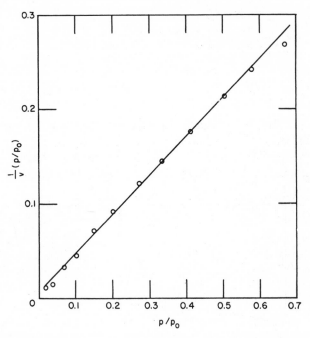

FIG. 6.   The data of Fig. 5 represented by the linear Langmuir equation.

bination of this gas and solid, the Langmuir isotherm is the only method of obtaining the area; all other adsorption theory methods fail.

5. THEORY OF BRUNAUER, EMMETT, AND TELLER

5.1. Introduction

The most general method for the determination of the areas of the surfaces of solids is that of Brunauer, Emmett, and Teller (18). This theory yields substantially the same results as an empirical method developed by Brunauer and Emmett (17, 24, 25, 26, 27, 28). Only the theoretical approach is discussed. The development of Brunauer, Emmett, and Teller is a theory of adsorption which attempts to explain the adsorption characteristics where only Van der Waals' forces are the means of interaction between the solid and gas. The results of the theory are useful as a method of area determination because one of the parameters in the resulting equations is v_m, the volume of gas required to form a monomolecular layer on the surface of the solid.

The fundamental postulate of the theory of Brunauer, Emmett, and Teller is that the adsorption of gases on a free surface is polymolecular. Because of the complexity of the general problem of polymolecular adsorption, a completely general solution is not possible. Many equations can be derived which depend upon the assumption concerning the energy of interaction of the adsorbed molecules with the molecules of the solid, the interaction of the adsorbed molecules with themselves, the packing of the molecules in the various layers, the number of layers actually formed, etc. The fewer the assumptions made, the more undetermined constants appear in the final result.

The simplest equation contains two parameters and is obtained on the assumption that the adsorbed molecules do not interact with each other, that the net energy of adsorption of the second and higher layers is zero and that an infinite number of layers can be adsorbed on the surface. The equation is

$$\frac{p}{v(p_0 - p)} = \frac{c-1}{v_m c}\frac{p}{p_0} + \frac{1}{v_m c} \tag{23}$$

By the proper choice of the values of the parameters the equation qualitatively reproduces all the known isotherms and in nearly all cases, better than 99% quantitative agreement can be obtained between the observed values and eq. (23), in the relative pressure region of 0.05 to 0.30.   The exact region in which agreement is obtained depends upon the system under observation.

The application of the theory is sufficiently successful so that it is generally accepted.   Recently, Cassie (19), with implausible arguments, derived an equation of exactly the same form by the use of statistical mechanics.   Hill (41) obtained the same result.   More recently, Hill (42) has shown that usable results can be obtained even when the restriction that the adsorbed molecules in the first layer do not interact is removed.   The statistical thermodynamic treatments of Cassie and Hill demonstrate beyond question the fundamental soundness of the Brunauer, Emmett, Teller theory.   The sole question is, how seriously do the assumptions made for mathematical reasons affect the value of v_m, which is used to calculate the area.   This question is answerable only by experiment, and the experiments indicate that the values for v_m are substantially correct.

5.2. Theory

Two approaches are possible in the treatment of multimolecular adsorption: (1) a kinetic treatment similar to that used by Langmuir in his derivation of monomolecular adsorption and (2) a statistical approach. The original kinetic approach of Brunauer, Emmett, and Teller is reproduced.

If a volume of gas is adsorbed onto the surface of a solid, s_0 cm.^{2} of the solid will be bare, s_1 cm.^{2} will adsorb one layer, s_2 cm.^{2} two layers, s_i cm.^{2} i layers, etc. The exact number of molecules in each layer will depend on the energy of the molecule in its particular position. If the energy of the molecule could be calculated or measured as a function of its position in the various layers, the Boltzmann distribution function could be used to determine the number of molecules that are present in any layer when the total number of adsorbed molecules is known. The total area of the solid is

$$A = \sum_{i=0}^{i=\infty} s_i \tag{24}$$

and the total number of adsorbed molecules is

$$v = v_0 \sum_{i=1}^{i=\infty} i s_i \tag{25}$$

where v_0 is the volume of gas required to cover the surface with a monomolecular layer of gas.

From eqs. (24) and (25)

$$\frac{v}{A v_0} = \frac{v}{v_m} = \frac{\displaystyle\sum_{i=0}^{i=\infty} i s_i}{\displaystyle\sum_{i=0}^{i=\infty} s_i} \tag{26}$$

Equation (26) is a completely general expression, and is true regardless of any condition or restraint that may be placed upon the system. For example, if only n layers can be adsorbed then all s_i greater than n are zero. The equation, however, is useless until the ratio of the summations can be evaluated. It is with respect to the evaluation of the sums that the various approximations are introduced into the theory.

When equilibrium is established between the gas on the surface of the solid and the vapor, the number of molecules in each layer must remain constant. However, molecules are always leaving the surface, and molecules from the gas phase are always entering the surface region. If a molecule evaporates from the ith layer, another molecule must condense in the ith layer. If the same assumptions are made as in the derivation of the Langmuir equation (see Section 4) then the following equations can be written:

$$a_1 p s_0 = b_1 s_1 1^{-\frac{E_1}{RT}}$$

$$a_2 p s_1 = b_2 s_2 1^{-\frac{E_2}{RT}}$$

$$a_3 p s_2 = b_3 s_3 1^{-\frac{E_3}{RT}} \tag{27}$$

$$\cdot \quad \cdot \quad \cdot \quad \cdot \quad \cdot \quad \cdot \quad \cdot$$

$$\cdot \quad \cdot \quad \cdot \quad \cdot \quad \cdot \quad \cdot \quad \cdot$$

$$\cdot \quad \cdot \quad \cdot \quad \cdot \quad \cdot \quad \cdot \quad \cdot$$

$$a_i p s_{i-1} = b_i s_i 1^{-\frac{E_i}{RT}}$$

where a_i and b_i are constants whose form is given in the previous section, and E, E_2, E_3, etc. are the energies of adsorption of the molecules in the respective layers.

If the following additional assumptions are made:

$$E_2 = E_3 = \cdots E_i = \cdots = E_L \tag{28}$$

$$\frac{b_2}{a_2} = \frac{b_3}{a_3} = \cdots \frac{b_i}{a_i} = \cdots = g \tag{29}$$

it becomes possible to express s_i in terms of s_0.

$$s_1 = y s_0 \tag{30}$$

where

$$y = \frac{a_1}{b_1} p e^{\frac{E_1}{RT}}$$

and

$$s_i = c x^i s_0$$

where

$$c = \frac{y}{x}$$

and

$$x = \frac{p}{g e^{\frac{E_L}{RT}}}$$

Equation (26) becomes

$$\frac{v}{v_m} = \frac{c s_0 \displaystyle\sum_{i=1}^{i=\infty} i x^i}{s_0 (1 + c) \displaystyle\sum_{i=1}^{i=\infty} x^i} \tag{31}$$

Both of the above summations are well known

$$\sum_{i=1}^{i=\infty} x^i = \frac{x}{1 - x} \tag{32}$$

$$\sum_{i=1}^{i=\infty} i x^i = \frac{x}{(1 - x)^2} \tag{33}$$

Thus eq. (31) becomes

$$\frac{v}{v_m} = \frac{cx}{(1-x)(1-x+cx)}$$

Returning to eq. (31) coupled with the realization that over a free surface at saturation $v = \infty$, it is seen that $x = p/p_0$. The final equation under all the assumptions is

$$v = \frac{v_m c p}{(p_0 - p)\{1 + (c - 1)p/p_0\}} \tag{34}$$

For computational purposes the most convenient form of eq. (34) is

$$\frac{p}{v(p_0 - p)} = \frac{1}{v_m c} + \frac{c - 1}{v_m c}\frac{p}{p_0} \tag{35}$$

if $\dfrac{p}{v(p_0 - p)}$ is plotted against p/p_0 the experimental points should fall on a straight line for those values of the pressure for which there is agree-

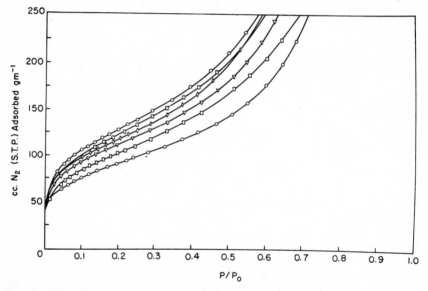

FIG. 7. The adsorption isotherms of nitrogen on some cracking catalysts. The areas of these solids are listed in Table II.

ment between theory and experiment. Figure 7 exhibits the isotherms of nitrogen on a group of cracking catalysts at about 77.8°K., while Fig. 8 illustrates the application of eq. (35) to the isotherms in Fig. 7. It is readily seen that the agreement between theory and experiment is excellent in the relative pressure region $0.05 \leq p/p_0 \leq 0.30$. Thus, this very simple theory is capable of reproducing the isothermal data. v_m, the volume of gas required to form a monolayer is obtained from the constants of the straight line; the intercept of this line is $\dfrac{1}{v_m c}$ and its slope $\dfrac{c-1}{v_m c}$.

Within the frame work of the original derivation many other equations can be derived depending upon the assumptions that are made. If it is

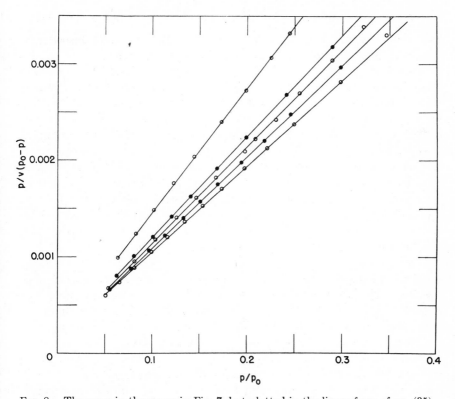

Fig. 8.   The same isotherms as in Fig. 7, but plotted in the linear form of eq. (35).

assumed that only a monomolecular layer can be adsorbed the resulting equation is

$$\frac{v}{v_m} = \frac{c(p/p_0)}{1 + c(p/p_0)} \tag{36}$$

which is the Langmuir equation. If it is assumed that n rather than an infinite number of layers can be adsorbed the result is

$$\frac{v}{v_m} = \frac{cx}{1-x} \frac{1 - (n+1)x^n + nx^{n+1}}{1 + (c-1)x - cx^{n+1}} \tag{37}$$

If it is assumed that the energy of adsorption of the second layer is greater than E_L and different and less than E_1 and that the packing of the molecules in the second and higher layers is different from that in the first, the following equation is obtained:

$$\frac{v}{v_m} = \frac{cx}{(1-x)} \frac{\delta + (b-\delta)(2x - x^2)}{1 + (c-1)x + (b-1)cx^2} \tag{38}$$

where $\delta = \dfrac{v_{m(1)}}{v_{m(2)}}$, and b has the same significance for the second layer as c has for the first. Finally, Brunauer *et al.* (16) have devised isotherms that consider the possible pore structure of the adsorbent.

It is evident that many more equations are possible. In each case, the final form is dependent upon the assumptions that are made. Remarkably, the more complex equations that have been studied so far yield remarkably self consistent values for v_m, the volume of gas required to form a monomolecular layer on the surface of the solid. For example, the simple theory yields 0.44 cm.^{3}g.$^{-1}$ as the value of v_m for the adsorption of n-heptane on a sample of ferric oxide. The theory of Hill (41), which considers horizontal interactions between the adsorbed molecules in the first layer, gives values for v_m ranging from 0.43 to 0.48 depending upon the assumed change in the internal electronic levels of n-heptane. The above comparison seems to be general. Thus, it appears that the simplest of all possible equations is satisfactory for area determinations.

The use of eq. (35) to determine v_m does not completely solve the problem of area determination. Before an area can be computed it is necessary to determine the cross section of the adsorbed molecule. Actually, estimation of the cross-sectional area probably introduces as much uncertainty in the final result as the approximations in the theory.

The adsorbed molecules are certainly not in the same state as if they were in a solid or liquid. When the molecules are adsorbed they are in an assymetric field, and their polarization is different from what it would be at the center of a condensed system composed of like molecules. Even the assymetry of the surface of pure material changes the distances between molecules. For example, Dent (21) has shown that for the 100-plane of ionic crystals such as sodium chloride, the equilibrium distance between ions is about 10% less than in the interior of the crystal. Rice (62) has shown that for nonpolar systems the distance between molecules is increased at the surface.

A potential field exists between the solid and the gas molecules. The potential field of the solid must have a pattern determined by the surface lattice of the solid. This pattern should affect the position of the adsorbed molecules on the surface in that a variation in the cross sectional area should be expected with a variation in the nature and spacing of the lattice of the solid.

Theoretically, it is not possible to resolve the above problem. The simplest possible assumption that can be made is that the cross sectional area of the adsorbed molecule is independent of the solid. This assumption cannot be rigidly correct, but it is capable of experimental verification. If the isotherms of a series of solids are determined with two or more gases, the ratios of v_m of the different gases for a given solid should be the same for all solids. Such a comparison is shown in Table IV.

TABLE IV

Ratios of v_m of Various Gases on Some Solids (20)

Solid	$\dfrac{N_2}{Kr}$	$\dfrac{N_2}{C_4H_{10}}$	$\dfrac{N_2}{CHCl_2F}$	$\dfrac{N_2}{i\text{-}C_4H_8}$
Glass spheres (200 mesh)	1.44	1.60	1.74	
Glass spheres (7 micros)	1.34	1.29	1.37	
Tungsten	1.37	1.61	1.56	
Zinc oxide	1.38	1.35	1.42	
Alumina				1.38
Silica gel				1.42
Average	1.36	1.46	1.52	1.40

The data in Table IV indicate that an error of the order of 20% is possible on the assumption of the constancy of the cross-sectional area. From data such as that given in Table IV it is possible to calculate the effective cross-sectional area for any molecule if the area of any one molecule is known.

From all available data, apparently the best choice is that of 16.2 A.[2] as the area of the nitrogen molecule at its normal boiling point 77.3°K. The above value, 16.2 A., was first proposed by Emmett and Brunauer (24). They arrived at this figure on the assumption that the adsorbed gas possessed the same packing as liquid nitrogen and that the molecules in the liquid had a close-packed hexagonal lattice. If this same method is used to determine the cross-sectional areas of other molecules, no area values are obtained higher than those obtained with nitrogen. Argon and oxygen, among others, give areas that agree with nitrogen (18) while krypton, water, n-butane and others yield results which are much lower.

Actually this method of computing cross-sectional areas should be close to the lowest possible value. From the determined distribution functions of liquids it is known that there are not twelve nearest neighbors as assumed by Emmett and Brunauer. Thus in a true liquid, the molecule actually must occupy more space than that determined on the assumption of close packing. Perhaps the greatest single reason for the acceptance of 16.2 A.[2] as the cross-sectional area of nitrogen is the agreement obtained when the results are compared with those obtained by the absolute method (Section II).

Table IV gives the best values, as of present, of the cross-sectional areas of various molecules. The values are subject to change.

5.3. Application

The most applicable method of area determination is that of Brunauer, Emmett and Teller. Regardless of the nature of the individual isotherm this theory is almost certain to be applicable. It is only under rather unusual circumstances that an unlikely answer is obtained from a single isotherm. Of the hundreds of isotherms known in detail to the writer, the theory in one form or another has been inapplicable only twice, and only in one case where the theory was applicable was a really poor answer obtained. The one poor result was obtained when n-heptane was adsorbed on copper powder at 25°C. The result was approximately one-half of that obtained with other gases.

The many possible variations in the shape of the adsorption isotherm can be satisfactorily explained by the proper variation of the parameter c in eq. (35). If c is equal to or less than unity the isotherm is convex to the pressure axis, while if c is greater than unity the predicted isotherm is concave to this axis. The greater the value of c, the steeper the rise of isotherm in the low pressure region. Figure 9 exhibits the effect of the variation of c in eq. (35).

In the original treatment of the theory, c was directly related to the energy of adsorption of the molecules in the first layer.

$$E_1 = E_L = RT \ln c$$

It was pointed out later by Cassie (19) and Hill (41) that $E_1 - E_L$ was not so simply related to the energy of adsorption. The treatment of Brunauer, Emmett, and Teller does not consider, among other things, the change in the electronic energy levels of the adsorbed molecules. Such changes do occur. This can be experimentally shown by the changes in the adsorption spectra that occur when the molecules are adsorbed. De Boer (10) has performed such experiments. The contribution of the change in the electronic energy may be greater than that obtained from a consideration of c alone. This defect in the energetic consideration of the theory does not affect the values obtained for v_m. The equations that consider this effect are of exactly the same form as the equation derived on purely kinetic considerations.

In general, the equations of this theory are valid in the relative pressure region 0.05 to 0.3.   Individual systems vary somewhat from the above limits, though not greatly.   Occasionally, the theory does not become valid until a relative pressure of 0.1 is reached.   This is found when the value of c is small, ca. 10.   For very high values of c, 500 to 1000, the theory may fail at pressures as low as 0.2 or 0.25.   Thus, if

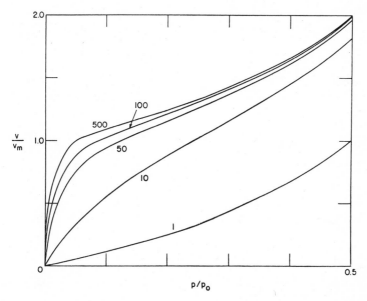

FIG. 9.   The effect of the parameter c in eq. 35 on the shape of the isotherm.

the adsorption points are taken between $0.1 \leqq p/p_0 \leqq 0.2$, there is almost certain agreement between theory and experiment.   These points may be used to determine the constants of the linear form, and from these constants v_m may be calculated.

For area purposes, three equations must be considered.   The first is the Langmuir form discussed in Section IV.   The other two apply when at saturation roughly $2v_m$ or less are adsorbed and when more than $2v_m$ are adsorbed.   When more than $2v_m$ are adsorbed eq. (35) is used while if less, Joiner and coworkers (45) recommend the use of eq. (37). Joiner claims that more self consistent results are obtained by the use of the more complicated equation.   The treatment of several activated carbons and gels is given in Table V.

The results of Brunauer and Emmett (18) using the simple two constant equation are given in Table VI.   The results are sufficiently self consistent to permit the assumption that the method yields at least relative areas.

The simple theory of Brunauer, Emmett, and Teller possesses one further advantage. If an area estimate to within only a few per cent is desired, the area can be determined from a single adsorption point, provided the point is taken at a sufficiently high relative pressure. The

TABLE V

Comparison of v_m of Nitrogen at $-195°C$. from the Application of Equations 35 and 37

Adsorbent	v_m (Eq. 37)	v_m (Eq. 35) *
Alumina—Silica I	49.5	49.2
Alumina—Silica II	63.3	62.4
Silica Gel	197.0	Not applicable
Anatase	3.314	3.198
Carbon 5	179.1	205
Carbon 6	311.8	350
Carbon 7	336.5	383
Carbon 2	318.3	356
Carbon 1	280.0	306
Carbon 4	426.6	456

TABLE VI

Area of a Silica Gel as Determined by Several Gases

Gas	T°C.	v_m (cc./g.)	Area (m.²/g.)
N_2	-195.8	127.9	560
N_2	-183	116.2	534
A	-183	119.3	464
O_2	-183	125.1	477
CO	-183	121.2	550
CO_2	-78	99.0	455
C_4H_{10}	0	58.2	504

intercept of eq. (35), $\dfrac{1}{v_m c}$ is usually small. Thus if a point is determined at high pressures ca. $p/p_0 = 0.3$ to 0.35, only a small error is made by assuming that the line passes through the origin and determined point. If the value of c is moderate or high, the error is on the order of 5% according to Emmett and Brunauer.

The writer has found that v_m can be determined by this method to within 10% with nitrogen at $77.3°K.$, water at $25°C.$, and n-heptane at $25°C.$ Large errors were made with n-butane at $0°C.$

6. Entropy Method

This method, due to Jura and Harkins (48) is presented not for its utility, but because it substantiates the results obtained in the previous section by an entirely different reasoning.   In this method attention is focused on the behavior of the entropy of the surface of the solid as a function of the amount of gas adsorbed on the surface.

The change in surface entropy has not been as yet directly determined, but must be obtained from the changes in free surface energy and enthalpy.   The change in free surface energy can be obtained by the application of the Gibbs adsorption equation to the isotherm as suggested by Bangham (4, 5, 6).   The change in free surface energy, π, is

$$\pi = \frac{RT}{V_M \Sigma} \int_0^p \frac{v}{p} \, dp \tag{38}$$

The change in surface energy, Δh, can be obtained by direct measurement.   The change in surface entropy, Δs is

$$\Delta s = \frac{\Delta h - \pi}{T} \tag{39}$$

If Δs is plotted against v for a system in which the isotherm is strongly concave to the pressure axis, it is found that a minimum occurs in the entropy.   Figure 10 illustrates this behavior for the adsorption of water on titanium dioxide in the form of anatase at 25°C.

Statistically, the minimum must occur when there is a maximum of order and orientation in the system.   The orientation is fixed by the nature of the adsorbent and adsorbate and need not be considered.   If the adsorbed gas goes into the first layer before an appreciable fraction enters the second and higher layers, the maximum ordering is obtained when a monomolecular layer has been adsorbed.   To a first approximation the minimum in the entropy corresponds to v_m.

A completely rigid analysis of the behavior of the surface entropy is not possible at the present time.   However, it can be shown that if $E_1 - E_L$ and $E_1 - E_2$ are large compared to RT, and no first or second order phase change complicates the behavior of the entropy in the neighborhood of a monomolecular layer, the minimum in the entropy corresponds to 0.87 to $0.92v_m$, depending upon the assumptions that are made in the calculation.   Table VII gives a comparison between the values of v_m obtained by the application of the B.E.T. theory and the entropy method for different gases on titanium dioxide.

The values are in excellent agreement.   It appears that for water, n-butane, and n-heptane, larger values are obtained than those of the B.E.T. theory.   This discrepancy is not serious, since the value obtained

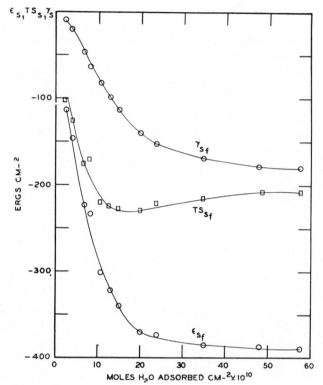

FIG. 10.   The changes in thermodynamic properties of the surface of TiO₂ (anatase) produced by the adsorption of H₂O at 25°C.

TABLE VII

Values of v_m for Various Gases on Titanium Dioxide (Σ = 13.8 m.²g.⁻¹) by Two Methods

Gas	T°C.	v_m cm.³g.⁻¹ B.E.T.	Entropy
N_2	−195.8	3.19	3.1
H_2O	25.0	3.55	5.0
n-C_4H_{10}	0.0	1.02	1.2
n-C_7H_{16}	25.0	0.80	0.9

from the entropy cannot be precise due to the broadness and shallowness of the minimum.

7. RELATIVE METHOD

7.1. Theory

The relative method of area determination was proposed by Harkins and Jura (40).   The fundamental approach of this method is entirely different from that used in any of the derivations of the theory of Brunauer, Emmett, and Teller.   Generally, the same data can be used for both methods, and an area obtained.

The fundamental concept used in the relative method is: the adsorption of a gas on the surface of a solid forms a film on the surface.   This film can be thermodynamically studied in the same manner as insoluble films on the surface of water.   The variables most generally used to describe the properties of insoluble films are the decrease in free surface energy (surface tension), π; the absolute temperature, T; and the surface concentration of adsorbed molecules, usually expressed in inverse form as, σ the area available for each molecule.   When insoluble films on water are studied it is found that the film exists in at least five different two-dimensional phases: gaseous, liquid expanded, liquid intermediate, liquid condensed, and solid condensed.   The gaseous, liquid and solid condensed phases may be considered as the two dimensional analogies of the three dimensional phases.   The liquid expanded and intermediate states do not have counterparts in three dimensions.   Different analysis of the states of films are those of Adam (1) Dervichian (22), and Harkins and Boyd (35).

Jura and Harkins have recently published a detailed comparison between the behavior of films formed by adsorption on solids and insoluble films on liquids (47).   This study indicates that the films on the surfaces of solids exhibit the same general relations as insoluble films on liquids. For the purpose of area determination it is the condensed film that is of interest.   On water, at constant temperatures, the plot of film pressure, π, vs. the area per molecule, σ, is a straight line over nearly the entire region of existence of this state.   At high pressures, the area decreases more rapidly than required by the straight line which represents the film at low pressures.   As a first approximation the equation of state of the film is

$$\pi = b - a\sigma \tag{40}$$

where b and a are unknown functions of the temperature.

The effects of temperature are as follows: the lower the temperature, the greater the value of a, which signifies a decrease in compressibility; (2) a decrease in the value of b, which indicates a smaller area at zero pressure, and (3) in general, a greater region of existence of the phase. The latter is not completely general, since the phase boundaries are determined by the temperature relations of the other phases.

One other possible effect on the state of the film as expressed by eq. (40) are the changes brought about by varying the subphase, by the introduction of various solutes at different concentration.   When any of these changes are made it is found that the phase may be completely suppressed or its region of existence increased. In general, if the phase still exists, the value of b is changed. The quantity a, however, is unchanged within experimental error. At present there is insufficient theoretical development to explain this behavior, and it must be accepted as an experimental fact.

The basis of the relative method can now be explicitly expressed. If the pressure area relations are those of eq. (40) it is assumed that the film is condensed. For condensed films on the surfaces of solids it is assumed that a is independent of the subphase, i.e., the solid. Stated differently, if eq. (40) represents the observed data, a depends only upon the gas and temperature.

To determine whether or not a condensed film exists, quantities proportional to π and σ could be plotted to determine whether or not a condensed film is formed. This would involve plotting $\frac{1}{v}$, the volume adsorbed per gram, which is proportional to σ, against $\int_0^p \frac{v}{p}\, dp$, which is equal to $\frac{\Sigma\pi}{RT}$. If the last two expressions are equated the result is the integrated form of the Gibbs adsorption equation first proposed by Bangham (4, 5, 6) for the evaluation of the decrease of free surface energy.

A use of the Gibbs adsorption equation permits a change of variables in eq. (40) from π and σ to p and v. If σ is expressed in cm.^{2} molecule, then

$$\sigma = \frac{V_M \Sigma}{v N_0}$$

(41)

The Gibbs adsorption equation can be written

$$\frac{v}{\Sigma} = \frac{1}{RT}\left(\frac{\partial \pi}{\partial \ln p}\right)_T$$

(42)

σ as expressed in eq. (41) is substituted in eq. (40) and differentiated with respect to $\ln p$, the resulting expression for $\left(\frac{\partial \pi}{\partial \ln p}\right)_T$ is substituted in eq. (42). The result is a differential equation in v and p, which integrated is

$$\log p = -\frac{A}{v^2} + B$$

(43)

where

$$A = \frac{(V_M \Sigma)^2 a}{2.303 R T N_0}$$

(44)

and B is the constant of integration.

From eq. (43) it is apparent that if the film obeys the equation of state of a condensed film a straight line results when $1/v^2$ is plotted against log p. Figure 11 exhibits this plot for the adsorption of nitrogen at $-195.8°C$. on a group of catalysts whose areas vary from 60 to 420 m.²g.$^{-1}$. It is observed that each of the isotherms is linear over a wide

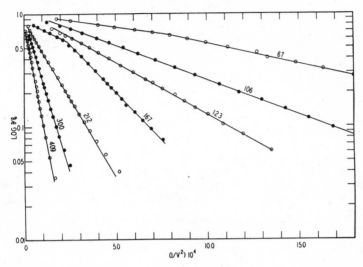

FIG. 11.   The application of eq. 43 to the adsorption of N_2 on various porous solids at ca. $77.8°K$.

range of pressures in this representation.   Also, several of the isotherms are represented by two straight lines.   The interpretation of the two lines is that two condensed phases formed.   For the purpose of area determination, the condensed phase appearing at the lower pressures is used.

If eq. (44) is solved for Σ it is found that

$$\Sigma = \sqrt{\frac{2.303RTN_0}{aV_M{}^2}} A^{\frac{1}{2}}$$

Since it has been assumed that a is dependent only on the gas and temperature

$$\Sigma = kA^{\frac{1}{2}} \tag{45}$$

A is determined from the experimental data.   Before k can be determined, the area of at least one solid must be known.   If the absolute area is not known, the method will yield directly the ratios of the areas, which is the ratio of the square roots of the slopes of the linear portion the lines in the log p vs. $1/v^2$ plot.

7.2. Application of Relative Method

The first problem in the use of the relative method is the determination of the value of k for various gases.   Table VIII gives the values for k thus far determined.

TABLE VIII

Values of k for Area Determination by Relative Method

Gas	T°C.	k	Reference
N_2	-195.8	4.06	40
Kr	-194.5	4.20	19
H_2O	25.0	3.83	40
n-C_4H_{10}	0.0	13.6	40
n-C_7H_{16}	25.0	16.9	40
NH_3	-40.0	3.23	63
n-C_6H_{14}	0.0	14.3	58
Triptane	0.0	16.2	58

The values given for k are valid only at the temperatures given.   For small temperature differences a suitable value of k is given by the equation

$$k_2 = k_1 \sqrt{\left(\frac{T_2}{T_1}\right)} \tag{46}$$

Equation (46) is derived on the assumption that for a small temperature change, the amount of gas adsorbed at a given relative pressure is independent of the temperature.   This is not strictly correct, but too large an error is not made by this procedure.   For example, eq. (46) is found to be true within experimental error for n-heptane at 15 and 25°C., but not true for nitrogen between -195.8 and -183.0°C.

The application of the relative method to the determination of the areas of several nonporous solids with various gases is given in Table IX.

TABLE IX

Areas of Solids by the Relative Method

Solid	N_2	H_2O	n-Butane	n-Heptane
TiO_2 I	13.8*	13.8*	13.8*	13.8*
TiO_2 II	8.7	8.4	—	8.7
$ZrSO_4$	2.9	2.7	—	—
$BaSO_4$	2.4	2.3	2.2	2.3
SiO_2	3.2	3.3	—	3.3

* Assumed to be correct as determined by the absolute method described in Section II.

The self consistency of the values determined by this method is remarkable. Determinations other than those listed in Table IX show equally good agreement. Unfortunately there are no published values to judge how this method would work with porous solids. The author has determined the isotherms of both nitrogen and n-butane on several catalysts. On two of these solids the relative method was applicable with both gases. The areas obtained were 118 and 125 m.^{2}g.$^{-1}$ with nitrogen and n-butane, and 242 and 232 m.^{2}g.$^{-1}$ on the other sample with the same gases. The above results are encouraging and indicate that the method is equally applicable regardless of the structure of the solid.

The two greatest advantages of the relative method are (1) an effective cross-sectional area of the molecules need not be known and (2) it yields consistent results.

There are several disadvantages of the relative method for routine work. First, it is not generally applicable. A condensed film is not formed on every solid at all temperatures. Nor is a condensed film formed in the same pressure region for all solids. For example, over 120 different solids have been investigated with nitrogen by the author and coworkers at $-195.8°C$. Every one of these solids exhibited a linear region in the log p vs. $1/v^2$ plot, thus permitting an area calculation for each. Of twenty or more determinations made with n-butane at $0°C.$, the method was applicable to only eight. It appears certain, though it has not as yet been attempted with n-butane that, if the temperature is reduced, a condensed phase may appear, or if it is present it will appear at a lower pressure. In contrast to the B.E.T. theory, the relative pressure region in which the method is applicable cannot be sharply defined. The region in which the necessary relationship is obeyed is dependent on the solid. For example, if nitrogen is adsorbed on the titanium dioxide, it is found that the log p vs. $1/v^2$ plot becomes linear at $p/p_0 = 0.03$, while for a silica-alumina cracking catalyst, $\Sigma = 480$ m.^{2}g.$^{-1}$, the condensed phase does not appear until $p/p_0 = 0.18$. With other gases, it has been found that relative pressures as high as 0.35 are reached before the method is applicable. The above factors indicate that the method is not too useful for routine work where it is most convenient to take a few points at given relative pressures. The precision obtained with the method, however, is such that for extended investigation, where the maximum amount of information is desired, the method becomes of value. In the last section of this chapter, several instances of great utility are cited when the areas of the solids are obtained by both the B.E.T. and relative method.

One further factor influences the region of applicability of eq. (43), namely, the structure of the solid. Σ appears specifically in eq. (43).

If the solid is porous, the pores are filled as more gas is adsorbed. As the pores are filled Σ is reduced. Consequently, $1/v^2$ no longer can be a linear function of log p. The smaller the pores, the lower the pressure at which deviations occur from linearity. These deviations are such that less gas is adsorbed than predicted. If the solid is nonporous deviations from linearity also occur at high relative pressures, but in the other direction.

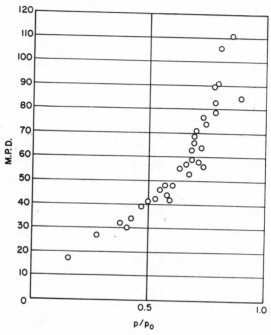

FIG. 12.   The relative pressure at which the relative method fails as a function of the mean pore diameter.

Since, with good data, a 2% deviation can be detected, the pore structure of a solid can be practically characterized by the pressure at which deviations start. This is illustrated in Fig. 12 where the relative pressure at which deviations occur is plotted against the mean pore diameter. The mean pore diameter used is

$$M.P.D. = \frac{4V}{\Sigma}$$

where V is the pore volume and Σ the specific area. If more than one condensed phase appears, then it is the deviation from the second phase that is considered.

For small mean pore diameters, the points fall on a fairly smooth curve, while for large mean pore diameters there is a considerable spread. This behavior is to be expected.

If it is merely desired to determine the area of a solid in routine work, the B.E.T. theory is more convenient, since a few points can be taken in a certain pressure region.   This can not be done with the relative method. However, the relative method is capable of yielding information other than that of an area.

7.3. Comparison of Results Obtained by B.E.T. and Relative Methods

The areas for the same solids obtained by the two methods are in remarkable agreement.   For nitrogen at $-195.8°C.$, the areas of a group of 120 solids agree to within 19% or less if 15.2 A.^{2} is used as the effective cross-sectional area of the nitrogen molecule in the B.E.T. theory.   The maximum discrepancy between the two is less than 20% if 16.2 A.^{2} is used as the effective cross-sectional area.   The comparison is equally good with other gases if the proper choice of the cross-sectional area is made.   This agreement, between the two methods, indicates strongly that both methods yield relative areas of solids.   The agreement of these methods with the results of the absolute method and the entropy method leave little doubt that the true areas of the solids are actually measured.

8. Comparison of Area Methods

Besides the methods of area determination that have already been discussed, many other methods have been proposed.   Most of the methods have not proven themselves reliable, either because of an incorrect theoretical development or insufficient experimental application to check their validity.   The large majority of these methods depends upon adsorption of gases or adsorption from solution.   Individual methods have been proposed that depend upon heat conductivity (52), overvoltage (11), permeability (15) and others.   None of the above methods appears to be reliable.

Among the methods which have not been discussed in detail and has been used moderately is that of adsorption from solution.   This method is doomed to failure.   Experimentally self-consistent results have not been obtained.   An extreme case of the unreliability of the method is illustrated by the recent work of Ries and co-workers (64).

The basis of area determination from solution is that the adsorption is monomolecular and that the Langmuir isotherm is applicable.   Experimentally, the postulate of monomolecular adsorption has been shown to be invalid by the work of Shephard (66), who has shown that certain cyanine dyes form polymolecular films on silver bromide.   Theoretically, it can be seen that only under certain conditions will a monomolecular film be formed. The reduction of free surface energy of the solid when exposed to a solution is

$$\Delta\gamma = -\frac{RT}{\Sigma} \int_{a_1=0}^{a_1} \Gamma_1 d\ln a_1 - \frac{RT}{\Sigma} \int_{a_2=a_2^0}^{a_2} \Gamma_2 d\ln a_2 \qquad (47)$$

where Γ_1 is the number of moles of solute in the interfacial region between the solid and solution, Γ_2 the number of moles of solvent in the interfacial region, and a_1 and a_2 are the activities of solute and solvent.

For any solute-solvent system $\Delta\gamma$ at saturation is determined by the reduction in free surface energy of the solvent and of the solute when adsorbed individually. Since in general different molecules will have a different effect upon the reduction of free surface energy, the limiting amount of various solutes will be different. Because of this it would not appear that adsorption from solution can be a reliable method of area determination.

Of the methods of area determination that have been presented, only two need be considered in any detail, the theory of Brunauer, Emmett, and Teller and the relative method of Harkins and Jura. The entropy method has been presented to show that an entirely different line of reasoning yields results in agreement with those of the theory of Brunauer, Emmett, and Teller. The absolute method shows that the results obtained by other methods are absolute values.

Of the two gas adsorption methods recommended, that of Brunauer, Emmett, and Teller is easier to apply. It is almost certain to fit the adsorption data in the relative pressure region of 0.1 to 0.25 regardless of the adsorbate or adsorbent or the temperature. The region of validity, if any, of the relative method cannot be predicted. It may become valid for a given gas and temperature at relative pressures ranging from 0.03 to 0.20. The inability to specify an exact region in which concordance is obtained between experiment and equation means that if this method is to be applied many points must be determined over a moderate pressure region.

The relative method has one further disadvantage, it must be calibrated for every gas at every temperature. The easiest manner of accomplishing this is to have a solid of known area available. The necessary constant can be determined from this one solid. The above difficulty also arises with the B.E.T. method, except that temperature variations for a given gas can be approximately computed. This is done by assuming that the cross-sectional area varies inversely as the two-thirds power of the density of the liquid.

The one great advantage of the relative method is that it appears

to yield more self consistent results.   That is, if the area of the same
solid is determined with different gases, there is less variation in the area
than that obtained with the B.E.T. method.   A second advantage of
the relative method is that a knowledge of the effective cross-sectional
area of the adsorbed molecule is unnecessary.

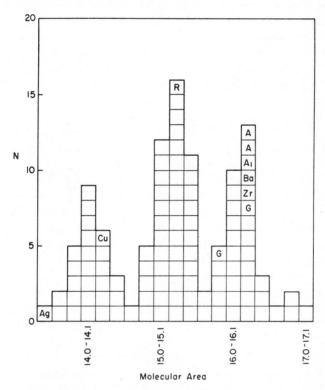

FIG. 13.   A comparison of the areas of solids by the relative and Brunauer,
Emmett, and Teller methods.   The gas used was nitrogen.   The comparison is made
by computing the cross-sectional area of nitrogen which with the computed v_m is
necessary to yield the area obtained by the relative method.

The two methods give substantially the same results for the areas
of the same solids.   The comparison between them is not as extensive
as desired.   Figure 13 exhibits the most exhaustive comparison of the
two methods.   In this comparison the effective cross-sectional area of
the nitrogen molecule is calculated in order that the v_m obtained from
the theory of Brunauer, Emmett and Teller agree exactly with the
area calculated by the relative method of Harkins and Jura.   On the
above basis the effective cross sectional area varies from 13.8 to 16.8 A^2.

per molecule. This agreement in over 110 cases is satisfactory. Somewhat similar results have been obtained with n-heptane but the results are not reproduced here since the comparison is available for only 23 solids.

Emmett (23) has attempted to explain the variation in the cross-sectional area by a variation in the value of c in eq. (35). He has shown that if the two isotherms are applicable to the same data, that the larger the value of c the greater the required value of the cross-sectional area required to obtain agreement between the two methods. Actually 80% of the comparisons in Fig. 13 have c values between 75 and 125, a rather narrow region. Apparently, Emmett's proposal is not the entire explanation.

Perhaps the most salient feature of the comparison is the existence of three maxima at 14, 15.4, and 16.2 A.[2] per molecule. Statistically, there are insufficient values to establish the three maxima with certainty. In the work with n-heptane, it appears as if there will be but one maximum, which is the expected situation.

There is some evidence which indicates that the maxima may be real. A typical example of a known change of surface is the following: a silica-alumina gel gave a molecular area for nitrogen of 14.1 sq. A. The surface was then coated with a carbonaceous deposit by exposing the solid to hydrocarbon vapors for a short time at an elevated temperature. The deposit reduced the area of the solid, but increased the area determined for the nitrogen molecule to 16.2 sq. A. After the deposit was removed, the area of the solid returned to its original, and the area of the molecule was found to return to 14.2 sq. A., its initial value within the limits of error.

Five such instances have been investigated. The values with the carbon deposit on the surface were found to be within the narrow range of from 16.0 to 16.3 sq. A., regardless of the initial value exhibited by the solid without the deposit.

In one series of solids composed of two components, silica and aluminum oxide, the ratio of the two was varied at concentrations of aluminum oxide of 6% or less. The area of the nitrogen molecule was found to be almost constant at 15.2 sq. A., but at 8% or more this shifted to 14.0 sq. A.

A second two component porous solid, of very different composition, gave a shift in the opposite direction. This exhibited an area of the nitrogen molecule of 15.2 sq. A. for all samples in which the content of the second component was 2, 4, and 6% by weight, but with 10 to 12% shifted to 16.2 sq. A.

The x-ray analysis of this solid shows a certain structure at all of the lower percentages but indicates that at 12% a partial change to a second crystal form has occurred. Since x-rays are not sensitive to a small percentage change of structure, it is probable that the shift in the area of the nitrogen molecule was caused by this change in structure and this change was detected at a lower concentration by gas absorption.

The above comparisons are interesting but it is difficult from the meager data available to evaluate their significance exactly. It appears that the method of comparing the results is capable of yielding useful information other than that concerning the area of the solid.

In brief summary the following can be stated. The only general, convenient, reliable methods of area determination known at present depend upon the physical adsorption of gases. Two such methods are available. The simplest to apply is that of Brunauer, Emmett, and Teller. The advantages of the method are its almost universal applicability and a predictable region of agreement between experiment and theory. Its disadvantage is the uncertainty that arises from an incomplete knowledge of the cross-sectional area of the adsorbed molecule.

The relative method of Harkins and Jura has an advantage in that more self consistent results are obtained. Its disadvantages are that it must be calibrated for each gas and at each temperature and its variable region of application.

If an approximate, i.e., 20% or less, value of an area is desired with a minimum expenditure of time, the B.E.T. theory should be used. For research projects where time is of secondary importance to results, both methods should be used. The application of both methods may yield important information other than the area.

REFERENCES

1. Adam, N. K., Physics and Chemistry of Surfaces, Clarendon Press, Oxford, 1938.
2. Adinoff, B., Thesis, University of Chicago, 1943.
3. Armbruster, M. H., and Austin, J. B., *J. Am. Chem. Soc.* **61**, 1117 (1939).
4. Bangham, D. H., *Trans. Faraday Soc.* **33**, 805 (1937).
5. Bangham, D. H., and Razouk, R. I., *Trans. Faraday Soc.* **33**, 1463 (1937).
6. Bangham, D. H., and Razouk, R. I., *Proc. Roy. Soc. London* **A166**, 572 (1938).
7. Barrett, H. M., Birini, A. W., and Cohen, M., *J. Am. Chem. Soc.* **62**, 2839 (1940).
8. Basford, P. R., Harkins, W. D., and Jura, G., Unpublished data.
9. Beebe, R. A., Beckwith, J. B., and Honig, J. M., *J. Am. Chem. Soc.* **67**, 1554 (1945).
10. de Boer, J. H., and Custers, J. F. H., *Physica* **4**, 1017 (1937).
11. Bowden, F. P., and Rideal, E. K., *Proc. Roy. Soc. London* **A120**, 59 (1920).
12. Boyd, G. E., and Harkins, W. D., *J. Am. Chem. Soc.* **64**, 1190 (1942).
13. Boyd, G. E., and Livingston, H. K., *J. Am. Chem. Soc.* **64**, 2383 (1942).
14. Brunauer, S., The Adsorption of Gases and Vapors, Physical Adsorption. Princeton University Press, Princeton, N.J., 1943.

15. Brunauer, S., The Adsorption of Gases and Vapors, Physical Adsorption. Princeton University Press, Princeton, N.J., 1943, Chapter IX, p. 271.
16. Brunauer, S., Deming, L. S., Demining, W. E., and Teller, E., *J. Am. Chem. Soc.* **62**, 1723 (1940).
17. Brunauer, S., and Emmett, P. H., *J. Am. Chem. Soc.* **59**, 2682 (1937).
18. Brunauer, S., Emmett, P. H., and Teller, E., *J. Am. Chem. Soc.* **60**, 309 (1938).
19. Cassie, A. B. D., *Trans. Faraday Soc.* **41**, 450 (1945).
20. Davis, R. T., Jr., DeWitt, W., and Emmett, P. H., *J. Phys. Colloid Chem.* **51**, 1232 (1947).
21. Dent, B. E., *Phil. Mag.* [7] **8**, 530 (1929).
22. Dervichian, D. G., *J. Chem. Phys.* **7**, 932 (1939).
23. Emmett, P. H., *J. Am. Chem. Soc.* **68**, 1784 (1946).
24. Emmett, P. H., and Brunauer, S., *J. Am. Chem. Soc.* **56**, 35 (1934).
25. Emmett, P. H., and Brunauer, S., *J. Am. Chem. Soc.* **59**, 310 (1937).
26. Emmett, P. H., and Brunauer, S., *Trans. Electrochem. Soc.* **71**, (1937).
27. Emmett, P. H., and Brunauer, S., *J. Am. Chem. Soc.* **59**, 310 (1937).
28. Emmett, P. H., and Brunauer, S., *J. Am. Chem. Soc.* **59**, 1553 (1937).
29. Eyring, H., *J. Chem. Phys.* **3**, 107 (1935).
30. Fowkes, F. M., and Harkins, W. D., *J. Am. Chem. Soc.* **62**, 3377 (1940).
31. Fowler, R. H., *Proc. Cambridge Phil. Soc.* **31**, 260 (1935).
32. Fowler, R. H., and Guggenheim, C. A., Statistical Thermodynamics. University Press, Cambridge, p. 429, 1939.
33. Giauque, F., and Stout, J. W., *J. Am. Chem. Soc.* **60**, 393 (1938).
34. Gross, P. L. K., Thesis, University of Chicago, 1926.
35. Harkins, W. D., and Boyd, G. E., *J. Phys. Chem.* **45**, 20 (1941).
36. Harkins, W. D., and Boyd, G. E., *J. Am. Chem. Soc.* **64**, 1195 (1942).
37. Harkins, W. D., and Dahlstrom, R., *Ind. Eng. Chem.* **22**, 897 (1930).
38. Harkins, W. D., and Jura, G., *J. Am. Chem. Soc.* **66**, 919 (1944).
39. Harkins, W. D., and Jura, G., *J. Am. Chem. Soc.* **66**, 1362 (1944).
40. Harkins, W. D., and Jura, G., *J. Am. Chem. Soc.* **66**, 1366 (1944).
41. Hill, T., *J. Chem. Phys.* **14**, 263 (1946).
42. Hill, T., *J. Chem. Phys.* **14**, 441 (1946).
43. Hoag, J. B., Electron and Nuclear Physics. Van Nostrand, New York, 1938.
44. International Critical Tables. Vol. 4, p. 420.
45. Joiner, L. G., Weinberger, E. B., and Montgomery, C. W., *J. Am. Chem. Soc.* **67**, 2182 (1945).
46. Jura, G., and Harkins, W. D., *J. Am. Chem. Soc.* **66**, 1356 (1944).
47. Jura, G., and Harkins, W. D., *J. Am. Chem. Soc.* **68**, 1941 (1946).
48. Jura, G., and Harkins, W. D., unpublished.
49. Jura, G., Harkins, W. D., and Loeser, E. H., *J. Chem. Phys.* **14**, 344 (1946).
50. Jura, G., Loeser, E. H., Basford, P. R., and Harkins, W. D., *J. Chem. Phys.* **14**, 117 (1946).
51. Kennard, E. H., Kinetic Theory of Gases. McGraw-Hill, New York, 1938, p. 330.
52. Kistler, S. S., *J. Phys. Chem.* **46**, 19 (1942).
53. Krieger, K. A., *Ind. Eng. Chem., Anal. Ed.* **16**, 398 (1944).
54. Laidler, K. J., Glasstone, S., and Eyring, H., *J. Chem. Phys.* **8**, 659 (1940).
55. Langmuir, I., *J. Am. Chem. Soc.* **40**, 1361 (1918).
56. Langmuir, I., *J. Am. Chem. Soc.* **54**, 2798 (1932).
57. Lewis, G. N., and Randall, M., Thermodynamics. McGraw-Hill, New York. 1923, p. 249.

58. Loeser, E. H., Jura, G., and Harkins, W. D., unpublished.
59. McBain, J. W., Sorption. Rutledge, London, 1932.
60. McBain, J. W., and Bakr, A. M., *J. Am. Chem. Soc.* **48**, 690 (1926).
61. Ostwald-Luther, Hand-und-Hilfsbuch zur Ausführung physikochemischer Messingen. Dover Publications, New York, 1943.
62. Rice, O. K., *J. Chem. Phys.* **15**, 314 (1947).
63. Ries, H., Private communication.
64. Ries, H. E., Johnston, M. F. L., and Melik, J. S., *J. Chem. Phys.* **14**, 465 (1946).
65. Scheele, C. W., as quoted in reference 17, p. 1.
66. Shephard, S. E., *Revs. Modern Phys.* **14**, 303 (1942).
67. Sieverts, A., *Z. physik. Chem.* **77**, 598, 1911.
68. Smith, D. P., *J. Phys. Chem.* **23**, 186 (1919).
69. Strong, J., Procedures in Experimental Physical Chemistry. Prentice-Hall, New York, 1938.
70. Volmer, M., *Z. physik. Chem.* **115**, 253 (1925).
71. Wooten, L. A., and Brown, C., *J. Am. Chem. Soc.* **65**, 113 (1945).

Surface Tension Measurements

BY

MALCOLM DOLE

Department of Chemistry, Northwestern University, Evanston, Illinois

1. INTRODUCTION

1.1. Definitions

Surface tension is defined as the force in the interface between a liquid and gas phase or between a solid and gas phase that opposes an extension of the surface, that is measured along a line, and that is expressed with the symbol γ having the units of dynes per centimeter. The force lying in the interface between two liquid phases, or between solid and liquid phase, that opposes an extension of the interface is defined as the interfacial tension and also has the symbol γ with the units dynes per centimeter. Thus surface tension is a force per unit of length.

Surface energy of an area A cm.^{2} is defined as $\gamma \cdot A$ ergs.

1.2. Methods

There are many methods of surface and interfacial tension measurement among which may be mentioned the capillary rise, the ring, the maximum bubble pressure, the drop weight, the Wilhelmy, the pendant drop, the centrifugal, the sessile drop, the ripple, the vibrating jet methods, and modifications of these. Double capillary tubes, twin-rings, straight wires, plates, discs, parallel plates, horizontal capillary tubes, etc. have been used. In fact the study of surface tension techniques might be described as a study of scientific inventiveness and ingenuity.

We do not have space here to describe and review all methods and modifications that have been used in the past; instead the four most important and convenient methods will be discussed. Of these, the maximum bubble pressure method and the drop weight method have most often been used in studying the surface tension of liquid metals and alloys, and the maximum bubble pressure method in the analysis of solutions. Many of the principles of one method are at once transferable to another method, so that if, for example, the theory underlying the capillary rise method is well understood, it is not difficult to comprehend the techniques of many of the other methods.

1.3. Applications

As most metals are formed in the liquid state it is clear that surface tension forces may influence some of their properties, in particular the spreading of one liquid metal over another, possibly solid, metal is affected by the surface forces. Thus, Chalmers (10) has investigated the relationship between surface tension and the tinplating of steel by the hot dipping process. Coffman and Parr (11) found that HCl gas not only lowers the surface tension of a Zn-Pb solder, but also markedly improves the spreading. The connection is obvious since, as the surface tension of the liquid phase is larger, the tendency for it to spread is less (the work of adhesion of the liquid to the solid and the contact angles must also be considered). As the surface tension of molten metals is remarkably high (10 times or more greater than that of water in many cases) with sometimes an unusual positive temperature coefficient, it is not surprising that surface tension forces play a significant role in all processes where the spreading of a liquid metal is concerned.

The accurate determination of the surface tension of molten metals is difficult because of two factors, first the ease with which metals combine with gases of different types to form surface compounds such as oxides or hydrides that upset the measurements, and second the large contact angle usually exhibited between metals and glass or quartz. In the drop weight method, for example, this means that the inner radius determines the size of the drop whereas when water is used with a quartz capillary, it is the outer radius which must be used in the surface tension calculation.

Grain size in alloys is undoubtedly affected by surface tension: see, for example, the remarks of Bastien on grain size in Al-Mg alloys (5).

Many solutions containing surface active solutes can be analyzed by adding base, let us say, which converts the surface active acid to a surface inactive compound and causes a sharp rise in the surface tension until the end point in the titration is reached, at which time the surface tension becomes constant (see Taubmann, 63, and Preston, 48). The maximum bubble pressure method is used, the pressure rising rapidly to the end point. Reference can also be made to the filter-paper strip method of capillary analysis carried out by Liesegang (38).

The flotation of solids, as in the separation of minerals by flotation, is entirely dependent on surface forces; in particular the property of the solid, or of the solid plus "collector," that largely determines the flotation is the contact angle between the liquid and solid phase. The stability of the floated ore will increase with increase in the value of $\gamma(1 - \cos\theta)$ where γ is the surface tension of the liquid phase and θ is the contact angle.

The rate of penetration of liquids into solid powders and capillary tubes is a function of the "penetrating pressure," which is given by the term

$$\frac{2\gamma \cos\theta}{r};$$

again showing the importance of surface tension and contact angle.

As this chapter will include only a description of methods of surface tension measurement, the reader who is interested in contact angles, frothing agents, surface film pressures, and other surface phenomena is referred to the excellent treatise of Adam (2).

2. CAPILLARY RISE METHOD

2.1. Absolute Measurements

2.1.1. Introduction. Since the capillary rise method has been in the past the standard surface tension method to which all other methods

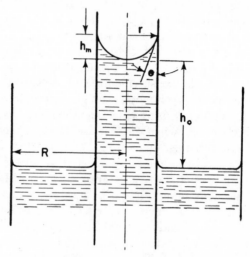

FIG. 1.   Diagram for discussion of the capillary rise method.

have been referred, we shall consider it first in some detail.   The theory underlying this method should be well understood because it is fundamental and applicable in part to all other types of surface tension measurement.   It is interesting to note that since the exhaustive studies of Richards and Coombs (52), Richards and Carver (51), and Harkins and Brown (26) there have been no important attempts to improve the precision of absolute surface tension measurements; the tendency has been on the other hand to increase the accuracy by relative methods which enable slight changes in surface tension to be measured.   These relative methods will be described later.   The absolute capillary rise method is nearly as precise as we can at the moment interpret the data.

2.1.2. General Theory.   The forces that, at equilibrium, act on a capillary tube liquid column (see Fig. 1) above the surface of the liquid in the wide tube, are as follows: a surface tension force acting around a periphery $2\pi r$, with γ dynes per centimeter of length and a vertical component proportional to $\cos \theta$ where θ is the so-called contact angle, or the angle between the vertical wall and a tangent to the meniscus at the point of contact; the buoyancy force due to air and vapor displaced equal to $\pi r^2 g h \rho_v$ dynes where h is the corrected height of capillary rise, ρ_v is the density of the vapor phase, and g is the gravitation constant; the downward pull of gravity on the liquid supported in the column equal to $\pi r^2 g h \rho_l$ where ρ_l is the density of the liquid phase. Equating these forces at equilibrium we have

$$\gamma = \frac{rgh(\rho_l - \rho_v)}{2 \cos \theta} \tag{1}$$

As most pure liquids wet clean glass, the contact angle θ is usually assumed to be zero. Richards and Carver (51) in fact could find no evidence of a finite contact angle between water and glass using a sensitive optical method, but they do not state how small a contact angle could have been detectable in their equipment.

The weight of liquid supported by surface tension forces includes that of the meniscus, which must be taken into consideration; in other words the true height of rise is not h_0 but $h_0 + h_m$ or h. If the radius of the capillary tube is 0.02 cm. or below, in other words if the meniscus has the shape of a perfect hemisphere, the true height can be calculated from the equation

$$h = h_0 + \frac{r}{3} \tag{2}$$

which may be obtained for small values of r from Poisson's (46) equation

$$h = h_0 + \frac{r}{3} - \frac{r^2}{h_0}(0.1288) \tag{3}$$

or from that of Hagen and Desains (23)

$$h = h_0 + \frac{a^2 r}{3a^2 + r^2} \tag{4}$$

where a is the capillary constant,

$$a^2 = rh \tag{5}$$

The equation of Hagen and Desains is to be preferred up to a value of $r = 0.1$ cm. For still higher values of r/h up to $r/h = 0.3$ the equation of Porter (47) can be used

$$a^2 = r^2 \xi^2 \left[1 - \frac{0.03219}{\xi^4} + \frac{0.01103}{\xi^6} - \frac{0.0010}{\xi^8} \right] \tag{6}$$

where

$$\xi = \frac{1}{2} \left[\frac{h}{r} + \frac{1}{3} \right] \tag{7}$$

Equation (6) is also based on the assumption that the tube holding the bulk of the liquid is wide enough so that the surface of the liquid is essentially flat.

A correction to the observed height, h_0, must also be made because of the fact that the lower level of liquid that serves as a reference point in measuring the height, h_0, is somewhat higher because of capillary rise on the walls of the wide tube than a free flat surface would be. The following equation of Lord Rayleigh (50) makes possible the calculation of this correction for wide tubes:

$$1.4142 \frac{r}{a} - \ln \frac{a}{h_0} = 0.6648 + 0.19785 \frac{a}{r} + \frac{1}{2} \ln \frac{r}{a} \qquad (8)$$

As tested by Richards and Carver (51) this equation is valid for values of r/a greater than 2.75. The correction factor in the case of smaller tubes can be obtained from the experimental curve given by these authors.

For the most refined work a final correction needs to be made if the capillary tube is not perfectly circular in cross section. If the tube is elliptical instead of circular, with a ratio of major to minor axis given by Q, then the capillary rise will be greater in hundredths of one per cent by the factor (from Richards and Carver),

$$1900(Q - 1.00) - 4 \qquad (9)$$

This expression is valid only for Q values up to 1.10 (10% ellipticity). Apparently unaware of the work of Richards and Carver, Smith and Foote (58) have also discussed and given mathematical equations for the surface tension in elliptical tubes.

2.1.3. Experimental Precautions. Since the surface tension as measured by the capillary rise method is directly proportional to the height, the density, and the radius of cross section, it is essential that all of these quantities be known with as great a precision as desired in the final surface tension value. The density of the pure liquid is readily determined with great accuracy, the height also is fairly readily measured, but the radius of cross section offers the greatest difficulty in its determination. The usual procedure is to force a small slug of mercury through the capillary measuring its length at various points along the tube with an accurate comparator. Harkins and Brown (26) point out that gravitational forces may distort the meniscus when the tube is in a horizontal position and Harkins (25) recommends the adoption of Young's scheme, which eliminates the meniscus correction by using a long and short section of mercury. Richards and Carver (51) could not observe any gravitational distortion in the case of small bore tubes, but applied a correction for the mercury meniscus by measuring its length (a distance corresponding to h_m) and computing the volume of mercury in the meniscus, assuming it to be a hemisphere. One wonders why capillary tubes have not been studied in a vertical position with the mercury column supported on a column of water or some other liquid. From theoretical considerations which we shall discuss later, it would appear that the diameter of the tube wet with a film of water is of greater significance for surface tension measurements than that of a dry tube. The greatest care in selecting capillary tubes of uniform true right cylindrical shape should be exercised.

Capillary height measurements are made with accurate cathetometers with a sharp edged black screen immersed in the thermostat tank just under and back of the meniscus, as recommended by Richards and Coombs (52). The apparatus should be tested for optical distortion by measuring the distance between two ruled lines on a glass plate inserted in the bath at the location of the capillarimeter and comparing this distance with a similar measurement made in the air. Richards and co-workers measured the height of rise with the capillary tube in four positions, front, back, inverted front, and inverted back, and took the average to eliminate the distortion of the image. The capillarimeter, as well as the plates through which the observation is made, should be, of course, exactly vertical.

The final experimental precaution has to do with cleanliness of equipment and purity of liquids studied. A slight amount of grease on glass surfaces will change the contact angle between liquid and glass, thus vitiating the measurement. The best technique for the removal of grease is to wash the glass apparatus with a hot mixture of nitric and sulfuric acids (cleaning solution should not be used since chromic oxide seems to penetrate slightly into the glass structure—as we have often noticed in making accurate density measurements in the Northwestern Laboratory), to rinse with redistilled water, and finally to steam out the apparatus for about an hour using steam generated from redistilled water. The chief criticism of the work of Richards and his school lies in their use of chromic acid cleaning solution. Nevertheless, their results agreed very closely with those of Harkins and Brown who applied the steaming out technique to the cleansing of their glass capillarimeters.

Young et al. (69) describe a useful overflow method of renewing the surface by flowing the liquid in the capillary tube out into a trap. (The surface could also be renewed in the apparatus of Richards and Coombs (52) and, indeed, was, in their habit of inverting their apparatus.)

2.1.4. Experimental Accuracy and Reproducibility. Table I gives some data from which the degree of accuracy obtainable can be judged.

Richards and Carver (51) found that removal of air increased the surface tension by the following amounts: water 0.02, benzene 0.14, chloroform 0.10, carbon tetrachloride 0.15, ether 0.05, and dimethyl aniline 0.10 dynes/cm. These values represent the increase in surface tensions on readmitting air to the evacuated capillarimeter; one wonders

TABLE I

Surface Tension Data by Capillary Rise Method

		Observer
h_0 ($r = 0.4$, $R = 20$ mm.)	34.33 mm.	Richards and Carver (51)
Small meniscus correction	.143	
Large meniscus correction	.013	
Corrected Height	34.49 mm.	
Surface tension of water at 20°	72.75 dynes/cm.	Richards and Carver
	72.77	Richards and Coombs (52)
	72.80	Harkins and Brown (26)
Surface tension of benzene at 20°	28.88	Richards and Carver
	28.88	Harkins and Brown

if sufficient time was allowed for the liquids to become resaturated with air.

2.2. Relative Measurements

2.2.1. Double Capillary Tube Methods. Sugden (60), Mills and Robinson (43), and Bowden (8) are among those who have advocated the use of two small capillaries attached to a large tube instead of one small tube. The apparatus of Sugden is illustrated in Fig. 2 where r_1 and r_2 represent the two small capillary tubes of radii r_1 and r_2 respectively, A is a solid rod on which tubes r_1 and r_2 are fused and which fits into the socket B of the wide tube C. The capillary system is thus easily removable from C for cleansing purposes.

If both capillary tubes r_1 and r_2 are so small that each meniscus has the shape of a hemisphere, and if h is the observed difference in the height of rise in the two capillaries, then the surface tension is given by the equation (for zero contact angle) (43)

$$\gamma = \frac{r_1 \cdot r_2 \cdot g \ (\rho_l - \rho_v)(3h + r_2 - r_1)}{6(r_1 - r_2)} \tag{10}$$

As is obvious from equation (10) this method requires an accurate knowledge of the capillary radii and of the heights of rise.

Advantages are first, that it is suitable for small quantities of liquid, second, for corrosive liquids, and third, that it permits a study of changes of height of rise with time. Thus Mills and Robinson (43) observed irregularly falling or rising menisci, followed by a slow rise to a stationary maximum value in both tubes.

2.2.2. Relative Method of Jones and Ray. Although it had been realized by previous workers that changes in the height of rise could be measured by weighing the quantity of liquid in the wide tube required to bring the meniscus in the narrow tube always to the same point, it was

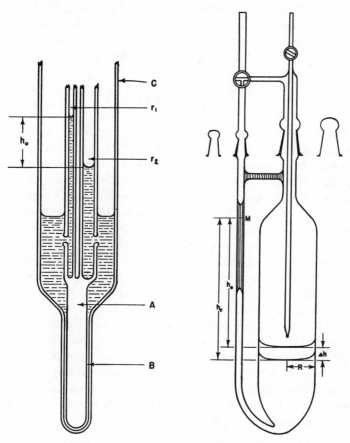

FIG. 2. Double tube capillarimeter of Sugden (1921).

FIG. 3. Silica capillarimeter
of Jones and Ray (1937).

Jones and Ray (33) who first brilliantly carried this method to a high state of perfection. Using a fused quartz capillarimeter, illustrated in Fig. 3, whose wide tube was ground internally and externally to a true right circular cylinder, they were able to measure changes in surface tension amounting to 0.001% or 0.0007 dyne/cm. After water had been dropped, by pipet, into the wide tube until the upper meniscus came to M, the apparatus was weighed to obtain the weight of water, W_0, contained therein. After drying, solution was admitted to the capillarimeter until once again the upper meniscus stood at M. Knowing the weight of solution W_c required to bring this about, knowing the densities of water and solution $\rho_{l,0}$ and $\rho_{l,c}$ and knowing the radii of the larger and smaller tubes R and r respectively (an exact knowledge of the radius of the large tube became important in concentrated solutions, but apart from this it was unnecessary to determine the radii exactly), the relative surface tension, γ, could be calculated from the equation

$$\gamma = \frac{\gamma_c}{\gamma_0} = \left[\frac{\rho_{l,c} - \rho_{v,c}}{\rho_{l,0} - \rho_{v,0}} \right] \left[1 + \frac{1}{\pi R^2 h \left(1 - \dfrac{r}{h} \right)} \left(\frac{W_0}{\rho_{l,0}} - \frac{W_c}{\rho_{l,c}} \right) \right] \tag{11}$$

where h is the true height of rise with pure water in the capillarimeter.

The outstanding observation of Jones and Ray was that addition of salts up to 0.001 N concentration *lowered* the surface tension, apparently, by 0.02%. At higher concentrations, the surface tension then rose in accordance with the prediction of the Debye-Wagner-Onsager-Samaras surface tension theory of strong electrolytes (45). Langmuir (36) has explained the initial decrease in surface tension, called the Jones-Ray effect, as the result of a methodological error, arising from a vertical film of water held above the meniscus because of ζ-potential forces which diminishes in thickness in the presence of electrolytes, thus producing an apparent widening of the small tube and an apparent decrease of surface tension. Langmuir's theory has been further investigated by Jones and Frizzell (32), Jones and Wood (34), and Wood and Robinson (67), with nearly complete verification. Harkins (25) states that the water film is about 25 A. thick, but Langmuir's calculations and the Jones-Ray effect require it to be about 500 A. thick at the meniscus in the capillary tube. Until this methodological uncertainty is resolved, all surface tension measurements by the capillary rise method will be uncertain to the extent of a few thousandths or hundredths of a per cent.

2.3. Combined Capillary Tube-Pressure Methods

2.3.1. Single Capillary Tubes. Single capillary tubes with the meniscus forced to a predetermined point by means of air pressure have been used in both the vertical and horizontal positions. The essential part of Ferguson and Dowson's (17) apparatus is shown in Fig. 4 where A is the tip of the capillary tube that is immersed in a vertical position under the surface of the liquid whose surface tension is desired. E is the sharp end of a pointer which is sealed into the capillary tube at a convenient height and serves as a reference mark so that the height of the liquid in the wide dish can always be adjusted to the distance h_2 above the flat bottom end of the capillary tube.   This adjustment can be made with great accuracy.   Pressure is now applied at B until the lowest point of the meniscus of liquid in the capillary tube falls to a position flush with the flat end.   If the capillary tube is small enough so that the meniscus is hemispherical, the surface tension is given by the equation

$$\gamma = \frac{\rho r \cdot g}{2}\left(h_2 - \frac{r}{3} - \frac{P}{\rho \cdot g}\right)$$ (12)

If the liquid in the manometer used to measure the pressure is the same

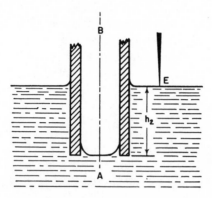

FIG. 4.   Apparatus of Ferguson and Dowson (1921).

as the liquid under test and if h_1 is the difference between the heights in the manometer, equation (12) may be written

$$\gamma = \frac{\rho r \cdot g}{2}\left(h_2 - h_1 - \frac{r}{3}\right).$$ (13)

This method can be carried out with great accuracy and has the advantages that (1) the same point on the capillary tube, namely its tip end, is always used, (2) the radius is easily measured at various orientations with a dividing engine, (3) it is unnecessary to measure the height of rise in the capillary, only the relative measurements of h_1 in the manometer have to be carried out with a cathetometer, (4) the capillary tube can be made quite short and is thus more easily cleaned, and (5) the experiment can be quickly performed.   Ferguson and Hakes (18) point out that by varying h_2 and making simultaneous measurements of h_1 and h_2, the density of the unknown liquid can be determined from the slope of a plot of $\rho_1 h_1$ versus h_2 (in this case the manometer liquid must have a known and different density).

Ferguson and Kennedy (19) eliminate density considerations entirely by measuring the pressure necessary to produce a flat meniscus of liquid at the open end of a horizontal capillary tube (contact angle of 90° at open end). No height of rise measurement is necessary and no meniscus corrections are involved, the surface tension being given by the equation

$$\gamma = \frac{P \cdot r}{2} \tag{14}$$

where r is the radius at the curved meniscus end of the liquid column.

2.3.2. *Double Capillary Tubes.* Double capillary tubes have also been used in both vertical and horizontal positions. Sutton (62) seals two tubes of radii r_1 and r_2 together end to end and measures the pressure required to bring a column of liquid of length l_1 to a predetermined point on the smallest capillary with the system in a vertical position. The apparatus is inverted and the pressure again recorded. If P_1 and P_2 are the pressures in the two positions, we have

$$\gamma = \tfrac{1}{2}k(P_1 + P_2) \tag{15}$$

$$\rho = \frac{P_2 - P_1}{2gl} \tag{16}$$

$$\frac{1}{k} = \frac{1}{2\pi r_1} - \frac{1}{2\pi r_2} \tag{17}$$

where r_1 is the radius of the smaller tube. Thus from these two pressure measurements both the density and the surface tension can be determined. If the apparatus is calibrated with a liquid of known surface tension, γ', we can write

$$\gamma = \gamma' \left[\frac{P_1 + P_2}{P_1' + P_2'} \right] \tag{18}$$

In these equations meniscus corrections have been neglected. Sutton obtained results accurate to about 1%, but the technique could no doubt be refined. Speakman (59) seals two parallel capillary tubes of radius r_1 and r_2 into a wider tube whose vertical arm has a radius r_3. He then measures first the pressure required to bring the liquid in r_1 to a predetermined level and second the pressure required to bring the liquid in r_2 to the same level, the surface tension is then given by the equation

$$\gamma = \frac{\Delta P}{2 \left[1 + \dfrac{r_1{}^2 + r_2{}^2}{r_3{}^2} \right] \left(\dfrac{1}{r_2} - \dfrac{1}{r_1} \right)} \tag{19}$$

where ΔP is. the difference in the two pressure measurements. For accurate calculations meniscus corrections must be applied.

Achmatov (1) uses a double capillary tube system similar to Sutton's described above, but by laying the tube in a horizontal position, the surface tension can be computed from the following equation without a knowledge of the density of the liquid

$$P = 2\gamma \left(\frac{1}{r_1} - \frac{1}{r_2} \right) \tag{20}$$

where P is the pressure difference at the ends of the two capillaries just sufficient to prevent the liquid from moving in either horizontal direction. No capillary correction is necessary for this method but the possibility of gravity distortion of the meniscus would have to be investigated for precise results.

3. Maximum Bubble Pressure Method

3.1. Single Tube Methods

3.1.1. Introduction. One of the most attractive methods of surface tension measurement involves the measurement of the pressure required to form a bubble of gas in the liquid whose surface tension is desired. It is particularly applicable to corrosive liquids like molten phosphorus (30) or molten metals and alloys (7) and has the distinct advantage of

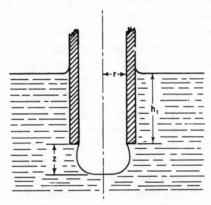

Fig. 5.   Diagram for discussion of maximum bubble pressure method.

giving results independent of the contact angle.   By exerting the necessary precautions great precision of technique is obtainable.

3.1.2. Theory.   If we assume for the moment that the radius of the capillary tube, Fig. 5, is so small that the shape of the bubble at maximum pressure is hemispherical, then the equation for the total gas pressure in the capillary tube is

$$P_{\text{total}} = P + P_1 = \frac{2\gamma}{r} + gh_1(\rho_l - \rho_v). \tag{21}$$

The contact angle is zero at this point; any lowering of the pressure will cause the bubble to grow smaller, any attempt to increase the pressure will produce an increase in the size of the bubble with an increase in the contact angle to a value greater than 180°, as illustrated in Fig. 5.   The pressure will decrease as the bubble rapidly expands.

The pressure across the interface, P, is given for small values of r/L by the equation of Schroedinger (54)

$$\gamma = \frac{Pr}{2}\left[1 - \frac{2}{3}\frac{r}{h} - \frac{1}{6}\left(\frac{r}{h}\right)^2\right] \tag{22}$$

where h is given by the equation

$$P = gh(\rho_l - \rho_v) \tag{23}$$

(In the case of a perfect hemisphere, h of equation (23) would be identical with Z of Fig. 5.) For more accurate calculations the tables of Bashford and Adams (4) can be used. Sugden (61) has worked out a method for the use of these tables in connection with the maximum bubble pressure method and gives additional tables which make it unnecessary to refer to the work of Bashford and Adams. The height h, must be measured with reference to a flat surface; i.e., if the outer vessel holding the liquid under investigation is not wide enough to give a flat surface, a correction for capillary rise must be included.

3.1.3. *Applications.* Harkins (25) quotes Young as recommending that the maximum pressure be measured in the formation of a single bubble, rather than measuring the pressure necessary to give a stream of bubbles. Long and Nulting (40) could detect no difference between a rate of 9 and 100 seconds per bubble in their accurate relative surface tension studies. The capillary tip should be thin-walled.

Inasmuch as the pressure drops as each bubble breaks away from the tip, it is possible to measure the maximum pressure even though the bubble cannot be watched. Thus, Hutchinson (30) has recently measured the surface tension of white phosphorus against CO_2 by observing the maximum pressure required to form bubbles of this gas in the molten phosphorus. His apparatus was calibrated with known liquids before use, and a Bourdon gauge was used to measure the pressure (as the system had to be completely evacuated before use). Using a quartz capillary tube placed under the surface of fused metals, Sauerwald (53) and Drath and Sauerwald (13) were able to measure the surface tension of a number of fused metals and alloys. In this case hydrogen was the gas forced through the capillary tip.

Hogness (29) has developed a maximum pressure method for the measurement of the surface tension of mercury and fused metals in which the pressure necessary to force a drop of the liquid metal upwards through a vertical capillary is measured. His apparatus is illustrated in Fig. 6 where A is a tube into which a cylinder of the metal is inserted and later melted by raising the temperature. Pressure is applied at B until liquid metal drops begin to flow out of the quartz capillary tube D. At this point the difference in height between the column of metal in C and capillary tip is measured and the surface tension calculated from the equation

$$\gamma = \frac{rP}{2}\left(1 - \frac{2}{3}\frac{r\rho g}{P} - \frac{1}{6}\frac{r^2\rho^2 g^2}{P^2}\right) \tag{24}$$

where P is the maximum pressure and ρ is the density of the liquid metal. Hogness found it necessary to use hydrogen gas and to bake out his glass apparatus thoroughly before admitting the metal in order to eliminate all traces of water. Bering and Pokrowsky (6) have more recently carried out a similar investigation in which they studied the surface tension of mercury and amalgams against a vacuum as well as hydrogen gas. Hogness's method has the advantages of continually supplying a fresh surface and of being independent of the contact angle.

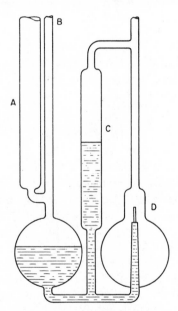

FIG. 6. Apparatus of Hogness (1921) for the measurement of the surface tension of fused metals and alloys.

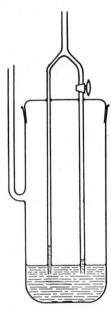

FIG. 7. Double capillary tip surface tension apparatus of Sugden (1924).

3.2. Double Tube Methods

3.2.1. *Apparatus of Sugden.* Figure 7 illustrates a convenient apparatus invented by Sugden (60) for the measurement of surface tension by a relative method. First the pressure necessary to produce bubbles from the small tip, radius r_1, is determined. The stop cock is then opened and the maximum pressure measured for bubbles formed at the tip of the larger capillary tube, radius r_2. If P is the difference in pressures measured, the surface tension can be calculated from the equation,

$$\gamma = \frac{P}{2\left[\dfrac{1}{x_1} - \dfrac{1}{x_2}\right]} \tag{25}$$

where $x = \dfrac{a^2}{h}$ and must be calculated from the tables given by Sugden (61). This is particularly true for the large capillary tube; for the small tube

$$\frac{a^2}{h} = r\left(1 - \frac{2}{3}, \frac{r}{h} - \frac{1}{6}\frac{r^2}{h^2}\right) \tag{26}$$

with sufficient accuracy. The recommended values of r_1 and r_2 in centimeters are

$$0.005 < r_1 < 0.01$$
$$0.1 \quad < r_2 < 0.2 \text{ cm.}$$

Sugden points out that for approximate calculations, good to 1 part in 1000, the following equation is satisfactory

$$\gamma = A \cdot P\left(1 + 0.69 r_2 g \frac{\rho_l}{P}\right) \tag{27}$$

where A is a constant, r_2 is expressed in centimeters and P in dynes/cm^2. Both capillary tips must be at the same level in the liquid.

Bircumshaw (7) carried out an extensive study of the surface tension of liquid metals and alloys using the double tip maximum bubble pressure method. Good agreement with the data of Hogness was obtained.

Using a similar double capillary tip apparatus Hutchinson (30) determined the interfacial tension of a number of liquid pairs by measuring the pressure required to form a liquid bubble of one liquid in another. This is a particularly good method for interfacial tension measurements as here again the contact angle does not enter into the phenomenon.

3.2.2. The Relative Method of Warren. In the double tube apparatus of Warren (66) two identical tips (made by carefully breaking a capillary tube at one point) are immersed in separate vessels, both containing the same fluid at first. By suitable mechanical means it is possible to adjust and measure accurately the depth of immersion of the jets. One of the jets is moved up or down until the rate of escape of bubbles from its tip is exactly equal to the rate of bubble formation at the other tip. The liquid in the second vessel is then removed and replaced by the liquid under investigation. The difference in surface tension between the two liquids is then given by the equation

$$\gamma_1 - \gamma_2 = g\frac{r}{2}(\rho_2 h_2 - \rho_1 h_1) + \frac{1}{6}gr^2(\rho_1 - \rho_2) \tag{28}$$

where h_1 and h_2 are the depths of immersion of the tip in the experiments on the two liquids plus the radius r in each case. Warren's mean error in the determination of the surface tension of sodium chloride solutions was 0.022 dynes/cm.

3.2.3. Method of Long and Nutting. Long and Nutting (40) describe a relative method similar to Warren's in which the change in the depth of immersion was calculated from the weight of liquid added and from the depth of immersion of a rod of known volume. (By careful regulation of the depth of the rod the height of the liquid level in one of the vessels is varied until the bubbling rate is equal from the two jets.) With pure water initially in both vessels, the depth of immersion, h_0, must necessarily be equal for the two jets. After a small amount of salt solution is added to one of the halves of the apparatus, and pure water to balance the bubbling rate added to the other half, the relative surface tension can be calculated from the equation

$$\gamma = \frac{\gamma_1}{\gamma_0} = 1 + \frac{gr}{2\gamma_0} \left[h_0(\rho_0 - \rho_1) + \Delta h_0 \rho_0 - \Delta h_1 \rho_1 \right] \tag{29}$$

The reproducibility of Long and Nutting's data is somewhat better than 0.01%.

Apparently the Langmuir film or possibly a finite contact angle which resulted in the Jones-Ray effect does not exist in the maximum bubble pressure method—which suggests that this method may be fundamentally sounder for surface tension measurements than others.

4. DROP-WEIGHT AND PENDANT DROP METHODS

4.1. Drop-Weight Method

4.1.1. Introduction. Another useful method of surface and interfacial tension measurement is the drop-weight method in which the surface tension can be calculated from the maximum weight of a drop. It is, perhaps, most important from the standpoint of interfacial tension measurements difficult to make by other methods. The closely analogous pendant drop method is in practice less accurate but has its own advantage in being particularly suitable for studying the variation of surface tension as a function of time.

4.1.2. Theory. The theory of the shape of drops has been investigated by Bashford and Adams (4), Lohnstein (39), Freud and Harkins (21) and a number of early workers. Harkins (25) has stressed the principle of similitude, namely that all drops have the same shape if their values of $r/V^{\frac{1}{3}}$ are equal where r is the radius of the tip from which the drop falls and V is the volume of the drop. Harkins and Brown (26) give a table of their so-called F-factors from which values of F can be obtained applicable to the particular liquid under study and which when multiplied by mg/r gives the surface tension in dynes per centimeter. In the case of interfacial tension measurements the equation for the tension is

$$\gamma = V(\rho_1 - \rho_2)\frac{g}{r} \cdot F \qquad (30)$$

where V is the volume of a single drop of liquid of density ρ_1 formed in a second liquid of density ρ_2.

The F-factors have been determined experimentally by first finding the surface tension of the liquids by the capillary-rise method, and then determining the drop-weights in a drop-weight apparatus. The F-factors are finally calculated from the equation

$$F = \frac{r\gamma}{mg} \qquad (31)$$

They are apparently valid for liquids having such diverse surface tensions as exhibited by benzene on the one hand and mercury on the other, as Dunken (14) has recently shown. Iredale (31) and Michelli (42) have suggested an alternate method of surface tension calculation for the drop weight method based on an equation of Worthington (68). If r is the capillary tip radius and α the radius of the drop assuming it to be spherical, then Iredale points out that the ratio r/α is roughly a linear function of r. Suppose α is determined for a liquid of unknown surface tension, the value of r/α is then calculated and from the nearly linear curve of r_0/α_0 as a function of r_0 for water, the value of r_0 for water is found which would give a value of r_0/α_0 equal to r/α for the unknown liquid. The surface tension can then be calculated from the equation

$$\frac{\rho_0\gamma}{\rho\gamma_0} = \frac{r^2}{r_0^2} \qquad (32)$$

where the subscript zero identifies the values for water. As a matter of fact this method is essentially that of Harkins and Brown inasmuch that, if

$$\frac{r}{\gamma} = \frac{r_0}{\gamma_0}$$

then

$$\frac{r}{V^{\frac{1}{3}}} = \frac{r_0}{V_0^{\frac{1}{3}}}$$

and the F-factors are equal.

4.1.3. Methods. The method of Harkins and Brown (26) is capable of a precision of 0.02 to 0.03% with certain liquids. The following precautions should be observed:

(a) A flat ground tip, circular with sharp edges and not polished on the bottom should be used.

(b) Its vertical sides should be polished to prevent liquid wetting the side walls.

(c) The size of the tips should be between 5–7 mm. in diameter for most liquids in the case of surface tension measurements and between 9–11 mm. in diameter for interfacial tension measurements. High density liquids call for smaller tips than low density liquids.

(d) The apparatus should be held in a vertical position, but a 3° inclination from the vertical can be tolerated as Gans and Harkins (22) have pointed out (the weight becomes less the greater the angle of inclination).

(e) As the weight of the drops increases with increasing velocity of flow, it is important to form each drop over a 5-minute interval. Actually the liquid is allowed to flow until the drop approaches its maximum size, then it is allowed to stand for a few minutes to reach equilibrium (some dilute liquids of long linear organic molecules may take half an hour to attain surface equilibrium). Finally, the volume of the drop is allowed to increase slowly and preferably automatically until it drops. The drops are collected in a suitable weighing bottle and weighed.

(f) It is not correct to calibrate the instrument with a liquid of known surface tension unless the proper F-factor correction is applied both to the known and unknown surface tension calculation.

(g) In interfacial tension measurements Ward and Tordai (65) collect drops of the heavier liquid by displacement of the lighter liquid from a special pycnometer. The increase in weight of the pycnometer gives just the required information needed for the interfacial tension calculation. The authors point out that a weight measurement of four drops is more accurate than a volume measurement of 40 drops.

Figure 8 illustrates the apparatus of Harkins and Brown (26), suitable for the study of volatile liquids. The capillary tip is shown at the right; the rod at the left which is attached to a rack and pinion device serves to raise gradually the reservoir of liquid, thus causing the drop to grow very slowly; the intermediate vessel containing a small amount of liquid prevents excessive evaporation from the surface of the drop.

Kurtz (35) points out that a film of plastic or other solid material forming on the surface of the drop can vitiate the surface tension measurements by preventing the drop from taking on its normal shape. Edwards

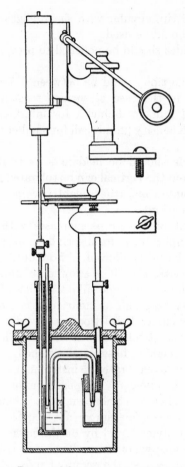

FIG. 8.   Drop-weight apparatus of Harkins (25).

(16) uses an electrical counter in measurements of interfacial tension of sulfuric acid against various oils.

4.2. Pendant Drop Method

Andreas *et al.* (3) as well as Smith (57) have applied a method involving the measurement of the shape of pendant drops to the study of surface tension.   This method has the advantage of being a static one, a single drop being investigated over a considerable period of time, or until its shape becomes constant.   This method is the only known surface tension method which permits an accurate study of surface composition (as indicated by surface tension) as a function of time.

The experimental problem is chiefly an optical one, once a proper dropping tip has been obtained. By proper choice of magnifying system and camera results having a probable error of $\pm 0.5\%$ are obtained. As with the drop weight method, correction factors given in tables must be used to convert measurements of the diameter of the drop at its equator and at a selected plane to surface tension. Good agreement for both surface and interfacial tension measurements on standard substances has been obtained. Andreas *et al.* believe that this method will prove to be particularly valuable for the study of (1) viscous liquids, (2) surface-active solutions (3) small samples of rare chemicals and (4) systems in which the contact angle is not zero.

5. Ring Methods

5.1. Single Ring

5.1.1. Introduction. Because of the ease and rapidity with which the force necessary to pull a ring out of the surface of a liquid can be measured, the ring method of surface tension measurement has had great popularity. Like the drop weight and the maximum bubble pressure methods this method is a dynamic one and requires a knowledge of the force necessary to rupture the liquid-air interface. The data obtained by the ring method are quite sensitive to the size of wire and dimension of ring employed, so that absolute values of surface tension cannot be obtained without applying corrections. In fact it is rather surprising to consider the large number of ring surface tension determinations in which the shape of the surface was not taken into account. It was not until 1924–26 when Lenard (37) who used a straight wire instead of a ring and Harkins *et al.* (28) first correctly calculated surface tension values from the surface rupture forces that the theory of the ring method was put on a sound basis. We are including the work of Lenard in this discussion as the problems involved in pulling a straight wire out of the surface are similar in many ways to those applicable to work with circular rings.

5.1.2. Theory of the Ring Method. If a ring pulled a true hollow cylinder of liquid with a vertical plane of contact with the ring from the surface, then at the moment the liquid surface ruptured, the weight of liquid supported to the point of rupture above a flat level surface would be given by the equation

$$W \cdot g = 4\pi R \gamma \tag{33}$$

where R is the radius of the ring measured to the center of the wire of which the ring is composed. However, the liquid surface will take on the shape illustrated in Fig. 9 as the ring is raised (or the liquid lowered).

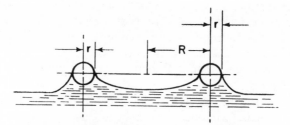

Fig. 9.   Schematic diagram of the ring method.

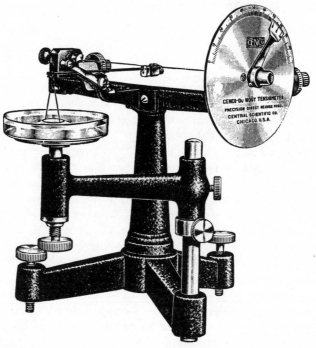

Fig. 10.   Cenco Du Noüy tensiometer.   (Courtesy of the Central Scientific Co.)

Harkins and Jordan (27) made an extensive study of the weight of liquid
supported by rings of various r and R values using liquids of known
surface tension and found that in the majority of cases the weight of
liquid supported is greater than the simple equation (33) would predict.
They have published tables of F-factor corrections for the ring method
which may amount to as much as 25% under certain conditions.   Thus,
the correction factors may be extremely large.   Knowing F, the surface

tension is to be calculated from the equation

$$\gamma = \frac{W \cdot g}{4\pi R} \cdot F \tag{34}$$

To determine F from the tables both R and r must be known as well as V, the volume of liquid supported at the moment of break ($V = m/\rho$).

Freud and Freud (20) have carried out numerical integrations of Laplace's equation relating surface curvature to surface tension and thus succeeded in calculating the F-factors theoretically. For this reason we can now regard the ring method as being an absolute method.

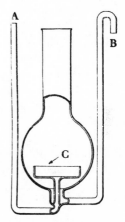

FIG. 11. Surface tension flask of Harkins and Jordan (1930).

5.1.3. *Methods.* For the most precise determinations using rings the technique of Harkins and Jordan (27) should be followed although Schwenker's straight wire method (55) seems to be somewhat more sensitive. The relative twin-ring method of Dole and Swartout (12) described below has the greatest precision of all methods involving a rupture of the surface. Various commercial tensiometers are on the market, the best known being the Du Noüy (15) tensiometer sold by the Central Scientific Co., Fig. 10. In the last instrument the liquid is lowered from the ring and the force at rupture measured by a torsion wire balance. The torsion force is calibrated by known weights in advance of the surface tension measurement. The Harkins F-factor corrections should be applied, of course.

Returning to the techniques of Harkins and Jordan, Fig. 11 illustrates their surface tension flask in which the pan holding the liquid is sealed into another flask in order to allow the whole to be immersed in a constant temperature bath, and which has the side tubes A and B so that the surface can be renewed by flushing through A and by sucking the overflow liquid out through B. During measurement the liquid is held stationary and the ring slowly raised by using a mechanical gear arrangement to raise the chainomatic balance on whose left beam the ring is supported. The chief difficulty comes from slight impurities, particularly in the case of aqueous solutions, which are picked up by the ring, thereby changing the contact angle. The pull on the ring at rupture is a rather sensitive function of the contact angle (44) as it also is of the angle of inclination of the ring (27). Precautions and experimental recommendations can be listed as follows.

(a) Harkins (25) recommends raising the ring rather than lowering the solution as the latter might produce disturbing ripples in the surface. Dole and Swartout (12), however, show that a precision of 0.002% is attainable on lowering the liquid (the precision of Harkins and Jordan was about 0.2%).

(b) The diameter of the pan should be such that it is 4–5 cm. greater than the diameter of the ring.

(c) The angle of inclination of the plane of the ring with the free surface should be less than 0.47° for the error of measurement to be less than 0.1%. A positive angle can be detected by carefully observing the ring as it approaches the surface of the liquid. If it makes contact with the liquid simultaneously all about its circumference, then no angle of inclination exists (assuming, of course, that the ring is plane).

(d) Harkins and Jordan adjusted the volume of liquid in the pan so that the surface would be plane at the moment of rupture.

(e) The ring should be circular and all in a plane.

(f) The apparatus should be cleaned with a hot mixture of nitric and sulfuric acids, rinsed with redistilled water, steamed (the steam generated from water that had previously been refluxed with $KMnO_4$), and rinsed again. The pH of the rinse water should be checked to insure the complete removal of the acid. These rigorous cleaning directions are of significance chiefly in the measurement of the surface tension of aqueous solutions.

(g) The ring is preferably made of platinum-10% iridium and should be ignited in a flame shortly before use.

(h) The dry weight of the ring must be known. The W of equation (34) is the weight at the moment of rupture less the dry weight. The fact that drops of liquid adhere to the ring after the rupture is of no significance except that it indicates a desirable wetting of the ring by the liquid.

5.2. Double Ring Method

Dole and Swartout (12) have recently invented a twin-ring tensiometer, illustrated in Fig. 12, which makes possible the attainment of a relative precision to 0.002%. In this method it is unnecessary to observe the maximum weight of pull or the weight at the moment of rupture; instead notice is taken merely of the ring which breaks from the surface first as the two liquid surfaces are lowered. The weaker tension on this side is then balanced by the addition of weights to this side of the balance and the process repeated. It is possible to obtain a balance between the forces of tension and the weights such that 0.1 mg. increase in weight on one side will cause the ring on the other side to break first from the surface. As the total pull on either ring amounted to 5.7 g., the relative uncertainty is 1/57,000 or about 0.002%. With a more accurate balance an even greater sensitivity might be obtainable.

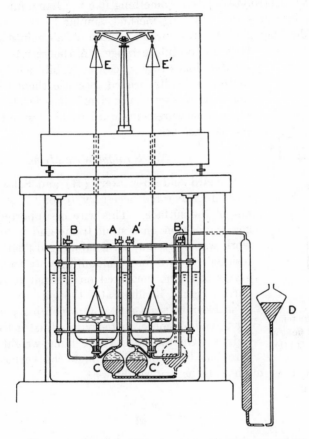

Fig. 12. Twin-ring tensiometer of Dole and Swartout (1940).

After the surface tension forces have been balanced by weights, the liquid being the same in both pans, one of the liquids is removed and replaced by an unknown (in Dole and Swartout's work by a dilute aqueous solution). The change in weight required to bring about a new balance ΔW is a measure of the difference in surface tensions, or

$$\frac{\gamma}{\gamma_0} = \frac{W + \Delta W}{W} \qquad (35)$$

where W is the total pull on the ring in contact with liquid of surface tension γ_0. In the range of dilute solutions studied by Dole and Swartout it was unnecessary to apply a Harkin's F-factor correction.

The Jones-Ray effect was observed using the twin-ring apparatus which indicates that either the contact angle is changed slightly by the addition of electrolytes or that something like the Langmuir film enters in. This indicates that the ring method, similar to the capillary rise method, does not give the true surface tension of salt solutions, particularly in the dilute range. A theoretical explanation of the Jones-Ray effect as exhibited by the ring method is badly needed, because there will be some doubt as to the precise significance of all ring surface tension measurements until we understand the reason for its existence.

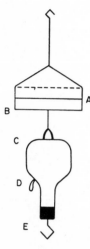

5.3. Straight Wire Method

Lenard and co-workers (37) and Schwenker (55) measure the force necessary to pull a straight wire out of the surface. This wire is supported in a horizontal position on a stout frame and in Schwenker's work was buoyed up by a submerged float so that the residual rupture force amounting only to a few milligrams could be measured on a sensitive torsion balance. Figure 13 illustrates the wire, A, in its frame B sealed into a glass float C which has a side arm D for the admission of mercury to adjust it to a suitable weight. On the hook E are hung weights after the wire has been pulled through the surface so as to obtain what we might call the dry weight.

F I G .   1 3 .
Straight wire tensiometer and float of
Schwenker (1931).

Letting

$$\alpha = \frac{W - W_0}{2l} \tag{36}$$

where W is the weight of maximum pull, W_0 is the weight after the wire has ruptured the surface and l is the length of the wire, the surface tension can be calculated from the equation

$$\frac{\gamma}{g} = \alpha - r\left(\sqrt{2\alpha\rho} - \frac{2\alpha}{l}\right) + r^2\left[\left(1 + \frac{\pi}{4}\right)\rho - \frac{3}{l}\sqrt{2\alpha\rho}\right] \tag{37}$$

In equation (37) r is the diameter of cross section of the wire. Schwenker obtained results with an uncertainty of somewhat less than 0.01%.

It is interesting to note that this straight wire or rod method was suggested by Michelson in 1891 while at Clark University and was first carried out experimentally by Hall (24). Hall discovered the maximum in the weight as a function of rod distance above the surface (see also Harkins and Jordan (27)) and eliminated end effects by the use of two rods of different length.

There are a number of other methods of measuring surface tension among which can be mentioned centrifugal methods (41, 56), method of impacting jets (9, 49) ripple method (64), etc. all of which require rather complicated apparatus or have not yet been developed to great accuracy; hence they will not be discussed here.

REFERENCES

1. Achmatov, A., *Kolloid. Z.* **66**, 266 (1934).
2. Adam, N. K., The Physics and Chemistry of Surfaces. 3rd ed. Oxford University Press, London, 1941.
3. Andreas, J. M., Hauser, E. A., and Tucker, W. B., *J. Phys. Chem.* **42**, 1001 (1938).
4. Bashford and Adams, An Attempt to Test the Theory of Capillary Action. Cambridge, 1883.
5. Bastien, P., *Chimie & industrie* **45**, No. 3 bis, 27 (1941).
6. Bering, B. P., and Pokrowsky, N. L., *Acta Physicochim. U.R.S.S.* **4**, 861 (1936).
7. Bircumshaw, L. L., *Phil. Mag.* [7] **3**, 1286 (1927); **12**, 596 (1931); 17, 181 (1934); and others.
8. Bowden, S. T., *J. Phys. Chem.* **34**, 1866 (1930).
9. Buchwald, E., and König, H., *Ann. Physik.* **26**, 659 (1936).
10. Chalmers, B., *Trans. Faraday Soc.* **33**, 1167 (1937).
11. Coffman, A. W., and Parr, S. W., *Ind. Eng. Chem.* **19**, 1308 (1927).
12. Dole, M., and Swartout, J. A., *J. Am. Chem. Soc.* **62**, 3039 (1940).
13. Drath, G., and Sauerwald, F., *Z. anorg. allgem. Chem.* **162**, 301 (1927).
14. Dunken, H., *Ann. Physik* **41**, 567 (1942).
15. Du Noüy, P. Lecomte, Surface Equilibria of Biological and Organic Colloids. Chemical Catalog Co., New York, 1926.
16. Edwards, J. C., *J. Sci. Instruments* **6**, 90 (1929).
17. Ferguson, A., and Dowson, P. E., *Trans. Faraday Soc.* **17**, 384 (1921).
18. Ferguson, A., and Hakes, J. A., *Proc. Phys. Soc. London* **41**, 214 (1929).
19. Ferguson, A., and Kennedy, S. J., *Proc. Phys. Soc. London* **44**, 511 (1932).
20. Freud, B. B., and Freud, H. Z., *Science* **71**, 345 (1930); *J. Am. Chem. Soc.* **52**, 1772 (1930).
21. Freud, B. B., and Harkins, W. D., *J. Phys. Chem.* **33**, 1217 (1929).
22. Gans, D. M., and Harkins, W. D., *J. Am. Chem. Soc.* **52**, 2287 (1930).
23. Hagen and Desains, *Ann. chim. phys.* [3] **51**, 417 (1857).
24. Hall, T. P., *Phil. Mag.* **36**, 390 (1893).
25. Harkins, W. D., in Physical Methods of Organic Chemistry. Edited by Arnold Weissberger, Interscience, New York, 1945, Chapter VI.
26. Harkins, W. D., and Brown, F. E., *J. Am. Chem. Soc.* **38**, 246 (1916); **41**, 499 (1919).
27. Harkins, W. D., and Jordan, H. F., *J. Am. Chem. Soc.* **52**, 1751 (1930).
28. Harkins, W. D., Young, T. F., and Cheng, L. H., *Science* **64**, 333 (1926).
29. Hogness, T. R., *J. Am. Chem. Soc.* **43**, 1621 (1921).
30. Hutchinson, E., *Trans. Faraday Soc.* **39**, 229 (1943).

31. Iredale, T., *Phil. Mag.* [6] **45**, 1088 (1923).
32. Jones, Grinnell, and Frizzell, L. D., *J. Chem. Phys.* **8**, 986 (1940).
33. Jones, Grinnell, and Ray, W. A., *J. Am. Chem. Soc.* **59**, 187 (1937).
34. Jones, Grinnell, and Wood, L. A., *J. Chem. Phys.* **13**, 106 (1945).
35. Kurtz, S. S., Jr., *J. Am. Chem. Soc.* **49**, 1991 (1927).
36. Langmuir, I., *Science* **88**, 430 (1938); *J. Chem. Phys.* **6**, 894 (1938).
37. Lenard, P., v. Dallwitz-Wegener, R., and Zachmann, E., *Ann. Physik.* **74**, 381 (1924).
38. Liesegang, E., *Z. anal. Chem.* **126**, 172 (1943); **126**, 334 (1944).
39. Lohnstein, T., *Ann. Physik.* **20**, 237 (1906).
40. Long, F. A., and Nutting, G. C., *J. Am. Chem. Soc.* **64**, 2476 (1942).
41. Meyerstein, W., and Morgan, J. D., *Phil. Mag.* **35**, 335 (1944).
42. Michelli, L. I. A., *Phil. Mag.* [7] **3**, 581 (1927).
43. Mills, H., and Robinson, P. L., *J. Chem. Soc.* **1927**, 1823.
44. Nietz, A. H., and Lambert, R. H., *J. Phys. Chem.* **33**, 1460 (1929).
45. Onsager, L., and Samaras, N. N. T., *J. Chem. Phys.* **2**, 528 (1934); also Wagner, C., *Physik. Z.* **25**, 474 (1924).
46. Poisson, Nouv. Théor. d. l'act. capill. Paris, 1831.
47. Porter, A. W., *Trans. Faraday Soc.* **27**, 205 (1931); **29**, 1307 (1933).
48. Preston, J. M., *J. Soc. Dyers Colourists.* **61**, 161 (1945).
49. Puls, H. O., *Phil. Mag.* **22**, 970 (1936).
50. Rayleigh, Lord, *Proc. Roy. Soc.* **A92**, 184 (1915).
51. Richards, T. W., and Carver, E. K., *J. Am. Chem. Soc.* **43**, 827 (1921).
52. Richards, T. W., and Coombs, L. B., *J. Am. Chem. Soc.* **37**, 1656 (1915).
53. Sauerwald, F., *Z. Metallkunde* **18**, 137, 193 (1926).
54. Schroedinger, E., *Ann. Physik.* **46**, 410 (1915).
55. Schwenker, G., *Ann. Physik.* **11**, 525 (1931).
56. Searle, G. F. C., *Proc. Phys. Soc. London* **53**, 681 (1941).
57. Smith, G. W., *J. Phys. Chem.* **48**, 168 (1944).
58. Smith, W. O., and Foote, P. D., *Ind. Eng. Chem.* **21**, 567 (1929).
59. Speakman, J., *J. Chem. Soc.* **1933**, 1449.
60. Sugden, S., *J. Chem. Soc.* **119**, 1483 (1921).
61. Sugden, S., *J. Chem. Soc.* **121**, 858 (1922); **125**, 27 (1924).
62. Sutton, T. C., *Proc. Phys. Soc. London* **45**, 88 (1933).
63. Taubmann, A., *Z. physik. Chem.* **A161**, 129 (1932).
64. Tyler, E., *Phil. Mag.* **31**, 209 (1941).
65. Ward, A. F., and Tordai, L., *J. Sci. Instruments* **21**, 143 (1944).
66. Warren, E. L., *Phil. Mag.* [7] **4**, 358 (1927).
67. Wood, L. A., and Robinson, L. B., *J. Chem. Phys.* **14**, 258 (1946).
68. Worthington, *Proc. Roy. Soc. London* **32**, 362 (1881).
69. Young, T. F., Gross, P. L. K., and Harkins, W. D. See Harkins (25).

Vacuum Techniques and Analysis

By

BENJAMIN B. DAYTON

Distillation Products, Inc., Rochester, New York

CONTENTS

333

1. INTRODUCTION

Several of the unit operations described in other chapters involve vacuum techniques. It is the purpose of this section to outline the proper methods of assembly and operation of vacuum systems constructed with the aid of modern diffusion pumps and unit parts available from manufacturers of scientific glass apparatus and vacuum equipment. This outline is supplemented by a fairly complete bibliography on vacuum technique. As examples of typical vacuum systems certain unit operations not described elsewhere in this volume will be briefly treated.

2. THE MEASUREMENT OF LOW PRESSURES

2.1. Range of Common Types of Vacuum Gauges

The adjacent diagram (Fig. 1) shows the useful range of pressure measurement for various common types of vacuum gauges (8, 12). The width of the band indicates the relative accuracy of the gauge at a given pressure. The pressure scale is logarithmic from 10^{-8} to 10^2 millimeters of mercury. Among the other types not shown on the chart are glow discharge tubes (2, 31, 41), which give a rough estimate of pressure in the range from 10^{-2} to 10 mm., and Gaede's "Molvacuumeter" (100), which is a special type of radiometer gauge with a range from 10^{-7} to 10 mm. The Alphatron (83, 144, 154) is a new type of ionization gauge using the alpha particles from a radioactive source to ionize the gas.

2.2. Absolute Gauges

The McLeod gauge (1, 6, 193) (Fig. 2a and b), the mercury manometer (1, 92, 212, 227), and the butyl phthalate (or oil) manometer (69, 109, 116, 203) are "absolute" gauges, that is, they measure the pressure directly in a way that can be predicted from the geometry of the instrument and have the same calibration for all gases (except that the McLeod gauge can not be used with gases or vapors which deviate considerably from the ideal gas law). These three are in general the only gauges which can be trusted for analytical work in which the pressure enters into the final calculations. The other types of vacuum gauge do not measure the pressure directly, but rather some other physical property of the gas such as the transport of heat (Pirani and thermocouple gauges) or the ionization produced by a stream of electrons (ionization and Philips gauges). They are usually calibrated against a McLeod gauge on a manifold with cold traps to eliminate vapors, and the calibration

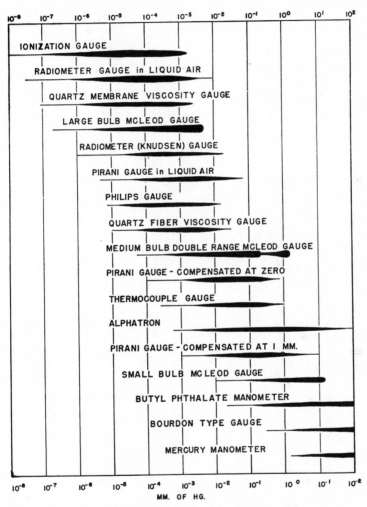

FIG. 1. Range of vacuum gauges.

factor is not the same for all gases. The construction and calibration of McLeod gauges is described briefly in Section 2.6.

The Knudsen gauge is sometimes classed as an absolute gauge, but its calibration varies slightly with different gases because of differences in the accommodation coefficient and other factors (6, 38, 84, 97).

There are many variations in the design of Knudsen gauges, which are also known as radiometer gauges (70, 96, 97, 121, 140) and Klumb and Schwarz (131) have described a type involving a suspended cylindrical vane system with a heater inside and liquid air cooling on the outside

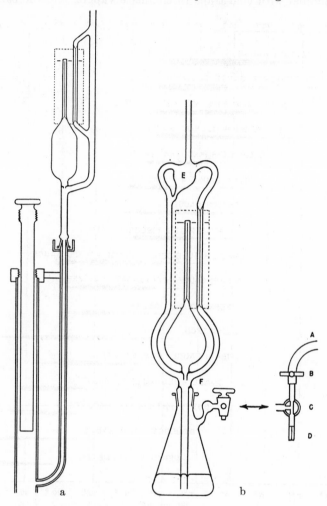

FIG. 2. a) McLeod gauge (long form), b) McLeod gauge (short form).

capable of measuring to less than 10^{-7} mm. of Hg. The principle of operation of Knudsen gauges is to move a suspended vane system by directing rapidly moving molecules, which have come in contact with a hot surface, against one side of the vanes while less energetic molecules coming from a cool surface impinge on the opposite side (132, 208).

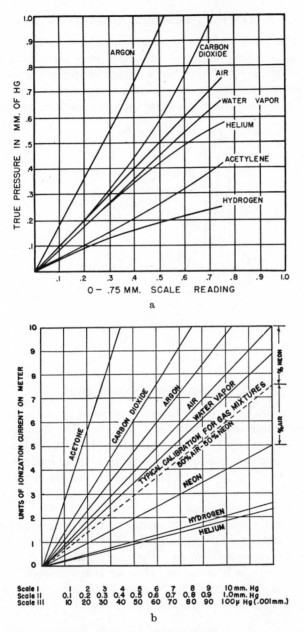

FIG. 3. a) Calibration of Pirani gauge, type PG-1A, for various gases. (Distillation Products, Inc.) b) Calibration of Alphatron for various gases. (National Research Corp.)

2.3. Analysis of Gases with Nonabsolute Gauges

While it is possible to take advantage of the fact that the "non-absolute" gauges have different calibration curves for various gases in analyzing simple gas mixtures, the accuracy obtainable is not very good unless extreme precautions are taken to eliminate variations in the calibration due to surface changes (accommodation coefficient, etc.)

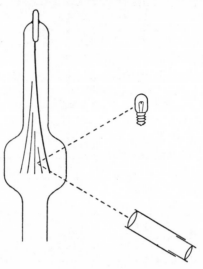

FIG. 4.   Quartz-fiber viscosity gauge.

presence of vapors from rubber or grease exposed in the system, fluctuations in the power supply, electrical leakage, electrical clean-up, etc. While the standard types of ionization gauge (1, 6, 12, 86, 152) have been calibrated for various gases, this gauge is very unreliable because of clean-up effects (7, 56, 183). Calibration curves for the Pirani gauge (Type PG-1A) and a radioactive-source ion gauge (Alphatron) for various gases are shown in Fig. 3a and b.

Corrosive gases react with the metal parts of gauges and even relatively inert gases (e.g., carbon dioxide) may react with the incandescent filament of the ionization gauge. For analytical work with extremely corrosive gases such as bromine and chlorine at low pressures the quartz-fiber viscosity gauges (12, 38) are recommended since these can be made with all exposed surfaces of glass or quartz (Fig. 4).

2.4. Measurement of Ultimate Vacuum

It is frequently necessary to evacuate a system to as low a pressure as possible (ultimate vacuum) before admitting a gas sample or reagent.

Any of the gauges listed (except the McLeod) can be safely used to determine when the system is sufficiently evacuated to permit filling with some gas at a pressure over one hundred times the ultimate vacuum that can be measured with the gauge. However, while the usual Pirani gauge (6, 12, 31, 68, 87) or thermocouple gauge (1, 148, 177) can be read down to 1 micron (0.001 mm.) of mercury or lower, these gauges are subject to zero shifts of as much as 2 or 3 microns or more and hence an ionization gauge is to be preferred for checking the ultimate vacuum when gases are to be introduced at pressures less than 100 microns. The hot-filament type ionization gauge is used when pressures less than 10^{-5} mm. of Hg must be reached. The cold-cathode type, or Philips ionization gauge (165, 166, 167), has a shorter range as shown in Fig. 1 but has the advantage that there is no filament to burn out by accidental exposure to high pressures. Briefly, the principle of the Philips gauge is the measurement of the current transmitted through a glow discharge in the gas excited by voltages of about 2000 volts in the presence of a magnetic field that lengthens the path of the moving electrons, thus maintaining the discharge to lower pressures than are permitted in an ordinary Geissler tube.

The McLeod gauge does not show the presence of condensable vapors (95), and unless the system is completely protected at all times with a liquid air or dry ice trap the true pressure in the system is frequently somewhat higher than that indicated by the McLeod gauge. In general, vapors from oils, "vacuum" greases, and rubber, and "virtual leaks" (38) due to frosted cold traps are the chief sources of trouble in a high vacuum system. These can always be detected by comparing the reading of a McLeod gauge and some other type of manometer which does not condense the vapors, or by other procedures such as plotting the rate of rise of pressure on a Pirani gauge when the system is isolated by valves.

2.5. Theory of the Pirani and Thermocouple Gauges

The Pirani gauge consists of a Wheatstone bridge circuit, Fig. 5, to indicate the change in resistance of a heated filament (of tungsten, platinum, nickel, or other stable metal with large temperature coefficient of resistance) mounted in a tube attached to the vacuum system. The thermocouple gauge, Fig. 6, measures changes in the temperature of a heated filament by means of a thermocouple junction welded to the center of the filament. The sensitivity formula for both gauges depends on the nature of the gas through the factor

$$f = 4.38 \times 10^{-5} \frac{a(C_v + R/2)}{\sqrt{MT'}} \text{ in c.g.s. units}$$

where C_v is the specific heat of the gas at constant volume per mole, R is the molar gas constant 8.315×10^7, M is the molecular weight of the gas, T' is the temperature of the gas at the entrance to the Pirani or thermocouple tube, and a is the accommodation coefficient (128, 141). When the heat lost by conduction to the filament supports is negligible,

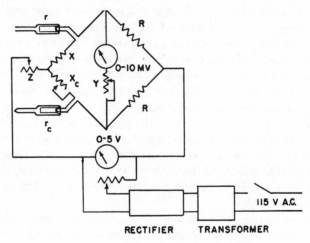

FIG. 5. Pirani gauge circuit.

it can be shown (87) that the rate of change of filament temperature, T, with pressure, p, is

$$\frac{dT}{dp} = \frac{-f(T - T_0)}{4ekT^3 + fp}$$

where T_0 is the wall temperature, k the Boltzmann radiation constant, and e is the total emissivity coefficient. At low pressures and high filament temperatures the term fp in the denominator can be neglected.

The change in filament temperature, dT, is measured as a change in resistance, dr, on the Pirani gauge and as a change in electromotive force, dV, on the thermocouple gauge. Since $dr/dT = r_0\alpha$, where r_0 is the filament resistance at $T = 273°$ absolute and α is the linear temperature coefficient of resistance, the rate of change of filament resistance with pressure, dr/dp, is obtained by multiplying the above formula for dT/dp by $r_0\alpha$. Similarly the rate of change of EMF with pressure for the thermocouple gauge is obtained from $dV/dp = (dV/dT)(dT/dp)$ where $V = (\alpha_1 - \alpha_2)(T - T_0) + \frac{1}{2}(\beta_1 - \beta_2)(T - T_0)^2$ is the ordinary formula for the EMF produced by two metals with thermoelectric coefficients α_1, α_2, β_1, and β_2 when the hot junction is at temperature T and the cold junction at temperature T_0. From these equations the response of the gauges for any gas could be predicted except for the fact that the emissivity, e, and accommodation coefficient, a, depend on the condition of the surface of the filament and must be determined experimentally for each filament and each gas.

The sensitivity of the gauges can be increased by lowering the wall temperature T_0. Normal variations in room temperature do not change the sensitivity by more than a few per cent. For example, at the higher pressures, as T_0 increases the filament temperature T also increases so that $T - T_0$ is nearly constant (when the watt input to the filament is constant), and the quantity $(T - T_0)/T^3$ is only slightly decreased because T is in absolute units.

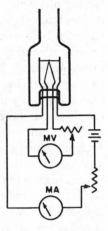

In the Pirani gauge the main purpose of the compensating tube is to decrease the effect of variations in the bridge voltage and to prevent slight zero shifts with changes in room temperature. The gauge is usually operated by calibrating the galvanometer deflection in terms of pressure. The galvanometer current is proportional to the resistance change dr and also to the voltage drop across the filament. It is inversely proportional to a term involving the resistances of the arms and the galvanometer resistance. The resistance of each arm and the galvanometer resistance should all be approximately equal for maximum sensitivity.

Fig. 6.   Thermocouple gauge circuit.

2.6. The Construction and Calibration of McLeod Gauges

Since the McLeod gauge serves as the laboratory standard for calibrating other gauges and is the principal gauge used in analysis at low pressures, the construction and calibration of this gauge deserves special attention. Barr and Anhorn (1) have presented an excellent treatment of this topic and the reader should also consult Dunoyer (6).

A method of sealing the top of the closed capillary by fusing a fitted plug of glass to obtain a flat closure is illustrated by Barr and Anhorn and was originally described by Ferguson (93). This reduces the zero error introduced by a rounded closure and also by bulbous tips which make difficult the adjustment of the top of the closed capillary to the zero line. Another important element of construction is a sharp cut-off which may be obtained by adding an orifice by means of a ring seal just above the opening to the side arm as shown in Fig. 2a, and at (F) in Fig. 2b, and also in the article by Barr and Anhorn. This orifice also diverts air bubbles which sometimes rise with the mercury along the tube wall below the cut-off. For large sensitive McLeod gauges Rosenberg (180) recom-

mends grinding the capillaries with No. 600 Alundum to reduce the sticking of the mercury. Care must be taken, however, to avoid the use of
coarse hard abrasives such as Carborundum, which may introduce deep
pits in the capillary wall that are not filled by the mercury because of
surface tension. It is also advisable to place a trap or splash bulb
(E in Fig. 2b) between the McLeod gauge and the system to avoid
forcing mercury into the system accidentally by expansion of air trapped
in the bulb at higher pressure when the operator forgets to lower the
mercury before reducing the pressure in the system. A trap for air
bubbles should also be provided between the cut-off and the mercury
reservoir, either by the orifice mentioned above or a bulb and ring seal
as shown attached to the rubber tube and leveling bulb in Fig. 10 (which
represents a Toepler pump but is similar in construction and operation
to a McLeod gauge).

There are many schemes for raising and lowering the mercury in a
McLeod gauge (1, 201). The use of rubber tubing in any form is to be
avoided because of contamination of the mercury and bubbles formed by
outgassing of the rubber. However, a leveling bulb and rubber connecting hose are frequently used on home-made gauges because of ease
of construction. The tubing, if used, should be of pure gum rubber free
of sulfur (6, 38). The short-form McLeod with reservoir is usually provided with a standard two-way stopcock to connect the reservoir to the
atmosphere or to a vacuum pump. However, some form of needle-
valve control is advisable. An arrangement which the author has found
to be very smooth acting is shown in Fig. 2b. It consists of the T type
of two-way stopcock (C) with a needle-valve on the vacuum line consisting of a short piece of rubber hose (A) through which a piece of No. 27
wire is threaded and pinched by a large screw clamp (B) while the air
line is throttled by a short piece of broken thermometer tube (D). By
opening the T stopcock to both air and vacuum and adjusting the screw
clamp the mercury can be raised, held stationary, or lowered at will in a
smooth and continuous fashion.

A method of calibrating McLeod gauges which are already assembled
and installed on a vacuum system has been described by Ramaswamy
(175). A calibrated burette with open end dipping in mercury (or a low
vapor pressure oil, such as Octoil) is attached to the system and a known
volume of air at atmospheric pressure admitted from the burette through
a stopcock to a previously evacuated section of the apparatus including
the McLeod gauge. The stopcock is opened only momentarily, the air
in the burette being maintained at atmospheric pressure by raising the
mercury reservoir to keep the levels equal inside and outside the burette.
The final pressure in the system is obtained by measuring the drop in the

level of the mercury meniscus below the cut-off of the McLeod, this fall being of the order of 5 or 6 cm. Boyle's law then gives at once the volume of the isolated system. The system is then re-evacuated and a small volume of air at atmospheric pressure admitted from a fine capillary tube of known diameter dipping in concentrated sulfuric acid until the pressure in the system is such that on raising the mercury in the McLeod a reading can be obtained at some point on the McLeod capillary. The compression ratio of the McLeod can then be computed by measuring the distance between the mercury and the top of the closed capillary and using the previously determined value of the system volume.

Usually, however, a McLeod is calibrated before installation on a vacuum system by direct determination of the capillary cross section (πr^2) with a weighed mercury pellet and measurement of the total bulb (and capillary) volume (V) by inverting the glass head and filling with water or mercury to the cut-off. The "quadratic" scale is prepared by plotting the equation $\log p = \log (\pi r^2/V) + 2 \log h$ on 3 cycle log-log graph paper, a straight line with slope equal to 2 being obtained. Suitable values of pressure (p) are listed with corresponding values of the distance (h) from the top of the closed capillary by reference to the graph, and a scale is then constructed lightly in pencil. After adjusting the pencil lines to give uniformity of spacing where inspection reveals obvious errors, the scale is inked or etched on a suitable plate. Correction for a rounded top of the capillary should not be necessary if the sealed-in plug method of closure is used; however, if necessary, then the zero line is shifted slightly without moving the other lines until agreement is obtained with previously calibrated McLeods.

Some gauges have multiple ranges, and usually the higher pressures are read from a "linear" scale prepared from the formula $p = v(p + h + x)/V$ where v is the volume trapped between the top of the closed capillary and the mercury when adjusted to a fixed reference·line h mm. below the top of this capillary, V is the total capillary and bulb volume to the cut-off, and x is the algebraic distance above or below the top of the closed capillary to which the mercury climbs in the open capillary.

Since the vapor pressure of water at room temperature is about 20 mm. of Hg, if the partial pressure of water vapor in the system is less than $20v/V$, the water vapor will not be condensed out when the mercury is raised to the mark corresponding to v. If the·partial pressure is greater than $20v/V$, some vapor will condense as moisture in the top of the capillary and the partial pressure of the remaining vapor in the volume v will be 20 mm. It is possible to surround the McLeod capillaries with a heat bath, such as a steam-jacket, to increase the operating range for condensable vapors. Correction must then be made for the change in the density of mercury with temperature and the change in pressure with temperature according to Charles law. Although many gases, such as NH_3, CO_2, SO_2, C_2H_2, etc., deviate appreciably from Boyle's law, it can be shown (6, 12) that the error from this cause is usually negligible. However, readings on chemically active gases, such as SO_2 and NH_3, are often meaningless because of the sorption of these gases by the walls of the gauge. The presence of moisture would presumably increase this effect. Data which illustrates the importance of eliminating all moisture and adsorbed gases from a McLeod by strong heating (360°C.) and prolonged pumping is given by Dunoyer (6). Gaede (99) observed that oxygen attacks the mercury (presumably aided by static charges and formation of ozone as the mercury moves in the tubes) forming a scum on the surface that causes sticking. This can be removed by gently heating the capillary. Incidentally, we have observed that the static charges developed by the moving mercury are sufficient to produce a red glow discharge near the meniscus when the McLeod is filled with neon gas.

Space limitations prevent a discussion of the technique of constructing, installing, and operating the other types of vacuum gauges beyond the special points of importance in analytical work. If the gauge is purchased from an equipment manufacturer, adequate installation and operating instructions usually accompany the instrument.

3. The Production of Low Pressures and the Transfer of Gases

3.1. Types of Pumps Available Commercially

Except for large electron microscopes, large mass spectrometers, and a few other special types of apparatus requiring high speed pumps exhausting through ports of 4-inch diameter or larger, most analytical procedures involve small systems with connecting tubes less than 2 inches in diameter. The pumps may therefore be relatively small and inexpensive. There are several excellent small oil-sealed rotary mechanical pumps available from different manufacturers and a great variety of small oil or mercury diffusion pumps* for reducing the pressure below the limit obtainable by mechanical pumps (about 10^{-3} mm. Hg).

Diffusion pumps consist of one or more jets of vapor from nozzles located in a pipe or tube through which air can diffuse easily only in the direction parallel to the vapor jet. The principle differs from that of a

---

* Ace Glass, Inc., Vineland, N.J.; Central Scientific Co., Chicago, Ill.; Distillation Products, Inc., Rochester, N.Y.; Eck and Krebs, New York, N.Y.; James G. Biddle Co. (Leybold dealer), Philadelphia, Pa.; Kinney Manufacturing Co., Boston, Mass.; National Research Corporation, Boston, Mass.; Scientific Glass Apparatus Co., Bloomfield, N.J.; W. M. Welch Scientific Co., Chicago, Ill.

water aspirator or a steam ejector in that the air is not entrained as a fluid by the formation of eddies in a boundary layer between air and vapor, but rather each molecule of air wanders more or less accidentally into a rapidly diverging jet of vapor with no sharp boundary, so that the molecule has a good chance of penetrating into the denser, forward-moving part of the vapor stream before it is driven to the wall and on towards the "fore vacuum." A fore vacuum (or forepressure) of the order of 0.1 mm. is usually required to permit the vapor to flow from the

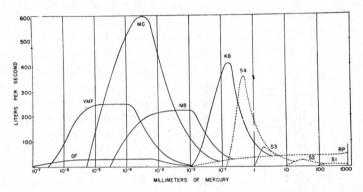

Fig. 7.   Performance curves for typical pumps.

nozzle to the wall since the mercury or oil vapor in diffusion pumps is generated in small boilers at pressures of 1 mm. or less and expands after leaving the nozzle. However, mercury and certain oils can be vaporized under high pressure (1 to 100 mm. of Hg) and ejected at high densities through nozzles and diffusers similar to those in steam ejectors, and under these conditions the air may be entrained by the ejector principle and passed into a fore vacuum of 0.5 to 50 mm. (depending on the boiler pressure).

There are seven distinct classes of vapor jet pumps, depending on the operating fluid and the range of pressure covered:

(1) Steam ejectors, 760–1 mm.

(2) Oil ejectors, 3–10^{-2} mm.

(3) Oil booster pumps, 10^{-1}–5×10^{-5} mm.

(4) Semifractionating oil diffusion pumps, 10^{-2}–5×10^{-6} mm.

(5) Fractionating oil diffusion pumps, 10^{-2}–10^{-7} mm.

(6) Mercury pumps with ejector stages, 40–10^{-7} mm.

(7) Mercury diffusion pumps, 10^{-2}–10^{-7} mm.

Figure 7 shows the performance curves for some typical pumps. Class (1) is illustrated by one stage (S1), two stage (S2), three stage (S3), and four stage (S4) steam ejectors. The long low curve (RP) is typical of a large rotary oil-sealed mechanical pump. The other curves represent typical oil vapor pumps. Class (2) corresponds to KB, class (3) to MB, class (4) to MC, and class (5) to VMF and GF. Ordinary mercury diffusion pumps, class (7), with a liquid air trap would have a performance curve similar to that marked GF.

Many analytical procedures require only a small oil-sealed mechanical pump and a cold trap to keep the vapors of the sealing oil out of the system or to keep water vapor out of the pump. However, rotary pumps can seldom produce a vacuum below 0.001 mm. in a complicated system because their efficiency is very low at pressures under 0.1 mm. They can easily produce the necessary fore vacuum for diffusion pumps and the latter are indispensable for reaching the low pressures required in the analytical procedures described in this chapter. Oil diffusion pumps are more convenient to operate than mercury pumps because they do not require a cold trap to reach low pressures and the vapor is not poisonous. However, the oil vapor is subject to decomposition and contamination by foreign organic molecules, and only when employed in "fractionating pumps" (115) can the oil be maintained sufficiently pure to permit vacuums of 10^{-6} mm. or less. Fractionation is accomplished by partial condensation and refluxing and by circulating the condensed oil through a series of boilers, see Fig. 9, so that the unwanted volatile constituents will be ejected in the first boilers and the best oil is fed to the last jet from whence only the least volatile vaporized fractions are exposed to the vacuum system. New pump fluids composed of certain silicone compounds are now available which are claimed to be less subject to decomposition than purely organic fluids (214).

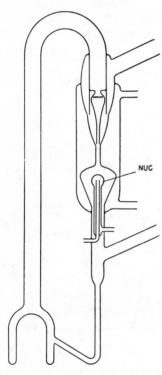

FIG. 8. Mercury pump.

3.2. Mercury Operated Pumps for Analytical Work

Mercury diffusion pumps with two or more stages (nozzles in series) capable of compressing a gas from 0.01 mm. or less up to 10 or 20 mm. of Hg are to be preferred for handling gases to be analyzed (Fig. 8).

Oil diffusion pumps (Fig. 9) are excellent for producing a high vacuum without cold traps, but in general they can not be used to store the gas

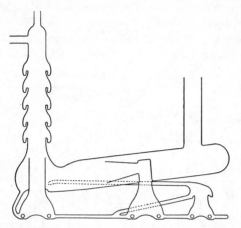

FIG. 9. Two-stage fractionating oil diffusion pump. (Distillation Products, Inc.)

by compressing it into reservoirs at pressures much above 1 mm. of Hg because the required oil vapor temperature would exceed the decomposition temperature at those pressures. The forepressure against which a diffusion pump will operate with full efficiency is in general about equal to one half of the boiler pressure, and the latter can be estimated by measuring the boiler temperature and referring to the vapor pressure curves supplied by the manufacturer of the pump fluid. The boiler pressure can be varied by changing the heater input and is roughly a linear function of wattage.

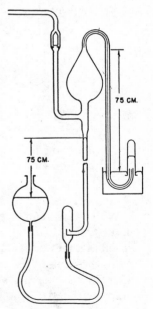

FIG. 10. Toepler pump and collecting tube.

For very accurate quantitative transfer of a gas from one reservoir to another a Toepler pump, or various modifications described below, must be used. The Toepler pump can also be used to obtain a high vacuum but is seldom used for this purpose since the advent of high speed diffusion pumps. The only good quantitative method of removing the whole of a gas sample for storage at atmospheric pressure is the use of a Toepler pump discharging through a long vertical capillary tube extending under a bottle of mercury inverted in a dish of mercury (Fig. 10). An automatic Toepler pump and control circuit designed by Prescott and Morrison (32) is shown in Fig. 11. The mercury is lifted by compressed air admitted through a two-way solenoid valve to the reservoir. When the mercury overflows into the capillary at the top of the pump, the valve switches the reservoir from the compressed air line to the atmosphere and the mercury

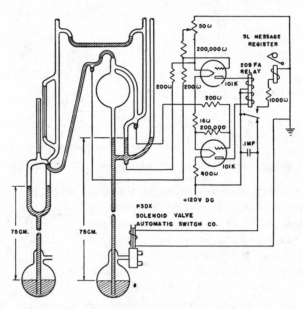

FIG. 11. Automatic Toepler pump.

falls. The valve is operated by a polarized telegraph relay controlled by a vacuum tube circuit and three contacts sealed into the pump.

3.3. Pumping Water Vapor

Water vapor can be passed directly through an oil or mercury diffusion pump without spoiling the pumping action, but the water vapor is condensed in a mechanical pump and after a short time enough will accumulate in the oil used to seal the pumps so that the partial pressure of water vapor on the vacuum side can not be reduced below a few tenths of a millimeter. Most types of diffusion pump discharging into a mechanical pump which has been saturated with water vapor will not operate efficiently since they usually require a forepressure of less than 0.2 mm. Hence the water vapor should be condensed out by a dry ice trap placed between the diffusion pump and the mechanical pump.

3.4. Traps and Baffles

Traps are necessary on the high-vacuum side of mercury diffusion pumps when the presence of mercury vapor within the system is not desirable. A trap cooled by liquid air is necessary for pressures of 10^{-7} mm. or less. Although the vapor pressure of mercury at dry-ice temperatures is about 10^{-9} mm., experience has shown that pressures less than 10^{-6} mm. are difficult to achieve with dry-ice traps designed to have low resistance to gas flow. The trap may be partially filled with gold

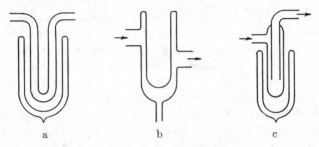

a   b   c

FIG. 12. Three types of cold traps.

foil or an alloy of one part sodium to two parts potassium (94) which acts as a "getter" for mercury vapor. In general no trap is required with oil diffusion pumps since the vapor pressure of the common pump fluids is less than 10^{-5} mm. Hg at room temperature, and by using a fractionating pump and a water cooled baffle pressures of the order of 10^{-7} mm. Hg can be obtained with fluids such as Octoil-S without a cold trap. However, certain equipment, such as the mass spectrometer, may be sensitive to traces of oil vapor and hence a cold trap should be used.

With the aid of a dry-ice trap a vacuum of 10^{-4} mm. or less can be produced with a good rotary oil-sealed mechanical pump, but without a trap a pressure of 0.005 mm. or higher is usually indicated by a Pirani gauge because of the vapor of the sealing oil. It is not uncommon to overlook the presence of this vapor when a McLeod gauge is the only manometer used. Dry-ice and acetone will cool a trap to about $-78°C.$, but it should be noted that the vapor pressure of ice is about 10^{-3} mm. at this temperature. If pressures below 10^{-3} mm. are desired, the water vapor should be allowed to pass untrapped through a diffusion pump or else trapped with liquid air. Traps must be defrosted when it becomes evident that they are giving rise to "virtual leaks" (38).

Three standard forms of cold trap are illustrated in Fig. 12a, b, and c. Type a can be easily defrosted by lowering the Dewar flask and gently flaming the U tube, but to defrost type b the refrigerant must be scooped or blown out of the reservoir, and type c is even more troublesome since frost collected on the inner tube is only slowly removed by flaming the outer tube, unless the pressure is allowed to rise above 100 microns. Type c is preferred when the vapor condenses to form a large quantity of liquid at the bottom of the trap.

For further information on cold traps, charcoal traps, and baffles consult references (1, 25, 35a, 38, 47a, 61, 129, 150, 151, 153, 195).

3.5. Assembly of Vacuum Systems

The assembly of the type of vacuum system commonly used in analysis usually involves simple glass blowing such as the bending and joining of Pyrex glass tubes of less than 20 mm. diameter. However, the system is often divided into units joined by standard taper or spherical ground glass joints, or by the introduction of rubber tubing, tape, or gaskets. Standard taper joints and stopcocks should be lapped together with a 900 mesh grit. Spherical joints are best sealed together with a thin film of vacuum wax (e.g., Apiezon W, Dekhotinsky, Picein, Myvawax). If grease is used, the joint should not be left unguarded overnight but should be protected with vacuum paint (glyptal) and always held together with the standard clamps for spherical joints. The silicone high-vacuum greases are recommended for stopcocks. Tests on stopcocks rotated at intervals in a vacuum line have shown that the greatest number of turns before "freezing" can be achieved with this type of grease, and the viscosity is less affected by changes in temperature.

The vapors and occluded gas escaping from rubber and "vacuum" grease are frequently the limiting factor in attaining a low pressure. Wherever possible joints should be made by fusing the glass or using a good vacuum wax applied carefully to avoid decomposition during melting. Further information on technique in making joints and seals is given in references (1, 6, 11, 12, 25, 38, 44, 85, 179, 181, 210).

3.6. The Flow of Gases through Vacuum Pipe Lines and Absorption Tubes

The time required to evacuate the system and also to transfer gas at low pressures from one part of the system to another depends on the rate of flow of gases at low pressures through the connecting tubes and absorption tubes. At pressures below 1 mm. this rate of flow is usually the limiting factor because of the practice of using long narrow tubes whose conductance is much less than the speed of the pumps at these pressures. If the conductance of a tube is U and the pump speed is S_0, then the net pumping speed available at the end of the connecting tube will be given by S in the formula

$$\frac{1}{S} = \frac{1}{S_0} + \frac{1}{U}$$

providing the pump speed, S_0, is measured under conditions consistent with the definition of U (75a).

The pump speed S_0 is usually given in the manufacturer's catalog in terms of liters per second or cubic centimeters per second, or some other units of volume and time for all pressures in the operating range. The conductance U may be computed from the geometry of the tube, the mean pressure, and the physical properties of the gas (6, 60, 72, 128, 141). Charts are available* which will give the conductance of any cylindrical tube at pressures up to the point at which the flow becomes turbulent.

The following table gives the approximate conductance in liters per second of 1-foot lengths (30 cm.) of small diameter tubing for various mean pressures of air at 25°C.

Inside diameter in mm.	Mean pressure in mm. of Hg					
	10^{-4}	10^{-3}	10^{-2}	10^{-1}	10^{0}	10
4	0.026	0.026	0.025	0.038	0.17	1.5
6	0.083	0.083	0.080	0.14	0.80	7.3
8	0.19	0.19	0.19	0.38	2.5	23
10	0.37	0.37	0.37	0.86	5.8	54
18	2.2	2.1	2.4	7.7	60	570

The conductance of a tube of length L inches can be found by multiplying the values in the table by $12/L$. The conductance is approximately constant until the product of the mean pressure in millimeters of Hg and the diameter in millimeters exceeds 0.2 and then increases rapidly as this product increases. When this product is less than 0.1, the mean-free-path of the air molecules is greater than the diameter of the tube and the Knudsen "molecular flow" formula applies. This formula states that the conductance is proportional to the quantity $\sqrt{T/M}$ where T is the absolute temperature and M is the molecular weight of the gas. For air at room temperatures the "molecular" conductance of a long tube in liters per second may be estimated by dividing the cube of the radius in millimeters by the length in millimeters. For short tubes (length less than ten times the diameter), such as the bore of a stopcock, the conductance is smaller because the maximum admittance in liters per second of the end of the tube is limited to 11.7 times the cross-section in square centimeters. This end correction is incorporated in the charts mentioned above according to Clausing's formula.

* These are contained in a pamphlet on "The Flow of Gases through Vacuum Pipe Lines" which may be obtained from Distillation Products, Inc., Rochester, N.Y. Charts are also available from Central Scientific Co., Chicago, Ill. and National Research Corporation, Boston, Mass. Cf. *J. Applied Phys.* **17,** 811 (1946).

Kenty and Reuter (128a) have made use of the fact that molecular flow is proportional to $\sqrt{T/M}$ in the identification of residual inert gases during the analysis of the minute quantities of gas impurities occurring in certain vacuum tubes. If a gas of molecular weight M is isolated in a system of volume V which contains no surfaces capable of evolving an appreciable amount of gas at the given temperature, and the system is then opened to the pump through a capillary whose conductance, U, is much smaller than the pump speed or the conductance of any other part of the system, then the pressure, p, will decrease with time, t, according to the formula (38)

$$p = p_0 e^{-(t-t_0)U/V}$$

where p_0, the initial pressure at time t_0, must be so small that the flow through the capillary is molecular. The conductance, U, which in this case is also equal to the "speed of exhaust," S, can be computed from

$$U = S = \frac{2.3V}{t_2 - t_1} \log \left(\frac{p_1}{p_2}\right)$$

providing p_2 is more than 20 times the "ultimate pressure" attainable in the system after pumping through the capillary for a very long time. The speed of exhaust will remain constant as the pressure falls and can be correlated with the molecular weight, M, by Knudsen's formula for molecular conductance or by calibrating the system with a known gas. The relative concentrations of two known gases can be determined by reference to a calibration curve as shown by Kenty and Reuter.

Absorption tubes packed with Ascarite, Anhydrone, copper oxide, etc. not only offer a high impedance to the flow of gases at low pressures but require a very long time for evacuating and outgassing. Accordingly the absorbent should be loosely packed granules not much smaller than 20 mesh retained by loosely wadded plugs of glass wool. Complete absorption may be insured by repeated circulation of the gas through the tube and hence a long densely packed tube is not needed. According to Vacher and Jordan (39) a 2-inch column of 20 mesh Ascarite in a $\frac{3}{8}$-inch diameter tube will absorb at least 0.2 g. carbon dioxide (100 ml. at N.T.P.).

3.7. The Circulation and Transfer of Gases with Diffusion Pumps and Toepler Pumps

The modern method is to circulate the gas through the absorption train with a mercury diffusion pump. Naughton and Uhlig (29) have designed a modified pump with an extra water-cooled member, labeled NUC in Fig. 8, which creates a sharp boundary between the vapor jet and the gas in the fore vacuum so that the gas can be compressed into a well-defined volume independent of the variations in heater input. Details of this method are given in the section on the vacuum fusion apparatus.

A circulating pump employing a rotating helical glass tube dipping in diffusion pump oil (or mercury) in a glass reservoir has been described by Harrington (110). The pump is driven by a rotating electromagnetic field and is reversible. A constant-volume pump for circulating gases designed by Puddington (172) consists of two Toepler pumps connected in tandem and alternately tipped by a cam mechanism so that the mercury oscillates between the pumps. An automatic Toepler pump involving an electrically operated valve for controlling the supply of compressed air for raising the mercury is described by Williamson (216). Other modifications of the Toepler pump will be found in references (6, 12, 123a, 173, 192). A simple method for the microanalysis of gases with dry reagents in which a combination Toepler pump and McLeod gauge is employed has been published by Haden and Luttropp (108). Puddington (171) has also described a scheme for collecting gases employing a mercury diffusion pump and a long capillary tube in which the exhaust gas is entrained by the condensed mercury on its way back to the boiler of the pump. Beeck *et al.* (51) designed a small glass turbine with magnetic drive for circulating gas in a glass system during adsorption studies. Nickels (159) has also described a glass circulating pump for gases and liquids using mercury, and Simons *et al.* (185) developed an automatic gas circulating pump using oscillating columns of mercury.

3.8. Mercury Cut-Offs, Needle Valves, and Stopcocks

Valves for controlling the flow and isolating gases in apparatus for analysis may be separated into six classes:

(a) Mercury cut-offs (1, 6, 12, 25, 37, 183a).
(b) Stopcocks lubricated with vacuum grease (1, 12, 25).
(c) Greaseless valves (12, 73, 202).
(d) Float or magnetic check valves (1, 25).
(e) Needle valves (12).
(f) Mercury controlled variable leaks (12, 50, 135, 178, 187).

Details of the construction and operation of individual types of valves in each class will be found in the references. Figure 13 shows a typical mercury cut-off with float-valves as used by Stock in his research on the boron hydrides. Figure 16 illustrates the use of several mercury cut-offs (at F, G, H, I and L). The mercury may be raised and lowered by any of the methods mentioned in Section 2.6 for operating McLeod gauges. In designing a cut-off the length of the arms of the U must be greater than the maximum possible pressure differential unless efficient float-valves are used. Large-bore, hollow-plug glass stopcocks lapped with 900 mesh corundum and lubricated with Apiezon N, Myvacene-S (silicone high-vacuum grease), or other good vacuum grease, are now often used where mercury cut-offs were considered necessary a few years ago.

Most of the valves described in the references as well as large high vacuum valves, solenoid valves, special vacuum stopcocks, and vacuum grease can be obtained from the manufacturers of vacuum equipment previously listed (see footnote, p. 344). Since valves and joints are two of the chief sources of trouble and contamination in a vacuum system, especially where rubber or a "vacuum" grease is employed, considerable care should be given to the selection of suitable designs.

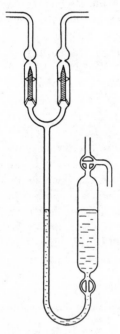

Fig. 13.   Mercury cut-off.

3.9. Manostats

A steady pressure must sometimes be maintained within specified limits of fluctuation as gas flows into a system and is either pumped out or absorbed. A large number of manostats have been described in the literature and while certain designs, such as the Cartesian Manostat* (104), are available commercially, most of them are home-made devices built for a special purpose and the reader must consult references (12, 25, 47, 66, 74, 81, 89, 92, 105, 109, 138, 139, 143, 160, 188, 196, 205) for designs which may suit his application. Note that some of the earlier models, for example, the Bailey pressure regulator (47), were found to have slight defects (bouncing) which were eliminated by later workers (74). Attention is called to the problem of variation in composition of a gas mixture flowing at low pressures through a tube system and in particular to the article by Honig (119) on this problem as related to the mass spectrometer.

3.10. Outgassing and Leak Hunting

Most laboratory equipment for analysis at low pressures is constructed of glass, and pinholes in the glass or leaks through joints can be quickly detected with a high-voltage spark coil (leak detector†). Care must be taken, however, to avoid puncturing the glass with strong

* American Technical Co., 532 Addison Street, Chicago 13, Ill.; Emil Greiner Co., 161 Sixth Ave., New York, N.Y.

† Central Scientific Co., Chicago, Ill.; W. M. Welch Scientific Co., Chicago, Ill.

sparks (more than 10 mm. in length) (2, 6, 38). Wherever possible the glass parts that may need leak testing should be supported on asbestos blocks well removed from any metal support which would draw the "leak detector" discharge away from the glass. Wood and felt supports can not be used if the glass is to be outgassed by torching with a Bunsen flame.

Leaks in metal apparatus (as well as glass apparatus) may be found by the following methods:

(1) Helium plus the "Mass Spectrometer Leak Detector" (197, 220).
(2) Acetone, hydrogen, illuminating gas, etc. plus a Pirani gauge, ionization gauge, etc. (38, 137, 209, 155, 156).
(3) Soap solution or tub of water plus compressed air (2).
(4) Sealing material (grease, glyptal, etc.) plus vacuum gauge (38).
(5) Freon gas plus copper-plate halide flame indicator (23).
(6) Rate of rise of pressure in sections isolated by valves, plugs, cover plates, etc. (2, 41).

Other methods have been used but these are the principle techniques, and the references must be consulted for details and special methods. The helium leak detector* is the most sensitive and quickest method but the apparatus is expensive to install and maintain. Method (3) is commonly used for large leaks, method (4) for porous areas and cracks in temporary set-ups, method (6) for complicated systems with numerous joints, seams, and valves where leaks might occur, while method (2) is the most common general procedure for small leaks and involves numerous variations in technique. In particular under method (2) the Pirani gauge, thermocouple gauge, glow-discharge tube, Alphatron, and Philips gauge may be used when the leak results in pressures from 10^{-3} to 1 mm. (or higher) and the probe gas may be hydrogen, illuminating gas (containing hydrogen, methane, etc.), carbon dioxide, methane, propane, helium, etc. or an organic liquid such as acetone, alcohol, ether, benzene, etc. may be brushed or sprayed over the suspected areas. If the leak is so small that the pump can maintain a pressure below 10^{-3} mm., the ionization gauge or the Philips gauge is used. With the ion gauge both the collector current and the electron current (emission from hot filament) may fluctuate as the probe gas enters the leak. For example oxygen gas entering a leak will cause a decrease in the emission from the tungsten filament of an ion tube which is more easily detected than a change in positive ion current (137, 156). Nelson (155) has

* Consolidated Engineering Corp., Pasadena, California; Distillation Products, Inc., Rochester, N.Y.; General Electric Co., Schenectady, N.Y.; National Research Corp., Boston, Massachusetts; Vacuum Electronic Engineering Corp., Brooklyn, N.Y.

developed a modification of this technique in which hydrogen entering the leak diffuses through a heated palladium tube* into an evacuated and sealed ionization gauge while other gases can not pass through the palladium.

"Virtual leaks" may be caused by vapors from grease, rubber, mercury, or condensate in cold traps and are most easily detected by comparing a McLeod gauge reading with that of a Pirani or other gauge which does not condense the vapors. The presence of vapor or occluded gas is also indicated by plotting the rate of rise of pressure and noting whether or not the slope of the curve decreases with time. When the system contains a saturated vapor, the pressure (as indicated by any gauge except a McLeod) will usually rise or fall much more rapidly with change in room temperature, or the temperature of a cold trap, than would be indicated by the perfect gas law $p = nkT/v$.

Leak hunting in a complex system should be systematic and in general begins with a check on the mechanical pump and then proceeds backwards toward the vacuum chamber, each section being isolated in turn, wherever possible, by valves or cover plates. Provision for such testing should be made when designing the system.

4. The Vacuum Fusion Method for the Analysis of Gaseous Elements in Metals

4.1. History and General Principles

When a steel sample is fused in a graphite crucible under vacuum at temperatures of 1600–1700°C. all oxygen-containing compounds are reduced to oxides of carbon, nitrides and hydrides are decomposed, and any dissolved gases are liberated. If the gases are removed quickly by a fast mercury diffusion pump and stored in a reservoir, the interference due to manganese and aluminum vapors, which condense as active metal films on the colder parts of the furnace and then reabsorb the gases, can be reduced to a minimum. The gases are then analyzed by circulating through absorption tubes or traps and noting the changes in pressure or the increase in weight of the absorption tube.

The present method was developed by Jordan (39, 124, 125) and his associates at the Bureau of Standards from 1925 to 1931. The history of the development from the original work of Walker and Patrick in 1912 to the time (1931) of Jordan's last article is summarized on pages 375–377 of reference (39) and additional references will be found in the footnotes on these pages. Subsequent improvements were made by

---

* A complete leak detector employing this principle is manufactured by the Radio Corporation of America, Harrison, New Jersey.

Chipman and Fontana (4) in 1935 and by Naughton and Uhlig (29) in 1943. Various means of simplifying the apparatus and reducing the time required for determination of oxygen have been developed by Derge (76) and by Alexander *et al.* (42).

No standard procedure has been adopted for the vacuum fusion method and the literature on various modifications of the technique is already quite extensive. Complete details of the apparatus and procedures used in England have been appearing regularly in a series of reports by the Oxygen Sub-Committee of the Joint Committee on the Heterogeneity of Steel Ingots, published by the Iron and Steel Institute (28 Victoria Street, London).* Most of the developments in Germany appear in the *Archiv für das Eisenhüttenwesen* in articles by Hessenbruch and Oberhoffer (111), Diergarten (80), Meyer and Willems (146), Willems and co-workers (215). In the United States numerous papers will be found in *Metals Technology* and the *Transactions of the American Institute of Mining and Metallurgical Engineers* as well as the Bureau of Standards publications and the *Analytical Edition* of *Industrial and Engineering Chemistry* (now *Analytical Chemistry*).

Oxygen has been the principal gaseous element of interest in steel analyses but hydrogen has also been the object of special study. Holm and Thompson (21) in 1941 recommended a low temperature (400–800°C.) extraction method instead of fusion for hydrogen. They found that the diffusion of oxygen and nitrogen through the solid steel is so slow that all of the hydrogen can be extracted without much contamination from the other gases. However Moore (149) and his co-workers have studied the rate of evolution of hydrogen as a function of temperature and conclude that the extraction is not always complete, even at 1000°C. A symposium on the determination of hydrogen in steel is reported in the *Trans. Am. Inst. Mining Met. Engrs.* (Jan. 1945) where a simplified fusion apparatus for hydrogen is described by Derge and co-workers (77). Carney, Chipman and Grant (3a) have described a "tin-fusion method" for the determination of hydrogen in steel in which the sample is dropped into a "lake" of molten tin at 1150°C.

4.2. Apparatus

A diagram of the apparatus designed by Vacher and Jordan is reproduced in Fig. 14. Chipman and Fontana used a similar system but modified the furnace (A) to include graphite radiation shields and a graphite "splash" plug. They also chose to introduce the samples by suspending them on a fine nickel wire wound on a stainless steel windlass rather than using the Oberhoffer sample loading device (illustrated in

* First report 1937, 75 pages; second report 1939, 15 pages; third report 1941.

the article by Vacher and Jordan (39)). Alexander *et al.* (42) found that the radiation shields and splash plug can be eliminated if the crucible is imbedded in graphite powder and a preliminary "lake" of molten metal is formed in the bottom of the crucible before running the samples.

The crucible and sample are usually heated by a high-frequency induction unit but Meyer and Willems (146) and Newell (158) have described graphite spiral furnaces (21, 22, 59). The induction unit

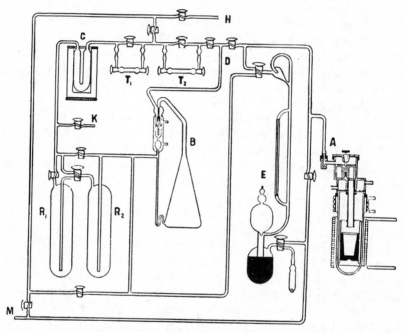

Fig. 14. Vacuum fusion apparatus of Vacher and Jordan.

should have a capacity of about 30 kva for fusion of 20-g. steel samples, about 20 kw being used to outgas the furnace during the blank while about 10–15 kw is sufficient to fuse the samples (22). However, only about 3 kva is required for bringing the samples to red heat (800°C.) in the extraction of hydrogen by the method of Holm and Thompson (21). Alexander *et al.* (42) used a 5-kva (output) power oscillator at 550 kc mean frequency for 5-g. steel samples.

The furnace tube is made of fused silica with a wall thickness of 2 to 5 mm. The crucible, shields, and "spatter plug" (or the insulating powder) are turned (or filed) from Acheson graphite. The head piece is made of brass or stainless steel and is sealed to the furnace tube with a vacuum wax, such as picein, Cenco Sealstix, Myvawax, or Apiezon W. The connection to the pump is usually located in the head and should be 20 mm. or more in diameter, if possible, similar to the tube used on Raine's carbon-spiral furnace (22) rather than the narrow tubes illustrated in the articles by Jordan and by Chipman and Fontana (4). An optical pyrometer is used to view the specimen through a small Pyrex glass window sealed in the head. Guldner and Beach (106a) have described an all-glass furnace.

The rest of the system is constructed of Pyrex glass,* although the mercury vapor pump may be of metal. The diffusion pumps should be equipped with the Naughton and Uhlig condenser (see Fig. 8) for providing a sharp gas-vapor boundary in the fore vacuum (29). They must be capable of compressing about 10 liter-millimeters (13 cc. at atmospheric pressure) of gas into the main reservoir. The general formula for storage of gas at room temperature (300°K.) is $PV = 19000 \ m/M$, where P is the pressure in millimeters in the reservoir of volume V liters when filled with m grams of a gas having molecular weight M. Thus if an 8-g. sample contains 0.1% oxygen, we may expect 0.014 g. CO for which $M = 28$ so that $PV = 9.5$ liter-millimeters. Usually the gas evolved from a 10- to 20-g. sample is less than 10 liter-millimeters, and therefore if the mercury pump is capable of operating against a forepressure of 5 mm., or more, the volume of the reservoir may be about 2 liters. Vacher and Jordan used a modified Stimson pump (191) capable of working against a forepressure of 15 mm. They found it advisable to use only one 700-ml. reservoir when analyzing 20-g. samples, a larger volume unnecessarily increasing the time for clean-up of oxidized gases (39). In cases where the gas evolution would make the pressure in the reservoirs exceed the forepressure limit of the pump, they recommend circulating the gases through the absorbents for short intervals without waiting to complete the extraction from the furnace. This is possible only when the gravimetric procedure is used (39). Chipman and Fontana adopted the practice of removing part of the stored gas, after reading the total storage pressure, by passing it out through the mechanical fore pump and then analyzing only the remainder in cases where considerably more gas was evolved than expected (4).

The McLeod gauge is usually specially constructed for this work with three or more scale ranges. Vacher and Jordan used a gauge covering the range 20 to 0.001 mm. In general the gauge should cover the range from 0.0001 mm. to slightly above the limiting forepressure at which the diffusion pump breaks down. A Pirani gauge may be included if desired

---

* A complete Vacuum Fusion Apparatus is manufactured by Distillation Products, Inc., Rochester, N.Y.

to aid in leak hunting and to give a continuous indication of the lower pressures, but the analysis should be done with the McLeod.

The analytical train consists of a reservoir with inlet tube reaching to the bottom, a U-tube filled with fresh copper oxide heated by an electric furnace followed by a tube containing anhydrous magnesium perchlorate (Anhydrone) or phosphorus pentoxide for absorbing water vapor, an absorption tube for carbon dioxide filled with sodium hydroxide on asbestos (Ascarite) backed by a drying agent such as Anhydrone, a mercury diffusion pump with Naughton and Uhlig condenser for circulating the gases, and the McLeod gauge for measuring the pressure at the reservoir and other points in the train. Alexander *et al.* (42) prepared the cupric oxide reagent by impregnating porous beryllia fragments with saturated copper nitrate solution under vacuum and then heating in a muffle furnace at 450°C. until evolution of nitrogen oxides ceased, reducing to copper by a stream of hydrogen at 350°C. and then reoxidizing by a stream of oxygen at 400°C. Stopcocks and connecting tubes are provided so that the gases can be circulated through any one of any combination of absorption tubes at will and so that any part of the train may be isolated, removed from the system, or evacuated by the mechanical pump without disturbing the pressure in the rest of the system. The absorption tubes may be attached by ground glass joints and in addition to the large tubes used for many consecutive runs by the volumetric method a set of small absorption tubes with matching ground glass joints should be provided for checking the volumetric method by the procedure of weighing the absorption tube on an analytical balance.

In the volumetric method the storage part of the system must be accurately calibrated while the diffusion pump is operating to determine the volume included by the reservoir, the McLeod gauge (with mercury at the cut-off), and the connecting tubes to the stopcocks and the boundary between vapor and gas in the forepressure end of the diffusion pump as determined by the Naughton and Uhlig condenser. An estimate is first made of this volume from the dimensions of the parts involved. A known volume of purified nitrogen at atmospheric pressure is then admitted from a calibrated burette. The pressure before and after admitting the nitrogen is read on the McLeod gauge, and the volume of the storage system is then readily calculated (4). The total volume can also be easily determined if the volume of some part of the system is accurately known, such as the volume of the reservoir to the stopcocks, or the volume of the bulb and capillary of the McLeod. Nitrogen is trapped in the known volume after measuring the pressure and the rest of the storage system is then evacuated. The trapped nitrogen is then expanded into the whole storage system and the pressure measured again.

4.3. Procedure

The references must be consulted for details of the procedure as well as a further description of the apparatus. A general idea of the steps involved in the fusion method can be obtained from the following outline.

(1) Preparation and loading of clean samples
(2) Evacuation of system and degassing of furnace (1900°C.)
(3) Blank run (1600°C.). Check base pressure and rate of rise (P_0)
(4) Fusion of sample (1600°C.). Reservoir pressure (P_1)
(5) Absorption of carbon dioxide (may be omitted) $(P_1 - P_2)$
(6) Oxidation of hydrogen and carbon monoxide by hot copper oxide
(7) Absorption of water vapor in Anhydrone $(P_2 - P_3)$
(8) Absorption of carbon dioxide in Ascarite $(P_3 - P_4)$
(9) Residual gas computed as nitrogen (P_4)
(10) Evacuate, check base pressure and rate of rise

The warm extraction method for hydrogen differs from the above procedure in omitting the degassing of the furnace at high temperature and in heating the sample to only 800°C. while the absorption train consists only of the copper oxide tube and furnace followed by a tube of anhydrous magnesium perchlorate (Anhydrone).

Derge (76, 77) prefers to analyze the gases by fractional freezing rather than by absorption and reads the pressure on a butyl phthalate manometer.*

4.4. Limitations and Accuracy

The vacuum fusion method yields only total oxygen and nitrogen and gives no information about the actual compound present in the steel. A fractional method suggested by Reeve (176) is useful for estimating the different types of oxide in weld metal. Manganese and aluminum interfere with the determination of oxygen by distilling on to the colder parts of the furnace, forming a film that readsorbs the oxygen. Previous investigators have published figures of the order of 0.5% for the amount of these metals that can be tolerated in the crucible and the samples under certain conditions, but Chipman and Fontana maintain that the error can be avoided by providing high speed removal of the evolved gases and by cleaning the furnace and using a new crucible after each analysis in which considerable manganese or aluminum was present (4, 22).

The precision and accuracy of the vacuum-fusion method has been well established by Chipman and Fontana and by cooperative analyses

* The Derge apparatus is available from the Central Scientific Co., Chicago, Ill.

of samples exchanged between the Bureau of Standards and laboratories in England, Germany, and the United States. Vacher and Jordan indicate values for oxygen and nitrogen reproducible to within 0.002%. Chipman and Fontana claim a precision of 0.001% and a probable accuracy of ±0.002%. Hydrogen by the fusion method is not very reliable unless the content is high, but the warm extraction method gives excellent results as indicated in the paper by Holm and Thompson (21). The question of the complete reduction of the oxides and nitrides present in steels has been thoroughly investigated and lengthy discussions will be found in the principle references already cited.

4.5. Extension to Nonferrous Metals

The vacuum extraction of gases from molten metals is limited only by the tendency of various metals to sublime to colder parts of the furnace and then readsorb part of the gas. Winterhager (217) designed a long furnace tube surrounded by a movable furnace coil and with connections at either end to the pump so that by means of valves the gases could be removed in either direction. When the metal sublimed to an adjacent colder portion of the tube, the coil was moved to this spot and the metal resublimed. Bobalek and Shrader (57) found that with fast pumping and rapid induction heating only one resublimation is necessary for extracting hydrogen, oxides of carbon, and nitrogen from magnesium alloys. Winterhager employed his method for extracting gases from magnesium and zinc. Walter (39a) has described a modified vacuum fusion apparatus for the determination of oxygen in titanium. Presumably almost any metal or alloy can be analyzed for gaseous impurities when a sufficiently powerful induction furnace and fast pumping system are used. The extent of the reduction of oxides and nitrides present must be separately investigated for each metal but in general these compounds are completely reduced at very high vacuums at temperatures of less than 2000°C.

5. DETERMINATION OF CARBON BY THE LOW-PRESSURE COMBUSTION METHOD

5.1. General Principles

The determination of carbon in iron and steel by the standard method of combustion in a stream of oxygen at normal pressures and absorption of the carbon dioxide in a suitable train, as described by Lundell et al. (142), is subject to many sources of error. The chief difficulties are the accurate measurement of the carbon dioxide from low-carbon steels by absorption and the relatively large blank. The low-pressure combustion method developed by Wooten and Guldner (40) and improved by Murray and co-workers (26, 27) avoids these difficulties by using an all-glass system in which the carbon dioxide is separated from the oxygen by freezing in a liquid nitrogen trap and then expanded into a known volume and measured by a McLeod gauge.

Similar methods for the determination of carbon in low-carbon iron were described previously by Yensen (221), Zhuravleva and Chufarov (225), and Ziegler (226), but Cioffi (71) and Wooten were the first to employ high-frequency heating and an all-glass system. Gurry and Trigg (15) have investigated the precision and accuracy of the method and claim a precision about three times that of the standard combustion method for low-carbon steel. Stanley and Yensen (190) have reduced the time for analysis of a 1-g. sample to 20 minutes, requiring only about 5 minutes for complete combustion whereas Murray and Niedrach allow 15 minutes for combustion of a 0.5-g. sample and a total analysis time of about 40 minutes per sample. The difference appears to be due to the use by Stanley and Yensen of a nickel boat containing the sample reduced to particles from -20 to $+100$ mesh on a bed of fused 100 mesh alumina in a narrow horizontal combustion tube with induction coil of small radius whereas Murray and Niedrach use larger particles transferred by a magnet to a crucible in a wide vertical combustion tube. Murray and Ashley (40) found that cutting the sample into small particles introduces too much contamination and that the combustion of large steel fragments was effected more easily and thoroughly.

Recently Nesbitt and Henderson (157) have described a new apparatus using a standard high-pressure combustion train with sodium hydroxide solution to absorb the carbon dioxide, the latter being subsequently released by acid into a low-pressure gasometric apparatus.

5.2. Apparatus and Procedure

The form of the apparatus, as described by Murray and Niedrach, is shown in Fig. 15. The oxygen enters from a cylinder connected by copper tubing to the point marked O_2 in the upper right corner. E is a mercury safety valve. The oxygen passes first through a liquid nitrogen trap T_1 and then over a palladium catalyst G heated to 400°C. or more by the electric furnace F to oxidize all organic impurities (such as methane) which might be present in the oxygen supply. The purified oxygen can be stored, if necessary, in the liquid nitrogen trap T_2.

The combustion system consists of a Pyrex tubular chamber in which is suspended a platinum crucible N with a magnesia or beryllia liner O and which is connected to the system through a dry ice trap T_3. The "hat rack" attached to the chamber is a multiple loading system by which successive samples can be moved by a magnet into the tube leading to the crucible without opening the system. A high-frequency heating coil is placed around the Pyrex chamber and the walls cooled by an electric air blower to prevent overheating by radiation from the platinum crucible. Murray used one 1.5-kva (output) converter with a frequency

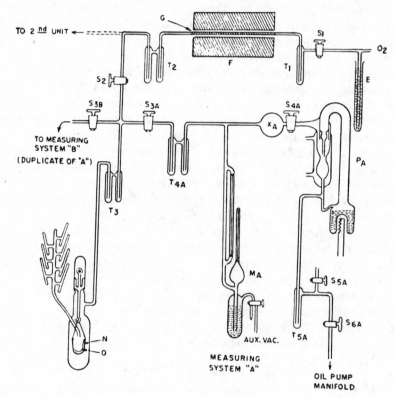

FIG. 15.   Carbon analysis apparatus of Murray and Niedrach.

range 170–500 kc for operating four combustion systems (26). A temperature of 1100–1300°C. is required (26, 40).

The analysis system consists of a liquid nitrogen trap T_{4A}, a McLeod gauge M_A, and a bulb X_A located between stopcocks S_{3A} and S_{4A}. In the earlier forms of the apparatus mercury cut-offs were used instead of stopcocks, but Murray and Niedrach have found that large-bore, precision-ground, hollow-plug stopcocks lubricated with Apiezon-L are quite satisfactory and much more convenient.

The pumping system consists of a two-stage mercury diffusion pump

P_A, a liquid nitrogen trap T_{5A}, and a small (0.5 l./sec.) oil-sealed mechanical pump.

The volume of the analysis system is calibrated by trapping gas in the McLeod gauge, whose volume is known, evacuating the rest of the system, and then expanding the trapped gas into the volume between stopcocks S_{3A} and S_{4A}.

The procedure of Murray and Niedrach will be outlined briefly here; the reader should consult the original articles for details. After the system is thoroughly evacuated and outgassed the traps T_1, T_2 and T_{5A} are surrounded by liquid nitrogen and T_3 by dry ice and acetone. Oxygen is then admitted slowly through the purification system until the pressure is 15 to 20 cm. as indicated by depression of the mercury column below the McLeod bulb. The oxygen supply is cut off at S_2 and trap T_{4A} cooled with liquid nitrogen. A blank is run first under the same conditions as used for a sample. The burning of a (0.5-g.) sample involves heating the platinum crucible to 1200–1300°C. and continuing for 15 minutes at this temperature. Stopcock S_{4A} is then opened very slightly and the gas pumped slowly from the combustion vessel through T_{4A} which traps out the carbon dioxide. The system is finally pumped rapidly to 0.1 mm., S_{3A} is closed and the measuring system evacuated to 10^{-5} mm. with the diffusion pump. S_{4A} is then closed and the carbon dioxide expanded into the known volume and measured with the McLeod. The small amount of carbon dioxide left in the combustion system at the time S_{3A} is closed can be shown to be negligible (27). The reason for closing S_{3A} at a pressure of 0.1 mm. is to avoid interference by transfer of water vapor from the dry ice trap T_3 to the liquid nitrogen trap T_{4A} (15). A second similar measuring system is attached at S_{3B} and a second sample can be burned for analysis in B while the first sample is being analyzed in system A.

5.3. Limitations and Accuracy

Wooten and Guldner (40) concluded that the method is not suitable for the analysis of samples containing greater than 0.1% sulfur, unless modified to ensure complete oxidation of sulfur to sulfur trioxide. However, most samples of low carbon content are also low in sulfur, and under the usual conditions only sulfur trioxide is formed which is adsorbed on the walls of the combustion vessel or condensed in the dry ice trap T_3.

Gurry and Trigg have established that the precision of the low-pressure method is about ±0.0005% carbon, although under favorable circumstances the precision may approach the value of the blank (about 0.0002%), and that it is at least three times as good as that of the ordinary combustion method (15). However, since the sample is usually small

(0.5 g.), great care must be exercised in selecting and handling samples. The accuracy was also determined to be of the same order as the precision.

Naughton and Uhlig (29a) investigated possible sources of discrepancies between the carbon content of Bureau of Standards samples as obtained by the low pressure method and the standard combustion-weighing method. They concluded that the low pressure method was more reliable.

As stated by Wooten and Guldner, the method deserves wide application not only to low-carbon alloys but also to higher carbon alloys where only very small samples are available. The method is generally applicable to the determination of microquantities of carbon.

6. The Microanalysis of Gases at Low Pressures

Several low-pressure methods have been developed for determining small amounts of hydrogen, oxygen, carbon dioxide, carbon monoxide, sulfur dioxide, water vapor, and gaseous hydrocarbons (methane, etc.) mixed with nitrogen. The gases may be separated by absorption in chemicals, adsorption and desorption with active carbon and cold traps, and fractional evaporation from cold traps. Combustion with an excess of pure oxygen may be employed to convert hydrogen, carbon monoxide, and the hydrocarbons to water and carbon dioxide which are easily separated from nitrogen. The gases are usually measured in a calibrated fixed volume with a McLeod gauge, but a differential manometer, Pirani gauge, or other type of vacuum gauge may be used, especially where water vapor and condensable gases are present. About 1 cc. of gas at standard temperature and pressure is normally used as the sample, but the methods are capable of fair accuracy when applied to as little as 0.001 cc. (N.T.P.) of gas (12, 16, 28, 32).

6.1. Methods of Langmuir and Ryder

Langmuir in 1912 described briefly an apparatus consisting of mercury cut-offs, a Toepler pump, a McLeod gauge, a U tube dipping into liquid air, and a platinum-wire combustion bulb which he used to analyze successfully samples as small as 1 cu. mm. of the gas liberated from incandescent lamps (6, 136). In 1918 H. M. Ryder (35) described a similar apparatus as shown in Fig. 16. Ryder used a diffusion pump, which Langmuir developed in 1916, to evacuate the system and an "optical lever" differential manometer (D) to measure the water vapor (12, 184).

The carbon dioxide and water vapor are first condensed in the liquid air trap (E), and the pressure of the noncondensable gases measured with the McLeod (M). The latter gases are then pushed by the Toepler pump (J) through a vertical capillary of length sufficient to balance the final pressure in the combustion bulb (K), which, in Langmuir's apparatus, consisted of a short piece (2 mm.) of fine platinum wire inside a bulb of about 1-cc. volume. The carbon dioxide in (E) is allowed to evaporate by removing the liquid air flask and replacing with a Dewar filled with dry ice and acetone. The CO_2 is measured by (M) and then completely pumped out at (A). Prolonged pumping must be avoided to prevent loss of H_2O from (E) since at $-80°C$. the vapor pressure of water is 10^{-3} mm. (12). The trap (E) is then brought to room temperature and

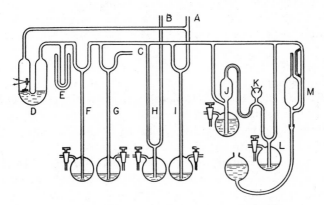

FIG. 16. Gas analysis apparatus of H. M. Ryder.

the pressure of the water vapor determined by the optical lever manometer (D). The volumes trapped between the manometer and the cut-off (F) and between (D) and (M) must of course be determined by means previously described. The quantity of CO_2 and H_2O can then be computed.

The gases in (K) are analyzed by admitting a measured quantity of oxygen, checking its pressure on (M), and transferring to (K) by operating (J). The platinum filament is brought to red heat for a few minutes and the resulting CO_2 and H_2O condensed in trap (E). The residual oxygen and noncombustible gas is measured on (M) and then returned to (K). The CO_2 and H_2O in (E) are then released and measured as described above (if the previous H_2O was not pumped out, then the last determination of H_2O must be diminished by the previous amount to find the part produced by combustion of hydrogen). The residual gas in (K) now contains only nitrogen and oxygen. If oxygen was present in the original mixture, then a measured amount of carbon monoxide must be introduced into (K) and the filament glowed again. The CO_2 formed is measured as before, and the original amount of oxygen can then be calculated.   The remainder is assumed to be nitrogen.   If a hydrocarbon is present as well as oxygen, the procedure must be modified (6).

6.2. Methods of Prescott and Morrison

In 1928 Prescott (12, 168) described a microgas-analysis apparatus in which the separation of the gases was accomplished by chemical absorption tubes rather than by cold traps as in the above methods.   The gas was measured on a McLeod gauge, circulated through the absorption tubes with a Toepler pump, soda lime being used for CO_2, hot CuO for H_2 and CO, and P_2O_5 mixed with powdered pumice for the H_2O formed, and the pressure on the McLeod noted after each absorption was complete.

In 1938 Prescott and Morrison (169) published details of an improved apparatus developed in connection with their study of oxide-coated filaments and in 1939 gave a complete description of their apparatus (32) of which a few key parts are shown in Fig. 17.   In the latest form of the apparatus they incorporated the miniature diffusion pump (Fig. 17, F) to circulate the gases through the absorption train.   When absorption is complete (about 2 minutes), the gas is passed from the diffusion pump to an automatic Toepler pump (see Fig. 11), which in four strokes collects the gas in a special capillary pipet operated like a McLeod gauge.

They substituted magnesium perchlorate for the P_2O_5 used earlier and packed about 0.3 g. of this reagent between plugs of glass wool in the tube shown in Fig. 17, D.   The soda lime is placed in a similar tube while the copper oxide (0.8 g. powdered wire segments) is sandwiched between Pyrex wool and copper screen in the middle of a special tube (Fig. 17, E).   The platinum filament lamp (Fig. 17, A) is used to determine oxygen by slow-combustion in an excess of hydrogen or carbon monoxide.   Since the authors found that platinum filaments are readily attacked by oxygen at 700°C. or above, they have introduced the explosion pipet (Fig. 17, B) for determining methane by adding an excess of oxygen.   The gas is compressed to about 17 cm. in this pipet and then exploded by a spark from an induction coil.   It should be noted that Ransley (175a) found that an alumina-coated platinum filament could be used at 1150°C. to achieve complete oxidation of methane without oxidation of the platinum.

Since the apparatus is designed to handle samples of 0.6 to 25 cu. mm. (at 0°C. and 1 atmosphere), when larger quantities are evolved in the process being studied, the gas is stored in special bottles as shown in Fig. 17, C.   The gas is transferred from the bottle to the system by bringing the upper porous plug (of baked Italian lavite) in contact with the plug sealed in the top of the soft glass bottle, the mercury (shown in black) being forced completely to one side by its surface tension.

For details of the procedure the article must be consulted. The authors claim that on samples of 5 to 25 cu. mm. (N.T.P.), errors for

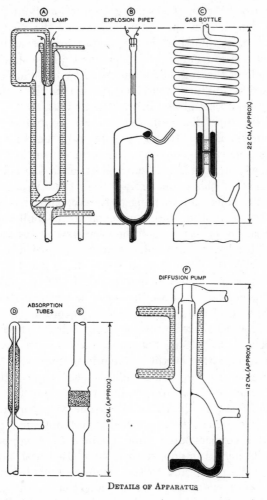

FIG. 17. Gas analysis apparatus of Prescott and Morrison.

each component will be as low as 2% of the total sample. One hour is required for a complete general analysis of H_2O, CO_2, H_2, CO, and oxygen or methane. The limit of detection for each component is about 0.025 cu. mm. (N.T.P.).

6.3. Low Temperature Method of N.R. Campbell

A method which is fundamentally different from the two already described was first developed by Campbell (3, 6) in 1921 for the common gases and extended by Sebastian and Howard (12, 16, 36) in 1934 to analysis of hydrocarbon mixtures using samples of about 1 cc. at N.T.P. This method depends on the determination of the dew-points of the gases and vapors by plotting the vapor pressure as a function of the temperature of a trap from which a condensed phase slowly evaporates.

The principle of the method is illustrated by the diagrams (12, 36) in Fig. 18. The gas mixture is first condensed in the appendix on the reservoir B by liquid air placed in the Dewar flask at T. On removing the Dewar, if the appendix is allowed to warm up uniformly and slowly, and the pressure in B is plotted as a function of temperature, the curve obtained for a single substance has the form shown in Fig. 18a. The curve rises slowly at first and then rapidly until the condensed phase disappears. Beyond this point (from b to c) there is practically no rise with temperature since the warming of the appendix has little effect on the vapor pressure in the bulb; and even if the bulb temperature is increased, the rise in pressure would be very slow at low vapor densities. If there is another less volatile substance present which does not form a solid solution with the first, then a second knee will be obtained at a higher temperature as shown in Fig. 18b. If the two substances form one phase in the condensed state, the curve depends on Raoult's law and the partial pressure of the vapor is lowered according to the concentration in the condensed phase so that the knee is less distinct as shown by the dotted curve in Fig. 18b. Sebastian and Howard have shown that an accurate determination is still possible in many cases where the mixture gives a curve with only slight inflections. Their article should be consulted for complete details on the interpretation of the curves.

The design of the cooling bath is extremely important. Campbell used mercury or organic solvents chilled with liquid air. Sebastian and Howard used a copper-plated tube bonded to a copper-constantan thermocouple immersed in copper turnings chilled with liquid nitrogen. Campbell applied the method to the common gases, hydrogen, carbon monoxide, carbon dioxide, etc., and used a special Pirani gauge which he had calibrated for the various gases using a null method in which the Pirani filament is maintained at constant temperature. Sebastian and Howard used a special McLeod gauge. However, as stated by Farkas and Melville (12), the Pirani gauge, or any other continuously reading gauge would be more convenient since the apparatus is preferably calibrated with a known mixture in any case. All of the gases except one must be

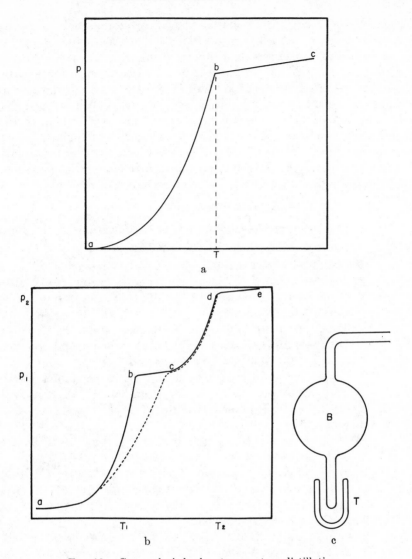

FIG. 18. Gas analysis by low temperature distillation.

easily condensable by liquid air. It is therefore necessary to convert hydrogen to water vapor and carbon monoxide to carbon dioxide by passing over hot copper oxide. Since the method depends merely on a temperature difference between the evaporation bulb and the space for storing and measuring the vapor, it is apparent that the method is not limited to analyses in which the temperature rises from that of liquid air to that of the room. By enclosing the vapor storage and measuring system in a controlled-temperature bath, the method could be applied to higher boiling substances than tertiary pentane or water.

The time required for an analysis of a hydrocarbon mixture in the apparatus described by Sebastian and Howard is 3 to 5 hours and an accuracy of about 1% may be expected (16). Campbell claimed that 1% water in carbon dioxide may be detected and 0.0005 mm. of CO_2 could be detected in an unlimited quantity of vapors with higher evaporation temperatures, or in 0.05 mm. of permanent gases. He was able to run complete analyses on the common gases in about half an hour. Dunoyer estimated the accuracy to be between 5 and 10% (6).

6.4. Other Methods and Special Techniques

For easy reference we have classified the modifications of the above methods and special techniques in the following outline.

(1) Microanalysis of the common gases with dry reagents:
    (a) Using combined Toepler pump and McLeod gauge, 1916, Guye and Germann (6, 107); 1941, Haden and Luttropp (108); 1946, Nash (28).
    (b) Using cold trap and separate Toepler pump, 1935, Dalton (12, 75); 1940, Spence (189); 1944, Norton and Marshall (30a); 1949, Keilholtz and Bergin (126a).
    (c) Separating hydrogen by diffusion through palladium or iron, 1946, Thoneman (197a); 1947, Ransley (175a); Somerville (187a); 1949, Pepkowitz and Proud (166a).

(2) Microanalysis of hydrocarbons:
    (a) By fractional desorption from active carbon, 1936, Euchen and Knick (90); 1939, Küchler and Weller (134).
    (b) By fractional distillation, 1940, Aristarkhova (45); 1941, Bensen (52); Savelli (181b); 1947, Hooper (119a).
    (c) By fractional condensation, 1947, Kenty and Reuter (128a).

(3) Thermal conductivity methods:
    1924, Hurst and Rideal (123); 1935, Barrer and Rideal (48); H. A. Daynes (5); Farkas and Melville (12); 1947, Kenty and Reuter (128a).

(4) Analysis of the hydrides of boron and silicon:
    A. Stock (37).

(5) Microanalysis of helium, neon, argon, krypton, and xenon by adsorption on calcium, activated charcoal, etc. and by fractional distillation and desorption (Cady and Cady, 65).

(6) Microanalysis of inert gases by speed of exhaust:
    1947, Kenty and Reuter (128a).

Special attention is called to the article by Nash (28) in which a simple and compact apparatus is described for analysis of 1-cc. samples of the common gases, including methane, with an accuracy of a few tenths of a per cent, the methane being determined in the presence of hydrogen and carbon monoxide by fractional combustion on a platinum catalyst. The outline lists the principle references which must be consulted for the details. Many of these schemes were devised before the modern development of accurate methods using capillary tubes and microburettes at atmospheric pressure which may provide a more convenient means of microgas analysis when vacuum is not otherwise required (12, 16).

7. ANALYTICAL MOLECULAR DISTILLATION

7.1. Boiling Points and the Elimination Curve

The boiling point of a pure organic compound is sometimes used as evidence in the identification of the substance. Compounds that decompose unless distilled under vacuum can also sometimes be characterized by the distillation curve at a given pressure, most of the material distilling in a narrow temperature range. However, when the vacuum is so high that the organic molecules can evaporate freely and pass directly to the condenser without colliding with gas molecules, there is no well defined boiling point or narrow range of distillation. The rate of evaporation under these conditions (molecular distillation) is given by Langmuir's equation (10)

$$n = PA \sqrt{\frac{1}{2\pi MRT}}$$

where n is the moles per second of compound of molecular weight M evaporating from a distilling surface of area A and absolute temperature T, R is the ideal gas constant, and P is either the vapor pressure of the pure substance at temperature T or, in the case of impure substances, the partial pressure of the vapor above the solution at equilibrium.

The identity of a pure substance could be partially established by measuring the saturation vapor pressure above a liquid phase at a given temperature. Such a measurement is always possible but frequently difficult when the vapor pressure is low and the sample small. Jacobs and Kapff have recently described (126) a "molecular dew-point apparatus" which is suitable for small quantities of oils with very low vapor pressure. However, the substance to be analyzed can not always be obtained in a pure state and frequently occurs in mixtures that can not be separated by crystallization, absorption, or processes other than distillation. In these cases molecular distillation becomes necessary, and by a special method known as the "elimination curve technique" much information about the relative boiling points, heats of vaporization, and concentration of two or more constituents can be obtained directly while distilling the material into a number of fractions.

This method requires a rather complicated apparatus (Fig. 19), and can only be applied to substances whose relative concentration in a

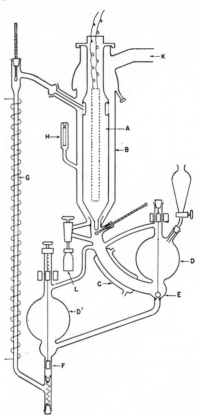

FIG. 19.   Falling film molecular still.   (Distillation Products, Inc.)

series of fractions can be easily determined by some quantitative procedure such as titration, color comparison, biological assay, or absorption spectroscopy.   Moreover the original mixture must be relatively simple and capable of partial fractionation by repeated molecular distillations.   In spite of these limitations the technique has proved quite valuable in the study of the natural fats and oils, especially in connection with the resolution of vitamin complexes.   The apparatus itself is not limited to analytical distillation but serves as an all-purpose laboratory molecular still for fractionation and purification of a wide variety of organic materials.

The elimination curve is obtained by plotting as a function of temperature the per cent yield of the key constituent in each fraction obtained by passing the residual distilland over the hot column of a falling-film cyclic molecular still (described below) in a predetermined constant time interval (e.g. 10 minutes), the temperature of the distilland being kept

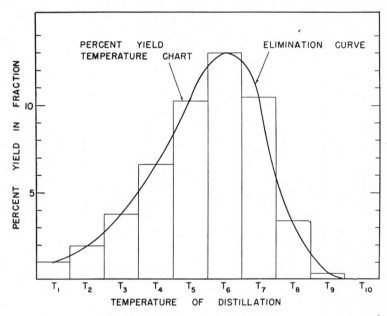

FIG. 20.   Theoretical elimination curve.

constant during the time interval but jumped quickly by a uniform increment (e.g. 10°C.) between cycles.   Pilot dyes may be added to the mixture so that the distillation can be "calibrated" by plotting simultaneously the curve for the pilot dye (18).

The elimination curve has the form of the Gaussian error curve (Fig. 20), rising to a maximum at a temperature which can be reproduced by a careful operator to within ±1°C.   The position of this maximum has been shown experimentally by Hickman (18) and theoretically by Embree (10) to be as characteristic of the compound as a boiling point. The exact shape of the curve and position of the maximum is dependent on the distillability of the substance and the length of the time intervals. The viscosity of the material may also affect the curve if the oil does not spread in a thin uniform film over the hot column or if the distillate clings to the condenser without draining into the receiver. Hickman (18, 49) has advocated the use of "constant-yield" oil as a diluent to promote uniform flow and complete drainage. Quackenbush and Steenbock (33) have designed a still in which a constant-yield oil is not necessary, the condenser being easily removed for washing or scraping

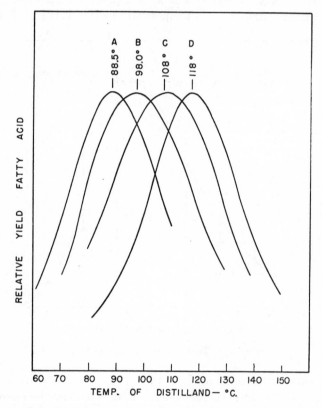

FIG. 21.   Elimination maxima of saturated fatty acids.

the last of the distillate into a receiver and the evaporating surface being designed to provide uniform heating and flow.   The elimination curve technique can also be applied to small centrifugal molecular stills (54a).

Examples of elimination curves for four saturated fatty acids (A, lauric acid; B, myristic acid; C, palmitic acid; D, stearic acid) are shown in Fig. 21 and curves for four unsaturated fatty acids and stearic acid (A, linoleic acid; B, oleic acid; C, stearic acid; D, 9, 11-linoleic acid; E, α-eleostearic acid) are given in Fig. 22.   It has been shown (106) that the addition of one CH_2 group to a compound increases the temperature corresponding to the elimination maximum by 5°C. as shown in Fig. 21. Unsaturation without conjugation lowers the maximum 2°C. The addition of a conjugated double bond raises the màximum about 3°C.

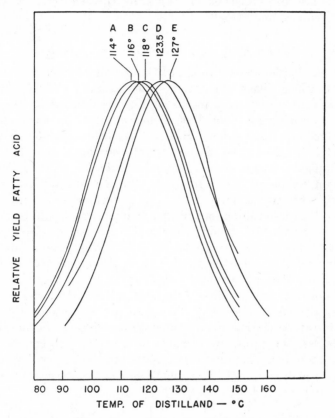

FIG. 22. Effect of structure on the elimination maximum.

7.2. The Cyclic Molecular Still

The method of operation of a cyclic still is made clear by the diagram, Fig. 19. The oil flows by gravity down the heated cylindrical column A. The distillate collects on the cooled walls, B, and the residue drops over the bulb of the thermometer through a cooling tube, C, into the upper reservoir, D. The residue may be recycled as many times as necessary by opening the magnetically operated ball valve, E, and passing the oil into the lower reservoir, D, from which it is boosted by the magnetic circulating pump, F, through the preheater tube, G, to the top of the hot column. The distillate flows down the walls of the Pyrex casing,

B, and is guided by an alembic into a receiving bottle, L. The pressure in the still is measured on a Pirani gauge, H. The principles involved in the design and operation of this apparatus and similar cyclic falling film stills are fully discussed in articles by Hickman (17, 18, 112) and by Quackenbush and Steenbock (33).

7.3. Future of the Elimination Curve Technique

The elimination curve is a new means of characterizing organic molecules which, like the parachor, when properly defined, measured, and tabulated serves as a means of identification and classification. The curves for several pilot dyes, biologically active compounds, fatty acids, glycerides, cholesterol esters and petroleum residues have been obtained (17, 94a) but no reliable and self-consistent table of values has been compiled. The method was found useful a few years ago in studies of vitamin complexes in fish liver oils (18, 117) and the relative "distillability" of various fatty acids and glycerides (88). The method deserves wider application, but further standardization will be necessary before the curves for various compounds can be correlated and the technique adopted by various laboratories. While many laboratories now have cyclic batch stills of this type, the practice of "analytical molecular distillation" has nearly died out in recent years. This may be due in part to the experience of those using the method who have found it rather tedious because of the frequent adjustment of heater input required to maintain the correct temperature over the exact time interval. Nevertheless, the procedure remains as a unique method of gaining information about materials which evaporate readily between 100 and 300°C. in a high vacuum (e.g., organic compounds with molecular weight between 100 and 1000).

8. Miscellaneous Vacuum Techniques Used in Analysis

The per cent of volatile solvents or moisture in various materials is frequently determined by placing the sample on a shelf in a glass or metal jar (vacuum desiccator) and pumping for several hours with a small mechanical vacuum pump protected by a cold trap. The loss in weight is interpreted as moisture content, plasticizer content, or solvent content according to the known history of preparation of the sample. In some cases the condensate in the cold trap may be removed and analyzed. Frequently it is advisable to warm the sample by heating coils or radiant heat to compensate for the cooling by evaporation, thus speeding up the analysis. The method is obviously applicable to a wide variety of materials; for example, it has been applied to the determination of the moisture content of photographic film and the plasticizer content of cellulose ester plastics (55, 127).

Vacuum distillation techniques have been applied to the analysis of alloys. Treadwell and Frey (199) described a method of analyzing brass by sublimation at 800°C. in a vacuum of 10^{-4} mm. Hg. The components are made to condense in different parts of a tube. Price (170) extended this technique to other alloys and he determined Zn in Sn-Zn, Zn-Cu and gun metals; Pb in Sn-Pb, Cu-Pb and gun metals; P in phosphor-tin; and Cd in copper alloys.

Many organic substances, which can not be distilled at atmospheric pressure without rapid decomposition, can be distilled at lower pressures,

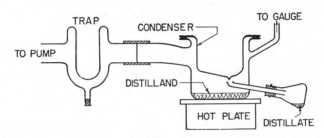

FIG. 23.   Hickman molecular pot still.

and many types of distilling columns and techniques have been developed for fractional distillation at low pressures. The high-vacuum techniques described in this chapter are particularly useful for "molecular distillation" where the pressure is maintained so low that molecules can pass from the surface of the heated distilland to a nearby condensing surface without in general colliding with other molecules. Analytical molecular distillation has been described in Section 7. Other analytical applications of molecular distillation are limited to separation and purification of compounds prior to identification. For work with small samples the Hickman (118) molecular pot still, Fig. 23, is frequently used for partial separation of organic fluid or solid mixtures which would decompose in conventional types of fractionating stills. References (17, 62, 63, 78, 79, 91, 98, 113, 114, 120, 122, 182, 206, 207, 218, 219) consist of long review articles on vacuum distillation in which extensive bibliographies will be found.

Special vacuum techniques are required in the analytical procedures using isotopes of carbon, oxygen and nitrogen (2a, 50a, 106b).

The bibliography at the end of this chapter includes most of the important applications of high vacuum techniques described in the *Analytical Edition* of *Industrial and Engineering Chemistry* (renamed

Analytical Chemistry on January 1947) up to March 1950. A few references not previously mentioned are given in (46, 53, 54, 58, 64, 67, 82, 102, 104a, 117, 130, 133, 145, 147, 161, 162, 163, 164, 174, 181a, 186, 192a, 194, 198, 200, 204, 211, 213, 222, 223, 224).

REFERENCES

General References on Vacuum Technique and Vacuum Analysis

1. Barr, W. E., and Anhorn, V. J., Scientific and Industrial Glass Blowing and Laboratory Techniques. Instruments Publishing Co., Pittsburgh, 1949. Appeared in serial form in *Instruments* **18**, 874; **19**, 14, 82, 150, 214, 344, 406, 460, 514, 604, 666, 734 (1946); **20**, 39, 151, 240, 454, 542, 716.
2. Burrows, G., *J. Sci. Instruments* **20**, 21 (1943).
2a. Calvin, M., Heidelberger, C., Reid, J., Tolbert, B., Yankwich, P., Isotopic Carbon. Wiley, New York, 1949, Chapter 8.
3. Campbell, N. R., *Proc. Phys. Soc. London* **33**, 287 (1921).
3a. Carney, D. J., Chipman, J., and Grant, N. J., *Trans. Am. Inst. Mining Met. Engrs.* **188**, 397, 404 (1950) (J. Metals).
4. Chipman, J., and Fontana, M., *Ind. Eng. Chem., Anal. Ed.* **7**, 391 (1935).
5. Daynes, H. A., Gas Analysis by Measurement of Thermal Conductivity. Cambridge University Press, London, 1933.
6. Dunoyer, L., Vacuum Practice. Van Nostrand, New York, 1926.
7. Dushman, S., High Vacuum. General Electric Co., Schenectady, N.Y. 1922; Scientific Foundations of Vacuum Technique. Wiley, New York, 1949.
8. Dushman, S., *Instruments* **20**, 234 (1947).
9. Dushman, S., *J. Franklin Inst.* **211**, 689 (1931).
10. Embree, N. D., *Ind. Eng. Chem., Ind. Ed.* **29**, 975 (1937).
11. Espe, W., and Knoll, M., Werkstoffkunde der Hochvakuumtechnik. J. Springer, Berlin, 1936.
12. Farkas, A., and Melville, H. W., Experimental Methods in Gas Reactions. MacMillan, London, 1939.
13. Gaede, W., Handbuch der Experimental Physik. Vol. 4, Pt. 3, Leipzig 1930, pp. 413–461.
14. Goetz, A., Physik und Technik des Hochvakuums. Friedrich Vieweg und Sohn, Braunschweig, 1926.
15. Gurry, R., and Trigg, H., *Ind. Eng. Chem., Anal. Ed.* **16**, 248 (1944).
16. Hallett, L., *Ind. Eng. Chem., Anal. Ed.* **14**, 984 (1942).
17. Hickman, K. C. D., *Chem. Revs.* **34**, 51 (1944).
18. Hickman, K. C. D., *Ind. Eng. Chem., Ind. Ed.* **29**, 968, 1107 (1937).
19. Hickman, K. C. D., *J. Franklin Inst.* **213**, 119 (1932).
20. Hoag, J. Barton, Electron and Nuclear Physics. Van Nostrand, New York, 1938, Chapter 16.
21. Holm, V., and Thompson, J., *J. Research Natl. Bur. Standards* **26**, 245 (1941) (RP No. 1373).
22. Iron and Steel Institute (London), Special Report No. 16, 63–108 (1937).
23. Jacobs, R. B., and Zuhr, H. F., *J. Applied Phys.* **18**, 34 (1947).
23a. Jnanananda, S., High Vacua. Van Nostrand, New York, 1947.
24. Kaye, G. W. C., High Vacua. Longmans, Green, New York, 1927.
24a. Martin, L. H., and Hill, R. D., A Manual of Vacuum Practice. Melbourne University Press, Melbourne, 1947.

25. Mönch, G., Vakuumtechnik im Laboratorium. Edwards Bros. Lithoprint, 1944.
26. Murray, W. M., Jr., and Ashley, S. E. Q., *Ind. Eng. Chem., Anal. Ed.* **16,** 242 (1944).
27. Murray, W. M., Jr., and Niedrach, L., *Ind. Eng. Chem., Anal. Ed.* **16,** 634 (1944).
28. Nash, L., *Ind. Eng. Chem., Anal. Ed.* **18,** 505 (1946).
29. Naughton, J., and Uhlig, H., *Ind. Eng. Chem., Anal. Ed.* **15,** 750 (1943).
29a. Naughton, J., and Uhlig, H., *Anal. Chem.* **20,** 477 (1948).
30. Newman, F. H., The Production and Measurement of Low Pressures. Van Nostrand, New York, 1925.
30a. Norton, F. J., and Marshall, A. L.: *Trans. Am. Inst. Mining Met. Engrs.* **156,** 351 (1944); A.I.M.E.-T.P. No. 1643 (1943).
31. Pirani, M., and Newmann, R., *Electronic Eng.* **17,** 277, 322, 367, 422 (1945).
32. Prescott, C. H., and Morrison, J., *Ind. Eng. Chem., Anal. Ed.* **11,** 230 (1939).
33. Quackenbush, F. W., and Steenbock, H., *Ind. Eng. Chem., Anal. Ed.* **15,** 468 (1943).
34. Reilly, J., and Rae, W. N., Physico-Chemical Methods. Van Nostrand, New York, 1939, Vol. I, Chapter VII, pp. 573–582.
35. Ryder, H. M., *J. Am. Chem. Soc.* **40,** 1656 (1918).
35a. Sanderson, R. T., Vacuum · Manipulation of Volatile Compounds. Wiley, New York, 1948.
36. Sebastian, J., and Howard, H., *Ind. Eng. Chem., Anal. Ed.* **6,** 172 (1934).
37. Stock, A., The Hydrides of Boron and Silicon. Cornell University Press, Ithaca, 1933, Chapter XXX.
38. Strong, J., Procedures in Experimental Physics. Prentice-Hall, New York, 1938.
39. Vacher, H., and Jordan, L., *J. Research Natl. Bur. Standards* **7,** 375 (1931) (RP No. 346).
39a. Walter, D. I., *Anal. Chem.* **22,** 297 (1950).
40. Wooten, L., and Guldner, W. G., *Ind. Eng. Chem., Anal. Ed.* **14,** 835 (1942).
41. Yarwood, J., High Vacuum Technique. Chapman and Hall, London, 1945.

Other References Cited

42. Alexander, L., Murray, W. M., and Ashley, S. E. Q., *Ind. Eng. Chem., Anal. Ed.* **19,** 417 (1947).
43. Anderson, P. A., *Rev. Sci. Instruments* **8,** 493 (1937).
44. Archer, R. M., *J. Sci. Instruments* **13,** 161 (1936).
45. Aristarkhova, M., *Zavodskaya Lab.* **9,** 1096 (1940).
46. Aston, J. G., and Fink, H. L., *Ind. Eng. Chem., Anal. Ed.* **19,** 218 (1947).
47. Bailey, A. J., *Ind. Eng. Chem., Anal. Ed.* **15,** 283 (1943).
47a. Baldwin, R. R., *J. Chem. Soc. London,* **1949,** 720.
48. Barrer, R., and Rideal, E., *Proc. Roy. Soc. London* **A149,** 231 (1935).
49. Baxter, J., Gray, E., and Tischer, A., *Ind. Eng. Chem., Ind. Ed.* **29,** 1112 (1937).
50. Bazzoni, C. B., *Rev. Sci. Instruments* **8,** 171 (1937).
50a. Beamer, W. H., and Atchison, G. J., *Anal. Chem.* **22,** 303 (1950).
51. Beeck, O., Smith, A. E., and Wheeler, A., *Proc. Roy. Soc. London* **A177,** 62 (1940).
52. Benson, S., *Ind. Eng. Chem., Anal. Ed.* **13,** 502 (1941).
53. Benson, S., *Ind. Eng. Chem., Anal. Ed.* **14,** 189 (1942).
54. Berl, E., Rueff, G., and Carpenter, Ch., *Ind. Eng. Chem., Anal. Ed.* **10,** 220 (1938).
54a. Biehler, R. M., Hickman, K. C. D., and Perry, E. S., *Anal. Chem.* **21,** 638 (1949).

55. Biggs, B., and Erickson, R., *Ind. Eng. Chem., Anal. Ed.* **16**, 93 (1944).
56. Blears, J., *Nature* **154**, 20 (1944).
57. Bobalek, E. G., and Shrader, S. A., *Ind. Eng. Chem., Anal. Ed.* **17**, 544 (1945).
58. Booth, H. S., *Ind. Eng. Chem., Anal. Ed.* **4**, 380 (1932).
59. Bramley, G., and Raine, T., Iron and Steel Institute (London), Special Report No. 25, 87–96 (1939).
60. Brown, G., DiNardo, A., Cheng, G., and Sherwood, T., *J. Applied Phys.* **17**, 802 (1946).
61. Bull, C., and Klemperer, O., *J. Sci. Instruments* **20**, 179 (1943).
62. Burch, C., and van Dijck, W., *J. Soc. Chem. Ind.* **58**, 39 (1939).
63. Burrows, G., *J. Soc. Chem. Ind.* **58**, 50 (1939).
64. Burton, M., *Ind. Eng. Chem., Anal. Ed.* **9**, 335 (1937).
65. Cady, G. H., and Cady, H. D., *Ind. Eng. Chem., Anal. Ed.* **17**, 760 (1945).
66. Caldwell, M. J., and Barham, H. N., *Ind. Eng. Chem., Anal. Ed.* **14**, 485 (1942).
67. Cameron, A. E., *Ind. Eng. Chem., Anal. Ed.*, **5**, 419 (1933).
68. Campbell, N. R., *Proc. Phys. Soc. London* **33**, 287 (1921).
69. Chadwick, T. C., and Palkin, S., *Ind. Eng. Chem., Anal. Ed.* **10**, 399 (1938).
70. *Chem. Eng. News*, 2370 (Dec. 25, 1945).
71. Cioffi, P., *Phys. Revs.* **39**, 363–7 (1932).
72. Clausing, P., *Ann. Physik* **12**, 961 (1932).
73. Crist, R. H., and Brown, F. B., *Ind. Eng. Chem., Anal. Ed.* **11**, 396 (1939).
74. Dalin, G. A., *Ind. Eng. Chem., Anal. Ed.* **15**, 731 (1943).
75. Dalton, R. H., *J. Am. Chem. Soc.* **57**, 2150 (1935).
75a. Dayton, B. B., *Ind. Eng. Chem.* **40**, 795 (1948).
76. Derge, G., *Metals Technol.* **10** (Jan. 1943), A.I.M.E.-T.P. No. 1544.
77. Derge, G., Peifer, W., and Alexander, B., *Trans. Am. Inst. Mining Met. Engrs.* **162**, 361–368 (Jan. 1945).
78. Detwiler, S., Abstracts of Articles and Patents on Molecular or Short-Path Distillation. U.S. Regional Soybean Industrial Products Laboratory, Urbana, Illinois (1941).
79. Detwiler, S., and Markley, K. S., *Oil and Soap* **16**, 2–5 (1939).
80. Diergarten, H., *Arch. Eisenhüttenw.* **2**, 813–28 (1929).
81. Donahue, H. B., Russell, R. R., and Vander Werf, C. A., *Ind. Eng. Chem., Anal. Ed.* **18**, 156 (1946).
82. Douslin, D. R., and Walls, W. S., *Ind. Eng. Chem., Anal. Ed.* **16**, 40 (1944).
83. Downing, J. R., and Mellen, G., *Rev. Sci. Instruments* **17**, 218 (1946).
84. Du Mond, J. W., and Pickels, W. M., *Rev. Sci. Instruments* **6**, 362 (1935).
85. Durau, F., *Z. Physik* **89**, 148 (1934).
86. Dushman, S., and Young, A. H., *Phys. Rev.* **68**, 278 (1945).
87. Ellett, A., and Zabel, R. M., *Phys. Rev.* **37**, 1102 (1931).
88. Embree, N. D., *Chem. Revs.* **29**, No. 2, 317 (1941).
89. Emerson, R. L., and Woodward, R. B., *Ind. Eng. Chem., Anal. Ed.* **9**, 347 (1937).
90. Euchen, A., and Knick, H., *Brenstoff-Chem.* **17**, 241 (1936).
91. Fawcett, E., *J. Soc. Chem. Ind.* **58**, 43 (1939).
92. Ferguson, B., *Ind. Eng. Chem., Anal. Ed.* **14**, 164 (1942).
93. Ferguson, W., *Rev. Sci. Instruments* **11**, 134 (1940).
94. Finch, G. I., *Nature* **119**, 856 (1927).
94a. Fletcher, G. L., Insalaco, M., Cobler, J. G., and Hodge, H. C., *Anal. Chem.* **20**, 943 (1948).
95. Flosdorf, E. W., *Ind. Eng. Chem., Anal. Ed.* **17**, 198 (1945).

96. Fredlund, E., *Ann. Physik* **14,** 617 (1932).
97. Fredlund, E , *Ann. Physik* **30,** 99 (1937).
98. Furter, M., *Mitt. Gebiete Lebensm. Hyg.* **30,** 200 (1939).
99. Gaede, W., *Ann. Physik* **41,** 289 (1913).
100. Gaede, W., *Z. tech. Physik* **15,** 664 (1934).
101. Garner, L. P., *Rev. Sci. Instruments* **8,** 329 (1937).
102. Germann, F. E. E., and Gagos, K. A., *Ind. Eng. Chem., Anal. Ed.* **15,** 285 (1943).
103. Germann, F. E. E., Gagos, K. A., and Neilson, C. A., *Ind. Eng. Chem., Anal. Ed.* **6,** 215 (1934).
104. Gilmont, R., *Ind. Eng. Chem., Anal. Ed.,* **18,** 633 (1946).
104a. Gilmont, R., *Anal. Chem.* **20,** 474 (1948).
105. Gilmont, R., and Othmer, D. F., *Ind. Eng. Chem., Anal. Ed.* **15,** 641 (1943).
106. Gray, E., and Cawley, J., *J. Biol. Chem.* **134,** 397 (1940).
106a. Guldner, W. G., and Beach, A. L., *Anal. Chem.* **22,** 366 (1950).
106b. Grosse, A. V., Hindin, S. G., and Kirshenbaum, A. D., *Anal. Chem.* **21,** 386 (1949).
107. Guye, P. A., and Germann, F. E. E., *J. chim. phys.* **14,** 195 (1916).
108. Haden, W., and Luttropp, E., *Ind. Eng. Chem., Anal. Ed.* **13,** 571 (1941).
109. Hall, S. A., and Palkin, S., *Ind. Eng. Chem., Anal. Ed.* **14,** 652 (1942).
·110. Harrington, E., *Rev. Sci. Instruments* **3,** 476 (1932).
111. Hessenbruch, W., and Oberhoffer, P., *Arch. Eisenhüttenw.* **1,** 583 (1928).
112. Hickman, K. C. D., *Ind. Eng. Chem., Anal. Ed.* **14,** 250 (1942).
113. Hickman, K. C. D., *Colloid Chem.* **5,** 253 (1944).
114. Hickman, K. C. D., *Ind. Eng. Chem., Ind. Ed.* **32,** 1451 (1940).
115. Hickman, K. C. D., *J. Applied Phys.* **11,** 303 (1940).
116. Hickman, K. C. D., *Rev. Sci. Instruments* **5,** 161 (1934).
117. Hickman, K. C. D., and Gray, E., *Ind. Eng. Chem., Ind. Ed.* **30,** 796 (1938).
118. Hickman, K. C. D., and Sanford, C., *J. Phys. Chem.* **34,** 637 (1930).
119. Honig, R. E., *J. Applied Phys.* **16,** 646 (1945).
119a. Hooper, J., *Analyst* **72,** 513 (1947).
120. Howat, D., *Chem. Age London* **45,** 309, 323 (1941); **46,** 3 (1942).
121. Hughes, A. L., *Rev. Sci. Instruments* **8,** 409 (1937).
122. Hunger, H., *Seifensieder-Ztg.* **67,** 450, 473, 483, 497 (1940).
123. Hurst, W., and Rideal, E., *J. Chem. Soc.* **125,** 694 (1924).
123a. Johnson, M., and Glover, J., *Anal. Chem.* **22,** 204 (1950).
124. Jordan, L., and Eckman, J. R., National Bureau of Standards Scientific Paper No. 514 (1925).
125. Jordan, L., and Eckman, J. R., National Bureau of Standards Scientific Paper No. 563 (1927).
126. Kapff, S. F., and Jacobs, R. B., *Rev. Sci. Instruments* **18,** 581 (1947).
126a. Keilholtz, G. W., and Bergin, M. J., *Instruments* **22,** 320 (1949).
127. Kemp, A. R., and Straitiff, W. G., *Ind. Eng. Chem., Anal. Ed.* **17,** 387 (1945).
128. Kennard, E. H., Kinetic Theory of Gases. McGraw-Hill, New York, 1938.
128a. Kenty, C., and Reuter, F. W., *Rev. Sci. Instruments* **18,** 918 (1947).
129. Kerris, W., *Z. tech. Physik* **16,** 120 (1935).
130. Kline, E. R., *Ind. Eng. Chem., Anal. Ed.* **14,** 542 (1942).
131. Klumb, H., and Schwarz, H., *Z. Physik* **122,** 418 (1944).
132. Knudsen, M., *Ann. Physik* **28,** 75 (1909); **32,** 809 (1910).
133. Krieger, K. A., *Ind. Eng. Chem., Anal. Ed.* **16,** 398 (1944).
134. Küchler, L., and Weller, O., *Mikrochemie* **26,** 44 (1939).

135. Kunzl, V., and Slavik, J., Z. tech. Physik **16**, 272 (1935).
136. Langmuir, I., J. Am. Chem. Soc. **34**, 1310 (1912).
137. Lawton, E. J., Rev. Sci. Instruments **11**, 134 (1940); **5**, 42 (1934).
138. Lewis, F. M., Ind. Eng. Chem., Anal. Ed. **13**, 418 (1941).
139. Liebig, G. F., Ind. Eng. Chem., Anal. Ed. **6**, 156 (1934).
140. Lockenvitz, A. E., Rev. Sci. Instruments **9**, 417 (1938).
141. Loeb, L. B., The Kinetic Theory of Gases. 2nd ed. McGraw-Hill, New York, 1934.
142. Lundell, G., Hoffman, J., and Bright, H., Chemical Analysis of Iron and Steel. Chapter IX, Wiley, New York, 1931.
143. McConnell, C. W., Anal. Ed. **9**, 347 (1937); **7**, 4 (1935).
144. Mellen, G. T., Electronics **19**, 142 (April 1946).
145. Melpolder, F. W., Ind. Eng. Chem., Anal. Ed. **19**, 617 (1947).
146. Meyer, O., and Williams, F., Arch. Eisenhüttenw. **11**, 259 (1937).
147. Miller, V. A., Ind. Eng. Chem., Anal. Ed. **17**, 5 (1945).
148. Moll, W., and Burger, H., Z. tech. Physik **21**, 199 (1940).
149. Moore, G. A., and Smith, D. P., Metals Technol. **6** (April 1939), A.I.M.E.-T.P. No. 1065, 37 pages. Bibliography (ref. 123).
150. More, K. R., Humphreys, R. F., and Watson, W. W., Rev. Sci. Instruments **8**, 263 (1937).
151. Morse, R. S., Rev. Sci. Instruments **11**, 272 (1940).
152. Morse, R. S., and Bowie, R. M., Rev. Sci. Instruments **11**, 91 (1940).
153. Müller, E., Z. tech. Physik **16**, 177 (1935).
154. Müller, R. H., Ind. Eng. Chem., Anal. Ed. **18**, 25A (1946).
155. Nelson, H., Rev. Sci. Instruments **16**, 273 (1945).
156. Nelson, R. B., Rev. Sci. Instruments **16**, 55 (1945).
157. Nesbitt, C. E., and Henderson, J., Ind. Eng. Chem., Anal. Ed. **19**, 401 (1947).
158. Newell, W. C., Iron and Steel Institute (London), Special Report No. 25, 97 (1939).
159. Nickels, J. E., Ind. Eng. Chem., Anal. Ed. **19**, 216 (1947).
160. O'Gorman, J. M., Ind. Eng. Chem., Anal. Ed. **19**, 506 (1947).
161. Oliver, G. D., Bickford, W. G., Todd, S. S., and Fynn, P. J., Ind. Eng. Chem., Anal. Ed. **17**, 158 (1945).
162. Palkin, S., Ind. Eng. Chem., Anal. Ed. **7**, 434 (1935).
163. Pearlson, W. H., Ind. Eng. Chem., Anal. Ed. **16**, 415 (1944).
164. Pearlson, W. H., Brice, T. J., and Simons, J. H., Ind. Eng. Chem., Anal. Ed. **18**, 330 (1946).
165. Penning, F. M., Philips Tech. Rev. **2**, 201 (1937).
166. Penning, F. M., Physica **4**, 71 (1937).
166a. Pepkowitz, L. P., and Proud, E. R., Anal. Chem. **21**, 1000 (1949).
167. Picard, R. G., Smith, P. C., and Zollers, S. M., Rev. Sci. Instruments **17**, 125 (1946).
168. Prescott, C. H., J. Am. Chem. Soc. **50**, 3237 (1928).
169. Prescott, C. H., and Morrison, J., J. Am. Chem. Soc. **60**, 3050 (1938).
170. Price, J., J. Soc. Chem. Ind. **64**, 283 (1945).
171. Puddington, I., Ind. Eng. Chem., Anal. Ed. **16**, 592 (1944).
172. Puddington, I., Ind. Eng. Chem., Anal. Ed. **17**, 592 (1945).
173. Purushotham, A., Current Sci. India **12**, 15 (1944).
174. Quaife, M. L., and Harris, P. L., Ind. Eng. Chem., Anal. Ed. **18**, 707 (1946).
175. Ramaswamy, K. H., Phil. Mag. [7] **14**, 96 (1932).

175a. Ransley, C. E., *Analyst* **72**, 504 (1947).
176. Reeve, L., *Trans. Am. Inst. Mining Met. Engrs.* **113**, 82 (1934).
177. Robinson, H., and Flanagan, M. C., *Gen. Elec. Rev.* **49**, No. 5, 42 (1946).
178. Rollett, A., *Ber.* **73 B**, 1023 (1940).
179. Rose, J. E., *Rev. Sci. Instruments* **8**, 130 (1937).
180. Rosenberg, P., *Rev. Sci. Instruments* **9**, 258 (1938); **10**, 131 (1939).
181. Rubens, S. M., and Henderson, J. E., *Rev. Sci. Instruments* **10**, 49 (1939).
181a. Sanderson, R. T., *Ind. Eng. Chem., Anal. Ed.* **15**, 76 (1943).
181b. Savelli, J. J., Seyfried, W. D., and Filbert, B. M., *Ind. Eng. Chem., Anal. Ed.* **13**, 868 (1941).
182. Schröder, H., *Chem. App.* **19**, 169, 197 (1932).
183. Schwarz, H., *Z. Physik* **122**, 437 (1944).
183a. Shapiro, I., *Anal. Chem.* **21**, 888 (1949).
184. Shrader, J. E., and Ryder, H. M., *Phys. Rev.* **13**, 321 (1919).
185. Simons, J. H., Brice, T. J., and Pearlson, W. H., *Ind. Eng. Chem., Anal. Ed.* **17**, 404 (1945).
186. Smiley, W. G., *Ind. Eng. Chem., Anal. Ed.* **18**, 800 (1946).
187. Smythe, W. R., *Rev. Sci. Instruments* **7**, 435 (1936).
187a. Somerville, J., *Australian J. Sci.* **10**, 21 (1947).
188. Spadaro, J., Vix, H., and Gastrock, E., *Ind. Eng. Chem., Anal. Ed.* **18**, 214 (1946).
189. Spence, R., *J. Chem. Soc.* **1940**, Part II, 1300.
190. Stanley, J. K., and Yensen, T. C., *Ind. Eng. Chem., Anal. Ed.* **17**, 699 (1945).
191. Stimson, H., *J. Wash. Acad. Sci.* **7**, 477 (1917).
192. Stock, A., *Z. Elektrochem.* **23**, 35 (1917).
192a. Stover, C. N., Partridge, W. S., and Garrison, W. H., *Anal. Chem.* **21**, 1013 (1949).
193. Tarbes, P., *Le Vide* **1**, 9–11 (1946).
194. Taylor, R. C., and Young, W. S., *Ind. Eng. Chem., Anal. Ed.* **17**, 811 (1945).
195. Tellmann, W., *Glas u. App.* **16**, 27–28 (1935).
196. Thelin, J. H., *Ind. Eng. Chem., Anal. Ed.* **13**, 908 (1941).
197. Thomas, H. A., Williams, T. W., and Hipple, J. A., *Rev. Sci. Instruments* **17**, 368 (1946).
197a. Thoneman, P. C., *J. Sci. Instruments* **23**, 217 (1946).
198. Thorp, C. E., and Landay, H. L., *Ind. Eng. Chem., Anal. Ed.* **17**, 741 (1945).
199. Treadwell, W., and Frey, G., *Helv. Chim. Acta* **27**, 42 (1944).
200. Uhrig, K., Roberts, F. M., and Levin, H., *Ind. Eng. Chem., Anal. Ed.* **17**, 31 (1945).
201. U. S. Patent Nos. 1,542,913, 1,620,540, 1,984,994, 1,666,739, 1,666,743.
202. Vaughan, W. E., *Rev. Sci. Instruments* **16**, 254 (1945).
203. Van Hengel, G. H., and Starkweather, J. D., *Mech. Eng.*, 633–635 (October 1935).
204. Wang, T. J., *Ind. Eng. Chem., Anal. Ed.* **17**, 670 (1945).
205. Warner, B. R., *Ind. Eng. Chem., Anal. Ed.* **15**, 637 (1943).
206. Washburn, E., *Proc. Am. Petroleum Inst.* III **14**, 111–23 (1933).
207. Waterman, H., and Van Vlodrop, C., *Rev. chim. ind.* **48**, 314 (1939).
208. Weber, S., *Kgl. Danske Videnskab. Selskab., Math.-fys. Medd.* **14**, No. 13 (1937).
209. Webster, D. L., *Rev. Sci. Instruments* **5**, 42 (1934).
210. Webster, E. W., *Electronic Eng.* **17**, 53 (1944).
211. Wendell, C. B., *Ind. Eng. Chem., Anal. Ed.* **18**, 454 (1946).

212. Werner, J., *Ind. Eng. Chem., Anal. Ed.* **10**, 645 (1938).
213. Werner, J., *Ind. Eng. Chem., Anal. Ed.* **17**, 865 (1945).
214. Wilcock, D. F., *Gen. Elec. Rev.* **49**, 32 (1946).
215. Willems, F., and co-workers: *Arch. Eisenhüttenw.* **12**, 485 (1938/1939); **13**, 309 (1939/1940).
216. Williamson, A., *Rev. Sci. Instruments* **3**, 782 (1932).
217. Winterhager, H., *Aluminum-Arch.* **12**, 7 (1938); *Z. Ver. deut. Ing.* **83**, 898 (1939).
218. Wittka, F., *Angew. Chem.* **53**, 557 (1940).
219. Wittka, F., Neuere Methoden der Präparativen Organischen Chemie. W. Foerst, editor, Verlag Chemie, Berlin, 1944, Vol. I, pp. 513–546.
220. Worcester, W. G., and Doughty, E. G., A.I.E.E. Technical Paper No. 46–142, A.I.E.E., New York, May 1946.
221. Yensen, T., *Trans. Am. Electrochem. Soc.* **37**, 227 (1920).
222. Young, W. S., *Ind. Eng. Chem., Anal. Ed.* **17**, 742 (1945).
223. Young, W. S., and Taylor, R. C., *Ind. Eng. Chem., Anal. Ed.* **19**, 135 (1947).
224. Young, W. S., and Taylor, R. C., *Ind. Eng. Chem., Anal. Chem.* **19**, 133 (1947).
225. Zhuravleva, G., and Chufarov, G., *Zavodskaya Lab.* **9**, 498 (1940).
226. Ziegler, N., *Trans. Am. Electrochem. Soc.* **56**, 231 (1929).
227. Zimmerli, A., *Ind. Eng. Chem., Anal. Ed.* **10**, 283 (1938).

Gas Analysis by Methods Depending on Thermal Conductivity

By

E. R. WEAVER

National Bureau of Standards, Washington, D.C.

CONTENTS

1. PRINCIPLES OF THE METHOD

A method which depends on the different conductivities of gases seems first to have been applied to gas analysis with real success during the years 1913–1918. The development of practical apparatus and applications took place simultaneously or nearly so in Great Britain, Germany, and the United States. Among the numerous workers who contributed to the subject, a major share of credit probably belongs to Koepsel (55), who, in 1908, demonstrated the practicability of the method and suggested various applications, and to Shakespear (76), who developed the first commercial instrument of good construction known and used outside Germany. A brief review of the subject by Palmer and Weaver (66) and a description of experiments made at the National Bureau of Standards by them and their associates probably first brought the method generally to the attention of analysts in America. A text of 357 pages by H. A. Daynes, entitled "Gas Analysis by Measurement of Thermal Conductivity" (20), covered the subject thoroughly to 1930 and will probably remain the best source of basic and historical information for students of the matter. This text will be referred to frequently and briefly as "Daynes."

Shakespear's instrument was named the "Katharometer" and its use is often referred to as "the Shakespear method." Another instrument is called the "Thermic Diaferometer," but usually the instruments are constructed and sold for specific applications and are unpoetically named "gas analyzers," "furnace controls," etc., with the manufacturers' or other proprietary names attached. The term "thermal conductivity method" is never applied to anything else, but the "conductimetric method" may mean one employing either thermal or electrical conductivity. The terms "hot wire method" and "Wheatstone bridge method" are shared equally with the method depending on combustion at the surface of a wire, while the term "electrical method" is applied impartially to the three here mentioned and several others.

The principle employed is simple. If a wire enclosed in a "cell" is heated by a steady electric current, its temperature increases until the loss of heat in one way or another exactly balances the input of electrical energy, measured by the product of the applied voltage and the current through the wire. In a cell of suitable size, much the greater part of the heat from the wire is conducted to the walls of the cell through the gas which fills it, and the temperature of the wire when a balance is reached depends on how good a thermal insulator the gas is.

The hot wire, which is usually of platinum, becomes a resistance-thermometer which measures its own temperature; but it differs from an ordinary resistance-thermometer in one important respect. A resistance-thermometer is normally used to determine the temperature of its immediate surroundings, frequently to a thousandth of a degree, and the input of electrical energy involved in making the measurement must not change the temperature of the resistor by even that much. In the gas analyzer, on the other hand, a rather large difference of temperature between the wire and its surroundings is desirable. Frequently this is 100°C., and as much as 250°C. has been recommended (39) in certain cases. The heating current is also the measuring current. Consequently, with an equally good galvanometer and measuring circuit, it should be possible to determine the temperature of the wire in the analyzing cell to a very small fraction of the smallest change of temperature measurable with an ordinary resistance-thermometer. However, to utilize the possible precision of measurement of temperature of the wire in a single cell, say to 10^{-5}°C., would require that we know the temperature of the cell wall as accurately, for we are not concerned with the temperature of the wire as such, but with the gradient between wire and cell wall which depends on the properties of the gas. Even if we knew the temperature gradient to one part in a million, the information would be useless unless we knew the input of energy to the wire with equal precision.

Chiefly to avoid the necessity of knowing with great accuracy the temperature of the cell and the power dissipated, conductivity cells are seldom used singly but nearly always in pairs, one of which contains a "reference gas." Usually the reference gas is of known composition, as much like that of the gas to be analyzed as is convenient. The two cells are arranged electrically, usually in a simple Wheatstone bridge, so that the ratio of the resistance of the wire in one cell to that of the wire in the other cell is the quantity on which the measurement principally depends. If the cells are identical and if the same gas is in both, the ratio of the resistance must be unity, whatever the temperature of the cell walls and whatever electric power is being supplied. If the compositions of the gases are nearly the same, the effect of the difference of composition measured with the bridge is almost independent of the external temperature and power supply. The greater the difference between the conductivities of gases in identical cells, the more seriously are the measurements affected by these external conditions. Moreover, two cells never are exactly alike. Hence, although the comparison of two cells eliminates most of the trouble from external causes, if the highest accuracy is desired in the measurements, attention must always be given to the control of external temperature and the electrical supply.

Since the only measurement we ordinarily make with the pair of cells is that of the ratio or other simple function of their resistances, we are limited to a single equation and to only one conclusion regarding the composition of the gas. Basically, this conclusion can only be as to the proportions of the two constituents of a binary mixture. Fortunately, a "binary mixture" in this case is not limited to one containing only two chemical individuals. Any mixture may be considered to be one of the two components of the system, provided it remains of uniform composition. For example, the method is very useful in measuring the proportions of a mixture of air and carbureted water gas, although the air contains at least five constituents in sufficient quantity to affect its conductivity appreciably, and the water gas contains a dozen. But as long as air and gas are individually of constant composition, there is no difficulty in determining the ratio in which they are mixed.

The "reference gas" is not necessarily of known or even of constant composition. It is frequently obtained by making a change in the gas to be analyzed, such as removing one constituent, adding another, or producing a reaction between constituents already present. Conclusions are drawn as to the effect of the operation from the difference between the conductivities before and after it.

2. The Thermal Conductivities of Gases

A knowledge of the thermal conductivities of gases is of interest, but paradoxically of little use, to the analyst whose instrument depends on conduction for its operation. This is true because of the difficulty and uncertainty of making an absolute measurement of thermal conductivity. In their review of the subject Laby and Nelson (49) state that "The experimental determination of the thermal conductivity of gases is subject to very large error. For example, the 19 determinations of k for air deviate on the average from the weighted mean . . . by 7 per cent."

Although the instruments used in what are probably the best measurements of conductivities are identical in principle with those used for analysis and may even have been constructed originally for that purpose, it is necessary to know many things in determining conductivity that need not be known in making an analysis. Among these are the amounts of heat lost by convection, radiation, and conduction through the wire, each of which is discussed in detail by Daynes, pp. 30–40. In a cell of the type principally used in the development of the analytical method at the Bureau of Standards, consisting of a tube 1 cm. in diameter, with a straight axial wire 10-cm. long, the aggregate of these sources of heat loss amounts to about 4% of the heat transferred by conduction. Conductivities of gases change with temperature; hence there is a gradient of conductivity as well as of temperature within the cell. When mixtures are involved, a further complication is introduced by "thermal diffusion," as a result of which there is also a gradient of composition. The lighter gas is concentrated near the wire where its generally higher conductivity is most effective. Daynes' discussion of the subject shows that the effect of thermal diffusion may be more important than the several minor methods of heat transfer. Additional difficulties in measuring conductivity are that of knowing exactly where within the cell the wire is located, the "inherent errors" caused by the temperature discontinuity between the gas and solid surfaces, and imperfect interchange of energy between the gas molecules and the solid surfaces.

Fortunately, these numerous obstacles to measuring conductivity can be almost eliminated in analytical work by empirical calibration. The readings of the instrument when supplied with known mixtures of gases are simply recorded. In doing this we substitute for the uncertainty of measuring conductivity the difficulties of making known mixtures or analyzing unknown ones by an independent method; but experience has shown that the substitution is necessary.

Since empirical calibration in this way is universally employed for analytical purposes, a knowledge of the conductivities of gases serves only as a general guide in planning the instrument and its use. Probably it has enough value for that purpose to justify the inclusion of Table I.

In the preparation of the table, advantage has been taken of the fact that a selection of the best recorded values was made by Laby and Nelson (49) and again by Daynes (20), who recorded several values for many of the gases. Their selections were considered and are referred to in preference to earlier original data, and their list of references is thereby reduced from 63 to 2. To these reviews have been added later publications including summaries by Dickins (21) and by Grüss and Schmick (40) and a new selection of "best values" has been made. The exact values have not enough importance in connection with analysis to justify a discussion of the reasons for the selections, which were based as much on agreement among relative as among absolute values. Sometimes a choice was based on an average of the data of several observers; sometimes on only one. Some liberty was taken in reducing the conductivities measured at one temperature not far from 0°C. or 100°C. to those round numbers by the use of coefficients recorded in the literature or assumed from analogy to related compounds. Such cases are marked in the table by a superscript. A close student of the subject should not uncritically accept the present author's selections, but should consult the original references.

How completely the measurement of thermal conductivity has been isolated from its analytical use could not be better illustrated than by the fact that there is no good reported value of the conductivity of atmospheric nitrogen (the residue after the removal of oxygen, carbon dioxide, and water vapor from air), yet, in the applications made of thermal conductivity in analysis, atmospheric nitrogen is probably the most important of all gases, even including air itself. The value reported for atmospheric nitrogen in Table I was computed from the average composition of the atmosphere and the assumption that the conductivities

TABLE I
Thermal Conductivities of Gases

Formula	Name	$K \times 10^{7a}$	$R_0{}^b$	$R_{100}{}^b$	References
	Air	583	1.00	1.00	(20, 21, 35, 36, 49, 53, 58, 59, 77, 85, 89)
H_2	Hydrogen	4160	7.15	7.10	(2, 20, 21, 46, 49, 52, 53, 64, 85, 89)
D_2	Deuterium	3400	5.85	—	(2, 52, 64, 82)
He	Helium	3480	5.97	5.53	(16, 20, 21, 49, 53)
N_2	Nitrogen	581	.996	.996	(20, 21, 37, 46, 49, 85)
	Atmospheric nitrogen	579	.993	.993	Computed
O_2	Oxygen	589	1.013	1.014	(20, 21, 37, 49, 64, 85)
Ne	Neon	1110	1.90	1.84	(16, 20, 49, 53, 89)
A	Argon	398	.0684	.696	(16, 20, 21, 46, 49, 53, 81)
Kr	Krypton	212	.363	—	(10, 16, 17)
Xe	Xenon	124	.213	—	(16)
Cl_2	Chlorine	188	.323	—	(20)
CO	Carbon monoxide	563	.960	.962	(20, 21, 46, 49, 53, 81)
CO_2	Carbon dioxide	352	.605	.700	(20, 21, 46, 49, 53, 56, 77, 85)
NO	Nitric oxide	571	.980	—	(20)
SO_2	Sulfur dioxide	204	.350	—	(20, 21)
H_2S	Hydrogen sulfide	314	.538	—	(20)
CS_2	Carbon disulfide	370	.285	—	(20)
NH_3	Ammonia	522	.897	1.04	(20, 21, 49, 56)
H_2O	Water	—	—	.775	(20)
CH_4	Methane	721	1.25	1.45	(20, 49, 58, 81)
CD_4	Deutero methane	714	1.22	—	(82)
C_2H_6	Ethane	436	.750	.970	(20, 49, 58)
C_2D_6	Deutero ethane	370	.635	—	(82)
C_3H_8	Propane	358	.615	.832	(58, 81)
C_3D_8	Deutero propane	305	.523	—	(82)
C_4H_{10}	n-Butane	322	.552	.744	(58)
C_4H_{10}	Isobutane	332	.569	.776	(58)
C_5H_{12}	n-Pentane	312	.535	.702	(20, 58)
C_5H_{12}	Isopentane	300	.515	—	(20)
C_6H_{14}	n-Hexane	296	.508	.662	(20, 58)
C_7H_{16}	n-Heptane	—	—	.582	(20)
C_6H_{12}	Cyclohexane	—	—	.576[c]	(20)
C_6H_{12}	n-Hexylene	251	.431	.618	(20)
C_2H_4	Ethylene	419	.720	.980	(20, 49)
C_2H_2	Acetylene	453	.777	.900	(20)

TABLE I.—(*Continued*)

Formula	Name	$K \times 10^{7a}$	$R_0{}^b$	$R_{100}{}^b$	References
C_6H_6	Benzene	—	.370	.583	(20)
CCl_4	Carbon tetrachloride	—	—	.288	(20)
$CHCl_3$	Chloroform	158	.269	.328	(20)
CH_2Cl_2	Methylene dichloride	161	.276	.356	(20)
CH_3Cl	Methyl chloride	220	.377	.530	(20)
CH_3Br	Methyl bromide	150	.257	.350	(20)
CH_3I	Methyl iodide	113	.194	.254	(20)
CH_2F_2	Freon 12	196	.344	—	(77)
C_2H_5Cl	Ethyl chloride	228	.391	.540	(20)
C_2H_5Br	Ethyl bromide	—	.295^c	—	(20)
C_2H_5I	Ethyl iodide	—	.242^c	—	(20)
CH_4O	Methyl alcohol	345	.592	.727	(20)
C_2H_6O	Ethyl alcohol	—	—	.700	(20)
C_3H_6O	Acetone	237	.406	.557	(20)
C_3H_8O	Methyl ethyl ether	—	—	.772	(38)
$C_4H_{10}O$	Methyl propyl ether	—	—	.716	(38)
$C_4H_{10}O$	Ethyl ether	—	—	.747	(38)
$C_5H_{12}O$	Methyl butyl ether	—	—	.664	(38)
$C_5H_{12}O$	Ethyl propyl ether	—	—	.670	(38)
$C_6H_{14}O$	Ethyl butyl ether	—	—	.625	(38)
$C_6H_{14}O$	Propyl ether	—	—	.616	(38)
$C_6H_{14}O$	Isopropyl ether	—	—	.642	(38)
$C_7H_{16}O$	Propyl butyl ether	—	—	.566	(38)
$C_8H_{18}O$	Butyl ether	—	—	.534	(38)
$C_2H_6O_2$	Methyl acetate	161	.421	—	(20)
$C_3H_8O_2$	Ethyl acetate	—	—	.543	(20)
CH_5N	Methylamine	—	.657^c	—	(49)
C_2H_7N	Dimethylamine	—	.610^c	—	(49)
C_2H_7N	Ethylamine	—	.583^c	—	(49)
C_3H_9N	Propylamine	—	.517^c	—	(49)
C_3H_9N	Trimethylamine	—	.565^c	—	(49)
$C_4H_{11}N$	Diethylamine	—	.520^c	—	(49)
$C_4H_{11}N$	Isobutylamine	—	.511^c	—	(49)
$C_5H_{13}N$	n-Amylamine	—	.479^c	—	(49)
$C_6H_{15}N$	Di-n-propylamine	—	.440^c	—	(49)
$C_6H_{15}N$	Triethylamine	—	.457^c	—	(49)

^{a} K is the conductivity at 0°C. in cal. cm.$^{-3}$ sec.$^{-2}$ (°C. cm.$^{-1}$)$^{-1}$

^{b} R_0 and R_{100} are the ratios of the conductivities of the substance to those of air at 0° and 100°C.

^{c} Results reduced from a slightly different temperature by means of reported temperature coefficients or coefficients deduced from a homologous series.

of mixtures of nitrogen and argon are a linear function of composition, as reported by Eltzin (24). The deviation from linearity indicated by the observations of Weber (88) does not affect the last significant figure in the estimated value.

3. Effect of Temperature on Conductivity

The effect of temperature on conductivity is not well established theoretically. It has been represented by mathematical functions only less numerous than "equations of state" (1, 33, 59, 86, 90). For the purpose of this paper only the simplest of the relations has been used,

$$k_t = k_0(1 + At).$$

In this equation k_t is the conductivity at any temperature $t°$C., k_0 is the conductivity at $0°$C., and A is a constant temperature coefficient. The values for R_{100} in Table I have been obtained in some cases by direct observation, in other cases they were computed from R_0 and observed values of A according to this equation. In making the computation, it was assumed that the value of A for air is 0.0029, that is

$$k_{100} = 1.29k_0.$$

The values used for the mean temperature coefficient between 0 and $100°$C. for other gases can be obtained, if desired, from the equation

$$100A = \frac{1.29R_{100}}{R_0} - 1.$$

At ordinary temperatures, the values of A differ from about 0.0020 for helium to about 0.01 for such heavy vapors as benzene.

Beyond being an additional reason why the temperature of the analytical apparatus must be carefully controlled in accurate work, the fact that gases do not all have the same temperature coefficients is of interest to the analyst principally because the difference between certain pairs of gases may reverse its sign as temperature changes. An outstanding example is that of ammonia with air or nitrogen. At low temperature, ammonia is a poorer conductor than air; at high temperature a better one. Although the difference between the gases at either extreme of temperature is adequate for the analysis, it is at least theoretically possible to heat the wire of the analytical cell to such a temperature that pure ammonia could not be distinguished from air. In most cases, the effect of increasing temperature is only to bring the relative conductivities of two gases more closely together.

Bolland and Melville (6) have taken advantage of the differences in thermal coefficients to analyze ternary mixtures without separation by heating the wire to two different temperatures, thereby obtaining two equations from which the proportions of two gases in a third can be computed.

4. Effect of Pressure on Conductivity

As in the case of temperature effects, there is a lack of general agreement as to the exact effect of changes of pressure on the conduction of heat from the wire. The kinetic theory, in its simpler forms at least, indicates that conduction should be independent of pressures that are high enough to make the mean free paths of the molecules very small fractions of the distance between the confining walls. This is so nearly true that there is no general agreement as to whether the observed departure from the rule is to be attributed to convection and other interferences with the measurement of true conductivity (34) or to the operation of attractive forces between the molecules and other things not included in the kinetic theory for ideal gases (11, 84).

The fact of practical importance for the analyst is that in the usual instrument the heat transferred is nearly, but never quite, independent of gas pressure, so that in a large variety of applications changes of barometric pressure and other variations not easy to avoid are negligible; but in applications requiring the utmost available accuracy, pressures must be controlled with as much care as temperature and current.

5. The Conductivities of Mixtures

A review of the thermal conductivities of mixtures of gases, mainly theoretical, is given by Daynes, pp. 16–25, which is of interest to a student of the subject. Like the conductivities of pure gases, the laws governing mixtures are of limited use to the analyst and for the same reason; they simply are not known accurately enough to be of any use in calibrating instruments.

In most cases, a plot of conductivity with respect to the compositions of mixtures of two gases results in a curve that is almost indistinguishable from the shape taken by a thread suspended from the two ends of the curve when placed at the same level. Different curves correspond to different tensions of the string. In Fig. 1 are shown curves drawn mainly from the data of Weber (88) and of Ibbs and Hirst (46) one of which represents the conductivities of mixtures of hydrogen with carbon dioxide, nitrogen, carbon monoxide, and nitrous oxide, and of helium with argon. On the scale used, a single curve represents the observations for all of these mixtures equally well. Separate curves represent mixtures of argon with hydrogen and with nitrogen. In each case the linear scale used is such that the conductivity of the poorer conductor of the two gases is assigned the value 0 and the conductivity of the better conductor, the value 100. The straight line joining the two points would represent the composition corresponding to each conductivity if the simple law of mixtures were followed.   The actual curves do not coincide with the calibration curves of an analytical instrument because the gases in the cells are at different temperatures and because the circuits and indicating devices are seldom or never arranged to produce readings that are strictly proportional to conductivity.   They might easily mislead the

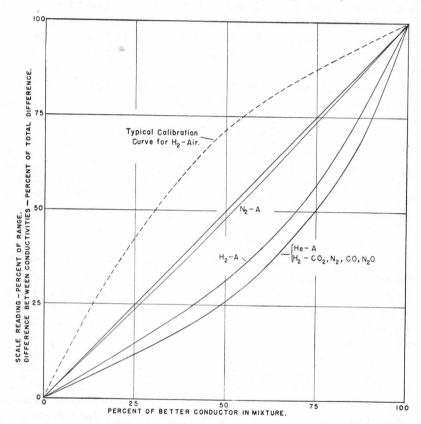

Fig. 1.   Conductivities of gas mixtures.   Each point on a solid curve represents the conductivity of a mixture minus the conductivity of one component as a percentage of the difference between the conductivities of the pure components.   The broken line is a typical calibration curve of an analytical instrument.

prospective analyst, for they indicate a much greater change of conductivity for 1% air in hydrogen (or helium) than for 1% of that gas in air. In most analytical instruments, the relation of readings to composition is just the reverse of this; the instrument is most sensitive to changes of composition near that of the less conducting gas, as is represented by the broken line which is an actual calibration curve for hydrogen in air.

In some cases of gases not too greatly different, the conductivities of mixtures pass through maxima. Probably the most important cases are those of water vapor and ammonia in mixtures with air or nitrogen. At 80°C., they show maxima at about 20 and 40% respectively (40). The addition of either of these gases to air increases its conductivity enough so that at ordinary temperature it is quite possible to determine the presence of ammonia or the absolute humidity of air with considerable accuracy (74). Near the maximum, small changes of composition would have no detectable effect. However, the position of the maximum shifts with a change of temperature, and it is at least theoretically possible to analyze any binary mixture by selecting a favorable temperature and power supply for the cell.

6. Construction of Analytical Cells—Early Types

The essential part of an analytical apparatus employing thermal conductivity is the combination of a heating and a temperature-measuring element, which are usually but not always the same wire, in a cell cavity, to the walls of which the heat is conducted through a gas-filled space. For brevity, the term "cell" will be used to mean this entire basic device, the cell body, and its contents. Usually more than one cell, as here defined, is enclosed in the same block of metal or other compact unit, and it is customary for instrument makers to refer to such combinations, with gas channels and essential wiring, as a cell. In this chapter, it will be called an analytical "unit."

Cells have been described in which heaters and resistance thermometers were different wires or in which the measurement involved the use of thermocouples, bimetallic strips, or even merely the thermal expansion of straight tubes or wire. The reasons for their design have been economy, ruggedness, or measurement with direct current instruments while heating with alternating current; but they have found little if any practical use and will not be mentioned again.

The early cells of Koepsel (55) and of Siemens and Halske (78), who apparently made the first commercial instrument, consisted of straight platinum wires in metal tubes of sufficient length to minimize end-losses. Cells of this form were used in most of the experimental work at the Bureau of Standards, and to some extent in commercial equipment in this country, and they seem always to have been favored for research by experimenters who made their own apparatus.

The "Bureau of Standards cell," as it was called by Daynes, will serve as a starting point in the description of cells.

The first cell cavities were glass tubes in a water bath; the next were drilled in pairs into brass blocks, but single ½-inch square bars were later used because they permitted matching the cells with one another to find pairs as much alike as possible. The square form permitted the pair of cells to be clamped into thermal contact not detectably inferior to cells in a single block.

A straight wire with a spring at one end was employed in preference to a coil because it was found easier for an experimenter to reproduce. The diameter of the cell, 1 cm., was chosen as a compromise between a larger one which would give more trouble with convection and a smaller one which would be more affected by any displacement of the wire or change in the dimensions of the cell by corrosion or the collection of dust or condensate. The length of the cell, 12 cm., was chosen as about the minimum that would permit the use of a wire not too delicate to be readily handled but with a resistance high enough for convenient use with the electrical instruments available. The diameter of the wire used was about 2 mils (0.05 mm.) and its resistance about 10 ohms.

Shakespear's Katharometer employed cells with a volume of only about 0.5 ml., with short helical coils of wire of very small diameter. The merits of the helix are the concentration of resistance into a shorter space and the fact that the helix itself acts as the spring that keeps the wire centered. Its disadvantage is the fact that mutual heating of one turn by another makes it difficult to reproduce with the accuracy of a straight wire. Straight wires are replacing coils even in the instruments of the former principal user of the coiled filament, the Cambridge Instrument Co.

When the Charles Englehard Co. became interested in the production of gas analyzers, it was already manufacturing a resistance thermometer consisting of a platinum coil imbedded in the wall of a quartz tube. The resistance thermometers, when cemented into chambers of suitable size, were found to make excellent analytical cells with which the recorders and other electrical equipment already used for thermometric work were quite satisfactory.

The active element of the Englehard cell is incomparably rugged, and is immune to physical or chemical change under ordinary conditions or by ordinary gases except hydrogen fluoride. It dissipates a much larger amount of heat than a cell of any other commercial type, but a correspondingly larger amount of power is available for the operation of indicating and control mechanisms. The relatively large amount of power required by the cell can be an advantage or a disadvantage, depending on the application made and the auxiliary instruments employed. The high cost of the cell and the lag associated with the large mass of the active element are definite disadvantages.

7. Sweeping Out the Cell

The three cells just described and the straight-wire cells of Siemens and Halske are the only ones mentioned by Daynes as being in commercial use in 1930. Daynes regarded the small size of the Shakespear cell and the fact that it had only one opening through which the gas changed by diffusion as its distinguishing features. All others were classed as "flow-type" cells because they have inlet and outlet connections at opposite ends, and provision is made to pass a flow of sample through them.

Gas that flows through a cell carries away heat and apparently increases conductivity. If the flow is not constant and taken into account in calibration, it can become a source of error. In the most precise work it is best to avoid this difficulty by stopping the flow entirely while a reading is made. If a continuous record or indication is required, steady flow and prompt response are provided for by by-passing the cell with a much larger flow than can be permitted to enter it. The fraction of the total flow which passes through the cell is determined in part by the relative resistance of the two parallel channels and in part by convection. Leeds and Northrup use a cell, devised by Peters (67), in which convection alone is depended on for purging, by connecting the inlet and outlet of the cell to the same point of the sampling line. This makes the flow through the cell independent of that in the sampling line, but somewhat more dependent on changes of density than would be the case with a moderate restriction in the by-pass.

8. Materials Used in Cells

In the past 15-years a score of cells of varied construction have been placed on the market by as many manufacturers. With one or two exceptions, the tendency has been to approach the Shakespear cell in small size and dependence on diffusion. Leeds and Northrup, who initially manufactured a close duplicate of the Bureau of Standards cell but with the convective circuit described above, has retained the approximate form and size of the original cell but employs a straight glass-covered wire in a glass body. The primary purpose of this is, of course, to resist corrosion. Several other manufacturers make glass cells with glass-covered filaments for chlorine and other very corrosive gases, but employ metal cell bodies for most purposes. The Englehard Co. encloses its quartz-platinum resistance thermometer in a quartz-glass body when corrosive conditions are anticipated. Other cell bodies have been made of brass, copper, aluminum, tin, lead, stainless steel, and brass with gold plating. Rolled metal is universally employed with the exception of lead, which is cast. By far the majority of cells are of brass, because of the ease with which it can be worked, brazed, etc. Copper costs more, is harder to machine, and offers few compensating advantages. Stainless steel is little used because of its cost. The difficulty of making secure connections to aluminum is its greatest fault; it has the merit of being completely resistant to hydrogen sulfide. Gold plating of brass, at one time extensively employed to prevent corrosion, has been generally abandoned because the coatings were often porous and consequently ineffective. "Active" wires of platinum, silver, tungsten, tantalum, nickel, "Kovar," and one or two other alloys have been used. Platinum is still the most commonly employed and would be selected by the writer for its known physical and chemical properties; but tungsten is known to be used by the General Electric Co. and to some extent by the Chas. Englehard Co., tantalum by the Davis-Hebler Co., and Kovar by the Gow-Mac Instrument Co. Data which would show the relative merits of the different metals in service are lacking. The Cambridge Instrument Co. normally employs platinum wires which have been gold plated to prevent catalytic effects. Glass and quartz coatings, of course, serve the same purpose.

9. Interchangeability of Cells

The importance of providing cells in well-matched pairs varies with the application to be made of them and their method of calibration. When an instrument is to be individually calibrated, exact matching of the cells may not be necessary, particularly if they are to be used for gases of a fairly wide range of composition. The accurate control of temperature and power supply is then necessary, however well the cells are matched, and when these conditions are constant, the calibration will be reproduced even if the cells are not alike. But when only small differences in conductivities are anticipated in the use of the instrument, the accuracy with which external conditions must be controlled becomes proportional to the difference between cells, and if this difference is small, elaborate controls may be dispensed with. When a large number of instruments is to be made for the same purpose, it is desirable, if possible, to make them generally interchangeable, both to avoid the necessity of individually calibrating the instruments and to facilitate replacements. In this case it is not enough to provide matched pairs; each unit should duplicate a standard. Cells are initially made as much alike as possible. When they are connected to form measuring bridges, an outside resistance is always adjusted to produce a predetermined reading, usually zero, with air in both analyzing and compensating cells. This is called a "zero adjustment." The electrical means of adjustment is usually retained in the final analyzer and is available for readjustment when desired. In most cases, at the present time, manufacturers consider their cells interchangeable without mechanical adjustment. In other cases, for exacting requirements, some mechanical adjustments are considered necessary to make the unit independent of small changes of temperature and applied voltage. Harrison (42) made a virtue of the usual fault of coiled filaments, by providing means for adjusting the tension on long helical cell wires. The resulting change of spacing of the helix permits ready compensation, which is probably the principal feature of the cells made by the Brown Instrument Co. R. H. Krueger (57) devised a short adjustable sleeve which fits over the lower part of a cell and alters its over-all conductance. The device is used in Englehard instruments. W. O. Hebler has described several devices for the purpose in the patent literature, but actually uses slight displacements of the position of the filament from the center of the cell.

10. CLASSIFICATION OF INSTRUMENTS

It will be convenient, in the further discussion of instruments, to classify them with respect to function and accuracy. In one group, which will be called laboratory instruments, a high degree of accuracy is needed and obtainable. Generally these instruments are used by competent observers who can interpret results of varied character, apply corrections, make necessary adjustments and calibrations, improvise accessories, and take the time required for simple manipulation. Usually, the manipulation needed is not more exacting or time-consuming than measuring a temperature with thermocouple and potentiometer. A single laboratory instrument may be adapted for a large variety of analyses.

In the second group, which will be called industrial instruments, each has only one purpose. Generally they are attached to units of a manufacturing or power plant; and sampling lines, filters, pumps, connections, wiring, and indicating, recording, and control equipment are permanent and may be elaborate and massive. Generally less accuracy is expected of industrial than of laboratory instruments, but they are required to be completely automatic, to give their results as directly as possible, and to serve for long periods without adjustment or recalibration. Cost is generally a secondary consideration.

In the third class are indicators, alarms, etc., of low accuracy, and portable equipment such as leak detectors and devices for adjusting automobile carburetors and the dampers of domestic heating appliances. They must be simple, with few accessories, require no trained personnel, and should be of small size and cost.   Because of their simplicity and the large fraction of them that are actually portable, they will be referred to for brevity as portable instruments.   There are, of course, gradations between these several types.

11. MEASURING CIRCUITS

Almost always the measuring circuits employed in analytical work consist of some form of the Wheatstone bridge in which one, two, or four cells are employed.   With each of these there are various ways of connecting resistances or measuring instruments, so that at least a score of different bridge arrangements are useful.   Daynes (pp. 26–48 and 70–91) has classified a majority of them and discussed their merits at greater length than is possible in the space of this chapter.

In Fig. 2 four bridges are represented.   They are chosen to show the various alternatives rather than for their relative importance among the arrangements in actual use.   The bridge represented by (a) is probably the best of three or four, each with a single cell, which have been used only by research workers, mainly in the study of isotopes.   The cell containing the gas to be analyzed is placed in a thermostat with resistance C made of wire of the same composition as is used in the cell.   Compensations for changes in the temperature of the bath are fair; they are not exact because the cell wire is at a higher temperature and changes its resistance by a smaller fraction per degree of change of temperature than does the compensating wire.   There is no compensation for variations of applied voltage; hence accuracy of measurement with this bridge depends on excellent thermostating and nearly perfect voltage control.

Bridge (b) is one of several that are suitable for varied laboratory uses.   The analytical cell A is compensated by a similar cell C which may contain a "standard" gas of predetermined composition, or a gas related to that being analyzed in a known way, for example, it may be the residue after one constituent of the gas in A has been absorbed by a chemical reagent. R_1 and R_2 are fixed resistances referred to as "end-coils" because they serve as extensions of a slide-wire S which is the real measuring instrument in this bridge.   All measurements are made with the bridge in balance; galvanometer G serves only to show when it is balanced.   The range of composition that can be measured with a given slide-wire can be adjusted by changing shunt T.   Decreasing the resistance of T increases the length of slide-wire that corresponds to a given change of composition, and accordingly increases the sensitivity of this factor in obtaining accurate readings; at the same time it decreases the sensitivity of the galvanometer.   It will be noted that current from the

battery flows through wires A and C in parallel so that there is exactly
the same difference of potential across each.

In bridge (c), which is much used in industrial instruments, the
analytical cell A and the compensating cell C are placed in series, so

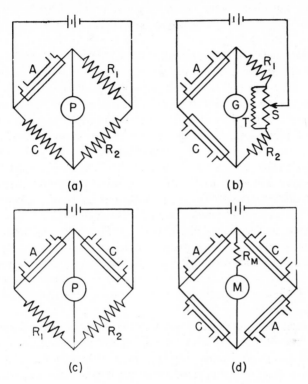

Fig. 2.   Types of bridges used with analyzers.

A, Cell containing gas for analysis
C, Compensating resistance or a cell containing a gas for comparison
P, Potentiometer
G, Galvanometer
M, Meter
R_1, R_2, Fixed resistances
S, Slide-wire
T, Shunt on the slide-wire

that, when the bridge is balanced, exactly the same current flows through
both. R_1 and R_2 are fixed resistances.   The bridge is normally unbalanced and the voltage across it is measured with a potentiometer.

In bridge (d), four cells are used, two of which are filled with the gas
to be analyzed and two with the gas with which it is compared.   The

analysis is indicated by a deflecting electromagnetic instrument usually of the milliameter range of resistance and sensitivity. Most of the portable instruments use a bridge of this form.

Reasons for choosing among some of the alternatives will now be discussed. The first choice is between the four-cell bridge (d) and one of the two-cell bridges. The advantage of the four-cell bridge is that, for a given applied voltage, it has twice the sensitivity of the two-cell form. A less delicate measuring instrument can therefore be used, or a lower voltage applied which saves batteries in a portable instrument. A smaller difference between the temperatures of the wires in analyzing and compensating cells also improves compensation in some cases. The advantage of the two-cell bridge is that it permits a greater variety and range of adjustments for various conditions and types of analysis. This is of particular advantage in the laboratory where the same bridge may be used for varied problems. Usually the four-cell bridge is made up in final form, adjusted, and calibrated by the manufacturer, and no attempt is made at readjustment, calibrations, or repair in service. The entire bridge is replaced when "servicing" is necessary.

The choice between a milliameter or other deflecting instrument on the one hand and a potentiometer or a balanced bridge and galvanometer on the other, depends primarily on whether an accuracy greater than that with which the milliameter scale can be read is desired and whether other conditions are controlled well enough to make more accurate readings significant.

For a manually-operated laboratory instrument, the balanced bridge with galvanometer and slide wire possesses slight advantages over the unbalanced bridge and potentiometer with respect to simplicity, directness, cost, adaptability, and number of sources of possible error; but the margin of advantage is small in each respect, and for temporary setups the average laboratory is more likely to have an available potentiometer than a detached slide-wire of the same accuracy. When this is the case, there should be no hesitation in using the potentiometer, unless work of very high accuracy is required. The most important item in favor of the balanced bridge is the fact that it is readily made to compensate for variations of applied voltage and the unbalanced bridge is not, at least when direct current is used. Leeds and Northrup uses alternating-current bridges in industrial work with alternating-current potentiometers and galvanometers. Since the potentiometer circuit is supplied (through a transformer) with current from the same source as the bridge, the dependence of the instrument on supply voltage is reduced to equality with that of a balanced bridge.

Among the industrial instruments, a great many of which are recording or controlling, the potentiometer has two important virtues. Its indications are independent of the length or temperature of the connections between the recorder and the analytical unit; switching from one unit to another can be done easily with little loss of accuracy, and several analyses, or both analyses and temperatures, can be recorded by a single multiple-point instrument with a single slide-wire. This is not practicable with balanced bridges. Bridge (c) is, therefore, the preferred type of two-cell bridge for industrial work. When instruments are well standardized and factory-calibrated, four-cell units are much used even when the potentiometer is employed for the measurements.

Whether the analyzing and compensating cells shall be arranged in parallel as in (b) or in series as in (c) is of minor importance. The series arrangement is slightly more sensitive, but the difference of sensitivity is appreciable only when there is a large difference between the two gases, and then it is likely to be unimportant. On the other hand, compensation for temperature and power supply is slightly better with the parallel arrangement, and the effect is greatest where it is most needed. The advantage is probably with the parallel arrangement for this reason. A more important advantage of the parallel arrangement in the case of the balanced bridge is that a higher potential exists between the slide-wire and its contact, and the effect of variable resistance in this contact is reduced.

Daynes and others have shown that good compensation between cells occurs when the temperatures of the wires are alike. It is sometimes a convenience to use a compensating gas that differs materially from the gas being analyzed; for example, to use air in a portable hydrogen-purity meter. In such a case, good compensation with a simple bridge requires that wires in the two cells be of different diameters if arranged in series. If they are in parallel they may be of either different diameters or different lengths.

Instruments made to produce the same wire-temperature in different gases are called "unsymmetrical" by Daynes in contrast to "symmetrical" units, in which analyzing and compensating cells are identical. The American tendency to produce interchangeable parts has made the commercial production of bridges unsymmetrical through the use of dissimilar cells decidedly uncommon.

The purpose of an unsymmetrical bridge is sometimes accomplished in a symmetrical bridge, when the gases compared are not too dissimilar, in the following manner as described by Rosecrans (73). In a two-cell bridge, it is determined which of the cell wires is most susceptible to a change of voltage and a manganin resistance is inserted in series sufficient to make the bridge arm change by the same fraction as does the arm containing the other cell. Then the effect on the bridge of a change of ambient temperature is determined, and enough nickel is inserted in series or in parallel with one of the manganin resistances R_1, R_2, to give it a compensating temperature coefficient.

12. POWER SUPPLY TO ANALYTICAL UNITS

Bridges are usually supplied with either constant current or constant voltage. The advantage of sensitivity is with constant current, but

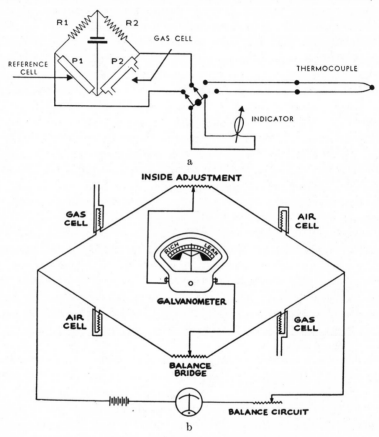

FIG. 3.   Wiring Diagrams.   a. Instrument to measure composition and temperature of flue gas.   b. Exhaust gas analyzer.

there is usually sensitivity to spare, and controls are sometimes simplified by using constant voltage. The means of controlling currents and voltages now available would be a suitable subject for a volume of large size; those described by Daynes and particularly by Palmer and Weaver are rather completely outmoded by developments in electronics, although they can still be used.

Permanent industrial installations are now almost universally designed for connection to 60-cycle power supplies. Transformers reduce the voltage as much as desired. In some cases reliance is placed on the constancy of the power supply, in others, automatic controls are added. Leeds and Northrup uses alternating current and alternating-current galvanometers directly with its bridges for reasons stated in the

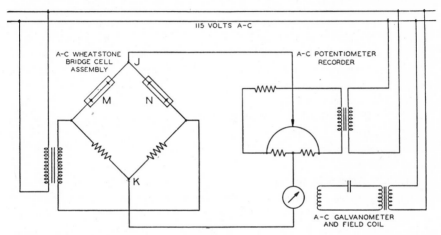

FIG. 4. Wiring diagrams of an industrial instrument with an alternating current bridge.

preceding section. Batteries are still used with many instruments of the portable class, but many of these instruments are also supplied with transformers and rectifiers and designed to plug into the lighting circuit. Instruments of this class are usually supplied with a rheostat to regulate the voltage to the analytical unit; and the voltage itself is measured, during adjustment, by switching the milliameter, with a series resistance, across the leads to the unit.

Figures 3 to 6 show self-explanatory wiring diagrams of several instruments. Figure 3a is the simple arrangement of a portable instrument for measuring the temperature and carbon dioxide content of flue gas. Figure 3b is the typical circuit of a four-cell bridge used as an exhaust-gas tester. Figure 4 is the circuit of a typical industrial instrument using a Leeds and Northrup alternating-current potentiometer.

13. Assembly of Units and Accessories

The two or four cells, if made of metal, are usually in the same metal block to facilitate maintaining them at equal temperatures. Glass or quartz cells are fitted rather closely into heavy metal covers for the same purpose. The block either contains the gas passages or is closely attached to another block which does. Insulation which carries the electrical connections and binding posts of the unit is rigidly attached to the blocks by screwing or molding in place. The entire assemblies of analytical units of the "diffusion" type with four cells are usually not more than 1- or 2-inches across (square or round) and 2- or 3-inches long. The industrial units of Brown, Englehard, and Leeds and Northrup are a little larger. Generally these units are placed, often with other equipment such as aspirators, filters, etc., in somewhat larger metal cases to protect the cells from uneven heating by external drafts or radiation and the wiring from mechanical damage. The cases are often but not always made into air thermostats with electric heating coils, bimetallic controls, and, rarely, circulating fans. For highly accurate work, the laboratory units are usually placed in thermostated and well-stirred oil baths similar to those used for other laboratory work at carefully controlled temperatures.

Sometimes the analytical units, with compensating cells sealed, are simply immersed in the gas to be analyzed; sometimes they are closely attached to the wall of an apparatus or plant unit and allowed to obtain their sample by convection or diffusion only; more frequently, samples are drawn through the units by jet pumps, small electric pumps or, in the portable instruments, by hand-operated rubber "aspirator" bulbs. In laboratory work with limited samples, the cells are evacuated and allowed to fill through suitable connections.

In most industrial installations, the gases to be analyzed are likely to contain dust or smoke which must be removed because their deposition would change the dimensions of the cell. It is almost standard practice to install porous thimbles of Alundum, porcelain, or the like at the intake of the sampling line, renewable pads of asbestos, cellulose, or glass fibers between that and the unit, and sometimes additional filters in the mouths of the cells themselves. It is one of the chief merits of cells of the Shakespear type that cell-mouth filters are provided which are especially effective because finely divided particles that are carried readily by the gentlest flow do not diffuse appreciably and will not penetrate a filter where there is no flow.

Water vapor is an almost universal constituent of industrial gas mixtures, and while it is sometimes to be determined as significant, its amount is more often the result of conditions of little interest to the analyst. Its variations tend to mask those of more important gases and in most cases are to be eliminated if possible. Two ways of doing this are employed with nearly equal frequency. One is to remove the water vapor from the gas with a drying agent; the other is to saturate both the gas to be analyzed and the gas with which it is compared with water at the same temperature. Leeds and Northrup and the Cambridge Instrument Co. prefer saturation for most of the gases produced by the combustion of fuels. Most others prefer to dry the gases. Drying agents depending on chemical action are to be preferred to those, such as silica-gel, which depend on adsorption because the latter retain constituents other than water, enough to retard seriously the purging of the sample line. Sulfuric acid is better than any solid reagent in this respect, but its use is limited because of its corrosive character. The anhydrous salts which can be used in convenient metal containers are therefore the drying agents principally used.

Saturating the gas to be analyzed at a definite temperature provides a standard condition of the gas for the purpose of calibration. If the temperature of saturation changes, so does the standard condition, and the saturation of the compensating gas at the same temperature does not eliminate the error unless the two gases are very much alike and have conductivities on the same side of that of water vapor. If air is being used as the compensator for methane, for example, the change in the compensating gas which accompanies a change in temperature of saturation is in the wrong direction, for additional water increases the conductivity of air and diminishes that of methane.

In the common case of analysis of mixtures of air or atmospheric nitrogen with not more than 20% carbon dioxide, it is beneficial to saturate the air used for comparison, and provisions for saturating the gas in a compensating cell are very common.

14. Characteristics of the Thermal Conductivity Method

It will be apparent from the preceding sections, though it has not been concisely stated, that, with all but single-cell analyzers, readings are obtained which depend on the properties, not of a single gas but of two gases. These have been referred to as the "gas to be analyzed" and the "compensating" or "reference" gases. The measurements made by the instrument may therefore be considered most simply as a *comparison* of two gases. What gases are to be compared and why will be the principal topic of the following sections.

The useful information we obtain from the comparison, which is usually but by no means always expressed in terms of the percentage of one constituent present in a gas mixture, depends in every case on an empirical calibration involving known mixtures or known conditions that we wish to reproduce or avoid.

Since all gases share to some degree the property of conducting heat, the readings have no qualitative significance. If they are to be inter-preted in terms of the compositions of the gases analyzed, we must know in advance the approximate composition of the mixture, qualitatively and quantitatively, and be able substantially to reproduce it at will for the purpose of calibration.

The fact that it is never specific for any one gas and the necessity of empirical calibration are two of the three major limitations of the method. The third is the fact that it gives only one answer at a time so that, in general, we cannot analyze a complex mixture except by combining thermal measurements with partial physical separations or chemical reactions. Complex mixtures offer opportunity for the exercise of the analysts' utmost ingenuity.

The method is of almost unlimited senistivity in the sense that almost any change of composition of gas could readily be made to produce a measurable effect. The limit of practical usefulness is determined by our ability to exclude other effects which would obscure the one in which we are interested. In most cases, uncertainty of chemical composition among constituents other than the one to be determined sets the ultimate limit rather than imperfect control of temperature and voltage or other instrumental difficulties. In some cases, the available sensitivity cannot be used only because there are no means for calibrating with correspond-ing accuracy.

Samples required are small. The industrial cells made by Leeds and Northrup are probably the largest in commercial use and have a volume of about 10 ml. The cells of the Shakespear Katharometer had a volume of about 0.5 ml. and they are understood not to have been changed much by the Cambridge Instrument Co. The cells made by the Davis-Hebler Co. are about half that volume. The cells used by Bolland and Melville (6) had a volume of 0.05 ml. and were used at low pressure with gas measuring only 0.01 ml. at atmospheric pressure. Hurst and Rideal (44) in a study of gases adsorbed by catalysts reported analyses reproducible to 0.04% of a sample of 0.001 ml.

The time required for an analysis varies with the construction of the cell, but depends mainly on the speed of purging. Once the sample is in a cell with a bare wire, practical equilibrium is reached within a second or two. The time required to purge a cell without noticeably affecting the reading depends less on the size of the cell than might be supposed. For example, compare two cells of the same diameter with straight-wire filaments at the same temperature, but one of which is twice as long as the other. Twice as much heat is dissipated in the longer cell, and twice as much can be carried away by the gas stream with approximately the same effect on the mean temperature of the wire. Hence, twice the rate of flow is permissible and the two cells may be swept out in approximately the same time. Another point to be noted is that if flow is constant, or a function only of composition, as it should be in the convection-purged cell, the effect is constant, though unknown, and can be taken care of with the numerous other unknowns by empirical calibration. Most of the commercial cells are purged in practice in about 30 seconds. The large mass of the active element of the Englehard cell adds about an equal lag, and there is some lag in the response of some of the electrical instruments. Generally, the practical lag of an industrial instrument is from $\frac{1}{2}$ to 1 minute plus that involved in the sampling line, filters, etc. If the problem requires it, attention given to speeding the analyses could be expected to cut the time at least in half, but not to change its order of magnitude. When the utmost attainable precision is required a longer time must be allowed for a steady state to be reached if large changes of composition are involved. This is true because the heat produced in the cell quite appreciably affects the temperature and the distribution of temperatures in the massive cell block, especially if it is in still air. With sensitive instruments, we may therefore expect readings to drift slightly for several minutes after a radical change of composition of the gas.

Other outstanding characteristics of the method may be quickly summarized. Its operation is continuous, and if the equipment is protected from mechanical damage or corrosion, practically permanent. Four analytical units installed with a 4-point recorder by the Bureau of Standards in the Navy's sulfuric acid plant at Indian Head, Md., in 1922, were reported still in continuous use in 1937.

The results of analysis are supplied by the analytical unit in the form of electrical energy which can be used with the great variety of readily available electrical instruments for indicating, signalling, recording, or controlling at the place where the analysis is made, or at a distance. The instrument can be made as free from disturbance by mechanical motion as its electrical meter and can be used with success on an automobile, airplane, or ship in motion.

The sample analyzed may be returned to its source unaltered in composition or amount. This fact combined with the continuous character of the analysis makes it especially valuable for following reactions without disturbing them. If desired, a small unit may be directly immersed in the sample.

The fact that the instrument is affected by all changes of composition, which limits its usefulness among complex mixtures, gives it a nearly universal applicability among simple ones including those of inert gases which cannot be analyzed chemically. The parts peculiar to it are simple, compact, rugged, inexpensive, and not too hard to improvise when suitable units are not immediately available from an outside source.

The cost of an analytical installation is determined principally by that of the electrical instruments and machinery used in conjunction with it, and by the cabinets, instrument boards, test stands, etc., which are not essential parts of the analyzer. Many "combination" instruments are made. For example, a favorite one is a carbon dioxide indicator, a thermocouple for measuring flue gas temperatures, and a draft gage, all in a portable case.

An element of first cost that must not be overlooked is that of "development" or adaptation to a particular product or process, including calibration. It is a characteristic of the method that most of the interpretation is done at one time when the character and range of composition of the gas mixtures likely to be encountered are considered in relation to the readings they produce and to their significance in the process or investigation involved. Thereafter, the readings and their interpretation are usually straightforward and require a minimum of time and little or no computation. This fact and the ease of maintenance combine to make the method almost unique among analytical procedures in the small amount of time usually required by trained personnel after the calibration and function of the unit have been established.

The first cost of calibration and interpretation is so large in comparison with the cost of construction that only two or three manufacturers are willing to udnertake special problems or make calibrations to which they are not already accustomed. Instead, they limit their products to stock items of standardized and calibrated equipment for one or a few specific purposes and to supplying interchangeable but uncalibrated units, for the calibration and application of which the purchaser takes all responsibility.

15. Sensitivity

As explained in the preceding section, the instrumental sensitivity is practically unlimited if one wishes to employ amplification with cells of high resistance and large thermal conductance. It will be of interest, however, to note the sensitivity of cells of the types most commonly used. If we start with a balanced bridge with gases of definite compositions in analytical and compensating cells and then change the composition of the gas in the analytical cell by 1% of a certain constituent, the unbalanced voltage produced may be considered to be the sensitivity of the instrument with respect to that gas. Daynes (pp. 109 and 110) shows that a unit made up with two cells of the Bureau of Standards type with 10-ohm wires and with 4 volts across the bridge, a Shakespear Katharometer with a resistance of 31 ohms and also a 4-volt potential across the bridge, and a standard Englehard unit with 12 volts across the bridge, all have about the same sensitivity, 1 mv. for 1% carbon dioxide in air. For the purpose of this discussion, the unbalanced voltage

TABLE II

Relative Deflections Caused by Different Gases When Compared with Air in Instruments of the Katharometer Type

Gas	Per cent of gas	
	100	1.0
Hydrogen	−1.92	−7.19
Argon	+0.98	+0.96
Helium	−1.85	−4.60
Oxygen	−0.035	−0.043
Nitrogen	+0.010	+0.007
Chlorine	—	+2.56
Carbon monoxide	+0.096	+0.10
Carbon Dioxide	+1.00	+1.00
Sulfur dioxide	+2.02	+3.00
Nitrous oxide	+0.98	+0.98
Water vapor		−0.48
Ammonia	+0.023	−0.57
Methane	−0.50	−0.87
Benzene		+1.36
Methyl alcohol		+0.57
Ethyl alcohol		+0.65
Acetone		+1.35
Ethyl ether		+0.94

The deflection produced by carbon dioxide is taken as unity.

produced by carbon dioxide in .any concentration may be considered to be proportional to the concentration.

Daynes, pp. 115–119, also gives data showing relative deflections of various instruments with hydrogen and with various other gases in air. From these data, Table II has been made up. It shows deflections produced by 1.0 and by 100% of each of the gases in terms of the deflection produced by the same percentage of carbon dioxide, which is taken as unity. These relative values were all obtained with Katharometers and will not be the same for different analyzers, in part, at least, because they are so dependent on wire temperatures. A unit used at low voltage with a sensitive galvanometer will not give the same relative readings as when used at high voltage with a less sensitive meter, for example.

Within the usual range of operation of commercial instruments, sensitivity is roughly proportional to the square of the applied voltage. One method of increasing sensitivity at will is therefore to increase the applied voltage. This method increases the chance of chemical reaction, especially with bare platinum wires, and may shorten the life of the instrument, however.

16. Adjustment and Calibration of the Instrument

In a great majority of the applications of the method, the gas mixtures of interest to the analyst are of limited range, and analyses of the greatest accuracy are desired only in the neighborhood of a particular composition. In adjusting carburetors of internal combustion engines, for example, a carbon dioxide content of about 14% in the exhaust gas is usually desired. If less than 10% is present, it is enough to know the fact. In this case, 10–15% would be a suitable range for the instrument scale, with 14% being the point at which the reading should be most accurate. A suitable range for the gases used in ammonia synthesis would be 70–80% hydrogen with the greatest accuracy at about 74%. For a gas required by specification to be 99.6% pure, a scale from 99 to 100% with an optimum at 99.6 is desirable. Usually, the range of interest is narrow enough to permit the analysis to be considered a linear function of the readings and only two points need be used for calibration. If the function is not linear, it may be nearly enough so for practical purposes if one calibrating mixture is chosen.

Both in the initial calibration and for the purpose of subsequent checking, the use of a "pure" gas, particularly air, as one of the calibrating "mixtures" is desirable because of the ease of reproducing the condition. For that reason, some accuracy of scale readings is often sacrificed by extending the range to cover a convenient calibrating point. Frequently, the calibrating gas is not one of the series of mixtures under analysis. Taking exhaust gas again as an example, it contains enough hydrogen to make its conductivity equal to that of air when the carbon dioxide content is about 11.3%. If the analysis is made in terms of carbon dioxide by a comparison with a standard gas, which in this case would certainly be air, the adjustment of range and the calibration of an unbalanced bridge and meter could be conveniently made as follows: The indicating instrument is graduated to read 10–15% of carbon dioxide. With a voltage across the bridge found by approximate trial to be a little greater than necessary to produce the required sensitivity, and with air in both analyzing and compensating cells, any zero adjustment needed in the ratio arms of the bridge to produce a balance is made. The analyzing cells are then connected to the exhaust of an engine and the carburetor adjusted until the previous reading of the bridge is exactly duplicated. The exhaust gas is analyzed, and with open circuit the zero of the indicator is mechanically adjusted to the percentage of carbon dioxide found. This point should be marked on the scale for future use in checking the zero adjustment. The carburetion is now changed to approximate the optimum, and the exhaust gas again analyzed. A resistance is now inserted in series with the indicating instrument such that the scale reading is equal to the percentage of carbon dioxide found. If a series of instruments is to be calibrated, a stock mixture of carbon dioxide and air with a conductivity approximately equal to that of the exhaust gas should be accurately matched with an analyzed exhaust gas and used in its stead for calibrating and adjusting other instruments.

The example given is about as complicated a one as is normally encountered. Usually, calibrations are simply made with mixtures the compositions of which are determined either by analysis or by making them up with measured quantities of the constituents.

Balanced bridges are a little more complicated to adjust to produce definite ranges and direct readings. The methods employed are described in T.P. 249 pp. 93–100 (66) and Daynes pp. 74–78, which should be consulted if the solution to a problem of this kind is not apparent.

In the case of instruments calibrated for mixtures of certain gases but used with mixtures of others of somewhat different composition, it is often desirable to avoid or minimize the labor of a new calibration. A common case of this is in the analysis of mixtures of air with a fuel gas or of one fuel gas with another. Ordinarily, the fuel gases change composition and conductivity more or less continuously, but not over wide ranges. A method of interpolation which is a modification of the graphic method of Dühring, is very convenient in such cases. Its application is shown by Fig. 5, which illustrates the general case of use of a calibration curve for mixtures of two gases A and B to determine, with the aid of two points, the complete calibration curve of two other gases C and D.

In the figure, the curve marked A + B is an ordinary calibration curve of compositions (abscissas) and corresponding scale readings (ordinates). A line drawn through the origin at an angle of 45° is called the "transfer line." Two mixtures of C and D of known composition, or more conveniently, the unmixed constituents, are plotted on the same scale but with compositions plotted as ordinates and scale readings as abscissas. From one point, W, representing one of these mixtures, lines are drawn vertically and horizontally. The vertical line intersects the transfer line at Z; from Z a line is drawn horizontally to intersect curve

A-B at Y, and from Y a line is drawn vertically to X, where it intersects the horizontal line from W. From the other calibration point, W′, another rectangle is constructed in the same way to locate point X′. Through X and X′ a straight line, called the Dühring line, is drawn. Any number of rectangles may now be constructed beginning with points

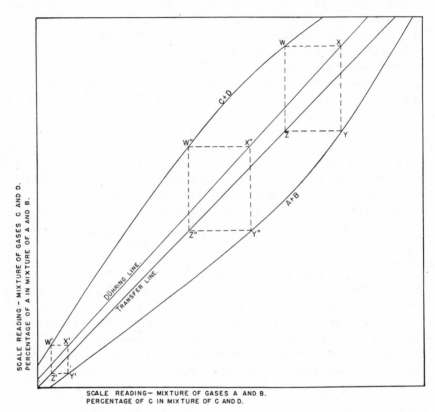

FIG. 5.   Construction of a calibration curve for one gas or instrument from that for another by a construction analagous to Dühring's rule.

such as X″ on the Dühring line and leading to points such as W″ on the calibration curve for C + D.

The same method may be applied to constructing a calibration for a second instrument, differing only slightly from one for which a calibration curve already exists. In this case, the compositions of mixtures of the same gas are plotted as both abscissas and ordinates with respect to the readings of one or the other of two instruments. As a matter of fact, the construction could be expected to apply to the case of different mixtures with different instruments, provided the differences were not too great.

Without attempting a demonstration, it may .be explained that this method will be exact if the following relation holds when we start from the same scale reading with both instruments:

$$\frac{Ra}{Rc} = K + k\Delta$$

in which Ra is the change of scale reading corresponding to a change of $\Delta\%$ gas A in the mixture in one instrument, Rc is the change of scale reading corresponding to the same change, Δ, in the percentage of gas C in the mixture in the second instrument, and K and k have any constant values.

The method does not apply to cases in which different instruments are to be adjusted to make certain percentages of the same or different gases fit the same scale-range by the method described above for calibrating an exhaust gas tester. For such a case, the graphical method shown in Fig. 6 may be useful. It depends on the simple assumption that the deviations from a straight-line calibration with different instruments or different gases are in the same ratio in all parts of the scale. Again, a calibration curve, A + B is drawn for mixtures of gas A and gas B, and a straight line L is drawn to connect its ends. This would be the calibration curve if the relation between composition and scale reading were linear. It is now necessary to determine by actual test one point on curve C + D, preferably near its middle. From that point, P, a perpendicular is drawn to L and from its base at O a distance equal to OP is laid off along line L, and the triangle OTS is completed. Similar triangles are constructed at other points, the lengths found along L are laid off perpendicular to L, and the calibration curve C + O for gas C in D is drawn.

Neither of the above methods can be relied on to give exact calibrations because the assumptions involved are only approximate as applied to real instruments, but both will usually give good approximations. Whether they are good enough for his purpose the investigator should determine in each particular case. The writer and his associates have found the first method entirely satisfactory for analyzing mixtures of air and carbureted water gas by the use of a calibration based on carbureted water gas of somewhat different composition, but not good enough to predict the calibration curve of mixtures of air and natural-gas from a curve for water gas. The second method would be the choice in such a problem as predicting the calibration curve of mixtures containing deuterium from corresponding mixtures of hydrogen.

A method of adjusting an instrument using an unbalanced bridge to accomplish roughly the purpose of these charts was described by Rosecrans (73). It consists in adjusting the bridge arms to produce balance with gas of the same composition as that with which the calibrated bridge is balanced, and then adjusting the resistance in series with the meter

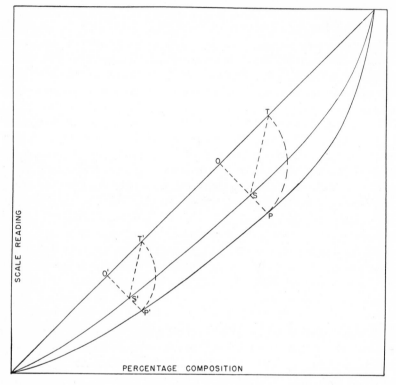

Fig. 6.   Construction of a calibration curve for one gas from that for another based on the assumption that the deviations of the curves from a straight line are everywhere proportional.

to give the same reading as the calibrated instrument with another gas. The same method can be applied to a balanced bridge, a variable shunt on the slide-wire replacing the variable resistance in series with the meter.

Adjusting the bridges by these means makes them direct reading and therefore more convenient to use than with the aid of calibration curves constructed by the graphical methods described. The electrical recalibration is considerably less accurate than the graphic one, however, unless the calibration curves are nearly straight.

The Cambridge Instrument Co. has announced the application of automatic electrical means for correcting an analysis for variation in the conductivity of one of the constituents, but details are lacking.

17. METHODS OF ANALYZING COMPLEX MIXTURES

Attention has already been called to the essential nature of the thermal-conductivity method as a comparison of two gases. Section 17 will deal with the question of what gases to compare to obtain useful results, particularly in the case of complex mixtures. The available procedures are described in T.P. 249, pp. 47–55 (66), and by Daynes, pp. 182–196. Those descriptions are still substantially complete, and there is not much need to depart from the classifications there given, which are nearly the same.

17.1. Method 1: Comparison With a Standard Gas

The simplest method of application of the thermal-conductivity instrument is the comparison of the gas to be analyzed with a gas of constant composition called a "standard" gas. The method is applicable to the following classes of gas mixtures:

a. *Mixtures containing only two components.* Examples that may be given are oxygen in electrolytic hydrogen, nitrogen in helium in the later stages of its separation from natural gas.

b. *Mixtures of two gases, one or both of which are mixtures in which the proportions of the various constituents are known to be constant.* Air is, of course, the most common of mixtures, and, when dry, fresh outdoor air is so constant in composition that only the most refined methods of analysis show any variation. The same is true of atmospheric nitrogen, the residue after oxygen, water, and carbon dioxide have been removed from air. An important example of analysis of this class is the determination of the ratio of hydrogen to atmospheric nitrogen in the gases entering the synthetic ammonia process.

c. *Mixtures in which it is known that the constituent of interest has a conductivity widely different from the conductivities of the other constituents, all of which have nearly the same conductivity.* Examples are the determination of hydrogen in an uncarbureted water gas from which steam and carbon dioxide have been removed. The other important constituents, nitrogen and carbon monoxide, have nearly the same conductivity, and a change in their proportions has almost no effect on the determination of hydrogen. Another example is the lifting power of balloon gas which can be determined with fair accuracy even when helium has been mixed with some hydrogen and contaminated with atmospheric gases. Hydrogen adds to the conductivity of helium in nearly the same

proportion that it increases its lifting power, and the probable contaminants, oxygen, nitrogen, and water vapor, are enough alike in conductivity to be classed together for approximate purposes such as determining when repurification should be undertaken.

d. *The proportions of other constituents of the mixture are related
in a predetermined manner to the quantity of the constituent being determined.*
This includes cases of equilibrium, of which automobile exhaust gas is
one of the most important.   The hydrogen, carbon monoxide, and carbon
dioxide in the gas occur in fairly definite relation, so that an empirical
calibration of the percentage of any one of the three could be made from
a comparison of the exhaust gas with air.   Another important case, in
which equilibrium is not involved, is that of sulfur dioxide from a sulfur
burner when mixed with excess air.   The sum of sulfur dioxide and
oxygen is a constant in this case, and a determination of sulfur dioxide
would be practicable even if oxygen and nitrogen differed widely in
conductivity.   Actually, they are nearly enough together to bring the
case under Method 1c also.

e. *Effect of an interfering substance is known from some external
condition.*   Daynes mentions as examples gases containing saturated
vapors and the accumulation of argon in the gases used in the synthesis
of liquid ammonia which are recirculated after partial reaction.   In
the first case, the amount of vapor can be learned from the temperature;
in the second, the argon can be calculated from the relation between
the amount of atmospheric nitrogen which has entered the system and
the amount of ammonia which has been produced.   In both cases, corrections can be made by a series of calibration curves.

f. *The compositions of the gases are not known and remain undetermined,
but practical use is made of a knowledge of changes that take place in them.*
The possibility of utilizing changes of composition of gases for process
control without knowledge of the actual compositions involved may
again be illustrated by carburetor adjustment.   Actually, the relation
between the compositions of exhaust gases and the conditions of operation
of engines was determined long before an attempt was made to apply
observations of thermal conductivity to the problem.   It was determined empirically what percentage of carbon dioxide in the exhaust gas
corresponded to a certain air-fuel ratio, to the production of maximum
power, etc.   When, later, definite readings of an instrument were found
to correspond to definite percentages of carbon dioxide, those readings
could be interpreted as indications of the conditions of adjustment; but
had the thermal conductivity instrument been used before exhaust
gases were studied by other methods, the relation between instrument
reading and carburetor adjustment could presumably have been estab-

lished as accurately and more directly than it is now. Thermal conductivity instruments are finding numerous and rapidly increasing applications in which the intermediate step of gas analyses has been omitted and instrument readings are applied immediately to judging the stage or results of a process in which the gas mixtures, if not too complicated for analysis, at least have not been analyzed.

Before leaving Method 1, something should be said about the standard gas. It is a great advantage to use air for this purpose, because leakage into the compensating cell will not change the contents, and the cell can be so easily swept out in case a change is suspected. When other gases are used in the standard cell to produce better compensation, they are usually sealed in glass or quartz. Alternatively, in a few cases, cylinders of gas such as hydrogen or carbon dioxide have been used to supply the compensator at a very small rate of flow; and in the synthetic ammonia process gases generated electrolytically have been used for the same purpose. The electrolysis of a solution of sodium hydroxide produces pure hydrogen and pure oxygen in the exactly equivalent ratio. Either may be used as a standard gas or they may be mixed in the 2:1 ratio. This is a fairly good compensator for the 3:1 mixture of hydrogen and nitrogen in the synthesis, which usually contains some inert argon and methane. Since the amount of gas required for replacing leakage is extremely small, the electrolytic cell may be made as tiny and designed to take as little current as is convenient.

17.2. Method 2: Comparison Before and After Treatment, Usually a Chemical Reaction Which Removes or Modifies the Constituent to Be Determined

a. *A constituent is removed by absorption.* The determination of a constituent by comparing mixtures from which it has and has not been removed has a wide applicability. Probably its greatest field of usefulness is that of determining carbon dioxide in gases, from furnaces, boiler plants, etc., which contain enough hydrogen to make the simple application of Method 1 inaccurate. The conductivity of the residue after the absorption has some effect on the differential readings obtained, but this effect is of a lower order of magnitude than that produced in Method 1. When the range of conductivity of the residue is too great, it can be compared, after the absorption, with a standard gas and a correction made by the use of a series of calibration curves or by electrical readjustment or compensation as described in the preceding section.

It is convenient in this case and others which follow to speak of comparing gases before and after an absorption or other treatment. Actually, it is best to use a divided stream, one part of which is treated while the other is not. Volumes and rates of flow in the two passages should be adjusted so that equal times elapse after the stream is divided before the portions reach their cells. If a single stream passes through the two in sequence, a change in the composition of the insoluble gas affects first one cell, then the other, confusing the record, which is intended only to indicate changes of the soluble constituent.

In some cases more than one constituent can be removed in succession and comparisons made "before and after" the removal of each. For example, sulfur dioxide and carbon dioxide are easily measured in the same gas by oxidizing the first with an acid solution of permanganate and absorbing the second with an alkali.

b. *One or more gases are removed by condensation or adsorption.* For example, water vapor can be removed practically completely by exposure to the temperature of solid carbon dioxide, or brought to a constant value at the freezing point. By fractional distillation at a series of rising temperatures or by differential adsorption on activated carbon, successive fractions of a hydrocarbon mixture may be removed. In the laboratory, the condensates, which are usually somewhat impure, can be vaporized and treated as binary mixtures according to Method 1, if desired. The Burrell Technical Supply Co. is manufacturing an "adsorption fractionator" in which this has been successfully accomplished.

c. *A chemical reaction is produced between constituents of the gas.* Usually the reaction is produced merely by heating with or without a catalyst. But copper oxide (or copper which has resulted from the reduction of the oxide) is excellent for application in an atmosphere that is either continuously reducing or continuously oxidizing. The method is particularly good for determining oxygen in hydrogen or hydrogen in air. It was used extensively for several years in gas appliance laboratories for determining "products of incomplete combustion." In this application, the combustible gases are carbon monoxide and hydrogen which occur in a nearly constant ratio of about 3:1. The carbon monoxide is burned to dioxide and the hydrogen to water. Both reactions result in a decrease of conductivity. Although the major part of the effect was produced by hydrogen, the instrument was usually given an empirical calibration in terms of carbon monoxide, by comparison with an iodine-pentoxide apparatus. Carbon monoxide can be determined alone by comparing the mixtures before and after passing over Hopcalite at room temperature, which does not oxidize hydrogen.

d. *A combination of c and a.* Organic vapors in air are being successfully measured by passing through a combustion furnace and comparing the resulting mixture with the residue after passing through a carbon-dioxide absorber. For heavy hydrocarbons, at least, the method is more sensitive than simple comparison of the vapor mixture with a standard, and it has the advantage of reducing the calibrations for all compounds to that already established for carbon dioxide.

17.3. Method 3: Treatment Before Analysis by Methods 1 or 2 to Make Them Applicable

a. *A disturbing constituent is removed.* Water vapor is a disturbing constituent in a great many analyses and may be removed by a drying agent. In the determination of oxygen in oxygen therapy and studies of metabolism, both water vapor and carbon dioxide are removed before the analysis. Sometimes a vapor may be condensed.

b. *The gas is saturated with a vapor.* As an alternative to drying a gas, we may bring it to a known condition for comparison by saturating it. The method is particularly applicable when there is no easy method of removing a vapor without disturbing other constituents detrimentally.

c. *"Double combustion" with the aid of electrolytic gas.* Enough oxygen is added to a gas to combine with all the combustible constituents present, and the mixture is passed through a combustion tube and a carbon dioxide absorber. The hydrogen from the same electrolytic cell is then added and the gas passed through a second combustion tube. Since the electrolytic hydrogen and oxygen are produced in equivalent quantities, the oxygen entering the second combustion tube is insufficient to burn the hydrogen by just the amount that reacted in the first tube. Hence, the final mixture contains hydrogen just equivalent to all the combustible constituents of the original mixture minus the oxygen, if any, initially present. If, as is usually the case, the final gas contains only hydrogen and atmospheric nitrogen, a comparison of the final mixture with air gives directly and with high sensitivity the amount of oxygen it would have been necessary to add to the original gas to produce theoretically complete combustion. In many cases the original gas, compared with a standard will show the hydrogen initially present with considerable accuracy (Method 1c). If in a second stream oxygen is absorbed before the double combustion, the mixture after it can be compared with that from the parallel process to give the oxygen initially present, and with a standard gas to give the oxygen equivalent of all the combustible gas.

By differentiating carbon monoxide with the aid of Hopcalite or methane by partial combustion over copper oxide and by making absorptions of various constituents in the customary reagents, it is theoretically possible with the aid of double combustion to make continuous analyses of all ordinary fuel gases and their products of partial and complete combustion with the same completeness, if not the same reliability, as by ordinary volumetric methods. Actually, the method is somewhat cumbersome and if the timing of flow in the various stages is not right, the records are difficult to interpret. For these reasons, while the method has been reported to be in industrial use, it is not employed frequently.

d. *Addition in constant proportion of another gas.* By permitting two gases to flow through capillary tubes under the same pressure to a point of mixing, they can be mixed in a ratio that, if not a constant, is at least a function of their composition. The same initial pressure can be assured by permitting both gases to flow to waste through a common outlet and supplying them in somewhat greater quantity than will flow through the capillaries. The very simple device required is illustrated in T. P. 249 p. 50 (66), and Daynes p. 179.

In this way, a gas to be analyzed is mixed with a pure gas, usually either hydrogen or oxygen, the purpose of which is (1) to act as a reagent, (2) to modify the conductivity of the·mixture so that the effect of removing one constituent will be accentuated, or (3) a combination of both (1) and (2).

The purpose for which mixing by the capillary device is now principally used is the addition of oxygen to gases formed during combustion with insufficient air to complete the reaction. Usually carbon dioxide is determined, then the mixture with added oxygen is passed through a combustion tube, and the carbon dioxide formed in there is measured (by Methods 1c or 2a).

When oxygen is to be determined in mixture with nitrogen, hydrogen may be added by capillary mixing, producing a gas of such high conductivity that the sensitivity to oxygen removal by absorption in pyrogallate is increased several fold. Or the added hydrogen may be used to burn out the oxygen in a combustion tube.

When oxygen is removed by absorption, the added hydrogen can be adjusted to produce a maximum effect. This is important, not because greater sensitivity is usually needed, but because at the maximum the measurement is insensitive to small changes in the quantity of the added hydrogen.

18. Present Status and Applications of the Method

In this section, an attempt will be made to give a comprehensive review of the extent to which the various procedures are used. Unfortunately, the information available for this purpose is very incomplete.

It is estimated that the total number of analytical instruments that have been made exceeds 100,000. It may be twice that number. The greatest number in any easily classified group is certainly that of exhaust gas analyzers which may be as much as half the total. These are nearly all simple and not very sensitive indicating instruments of the class that has been called portable. Quite commonly, they are mounted with numerous other devices on "test stands." Also numerous, simple, and more portable are instruments intended for use in the adjustment of burners and drafts of house heating systems, particularly those with oil burners. Usually, instruments in both these groups involve only the comparison of the gas produced by combustion, after the removal of water vapor, with air as a standard gas; but there are differences in their calibration and interpretation. The exhaust-gas analyzers may be graduated in per cent of carbon dioxide, in air-fuel ratio, or in "per cent completeness of combustion" and most of them indicate a range or point of "best" adjustment. The indications of the instrument depend largely on hydrogen as well as on carbon dioxide (60); hence the same reading will actually correspond to different percentages of that gas.

The ratio of hydrogen to carbon dioxide in the exhaust gas is affected to some extent by the composition of the original fuel (5). Minter (61) has demonstrated that by comparing the exhaust gas (1) with air and (2) with the residue after the removal of carbon dioxide, not only can the carbon dioxide in the gas be determined with much greater certainty, but the ratio of carbon to hydrogen in the initial fuel can be determined at the same time. Indeed, Minter's observations show that the two comparisons provide so easy, rapid, and accurate a method for analyzing fuels that it is probably not in extensive use only because few people have enough occasion to make the determination to justify keeping a gas engine as part of the analytical equipment for the purpose. Instead of using the dual set of observations to measure carbon dioxide in the exhaust and hydrogen in the fuel, they could have been used, with different calibrations, to measure the percentage of the maximum power developed and the hydrogen in the exhaust gas. So much space has been devoted to this case only because it suggests that valuable information may frequently be obtained by making two or more measurements as related tests even though they may not be interpretable in terms of percentages of known constituents.

Air-fuel ratio is sometimes obtained by a comparison of the conductivity of the mixture of fuel with air entering the cylinders. Diesel, jet, and rocket motors, on all of which exhaust gas analyzers have been used, present somewhat different conditions from gasoline engines; they at least require different interpretations of the optimum operating ranges in terms of instrument readings.

The analysis of flue gases in boiler plants as an aid to efficient combustion was probably the first application of analysis by thermal conductivity to reach major importance, but its later development has been disappointing. The explanation offered for this is that the presence of hydrogen and the nonuniformity of the gas mixture produced in burning coal make the simple comparison of the flue gas with air as a standard, or even the comparison of the gas before and after the absorption of carbon dioxide, a none too reliable guide to the condition of the fire. The deficiency can be met by the determination of oxygen and one or more of the unburned gases, hydrogen, carbon monoxide, and methane; but the making of several analyses in this way leads to complicated equipment that requires fairly skilled maintenance, and the practical use of the results may not be apparent. One of the chief reasons for the popularity of the method in its simpler forms is the fact that little skilled attention is needed. We find comparatively few simple instruments of the portable class in use in boiler control, and a much higher proportion of elaborate installations of the industrial type than in most other applications. Recording of the results is general, and there is some application of automatic control, but the extent of it is disappointing in comparison with the use of "combustion controls" of other types.

In a large majority of flue gas analyses, only the determination of carbon dioxide is undertaken. The methods used are fairly evenly divided between simple comparison of the flue gas with air and comparison before and after absorption. The trend is believed to be toward the latter method. The complication introduced by water vapor is dealt with about equally frequently by the method of drying both gases and that of saturating both gases, with the trend toward the latter. The reason for the trend to saturation is not to obtain a better analysis, but to avoid the inconvenience, interruption, and possibly the cost of frequently renewing the drying agent. Probably the dry gases would give the more accurate result, at least with a gas of stable composition.

Oxygen is the second most frequently determined constituent of flue gases. The methods employed industrially have been: a) to pass the gas remaining after absorbing carbon dioxide over carbon at a temperature of about 700°C., and to compare the resulting gas before and after absorbing the carbon dioxide produced; b) to mix the gas with all the hydrogen produced by an electrolytic cell and to compare the mixture before and after passing through a combustion furnace; c) to add hydrogen by capillary mixing, as described in the preceding section and to proceed as in b; d) to add the hydrogen by capillary mixing and to compare the mixture before and after absorbing the oxygen with a potassium pyrogallate solution. Method c seems to be the one principally used at present.

Oxygen in flue gas is usually in excess of the amount required to combine with all the reducing gas present. Hence, after the removal of carbon dioxide, carbon monoxide or all the reducing gases together are burned by passing through a combustion tube containing Hopcalite or copper oxide. Hopcalite at room temperature oxidizes only carbon monoxide; copper oxide at about 175°C. oxidizes that gas and hydrogen; at 700°C. it oxidizes all combustible gases present. In some cases, the carbon dioxide is absorbed and the gases compared before and after the absorption; but probably more often the combustible gases are all determined together simply by comparing before and after passing through the combustion tube. The indication may be designated either "combustible gas" or "carbon monoxide," which is the most abundant of the reducing gases, although most of the change of conductivity results from the burning of hydrogen. One manufacturer considers a difference of conductivity equal to that produced by 2% carbon dioxide in atmospheric nitrogen to represent 1% combustible gas. When a differentiation is made between the various reducing gases, it is usually done by comparing the gas after absorbing carbon dioxide with a standard and attributing the difference to hydrogen, burning some of the mixture over copper oxide at low temperature and attributing to carbon monoxide the difference before and after absorbing carbon dioxide, and finally burning the residue from this at high temperature and attributing the change of conductivity to methane. When gases are not expected to contain enough oxygen for complete combustion, oxygen is sometimes added by electrolysis, but more often the process of capillary mixing is used to add a little air. The powerful method of double combustion is seldom used because the timing is considered too troublesome. The Cambridge Instrument Co. has exhibited and advertises an instrument for the simultaneous recording of carbon dioxide, carbon monoxide, oxygen, hydrogen, and methane.

Products of combustion from kilns and furnaces are analyzed almost if not quite as frequently as those from boiler plants and by the same methods. They differ from the latter in the ranges of variation and the relation between various constituents. The carbonates decomposed in cement kilns affect the carbon dioxide to such an extent that oxygen and reducing gases are principally used to judge the conditions of combustion. Three ranges of carbon dioxide indication are desired in the firing of ceramic kilns, depending on the desired temperatures and the decomposition of materials at various stages of the process. A carbon dioxide indicator has been found useful in controlling lime kilns.

The maintenance of furnace atmospheres to produce desired conditions for bright annealing, nitriding, carburizing, and the safe melting of such metals as magnesium, employs large numbers of analyzers, and each type of furnace requires somewhat different conditions to produce the best results. Many instruments in this field are not calibrated in terms

of gas compositions at all, but adjustments of the furnace atmosphere are
made until the best results are obtained and the reading of the instrument
is noted. Subsequently, the same reading is maintained as well as possible until a change of fuel or some other condition makes necessary the
selection of another optimum. In furnace atmospheres, oxygen is likely
to be entirely absent, but carbon dioxide and water vapor act as oxidizing
agents if the reducing gases, carbon monoxide and hydrogen, are not
present in sufficient quantity. The relation between these four active
constituents of the furnace atmosphere is usually determined by the
water-gas equilibrium. This equilibrium changes with temperature.
Hence the simple comparison of the furnace atmosphere with a standard
gas can be expected to give reliable information only when the composition of the gas, the air introduced, and the temperature are all constant.
Two measurements, such as a comparison before and after removing
carbon dioxide followed by a comparison between the residue and a
standard, should give a much more positive and useful knowledge of
conditions. These measurements correspond nearly to determining
carbon dioxide and hydrogen. A third measurement made by burning
the residue after the removal of carbon dioxide and comparing the
resulting mixture before and after again absorbing carbon dioxide, will
complete the picture.

Thermal conductivity can be used for the complete analysis of blast
furnace gas, producer gas, and uncarbureted water gas; but the complete
apparatus is complex and few of the instruments in use are designed to
make more than one or two comparisons. Comparing the gas, untreated
except by filtering and drying, with a standard, gives a result that is
nearly a measure of the hydrogen content in the water gas, less so in the
producer gas, and still less so in the blast furnace gas, which contains a
large amount of carbon dioxide from the decomposition of carbonates.
Where a single comparison of this sort is used it is probably as an index
of departure from a composition of gas predetermined to represent
optimum conditions. Since the gases may vary in several ways, a change
from the prescribed conductivity must be interpreted from experience.
As in the case of furnace atmospheres, the simultaneous variation of
carbon dioxide and hydrogen, which are both easy to measure approximately in these gases, should give a much better basis for the expert's
diagnosis. Both single and multiple unit analyzers are known to be in
use with all these gases, but the number employed is small in comparison
with the number of plants. Whether the use of the instruments is to be
considered unsuccessful or merely experimental in this field, is not yet
apparent.

The application of the method to blast-furnace practice is not limited to the blast furnace gas. The air supplied to blast furnaces is frequently enriched with oxygen, and thermal-conductivity units are used to determine the extent of the enrichment. The measurement is usually a straight comparison of the enriched mixture with the unmixed air. Before using, blast furnace gas is frequently enriched with butane or other fuel gases, and thermal conductivity is used to indicate the proportions added. It has also been used to control the mixture of the blast furnace gas with air delivered to engines or burners and to analyze the products of combustion afterward.

Hardly any use of the method appears to have been made by the "manufactured gas" industry, for either coal gas or carbureted water gas, probably because of the complexity of the mixtures involved. In a few cases, instruments have been used to follow the proportions of fuel gases in a mixture, but this is usually done with the much more expensive recording calorimeter. The instrument has also been used, at least experimentally, to indicate the amount of hydrogen in gas as an index of flame properties; that is, the tendency of flames to blow from or flash back into burners. It has been used to some extent for determining the ratio of gas and primary air delivered to industrial burners and for the detection of leakage; but apparently the latter use has been much more common in Europe than in America. This is a simple application for which the method is well suited.

The method has numerous applications in the manufacture of synthetic ammonia (9). The proportioning of hydrogen and nitrogen in the mixture going to the converters, the determination of ammonia produced and later condensed or absorbed, and the accumulation of argon in the recirculated gases are followed, or automatically controlled, by thermal conductivity, probably in every plant. Hydrogen in the gas to be converted can be determined with enough accuracy by the simple comparison with a standard, which is conveniently the mixture of oxygen and hydrogen from an electrolytic cell. The ammonia can be determined accurately because of the high and nearly constant hydrogen content of the mixture by comparing the gas before and after its absorption in an acid. Argon is determined by burning out the hydrogen over copper oxide and comparing the residual gas with air. Oxygen must be added intermittently or continuously to keep the copper oxidized, and this is the only troublesome part of the process. Methane can be determined, if desired, from the carbon dioxide produced during the combustion in the argon analysis, or it may be measured with great accuracy by the "double combustion" method in which it appears as four times its volume of hydrogen, the original hydrogen being unaffected.

In the fixed nitrogen industry, thermal conductivity is also used in proportioning the air or oxygen in mixture with ammonia being oxidized to nitric acid, and in following the purity of the nitrogen used in the cyanamide process.

The determination of sulfur dioxide in the sulfuric acid industry is one of the most successful applications. Normally, in the now prevalent contact process for manufacturing sulfuric acid, sulfur dioxide is determined by comparison, with air as a standard, in the gas from the sulfur burners, again in the mixture of this gas with air going to the converters, and a third time in the gas coming from the converters to show the completeness of that reaction. Automatic control is frequently employed in this field. The method is also used in the lead chamber process, in the manufacture of lead pigments, and in the roasting of sulfide ores; but details are lacking.

Sulfur dioxide has many applications in the bleaching and cellulose industries and is used in large quantity in sugar manufacture. Analyzers have been supplied for all these applications, but how extensive their use has become is not known. An interesting application is to portable sulfur dioxide generators mounted on trucks, which travel from place to place for bleaching fruit.

In the compressed gas industries, the method has a large variety of applications. It is used for measuring concentrations and recovery of carbon dioxide in the manufacture of dry ice from products of combustion, for determining the purity of carbon dioxide produced by fermentation processes, and for following both the production and utilization of carbon dioxide in sugar factories. It is used in all stages of the production and utilization of helium, for which, in the absence of hydrogen, it is almost specific. It appears to have been used in the liquid-air industry in Europe much more generally than in this country. According to Daynes, pp. 241–7, substantially all stages of the fractionation of liquid air can be followed by comparing the gases with air as a standard as though only binary mixtures were dealt with, because the relative amounts of oxygen and argon in nitrogen, of nitrogen and argon in oxygen, and of oxygen and nitrogen in argon, change according to fixed rules, as each of the main constituents approaches purity. The impurity in nearly pure oxygen is mainly argon, which gives enough sensitivity for practical purposes. The impurity in nitrogen is mainly oxygen, which can be determined by the same methods applied for measuring oxygen in flue gases if greater sensitivity than is given by comparing with a standard gas is required. The impurity in argon is principally oxygen. In the preparation of pure argon, oxygen is burned out with hydrogen and cleaned up with hot copper. The control of the hydrogen used is a job for thermal conductivity. Helium and neon are collected together, and their proportions and subsequent purification are followed by comparing with a standard. At least one instrument has been made for determining nitrogen in krypton after the removal of oxygen by combustion.

In the electrolytic industries, the methods employed are so simple as to be obvious. Usually, the gases dealt with are nearly pure and the impurity is likely to be a known single substance. There are hydrogen in oxygen, oxygen in hydrogen, hydrogen in chlorine, hydrogen in hydrogen chloride, chlorine in hydrogen chloride, water vapor in chlorine, air in chlorine, chlorine in air, and hydrogen chloride in air, for all of which instruments have been made. If more complex mixtures are expected, such as air and another gas occurring together as impurities, the common methods of combustion and absorption are available. Hydrogen will burn in chlorine as well as in oxygen, and chlorine can be absorbed in either a strong alkali or a reducing solution.

One of the most extensive applications of the method is to the detection and recovery of volatile solvents in the plastics industries, including rubber and photographic materials. High concentrations of vapors up to 100% occur in treating and drying rooms with the more volatile solvents, and a few instruments have been made for use in this range. More commonly the analyses are applied only to determining the completeness of recovery of solvents, for testing the completeness of "drying" of paints and plastics by testing the atmospheres in which they are stored, and for detecting dangerous contamination of the atmospheres of work rooms. Two methods are commonly employed, simple comparison with uncontaminated air as a standard, and a combustion and subsequent determination of carbon dioxide. The first has the advantage of simplicity; the second is more sensitive, particularly for the heavier molecules, and easier to calibrate. Among the solvents for which analyzers have been made are methyl, ethyl, and amyl alcohols, gasoline, benzene, toluene, and xylene, acetone, ethyl acetate, ethyl ether, methyl and ethyl chlorides, ethylene dichloride, carbon tetrachloride, chloroform, and carbon disulfide. The atmospheres in which the solvents are determined are not necessarily air. In a varnish plant, the atmosphere above the solvent is nitrogen which is analyzed for oxygen; in a factory making rubber goods, the atmosphere is producer gas and the solvent benzene. A protective atmosphere of carbon dioxide above a flammable liquid used in dry cleaning is assured by an indicator.

The maintenance of concentrations of various materials in atmospheres, and their detection where not wanted, is another large field of application. It includes naphthalene, hydrogen cyanide, acetylene, propane, butane, and pentane in industrial atmospheres, and the control of hydrogen cyanide in fumigation and of carbon dioxide and ethylene when used for the preservation or ripening of fruits, flowers, vegetables, and coffee during transporation and storage. One instrument has been made to record ethylene in air over the range 0-200 p.p.m. Analyzers have been made for freon in air and for impurities in freon vapor. The detection of natural gas in air has been employed to a considerable extent in experimental work, but does not appear to have been extended to the important problem of mine gases. The margin between the conductivity of methane and air is not sufficient, in the presence of variable amounts of other gases, including ethane and carbon dioxide, to make reliable a simple comparison of the atmosphere with a standard. While a combustion method can be combined with thermal conductivity to give a reliable determination of mine gases, the equipment is not easily made sufficiently portable and nearly enough automatic for mine use. The determination of carbon dioxide by thermal conductivity has been used in studying the ventilation of buildings but not, so far as known, in controlling it.

Water vapor can be measured accurately in air if the composition of the air can be relied on (74). A few units are in use, but they are rare in comparison with the number of hygrometers of other types. There are at least two good reasons for this lack of use of the method. The first is that the method is not specific for water, and the conductivities of water vapor and air are so close together that large errors in apparent humidity are caused by small amounts of carbon dioxide or organic vapors. The second reason is that relative humidity is more often of interest than absolute humidity, because it determines whether or not drying will occur and how rapidly. The second objection alone would not be too serious, for the reading of the instrument could be combined with a temperature measurement with the aid of charts or tables such as are used for the great number of humidity measurements made with the wet- and dry-bulb thermometers. Duvander (22) has described an instrument for performing this correction automatically. The Cambridge Instrument Co. (13) has also pointed out the possibility of automatically determining relative humidity with the aid of two bridges, one of which has all its cells sealed and compares dry air with saturated air while the other compares the sample with dry air. It is also proposed to compare the sample with saturated air which produces a reading dependent on the difference between the sample and saturated air. This difference is also a measure of drying power and, if we were accustomed to it, might be as useful as the familiar relative humidity. The familiar psychrometer constantly changes the humidity of any confined space in which it is placed, and it requires the constant replenishment of liquid water. For certain locations and purposes, the thermal-conductivity instrument is decidedly superior to the psychrometer for these reasons, and perhaps superior to any other available method.

Among many miscellaneous uses of the method a few are of special interest. By bubbling hydrogen through water in constant ratio by volume and comparing the conductivities of the hydrogen before and after, the Cambridge Instrument Co. determines the content of dissolved gas. By comparing the conductivities of the gas before and after passing through a combustion tube, oxygen is determined specifically. The method is said to detect one part in 300 million of dissolved oxygen and to have great value in connection with boiler feed water. A unit with sealed comparison cells buried in roasting coffee is said to show when the best quality has been reached more accurately than can be judged from a measurement of temperature. This is a development of Hebler. The Gow-Mac Co. has developed a somewhat similar use. A unit buried in a grain bin will give an alarm if the grain begins to mold or to ferment. A similar unit in a warehouse or cargo space is an excellent means of giving warning of incipient combustion. This is not known to have been applied to coal storage, but it should be worth trying. Hansen (41) has described the use of the method in the control of the atmosphere in a hydrogen-cooled turbine generator. The comparison cells contain helium sealed in glass. Three scale ranges are provided, 0–15% air in hydrogen, 0–100% carbon dioxide in air, and 0–100% hydrogen in carbon dioxide. The first range is used during the operation of the machine; the other two during purging.

An important instrument is the permeameter developed by Shakespear (Daynes pp. 266–281), designed primarily for the testing of balloons and balloon fabrics. The fabric is clamped or held against a metal plate with many deep channels cut into its face. The channels communicate with a Katharometer. The atmosphere on the other side of the fabric is in contact with hydrogen, helium, or other gas, permeability to which is to be determined. As the gas diffuses through the fabric and into the analyzer, a reading is obtained that, when plotted against time, gives a curve a portion of which is practically straight. The slope of this line is a measure of the permeability of the fabric. This instrument has been applied extensively to the testing not only of balloon fabrics but of many other nearly impermeable materials. While the method of using the Shakespear permeameter is peculiar to it, a measured flow of one gas, such as air, over a material to be tested, then through an ana'ytical unit, is a general method of testing the permeability of membranes, the porosity of filters, etc., to the gas on the other side. The conditions of test may provide for measuring diffusion with no difference of pressure or any desired combination of diffusion and flow under pressure. Daynes

(19) has described an ingenious modification of this method for the measurement of minute rates of gas flow. An electrolytic cell produces hydrogen at a rate that can be determined by measuring the current, and the hydrogen is added to the flow to be measured and passed through an analytical unit. Air in the hydrogen is readily determined to a few parts per million and a flow can be measured to a corresponding fraction of the rate of production of the gas by electrolysis.

Several applications of thermal conductivity have been made to physiological studies and therapeutics, but the extent of their adoption into medical practice has been almost vanishingly small. Where helium has been used for decompression of divers and for other physiological uses, the method is generally used for such analyses as are involved.

A small number of analyzers are used in the control of atmospheres in oxygen therapy (12). They have also been employed, but to a very limited extent, in the carbon dioxide and oxygen determinations used in metabolism studies. Carbon dioxide is determined without too much difficulty (4, 12, 43, 54, 69) but the difference between oxygen and atmospheric nitrogen is so small that direct comparison with a standard gas to obtain the required accuracy of 0.01–0.02% puts quite a strain on the accuracy of the ordinary instrument. Nevertheless, the method has been used satisfactorily by several observers (12, 14, 51, 65, 68). Ledig and Lyman attempted to increase the sensitivity by introducing hydrogen and subsequently absorbing or burning out the oxygen, but encountered so much trouble in controlling the introduction of hydrogen that the procedure was abandoned in favor of the simple comparison with a standard. The method has been used to measure the rate of elimination of carbon tetrachloride through the lungs (50, 72) and its concentration in various tissues (71), to determine water vapor and carbon dioxide liberated by incubating eggs (3), to study the carbon dioxide evolved and oxygen absorbed by small amounts of living tissue under the effects of various drugs and diseases (17, 79), to measure respiration of insects (18), and of plants and germinating seeds (18). The effect of activity of a single fly was followed quite readily. The method seems ideally suited to the measurement of the gas mixtures employed in anesthesia, but a few applications to mixtures of oxygen and nitrous oxide are all that have been noted.

Reports of application of the method to laboratory research, as in the medical field, are disappointingly rare. It is to be expected that it will be used proportionately much less frequently for laboratory than for industrial analyses because in many cases the methods used for calibration can also be used to make the required analyses. Unless the analyses by usual methods are particularly time consuming or very numerous, the analyst is likely to adhere to them rather than to experiment with unfamiliar methods in which he has less confidence. In cases where there is too little material for determination by the method of calibration, where the process must not be disturbed by withdrawing samples, where the gases are chemically inert or isotopes with identical reactions, or where a continuous analysis is required, the thermal conductivity method may be indispensable. The most important applications in the physical chemical field in recent years are probably those having to do with deuterium and its compounds (25, 31, 32, 62, 63, 70, 75, 83, 91) and with *para*-hydrogen (7, 8, 23, 26, 31). It has been of great value also in the study of the diffusion of gases (80) particularly "thermal diffusion" (45, 47, 48) and in the study of catalysis and of adsorption (15, 44, 87).

ACKNOWLEDGMENTS

For the information contained in this chapter the author is indebted to an unusual extent to personal conferences and correspondence with the manufacturers of analytical instruments listed below, and particularly to the individuals named.

Allen Electric and Equipment Co., Kalamazoo, Mich.
Brown Instrument Co., Philadelphia, Pa.
   T. R. Harrison of the Brown Instrument Co.
Burrell Technical Supply Co., Pittsburgh, Pa.
Cambridge Instrument Co., New York City.
   R. H. Kruse of the Cambridge Instrument Co.
Davis-Hebler Co., Newark, N.J.
   W. O. Hebler of the Davis Hebler Co.
Electric Heat Control Co., Cleveland, O.
Electro-Products Co., New York City.
Charles Englehard Co., Newark, N.J.
   A. W. Taber of the Charles Englehard Co.
General Electric Co., Schenectady, N.Y.
Gow-Mac Co., Newark, N.J.
   C. C. Minter and W. G. Gow of the Gow-Mac Co.
Lantz-Phelps Corporation, Cincinnati, O.
Leeds and Northrup Co., Philadelphia, Pa.
   R. K. Davis of the Leeds and Northrup Co.

REFERENCES

1. Archer, C. T., *Phil. Mag.* **19**, 901 (1935).
2. Archer, C. T., *Proc. Roy. Soc. London* **A165**, 474 (1938).
3. Barott, H. G., private communication.
4. Bayliss, L. E., Miller, E. A., and Starling, E. H., *J. Physiol. London* **65**, 33 (1928).
5. Berg, H. H., *Automobiltech. Z.* **41**, 455 (1938).
6. Bolland, J. L., and Melville, H. W., *Nature* **140**, 63 (1937).
7. Bonhoeffer, K. F., Farkas, A., and Rummel, K. W., *Z. phys. Chem.* **B21**, 225 (1933).
8. Bonhoeffer, K. F., and Harteck, P., *Z. phys. Chem.* **B4**, 113 (1929).
9. Brown, E. H., and Felger, M. M., *Ind. Eng. Chem., Anal. Ed.* **17**, 273 (1945).

10. Brucke, E., and Littwin, W., *Z. Physik* **67**, 362 (1931).
11. Bullowa, J. G. M., *Instruments* **7**, 180 (1934).
12. Bullowa, J. G. M., and Lubin, G., *J. Clin. Invest.* **10**, 603 (1931).
13. Cambridge Gas Analyzers, List No. 144.
14. Carpenter, T. W., and Coropatchinsky, V. S., *Ind. Eng. Chem., Anal. Ed.* **14**, 159 (1942).
15. Coull, J., Engel, H. C., and Miller, J., *Ind. Eng. Chem., Anal. Ed.* **14**, 459 (1942).
16. Curie, M., and Lepape, A., *Compt. rend.* **193**, 842 (1931).
17. Curie, M., and Lepape, A., *J. phys. radium* [7] **2**, 392 (1931).
18. Daynes, H. A., *Proc. Roy. Soc. London* **97A**, 286 (1920).
19. Daynes, H. A., *Proc. Phys. Soc. London* **37**, 349 (1925).
20. Daynes, H. A., Gas Analysis by Measurement of Thermal Conductivity. Cambridge University Press, London 1933.
21. Dickins, B. G., *Proc. Roy. Soc. London* **143A**, 517 (1934).
22. Duvander, B. H., U. S. Pat. No. 2037409 (1935).
23. Eley, D. D., and Tuck, J. L., *Trans. Faraday Soc.* **32**, 1425 (1936).
24. Eltzin, I. A., *J. Tech. Phys. U.S.S.R.* **2**, 857 (1932).
25. Farkas, A., Orthohydrogen, Parahydrogen and Heavy Hydrogen. Macmillan, New York, 1935.
26. Farkas, A., *Z. phys. Chem.* **B22**, 344 (1933).
27. Farkas, A., and Farkas, L., *Nature* **132**, 894 (1933).
28. Farkas, A., and Farkas, L., *Proc. Roy. Soc. London* **152A**, 124 (1935).
29. Farkas, A., Farkas, L., and Harteck, P., *Proc. Roy. Soc. London* **144A**, 481 (1934).
30. Farkas, L., and Sachsse, H., *Z. phys. Chem.* **B 23**, 1 (1933).
31. Geib, K. H., and Harteck, P., *Z. phys. Chem.* Bodenstein Band 849 (1931).
32. Geib, K. H., and Steacie, E. W. R., *Z. phys. Chem.* **B29**, 285 (1935).
33. Gregory, H. S., *Proc. Roy. Soc. London* **A149**, 35 (1935).
34. Gregory, H. S., and Archer, C. T., *Phil. Mag.* [7] **15**, 593 (1926).
35. Gregory, H. S., and Archer, C. T., *Proc. Roy. Soc. London* **A121**, 285 (1928).
36. Gregory, H. S., and Archer, C. T., *Phil. Mag.* [7] **15**, 301 (1933).
37. Gregory, H. S., and Marshall, S., *Proc. Roy. Soc. London* **A118**, 594 (1928).
38. Gribkova, S. I., *J. Exp. Theoret. Phys. U.S.S.R.* **11**, 364 (1941).
39. Grüss, H., U. S. Pat. No. 1701181 (1929).
40. Grüss, H., and Schmick, H., *Wiss. Veröffentl. Siemens-Konzem* **7**, 202 (1928).
41. Hansen, C. A., Jr., *Gen. Elec. Rev.* **43**, 166 (1940).
42. Harrison, T. R., U. S. Pat. No. 1829649 (1931).
43. Hill, A. V., *Proc. Physiol. Soc.* **56**, XX (1922).
44. Hurst, W. W., and Rideal, E. K., *J. Chem. Soc.* **125**, 694 (1924).
45. Ibbs, T. L., *Proc. Roy. Soc. London* **A99**, 385 (1921); *Ibid.* **A107**, 470 (1925).
46. Ibbs, T. L., and Hirst, A. A., *Proc. Roy. Soc. London* **A123**, 134 (1929).
47. Ibbs, T. L., Grew, K. E., and Hirst, A. A., *Proc. Phys. Soc. London* **A1**, 456 (1929).
48. Ibbs, T. L., and Underwood, L., *Proc. Phys. Soc. London* **39**, 227 (1937).
49. Laby, T. H., and Nelson, E. A., International Critical Tables. Vol. 5, McGraw-Hill, New York, 1929 pp. 213–5.
50. Lamson, P. D., and Robbins, B. H., *J. Pharmacol. Exptl. Therap.* **34**, 325 (1928).
51. Ledig, P. G., and Lyman, R. S., *J. Clinical Invest.* **4**, 495 (1927).
52. Kannuluik, W. G., *Nature* **137**, 741 (1936).
53. Kannuluik, W. G., and Martin, L. H., *Proc. Roy. Soc. London* **A144**, 496 (1934).
54. Knipping, H. W., *Z. phys. Chem.* **141**, 1 (1924).
55. Koepsel, A., *Verhandl. deut. physik. Ges.* **10**, 814 (1908); *Ibid.* **11**, 237 (1909); *Chem. App.* **3**, 377, 401 (1908).

56. Kornfeld, G., and Hilferding, K., *Z. phys. Chem.* Bodenstein Band 792 (1931).
57. Krueger, R. H., U. S. Pat. No. 1698887 (1929).
58. Mann, W. B., and Dickins, B. G., *Proc. Roy. Soc. London* **A134,** 77 (1931).
59. Milverton, S. W., *Phil. Mag.* **17,** 397 (1934).
60. Minter, C. C., *Ind. Eng. Chem.* **17,** 687 (1925); *J. Soc. Automotive Engrs.* **16,** 613 (1925).
61. Minter, C. C., *Nat. Petroleum News* **25,** 69 (June 28, 1933).
62. Morikawa, K., Trenner, N. R., and Taylor, H. S., *J. Am. Chem. Soc.* **59,** 1103 (1937).
63. Newell, W. C., Purcell, R. H., Gregory, H., and Ellingham, N. J. T., *Nature* **137,** 69 (1936).
64. Nothdurft, W., *Ann. Physik* **28,** 137, 157 (1937).
65. Noyons, A. K. M., *Ann. physiol. physicochem. biol.* **13,** 909 (1937).
66. Palmer, P. E., and Weaver, E. R., *Nat. Bur. Standards U. S. Technol. Paper* 249, 100 pp. (1924).
67. Peters, J. C., Jr., U. S. Pat. No. 1504707 (1924).
68. Pieters, H. A. J., *Chem. Weekblad* **37,** 316 (1940).
69. Rabinowitch, I. M., and Bazin, E. W., *Can. Med. Assoc. J.* **16,** 638 (1926).
70. Reitz, O., and Bonhoeffer, K. F., *Z. phys. Chem.* **A174,** 424 (1935).
71. Robbins, B. H., *J. Pharmacol. Exptl. Therap.* **37,** 203 (1929).
72. Robbins, B. H., and Lamson, P. D., *J. Pharmacol. Proc.* **31,** 220 (1927); *Chem. Abstracts* **21,** 3978 (1927).
73. Rosecrans, C. Z., *J. Optical Soc. Am.* **14,** 479 (1927).
74. Rosecrans, C. Z., *Ind. Eng. Chem., Anal. Ed.* **2,** 129 (1930).
75. Sachsse, H., and Bratzler, K., *Z. phys. Chem.* **A171,** 331 (1934).
76. Shakespear, G. A., Brit Pat. No. 124455 (1916); U. S. Pat. No. 1304208 (1918); *Proc. Phys. Soc. London* **33,** 163 (1921).
77. Sherrat, G. G., and Griffiths, Ezer, *Phil. Mag.* **27,** 68 (1939).
78. Siemens and Halske, A. G., Ger. Pat. No. 283667 (1913).
79. Slater, W. K., *J. Sci. Instruments* **3,** 177 (1926).
80. Summerhays, W. E., *Proc. Phys. Soc. London* **42,** 218 (1930).
81. Trautz, M., and Zündel, A., *Ann. Physik* **17,** 345 (1933).
82. Trenner, N. R., *J. Chem. Phys.* **5,** 382 (1937).
83. Trenner, N. R., Morikawa, K., and Taylor, H. S., *J. Chem. Phys.* **5,** 203 (1937).
84. Ubbelohde, A. R., *J. Chem. Phys.* **3,** 219 (1935).
85. Ulsamer, J., *Z. Ver. deut. Ing.* **80,** 537 (1936).
86. Varhaftik, N. B., and Parfenov, I. D., *J. Exptl. Theoret. Phys. U.S.S.R.* **8,** 189 (1938).
87. Webb, G. A., and Black, G. S., *Ind. Eng. Chem., Anal. Ed.* **16,** 719 (1944).
88. Weber, S., *Ann. Physik* **54,** 481 (1917).
89. Weber, S., *Ann. Physik* **82,** 478 (1927).
90. Wilner, T., and Borelius, G., *Ann. Physik* **4,** 316 (1930).
91. Wirtz, K., *Z. phys. Chem.* **32B,** 334 (1936).

The Measurement of Radioactivity for Tracer Applications

By

ALOIS LANGER

Westinghouse Research Laboratories, East Pittsburgh, Pennsylvania

CONTENTS

1. GENERAL USE OF RADIOACTIVE MEASUREMENTS

1.1. Study of Radioactivity

The determination of radioactivity is of value in several fields of research. Predominant among these is the study of the phenomena concerned with the atomic nucleus. A considerable refinement in methods can be noted from the time of the discovery of radioactivity and the isolation of radium to the discovery of fission and the creation of transuranic elements. By radioactive measurements one seeks to establish the scheme and half period of the decay of unstable nuclei. This involves finding on a quantitative basis the type of the emitted radiation and its energy distribution.

1.2. Applied Radioactivity

The use of radioactive measurements as an analytical procedure is steadily gaining in importance, since radioactive elements and compounds have numerous applications in many branches of scientific and practical investigation. These applications were extended recently by the construction of uranium piles, which can supply perhaps a million times more of certain radioactive isotopes than a cyclotron.

The usefulness of these isotopes is due mainly to the sensitivity of radioactive measurements and the basic properties of the radioactive atoms. The radioactive elements can be detected and quantitatively determined in exceedingly small amounts. Under proper conditions of half-life, type, and energy of the emitted radiation, they are determinable by measurement of activity in concentrations many times smaller than by any other known chemical or physical method. Furthermore, by nature of its radioactivity, a given atom is labeled so that one can determine its position at the occurrence of the disintegration process among a great excess of nonactive species. The characteristics of the emitted radiation are also an identification of the radioactive isotope.

While the sensitivity and ease of detection makes the application of radioactive isotopes very convenient, for example in solubility and vapor pressure measurements, the labeled property is particularly useful in tracing the element through the process under investigation (49). Experiments like self diffusion and exchange reactions (45) can be performed, which, without labeled tracers, were impossible. Because radioactive elements are detected by their emitted radiation, the determination can often be made at a considerable distance from the sample. In some cases a continuous study of processes can be made, without any alteration or disturbance of the system (18), as in the study of metabolism on living organisms.

Since atoms having the property of spontaneous disintegration differ from the stable nuclei by only a slight shift in atomic weight, this difference does not ordinarily play a measurable role in the processes which are being studied, except for cases of isotope separation. This is particularly true of the heavier elements. Because minute amounts of the radioactive elements can be detected in an excess of the stable nuclei, the decay products or the emitted radiation do not alter the normal process of the investigated phenomena. These investigations, are. therefore, often called radioactive tracer or radioactive indicator methods, Radioactive tracer methods can sometimes be replaced or supplemented using the enriched heavy or light stable isotopes analyzed with a mass spectrometer.

Although the radioactive processes give rise to many kinds of radiation, their detection in principle, depends on the fact that the emitted radiation interacts with the surrounding matter, losing part or the whole of its energy and producing electrical, thermal, optical, chemical or other changes.

In nuclear physics one has to deal with many types of particles, such as neutrons, protons, deuterons, recoil atoms from fission, mesons, and others. In tracer work one encounters mainly alpha, beta, and gamma radiation, with a wide spread of energy content. In tracer application one rarely uses cloud chambers, differential calorimeters, or beta-ray spectrographs for measurements, but relies mainly on the action of radiation upon photographic emulsion and on the ionization effect, whereby gases and other normally insulating media are made conductive.

2. Photographic Method of Detection

2.1. Blackening of the Photographic Emulsion by Radiation

The effect on the photographic emulsion by electromagnetic and corpuscular rays has, since the discovery of radioactivity, never ceased to be an important detecting device for radiation. The blackening of a film is a complicated function of several parameters. The most important of these are the plate itself, the quality and intensity of the radiation, the time of exposure and the process of developing. The blackening (B) or density of a photographic emulsion is defined as $B = \log \frac{I_0}{I}$, where I_0 is the intensity of a parallel monochromatic beam of visible light falling on the film, and I the intensity transmitted by the film.

As a good approximation the blackening depends only on the amount (M) of the radiation received regardless of the time interval (t) during which the film is exposed. This reciprocity law, holding for energetic radiation, but not for visible light, can be expressed as: $B = f(M) = f(g \cdot t)$ where (g) is the intensity of the emitted radiation. The blackening of the emulsion is proportional to the amount of radiation in a limited range only. This is due to the fact that silver particles, once activated, are lost for activation by any further radiation impinging on the same point. Therefore, the blackening shows a saturation effect, following an exponential curve. If (A_0) is the quantity of available silver nuclei in the unexposed film then: $B = KA_0(1 - e^{-hM})$. For a quantitative determination of (M) constants (K) and (h) must be empirically evaluated.

2.2. Radioactivity Distribution Determinations

The present day use of the photographic emulsion is primarily for comparison of the two dimensional distribution of radioactive material in plane solid samples (18). The procedure is based on the fact that very small amounts of radiation can be recorded if long enough exposure times are used, and that an easily visible representation of the intensity distribution is obtained in a permanent picture. This procedure is more rapid than mapping the specimen point by point using small ionization chambers or counters.

Usually flat thin sections are prepared by the well known methods for microscopic examination, and the specimen is put on the photographic plate either in direct contact, or with a thin sheet of cellophane, paper, or mica interposed to eliminate blackening by effects other than radiation.

The exposure time, which varies from minutes to weeks, is determined conveniently from empirical tables. For a given radiation and film material the exposure time is adjusted to the overall radioactivity of the specimen and the half life of the isotope. In exposures lasting longer than two half lives no appreciable additional blackening is obtained. Fine grain x-ray films, metallographic plates, or special alpha-ray plates are satisfactory for this purpose.

These enlarged autoradiographs are compared with light microscope pictures of the same magnification, and valuable information concerning the distribution of the radioactive atoms in the material can be obtained. In case penetrating beta rays are emitted by the sample a diffuse image will result for several reasons. The blackened grains are spread along the whole track of the beta particle in the photographic emulsion and there is no collimation of the particles, which emerge with equal probability in any direction from the origin. In the case of alpha activity, because of reduced penetration in the emulsion, the first factor for diffuseness is reduced. The second factor can be minimized by using thin flat samples and by locating the plate in close contact with the specimen.

2.3. Radiation Dosimetry

Another valuable use of photographic films is in the dosimetry of radiation received by personnel working with radioactive materials or in the determination of the radiation strength of medical applicators of complicated shape. Small films cut from the same stock are carried in lightproof paper envelopes on any part of the body, or are placed for a certain length of time under the applicators and moulages in radio-therapeutic work. By developing the films simultaneously with films which received known amounts of the tolerance dose, any dangerous overexposure can be detected and precautions taken, or the strength of the radiator estimated. For more exact dosimetry, background corrections, corrections for scattered radiation and for the angle dependence have to be considered. Quantitative results can only be obtained under strictly standardized conditions. A major problem always remains, namely the varying response of the film to radiation of different energy. By covering part of the film with metal foils of different thicknesses and types it is possible to estimate the energy distribution of the received radiation.

3. ELECTRIC METHODS OF DETECTION

3.1. Collection of Charged Particles

If a strongly radioactive material is placed on one plate of a parallel plate condenser, the space between the plates evacuated, and the other plate connected to ground through a very sensitive galvanometer, a current can be detected. This current is caused, in the case of an alpha particle emitter, by the neutralization of two positive charges for each alpha particle striking the plate. In case of a beta-ray emitter one positive or negative charge is collected for each positron or electron. Gamma rays show a current caused by secondary radiation.

In such an arrangement the measured current (i) is proportional to the number of particles (m) reaching the plate in time (t) so that

$$i = \frac{dm}{dt} \cdot ne,$$

where (n) is the number of charges carried by the particle and (e) the charge of an electron. This arrangement, apart from a geometry factor and neglecting scattering, measures directly the intensity of the emitted radiation from the sample in a certain direction proportional to the over all radioactive strength of the material. Another advantage of such a device is, that one can act upon the charged particles by an electrostatic, magnetic field, or a combination of both. By proper arrangement of source and electrodes the nature and velocity distribution of the emitted particles can be determined.

This method is not very suitable for ordinary radiometric measurements for two reasons. For the accurate determination of the rather weak samples with which we ordinarily deal in tracer work, the best detecting device that present day amplification technique can provide is required since the collection of 6 electrons per second creates a current of only 10^{-18} amp. Also, the chamber with the sample has to be highly evacuated each time.

3.2. Ionization Measurements

3.2.1. *Principle of Ionization* (34). When a charged particle is emitted into a space filled with matter, elastic and inelastic collisions will occur. Elastic collisions merely influence the velocity of the colliding molecules. In inelastic collisions of the high energy projectile with the electronic cloud of the surrounding molecules a transfer of enough energy to the molecule results to bring it into an excited state, where it can lose one or more of its own electrons or can break up into charged and uncharged fragments. In the latter processes positively charged ions and free electrons are formed in equal numbers, and this phenomenon is described as the ionization and dissociation by impact. Similar effects are produced by roentgen and gamma radiation. The total number of ion pairs formed by a single particle depends on the energy content of the particle and on the nature of the surrounding gas. As an average for air 33 electron volts are used up in the creation of an ion pair. The total ionization produced is approximately obtained by dividing the initial energy of the particle by the mean ionization energy. The number of ions created by a particle in traveling 1 cm. in the gas at standard pressure and temperature is called specific ionization. The specific ionization is not the same throughout the whole path, but is usually denser shortly before the particle is brought to thermal velocities. The range of a charged particle in a substance is the distance it can travel before dissipating its energy.

Without a potential gradient between the condenser plates, the ions and electrons will diffuse and recombine sooner or later, so that almost no current will flow through the galvanometer. As soon as a potential is applied, the ions and electrons will separate and drift toward the oppositely charged electrode and a current will be detected. With an increase of the potential difference between the plates, the current will also gradually rise, but at a high enough potential an almost constant value will finally be reached. At this "saturation current" the recombination process is at a minimum and practically all the ions formed in the volume are collected at the electrodes. The saturation current (i_s) is:

$$i_s = k \frac{dm}{dt} \cdot ne,$$

where k is the amplification factor, a value depending on the specific ionization, dimensions of the apparatus, and the depletion of ions by recombination.

It is apparent that the measured saturation current is also an expression of the radioactivity of the sample, if k is constant and if one can evaluate the fraction o' particles entering the ionization chamber. In this simple picture, the formation of a space charge and the formation of negative ions by the capture of electrons by neutral molecules is neglected. The magnitude of the space charge, produced by the slower mobility of the positive ions compared to the electrons will depend on the intensity of the primary radiation. Since the space charge is influencing the field and, therefore, the potential at which saturation current occurs, it will also affect the saturation current.

Another important feature of this arrangement is that gamma quanta crossing the condenser volume produce a measurable current. This current is caused by the creation of electrons by the photoelectric. Compton, and pair production effect in the gas and surroundings, which in turn ionize the gas further in the same way as an electron coming directly from a radioactive substance. The main function of the ionization chamber is therefore a magnification of the current due to a primary ionization.

3.2.2. Ionization Chamber Constructions. One can consider an ionization chamber as a condenser with a gas as dielectric. The shape and size can vary considerably and is chosen to best suit the problem at hand. Thus very small ionization chambers with an air volume of only several cubic millimeters are used for mapping of gamma-ray intensity in radium and roentgen therapy. For cosmic ray studies the chambers can have a volume of many liters, sometimes with the gas above atmospheric pressure and of a low ionization energy. For ordinary radiometric work volumes of the order of 1 liter or smaller are used. Both, or only one of the electrodes are well insulated from the surrounding metal envelope. In the latter case the whole envelope serves as the second electrode. As insulation materials quartz, sulfur, amber, and plastics like polystyrene are satisfactory. Of these quartz is most desirable since it retains its insulating property at high humidity. To eliminate leakage current

across the insulator, guard ring protection is recommended. The guard
ring also provides electrostatic shielding for the electrode system if
properly designed against surface charges on the insulator.

In tracer assay one does not usually discriminate between the ionization produced by the different types of radiation. Instead, an attempt
is made to pass the largest possible fraction of the available primary
radiation into the sensitive volume of the chamber. Therefore, emitters
of alpha particles and of very soft beta radiation, which are appreciably
stopped even with the thinnest metal sheets, are placed directly inside
the chamber. For more energetic beta rays and for gamma radiation the
sample is usually outside the chamber and the radiation enters through a
suitable window. This latter construction avoids the contamination of
the inside of the chamber by accidentally spilled radioactive material.

Some of the common types of ionization chambers are shown in
Fig. 1. The parallel disc condenser is most frequently used. Because
of its simple shape, the geometry factor of radiation loss can be calculated and can approach almost one half. A more detailed drawing of an
ionization chamber of this type for samples placed outside the chamber is
shown in Fig. 2. The collecting electrode (E_1) is a brass disc, preferably
gold plated, held by the insulator (J). The guard ring (G) maintains a
low potential between the collector lead L_1 and ground, thus preventing
polarization effects in the insulator and also shielding the collector lead
from the surrounding space. The field defining part of the guard ring
(G_1) straightens the lines of force between the collecting electrode and
the electrode maintained at the potential above ground (E_2), thus
securing better reproductivity. This electrode is made of a heavier
ring with a stretched aluminum foil (F) from 0.1 to 0.5 mils thick serving
as the radiation window. Connection to the outside is made by an
insulated lead (L_2). The whole assembly is mounted in a metal housing
(H) for protection. The housing has slots (S) for the sample holder
(A) on which the sample can be deposited. If the plates E_1 and E_2
are apart at least as far as the range of the alpha particles (about 6 cm.)
all alpha radiation is stopped in this space and utilized for ionization,
thus rendering the chamber insensitive to pressure and temperature
variation. Normally, as in the case of penetrating beta rays, the
particles do not completely lose their energy in the chamber. The
current produced is sensitive to pressure and temperature variations,
and for precise measurements, corrections to normal conditions should
be made, by use of the equation $i_0 = i_{pt} \cdot \dfrac{760}{p} \left(1 + \dfrac{\tau}{273} \right)$ where i_{pt} is the
measured current at the pressure (p) and the temperature τ. For
samples outside the chamber, the construction of Fig. 1 using a hemi-

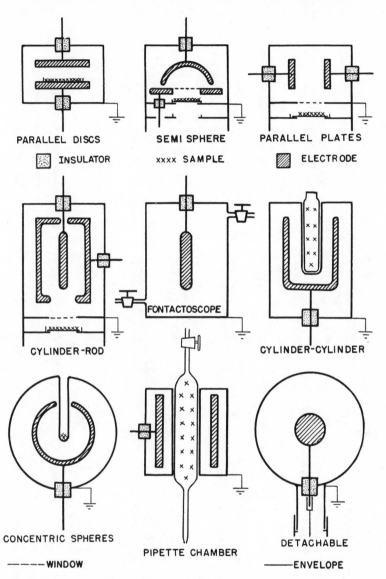

FIG. 1.   Schematic drawings of different ionization chambers used for tracer assay.

sphere as collector is recommended because of its favorable geometry factor.   Another construction consists of a cylindrical envelope with a rod as the collecting electrode.   This type is favored because of the ease of construction, high sensitivity, and adaptability.   A detailed drawing of such a chamber is shown in Fig. 2.   The sample can be placed

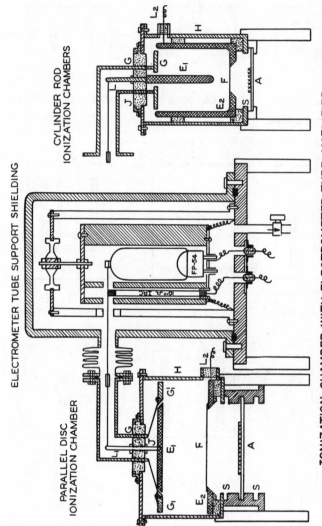

IONIZATION CHAMBER WITH ELECTROMETER TUBE AMPLIFIER

FIG. 2.   Detailed drawing of a circular parallel discs and cylinder rod ionization chamber with shielding and shock proof support for an electrometer tube amplifier.

inside or outside. A similar arrangement of electrodes with the envelope vacuum tight is used for measuring the ionization produced by radioactive gases introduced directly into the evacuated chamber through stopcocks. Samples with large amounts of foreign matter or those dissolved in a liquid can be measured in the concentric cylinder chamber The sample is put into a container which is introduced directly into the cavity of the inner cylinder. For the determination of radioactivity in liquids a pipette arrangement is more convenient. If only small samples are available the concentric spheres chamber offers increased sensitivity. The sample can be placed in the center of the inner electrode so that a large part of the emitted radiation is utilized for ionization between the spherical electrodes.

Spherical or cylindrical "thimble" chambers are used for radiation intensity measurement in the field of gamma and roentgen rays. They are made of a special air equivalent material for dosimetry and are detachable from the electrometer.

3.2.3. Detecting Devices. Galvanometers: The saturation current produced in the ionization chamber can be measured by galvanometers, electrometers, and electron tube amplifiers. Only with strongly active sample and the most sensitive galvanometers (10^{-12} amp./mm.) can a direct measurement of current be carried out (Fig. 4a). Photoelectric amplification and the use of a second galvanometer does not improve this condition in the region of radioactive measurements encountered in tracer technique. Ballistic discharge of a condenser through the galvanometer is slow and complicates the technique. Greater sensitivity can be obtained by the following instruments.

Electrometers: In electrometers a charged body moves under the influence of an electrostatic field of repulsion or attraction, until the restoring force, which may be gravity, elastic tension, or torsion, balances the electrostatic force. The new equilibrium position is an indication of the acting forces.

The energy (W) of a conductor with a capacity C, charged to a potential (V) is $W = \frac{1}{2}CV^2$. Since the restoring energy at equilibrium acting against the charged body is in the first approximation given by $W = K\rho^2$, where ρ is the displacement of the moving part, the new position indicates the potential which the body has acquired.

Electrometers can be divided into two classes. Those operating by their own repulsion in a grounded case are called electroscopes. In the electrometers proper the moving body is deflected in an artificially created electrostatic field. The actual construction of the various elements is so diverse that no generalized detailed description can be given.

The gold leaf electroscope, which played an important role in the early days of radioactivity, is not used any more as a measuring instrument due to the irregular jumping movements of the leaf drifting under gravitation. High capacity and low voltage sensitivity are also disadvantageous. Present day electrometers using the elastic property as the restoring force have light moving parts, such as noble-metal-coated quartz fibers, 3–5μ in diameter. Quartz fibers are favored because they have superior properties derived from their excellent elastic modulus and low temperature coefficient. Since the fiber weight is minute, these electrometers are not influenced by gravity and operate in almost any position. The capacity and capacity change can be kept small. The instruments are quite susceptible to air currents caused by a temperature gradient in the envelope and are disturbed by resonance vibration. Thermal shielding improves this condition. Evacuation of the casing reduces the unsteadiness of the fiber due to the effect of Brownian motion of the gas, if utmost sensitivity is desired.

Figure 3 shows a few of the better known types of electroscopes and electrometers. Many of them are commercially available. The Lauritsen quartz fiber (30) and the Wulf bifilar electroscope are convenient to use in the drift rate method. The Lutz monofilar electroscope, because of its high voltage sensitivity, is recommended as a null instrument in the compensation arrangement. The arrangement of the Lauritsen electroscope serves at the same time as the ionization chamber. The position of the fiber is determined in all the instruments by a low power microscope with a scale in the eye piece. Care should be taken to avoid any possible charge collected on the objective lens since this lens is often quite close to the fiber, and may therefore cause erratic movements of the indicator. All the glass parts, such as the window introducing the light for the illumination of the fiber, should be covered with a conductive but transparent film of metal. For the torsion instrument light reflected from a mirror is used to indicate the twist.

When electrometers and ionization chambers are operated, the apparatus should be kept dry by connection to a vessel with a good dehydrating agent. Electrometers are charged to the necessary potential by storage batteries, dry cells, frictional devices or best, by rectified and stabilized current from line operated power supplies. Any desired voltage can be tapped from a potentiometer. Enough resistance should be inserted in series with the fiber (0.5–1.0 megohms) to prevent the destruction of the fiber coating by an accidental short to ground. The regulated power supply can also be used as a permanently attached potential in the charging up and steady deflection method.

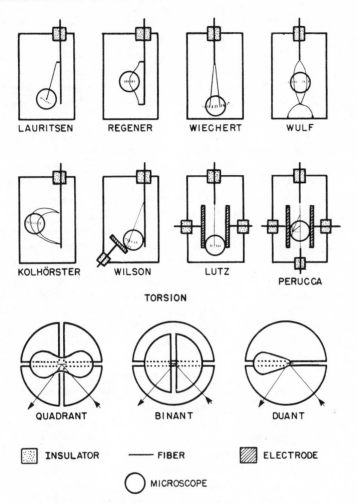

LAURITSEN   REGENER   WIECHERT   WULF

KOLHÖRSTER   WILSON   LUTZ

PERUCCA

TORSION

QUADRANT   BINANT   DUANT

INSULATOR   —— FIBER   ▨ ELECTRODE

⬤ MICROSCOPE

FIG. 3. Schematic drawings of some more frequently used fiber and torsion electrometers.

Electrometer tube amplifiers: Although electrometers are relatively inexpensive, rugged, and easy to operate, they are being replaced by the vacuum tube amplifier. Special tubes are often used where, by the arrangement of the electrodes and by careful insulation, a high grid resistance and low grid current is obtained. Various circuits are recommended to compensate automatically for small changes in filament and plate voltages (41). The tube, together with the grid resistor and the lead to the ionization chamber, is placed into an evacuated, heavy-walled iron container for shielding. The evacuation prevents leakage due to moisture and ionization by penetrating radiation. To minimize any microphonic disturbances, shock proof mounting is recommended. Such a mounting is shown in Fig. 2 where the electrometer tube is in a heavy iron tube suspended on a rubber shock absorber as a pendulum and located firmly by springs.

The connection of the electrometer tube to the ionization chamber and the experimental methods of measurements are similar to those used in electrostatic devices. The collection of a charge does not cause a mechanical movement but instead changes the potential of the tube grid, which in turn increases or decreases the flow of electrons from cathode to plate. In this way the primary current of the ionization chamber is amplified about a hundred fold. The resulting current can be further amplified. The output of such an amplifier can operate rugged galvanometers, oscillographs, or pen recording instruments. If these instruments are kept under power continuously to eliminate the unsteady warming up period, measurements of radioactivity can be performed rapidly with a very high precision, especially in the compensation arrangement. Weak and strong samples can be measured by changing the grid resistor. In the drift rate method the ionization chamber is coupled to the grid by a small condenser.

3.2.4. Methods of Measurements. By connecting the grid of the amplifier or the electrostatic electrometer to the ionization chamber a new unit is formed having a total capacity C_1. The charge (Q) is given by relation $Q = C_1 V$. A change of charge of such a system can be expressed by the equation $dQ = C_1 dV + V dC_1$. Since the movement of the fiber in the electrometer produces only a negligible change of the capacity C_1 of the system and because no change of capacity occurs with a tube amplifier, the term $V dC_1$ can be neglected. If a current (i) is flowing through the condenser, the insulated system will lose its charge, and the observed time rate change of charge is proportional to the change of voltage according to the equations $i = \dfrac{dQ}{dt} = C_1 \cdot \dfrac{dV}{dt} = C_1 \dfrac{V_0 - V_i}{t}$. The potential difference $V_0 - V_i$ is conveniently found by reading two positions on the calibrated electrometer scale or by the change in the output current of the vacuum tube indicator. By measuring the time (t) necessary to cause the potential change $(V_0 - V_i)$ the current (i) can be determined. Since (t) can be measured precisely, and if the device is voltage sensitive, the method is simple and fast. Two possibilities are offered by this "drift method," which are either to discharge the condenser plate with the attached electrometer or to charge it up.   The circuits are schematically indicated in Fig. 4, b and c.   In both cases measurements must be made at a potential in the saturation current region, so that $(V_0 - V_i)$ cannot be expanded over a wide voltage range.

With the discharge method one can join the electrometer and ionization chamber firmly together, or make the condenser detachable.   The latter arrangement is recommended for gamma-ray measurements: Only the condenser is exposed for a certain time to the radiation and the charge loss is determined upon reconnecting to the electrometer circuit.   In this way the discharge occurs in the condenser only and not in the electrometer proper.

For practical measurements one has to consider that the voltage scale, especially with fiber electrometers, is not linear.   The drift time, therefore, should be taken between the same defining marks.   The intensity (i) can then be expressed simply as $(1/t)$, the reciprocal of the time for drift between the chosen defining marks.   The measurements should be started with a moving indicator, since just after charging the movement of the fiber is often erratic.   All measurements are corrected for the background current, especially the leakage current.   The background current may vary considerably during the day and frequent blank measurements should be taken, especially with weak samples.

Reliable results can also be obtained by the steady deflection method. In this arrangement (Fig. 4d) the indicating instrument is shunted to ground by a high resistance (R) of the order of 10^{10} ohms.   If a radioactive sample is brought into the vicinity of the ionization chamber, the ionization current i will build up a potential V across the resistance R according to the equation $V = iR(1 - e^{-\frac{t}{RC}})$.   At a time interval large enough in comparison to RC, the potential will reach a constant value $V = iR$.   The steady deflection on the indicator of tne measuring instrument at equilibrium is not influenced by the capacity of the system. The current is therefore directly proportional to the reading in volts on the calibrated scale.   The value of this procedure is that it can be easily changed into a null method by compensating the current flowing in the resistor by a current of opposite sign.   This can be accomplished by a precise potentiometer, (P) (Fig. 4e) piezoelectrically or with a variable radioactive compensator.   Since in this case the indicator is not deflected, the electrometer can be very sensitive, especially at the balance point.   In case of a tube amplifier one does not have to take into account the corrections due to the nonlinearity of the tube characteristics, galvanometer readings, and other effects.   A complete circuit for the steady deflection method, where the current through (R) is compensated by a

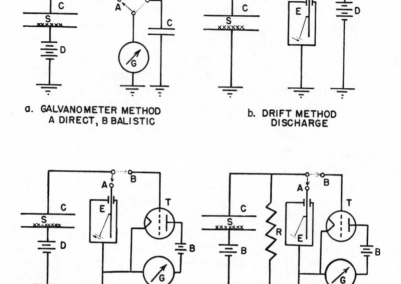

a. GALVANOMETER METHOD
A DIRECT, B BALISTIC

b. DRIFT METHOD
DISCHARGE

c. DRIFT METHOD
CHARGING UP

d. STEADY DEFLECTION
METHOD

e. STEADY DEFLECTION NULL METHOD

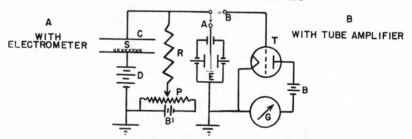

A
WITH
ELECTROMETER

B
WITH TUBE AMPLIFIER

Fig. 4. Idealized diagrams of ionization chamber connections in different methods of measurements.

C—Ionization chamber
S—Sample
D—Variable potential supply for the ionization chamber
P—Potentiometer
G—Galvanometer
E—Electrometer
T—Electrometer tube
R—Leakage resistance
B—Plate potential for the electrometer tube

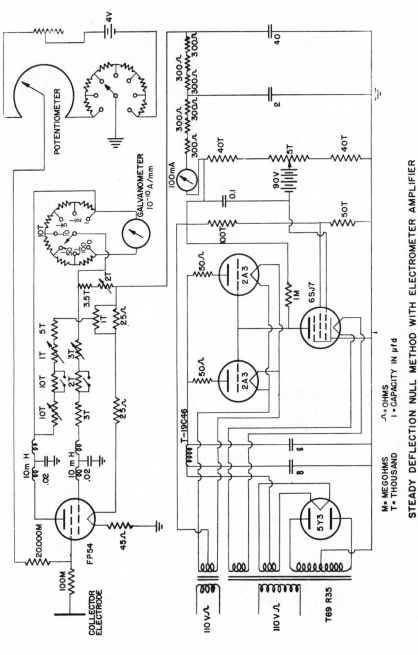

Fig. 5. Circuit diagram of a balanced electrometer tube amplifier with potentiometer compensation and regulated power supply.

potentiometer is given in Fig. 5.   The supply voltage is obtained from an electronically regulated pack.   The variable resistors are so chosen, that the circuit can be balanced to compensate for minor drifts in the supply voltage.   The proper operation of the instrument requires close supervision.   New possibilities are offered by the dynamic condenser electrometer, where a mechanical vibration of one plate of a condenser produces an alternating current.   The magnitude of the current depends on the impressed charge and can be easily amplified by A.C. amplifiers.

The Lauritsen ionization electroscope and the Wulf bifilar electroscope with an attached ionization chamber are simple and sensitive enough to turn out reliable data with the least effort in regard to the measuring technique.   The sensitivity of these methods is about one alpha particle per second.   Since better sensitivity and better procedures with weaker samples can be obtained with counters, they are replacing almost entirely the use of ionization chambers in the field of applied radioactive assay.   Because the preparation of samples and the necessary corrections applied to the results are similar for the ionization chamber as for counters, they will be discussed simultaneously in a later chapter.

3.3. Measurements by Counting (35)

3.3.1. Principle of Counters.   To explain the manner in which an ionizing particle produces discrete current pulses, large enough to be recorded, one has to return to the interpretation of the current in the ionization chamber.   At the saturation current the field gradient was strong enough to pull apart all the ion and electron pairs created by the primary particle and to give them sufficient energy to arrive at the electrodes.   If the ionization chamber has a low capacity and if the detecting instrument is sufficiently voltage sensitive by the use of a multiple stage vacuum tube linear amplifier, then by exposing the chamber to radiation of one particle at a time, pulses will be registered.   Because an appreciable number of ion pairs are formed by the entrance of a single alpha ray or any other particle of high specific ionization, the voltage pulses are large compared to the pulses detected at the arrival of a beta ray.   The output voltage of the amplifier is still proportional to the primary number of ion pairs created in the chamber by the single particle, whose duration is given by the time constant of the amplifier circuit.   The resulting electrical pulses can be fed into a thyratron circuit to operate a mechanical register.   The grid bias of the thyratron can be adjusted so that only pulses of preselected size are recorded.   In this way the "linear amplifier" is insensitive to beta and gamma rays below a certain noise level, which can be further decreased by bending away the beta radiation in a magnetic field.

The random fluctuations in the circuit of the linear amplifier, due to the high gain amplification, limit its use to detecting heavily ionizing particles.   This insensitivity to beta radiation can be overcome by utilizing secondary ionization in the ionization chamber proper, thus increasing the number of available ion pairs and therefore the voltage pulse.   As soon as the applied potential is raised on the plates of the ionization chamber above a certain value the current carried by the condenser starts to increase again.   The liberated electrons and ions are further accelerated between inelastic collisions so that they possess sufficient energy, greater than the ionization potential of the gas.   They produce, in turn, an ionization process of their own.   The newly created electrons are again speeded up during one mean free path, so that on collision with the electronic shells of the gas molecules they can cause further ionization.   Thus a rapidly progressing chain reaction, an "avalanche" is formed.   Such an avalanche produces many times more ion pairs, than the primary particle.

The greater the mean free path of the electrons or the steeper the potential gradient through which the electrons fall, the more energy they acquire.   Thus in a certain range of velocities they have a more favorable cross-section for the ionization and dissociation process.   In this way beta rays will produce enough charges to be detected as a short pulse.

The parallel plate condenser is not the most favorable arrangement for pulse production.   An ionization chamber in the form of a long cylinder is preferable wherein a thin wire is stretched concentrically, a very steep potential gradient being created close to the wire.   Usually the gas in the cylinder is rarefied to about 10 cm. Hg, increasing the mean free path proportionately and decreasing the potential at which the secondary electrons acquire ionization and dissociation ability.

The wire is usually made positive and connected to ground with a fairly high resistance (R) as indicated in Fig. 8a.   As a pulse indicator a fast and sensitive electrometer can be utilized, or one can use a tube amplifier in which a string oscillograph is inserted in the plate circuit.   This arrangement at low applied voltages will work as an ionization chamber sweeping the electrons to the wire and the ions to the cylinder.   In the voltage region of multiple collisions different particles will still produce different pulses.   A device of this kind is known as a "proportional counter" since it discriminates the energy content of the incoming radiation by the pulse size.   Valuable as linear amplifiers and proportional counters are in nuclear physics, they find only limited application in tracer work and will not be considered in detail.   The same is true for proportional counters filled with boron trifluoride for counting neutrons.

By increasing the potential between wire and cylinder in a proportional counter, the pulses will slowly approach equal size until at the so-called threshold voltage the pulses from any particle are almost identical. The process of internal pulse amplification is schematically shown in Fig. 13c.

Counters operated above the threshold voltage, where all pulses are of equal size are the Geiger-Müller counters proper (15). It is observed that in the Geiger region the current is much greater than would be produced by a single avalanche, and consequently it is postulated that the ionization process must take place in the whole counter volume.

One explanation of why such a spreading of discharge occurs is given by the fact that the colliding atoms are excited into higher energy states and upon returning to their normal states emit ultraviolet photons. These photons can liberate electrons in the walls and the gas by the photo- and Compton effects in any part of the tube, producing avalanches throughout the whole cylinder. Alternately the positive ions acquire enough energy so that in the act of being neutralized on the cylinder they can extract more free electrons from the wall than they need for neutralization. These electrons can act as primary particles, thus spreading and prolonging the discharge.

Let us investigate the process that terminates the discharge once started. A very dense concentration of ionized particles is produced close to the wire. Since the highly mobile electrons are rapidly collected on the wire, a positive sheath of ions is left behind, drifting relatively slowly to the cylinder. In this way an expanding space charge envelope is created, which can lower the effective field around the wire to such an extent that all production of secondary ion pairs is stopped. The space charge, therefore, causes a cessation of the discharge. Only after a large part of the positive ions are collected on the cylinder will the tube be restored to its sensitive condition. This mechanism of internal quenching will be especially effective if one can prevent delayed photon emission of the excited molecules and the additional electron liberation on the wall by the neutralization process. Certain polar organic vapors, like alcohols, acetone, esters, and many others, for example, organic metallic compounds (23), even in quite small amounts, absorb by collision the excitation energy of the counter gas, which is dissipated as kinetic energy instead of radiation. In this way the creation of photoelectrons is inhibited without preventing the initial spreading of the discharge through the whole volume of the tube. Organic vapors are also absorbed on the walls of the cylinder and thus can retard the formation of multiple discharges caused by the liberation of more electrons than the neutralization process requires. These additional electrons seem to be the origin of the spurious counts, which sometimes closely follow the actual discharge released by the primary ionizing particle. The spurious counts cause the tube to fire with increasing frequency, not proportional to the incoming radiation. Such a state always develops at sufficiently high potentials.

There is still another effective mechanism which will terminate the discharge. At the threshold voltage the pulses created by different particles become equal in size. This is the voltage where avalanches start to spread throughout the whole tube. However the actual counting is done at a higher operating voltage. The difference between the threshold and operating potential is called overvoltage. If after a discharge has started, one rapidly lowers the potential across the tube, below the threshold voltage, the spreading of avalanches terminates and the discharge is interrupted. Such a lowering of potential can be accomplished if the bleeder resistance to ground (R) is made high enough so that

$R > \dfrac{V_1}{i}$. In this way the potential across the counters will be automatically reduced below the starting potential as soon as enough charges are collected to produce a current (i). Normally, to obtain a potential drop of the order of the overvoltage, the resistance R has to be about 10^{10} ohms. Figure 13a, indicates a typical pulse created by a particle entering the counter as viewed on an oscilloscope with linear synchronized time sweep. The wire collecting the electrons acquires the potential V_0 rather suddenly. After that the pulse is dying, because the charge is leaking off

through R. The potential (V) at a time (t) will be given by $V = V_0 e^{-\frac{t}{RC}}$ where C is the capacity of the circuit. The recovery time (t_r) necessary to obtain a small enough potential (V) to restore the circuit to operating conditions will therefore depend on RC. Because R is large, t_r is also long (around 10^{-3} second) and counters quenched in this way are called slow counters. A sudden lowering of the potential can be achieved much more quickly by an electron tube arrangement.

The counters filled with an organic vapor are internally quenched and have a recovery time of the order of 10^{-5} second. They are called fast counters. The resistance R can have a much lower value. The disadvantage of counters filled with an organic vapor is that the organic compounds are dissociated into fragments by the discharge mechanism. The original filling is slowly used up with each count, changing the counter characteristic and giving the counter a lifetime of the order of 10^8 to 10^{10} counts. Small counters, in which the gases would be used up more rapidly, can be connected to a large gas storage vessel (51).

3.3.2. Construction of Counters. The counter constructions are not restricted to the cylinder and wire type. Any arrangement of electrodes where a steep potential gradient can be maintained close to one electrode will show self-quenching properties. Some constructions are indicated in Fig. 6.

The ball type counter consists of a small ball in the center of a hemisphere. A sharp point against a flat plate is usually called the point

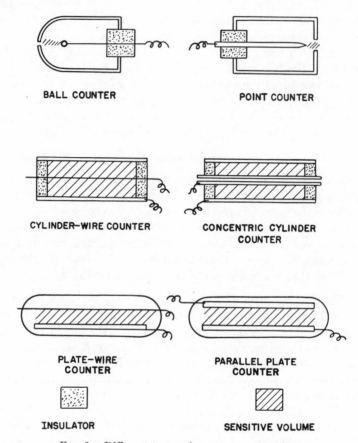

BALL COUNTER   POINT COUNTER

CYLINDER–WIRE COUNTER   CONCENTRIC CYLINDER
                            COUNTER

PLATE–WIRE   PARALLEL PLATE
COUNTER   COUNTER

INSULATOR   SENSITIVE VOLUME

Fig. 6. Different types of counter constructions.

counter. These arrangements actually furnished the first demonstration that it is possible to count individual alpha particles. They can be operated at atmospheric pressure and the particles enter the counter volume through a small hole in the larger electrode or through a wire gauze window. Their disadvantage is the rather small sensitive volume and insensitivity to beta and gamma radiation.

With the development of electronic quenching circuits almost any arrangement of electrodes can be utilized for counting, and one finds counters constructed as concentric cylinders, parallel plates, plate and a wire, and other forms. These and the concentric cylinder counter have the advantage of a large sensitive volume and a wide area for the penetration of the radiation. The cylinder wire counter is the best developed and most commonly used. Equipment like the Greinacher spark counter (14), the scintillation counters and the crystal counter show considerable promise, but must be considered of scientific interest only at this time.

The basic design of the Geiger-Müller cylinder-wire counter can be widely varied and adapted to any problem of radioactive measurement. In the determination of penetrating radiation, particularly gamma rays, cylinders of heavy metals, like copper, cobalt, molybdenum, and platinum, with sufficiently thick walls are recommended, so that optimal yield of photo and recoil electrons or pair production with gamma rays above 1 Mev is obtained in the sensitive volume (4). Screen wire cylinders of heavy metals will increase the gamma ray sensitivity because of their large surface (13). A counter with cylinders made of material made radioactive by neutron irradiation, like silver, can be used for neutron detection. The glass used in neutron counters should not contain boron because this element is a good neutron absorber. The cylinders are either completely inclosed in a glass envelope (Fig. 7a) or are sealed to glass ends if glass sealing metals are used for the construction (Fig. 7b). The practice of fastening hard rubber ends by wax to hold and insulate the central wire is now generally abandoned because such counters cannot be outgassed at elevated temperatures and because the wax absorbs the filling gas, changing the characteristic of the counter on storage. The diameter of the cylinder can vary from millimeters (8) to several centimeters; the length being at least four to five times that of the diameter. The inside of the solid tube should be smooth with ends slightly flared out to eliminate end effects. The metal is often treated for chemical stability and low photo emission. The surface should not change with time by the vigorous reactions taking place in the counter during each discharge. For that reason when employing a copper anode, a bright copper electrode is used with a hydrogen mixture. With mixtures of oxygen, on the other hand, the cathode is oxide coated. Iron or tungsten wire with a diameter from 1 to 30 mils is used as the central electrode. The diameter of the wire has an effect on the starting potential of the counter. The wire is preferably taken out at both ends of the counter tube. The counter, as a whole, is outgassed for several hours at 300°C. or higher. Before filling the wire is flashed for several seconds under vacuum to white heat, by passing current to release occluded gases, burn off all dust and grease, and smooth its surface. The wire is kept

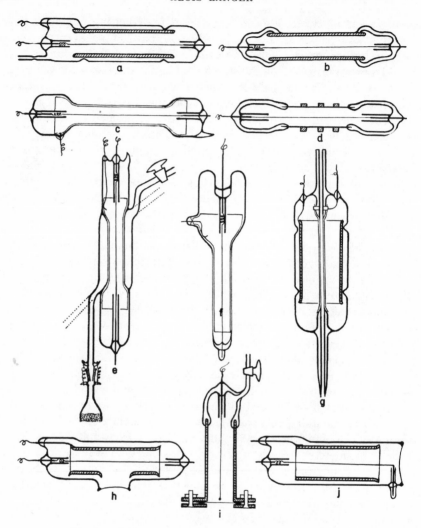

FIG. 7.   Commonly used Geiger counter constructions.
  a. Heavy solid cylinder glass envelope counter
  b. Solid cylinder with sealed on glass ends counter
  c. Thin walled glass envelope counter
  d. Thin metal cylinder counter
  e. Thin walled liquid-jacket pipette counter
  f. Thin walled dipping counter
  g. Capillary wire counter
  h. Front window counter
  i, j. Side window or bell type counters.

stretched by a small tungsten spring at one end and the weldings are protected by glass sleeves.   These sleeves should shield any sharp points resulting from the welding but should not be extended too close to the sensitive volume.   The glass might become charged, distort the field, and cause spurious counts.   Terminals for the wire and cylinder are taken to the outside by tungsten seals, or glass sealing alloys.   To obtain good seals and mechanical strength a combination of glasses, like Nonex and Pyrex, may be used in the construction.   The outside ends of the counter are covered with a film of wax by dipping into molten ceresin, to insure high leakage resistance even in humid weather.   A connection for sealing to the vacuum and filling system is also attached.

Many fillings are recommended in the literature to obtain best performance.   Pure hydrogen, dry air, 96% argon with 4% oxygen or helium are used in slow counters.   Argon saturated with ethyl alcohol at 0°C. with 1 cm. Hg amyl acetate or other polyatomic vapors perform satisfactorily in fast counters.   A total pressure of approximately 10 cm. Hg gives favorable operating potentials.   A good procedure is to test the counter during the filling stage before sealing off.   The helium filled counter at atmospheric pressure has many advantages and will probably be more widely used in the future.

To measure low energy beta rays an envelope thin enough to permit the penetration of the radiation into the sensitive volume is necessary, for this the walls of the metal tube are ground to the thinnest cylinder that can withstand the outside pressure (5).   The cylinder can be reinforced by heavier ribs (Fig. 7d).   The particles can also be admitted through a very thin walled glass envelope.   The solid cylinder is replaced by a screen or by a thin conducting layer of colloidal carbon, wet deposited silver, or copper, or other vacuum evaporated metal (Fig. 7c).   For better operating conditions it is recommended the glass be covered on the outside of the sensitive volume with a conducting layer.   Another useful type is the side window (Fig. 7g) and front window counter (Fig. 7h).   The former is known as a bell type counter since it has a very thin membrane of glass, mica, aluminum, or beryllium stretched across one side of the cylinder.

In the front window counter the radiation enters through a hole in the cylinder, in the bell type it passes axially.   In this way a large sensitive volume for radiation is obtained.   The glass membrane can be made by an indrawn glass bubble, or better and more uniformly by sealing a part of a large thin glass bubble to the softened end of the counter tube. Windows of mica or metal foils can be cemented to the cylinder by a Silicone plastic or clamped between lead or tin gaskets (10, 53).   Large windows can be supported by a grid.   The cylinder may be the metal envelope of the counter (Fig. 7i), or a solid metal cylinder in the glass tube (Fig. 7j). Sometimes the other end of the central wire is not brought to the outside but terminated with a small glass ball to prevent an irregular potential gradient due to a sharp point. The disadvantage of this construction is that the wire cannot be easily flashed and that vibrations can cause instability in operating such a counter tube.

Very thin glass, mica, and metal windows can be used if the counter is filled with helium at atmospheric pressure (17). In this case the membrane acts as a barrier for the gas only, without the necessity of withstanding any pressure. By this arrangement even very soft beta rays can penetrate into the sensitive region, without need of introducing the sample directly into the counter. For ordinary counter work the diameter of the cylinder is around 1 to 3 cm. with a glass membrane thickness of 0.02 mm. or mica windows as thin as 1.5 mg./cm.^{2}

3.3.3. Auxiliary Equipment. Each counter requires a high voltage supply. The potential should be continuously variable from about 300 volts to about 2000 volts to meet the operating range for different counters. The rectified current from the transformer should be stabilized either by a set of neon stabilizing tubes or by a vacuum tube circuit. With counters that have flat plateau small fluctuations can be tolerated. Since only a relatively small current is drawn from the circuit by the counter, inexpensive neon sign transformers with half-wave rectification prove satisfactory. Low voltage supplies can be regulated by standard gas filled tubes.

In practice one does not rely on the self quenching property of fast counters alone, but uses an external extinguishing circuit. The basic high resistance quenching circuit is not used frequently because it has a low resolving power. Instead, electronic quenching circuits are preferred for extinguishing the gas discharge as soon as it is established to a certain degree. Such circuits, which depend on the action of the collected charges on the grid of a vacuum tube, shorten the original discharge pulse and speed up the obtainable counting rate. They also amplify and broaden the pulses to a more uniform size for simpler further amplification or recording.

In the commonly used quenching circuits the electron tube represents a rapidly adjustable rheostat automatically controlled by the counter tube either to short circuit the counter by decreasing its resistance, or by increasing the resistance and hence cut off the counter tube from the high voltage.

The first principle is utilized in the Neher-Harper circuit (37), (Fig. 8b). The tube ·is negatively biased and therefore in a nonconducting state. Connected parallel to the counter tube, it represents a very high

a. GEIGER-COUNTER ARRANGEMENT

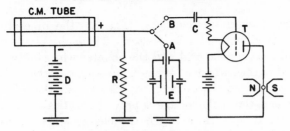

A—WITH ELECTROMETER, B—WITH TUBE DETECTION

b. QUENCHING CIRCUITS

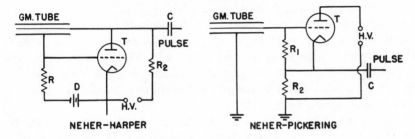

c. REICH SCALING CIRCUIT

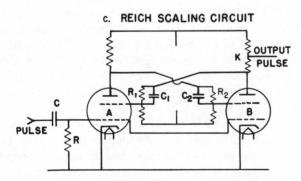

FIG. 8.   Diagram of Geiger counter circuit components.

resistor.   As soon as a pulse is created, the counter cylinder becomes more positive by the collected positive ions, the grid potential of T is raised, and a plate current starts to flow.   In this state the vacuum tube represents a rather low resistance and an appreciable potential drop will be established across the counter tube, which quenches the discharge.   As soon as the positive charge leaks from the grid through the resistor R, the electron tube again becomes nonconducting, the high voltage is re-established across the counter tube, and the counter is ready for the next count.

In the Neher-Pickering circuit (38) (Fig. 8b) the tube is normally conducting and functions as a low resistor. The high voltage is passing through the tube giving the grid and the counter wire almost the same potential as that of the cathode. When a pulse arrives, the grid becomes negative by the collected electrons on the center wire, the tube becomes nonconducting and the high voltage supply is practically disconnected from the counter tube. Again, when the charge leaks off to ground through R_1 and R_2 the previous active condition is restored.

Several modifications of these two basic principles of pulse extinguisher have been described (1). Multivibrator circuits using amplification and positive feedback have been constructed (16, 47). In the actual circuits pentodes are usually used. For tracer work the Neher-Pickering circuit is given preference because in this and similar circuits the cylinder of the counter tube is at ground potential. The cylinder acts as a protecting shield for the charged wire reducing disturbances when the counter is handled with the samples in the working condition. Such an arrangement is safer to operate.

The pulses from the quenching circuit can be directly fed into the recording circuit. Mechanical registers based on the movement of a ratchet actuated by a vane attracted by an electromagnet are relatively slow, not exceeding about 100 pulses per second for evenly spaced pulses, unless special precautions are taken (36). To increase the counting rate a scaling circuit is introduced (52). Such a circuit suppresses a definite number of pulses before reaching the mechanical recorder. Since scaling circuits are very fast, the resolving time of the counter system can be greatly improved. The function of such a circuit scaling by a factor of two is shown schematically in Fig. 8c (42).

The circuit has two stable conditions. Either tube A is conducting and tube B nonconducting or the reverse. The suppressor grids as well as the control grids control the action of the tube, and the circuit responds only to negative pulses. Suppose tube A is initially conducting and B nonconducting and a negative pulse is impressed at the control grid of tube A through a suitable condenser C. The current in tube A will decrease, the plate voltage will rise, and these changes are transmitted very rapidly through condenser C_2 to the suppressor grid of tube B and then held at their respective potentials through the resistance R. Since the suppressor grid of tube B becomes more positive, this tube will become conducting, the voltage across it will fall, and in a similar way as before the potential of the suppressor grid of tube A decreases to such an extent that tube A is now nonconducting. Since both tubes have their control grids connected together a second negative pulse will change the situation back to the original state, that is, tube A becomes conducting and B nonconducting. When this happens a negative pulse whose potential moves up or down each time the circuit trips is generated at point K. Through a condenser this pulse is transmitted to the next stage. Thus one negative pulse is transmitted to the output for every two pulses entering the circuit.

A battery of such circuits works in scals of 2^n, where n is the number of identical stages used. Every 2nd, 4th, and 8th pulse is passed and recorded. Scaling stages up to several thousand have been constructed. Interpolation of single counts, by means of the sequence of neon lamp indicators is incorporated. Recently ring circuits with a scale of 10 have been constructed (43). Such a decade scale reduction is more convenient for a large number of recordings. In order that the scaling circuit works properly the pulses from the extinguishing circuit are first converted by feeding them into a triode to change their sign and then applied to the grid of a thyraton. The grid bias of the thyratron acts as a discriminator, passing only pulses of one predetermined size, and the tube characteristics cause all the pulses to be sharpened and equalized. The output of the circuit are identical pulses equal in number to those from the counter tube.

The output from the scaling circuit are voltage pulses. In order to operate a mechanical recorder a transformation to current pulses must be made. This is accomplished by special circuits. A complete counting circuit using the described basic elements is shown in Fig. (9).

If pulses of uniform size and shape charge a condenser, which, after reaching a certain potential, trips a thyratron tube and then is completely discharged, the thyratron pulse can also operate a mechanical recorder. In this way large scaling numbers can be obtained, adjustable by the capacity of the condenser or by the pulse size used. If the charged condenser bleeds through a resistor and a galvanometer, the reading of the meter is proportional to the average counting rate with a time constant of $2\,RC$ seconds. Continuous graphical recording of the radioactivity is possible. The circuit is especially valuable for high counting rates (9, 25).

Recently properly designed counters and counter circuits have appeared on the market. Whether one uses self-built counter equipment or commercial models the counter tube and circuit have to be tested in their performance before use in any investigation.

3.3.4. Test of Counting Equipment. In this section some of the important tests to establish the reliability of the instrument will be mentioned (26). First the characteristic curve of the counter must be deter-

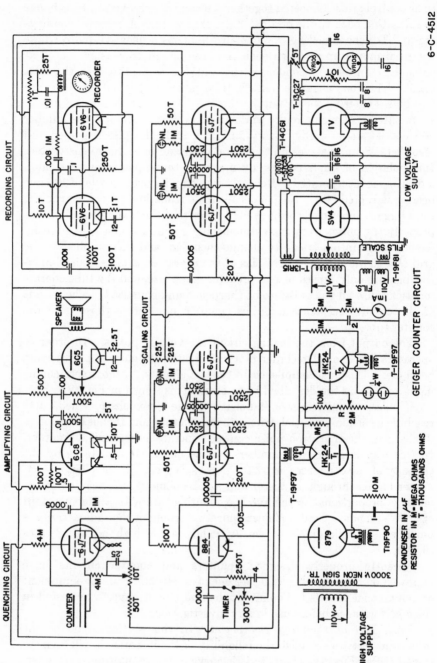

Fig. 9. Geiger counter circuit.

mined.   As one raises the high voltage potential on the counter from zero, no counts will be detected by the equipment at first, even when the counter is exposed to radiation.   After a certain potential, the starting potential, is reached, the counter begins to operate.   The starting potential depends on the biasing of the quenching circuit and is ordinarily above the threshold voltage.   From this point on the counting rate increases rapidly with increase of potential.   At a higher voltage over a limited range a shift in applied potential causes little or no change in the counting rate (Fig. 13b).   But further increase in potential will eventually cause the counting rate to rise very rapidly, soon leading to a continuous discharge.   Counters filled with organic vapors should not be exposed to this latter region of potentials because permanent damage might result. The region with a nearly constant counting rate is called the "plateau" of the counter.   Good reliable counter tubes have a wide plateau with almost no slope, although efficient stabilizing circuits permit the successful use of counters with quite narrow plateaus.   Because double counts are produced more frequently near the end of the plateau, the operating voltage is chosen closer to the low voltage side of the flattest portion. The plateau should be determined at a number of different counting rates since it might be shifted on the voltage scale.

At the operating voltage the background counts must be determined. Especially when dealing with weak samples the background counting rate has to be known with a fair degree of accuracy since it is subtracted from the measured counting rate of the sample.   The background must be taken under the exact conditions of the measurements, only without any source.   For laboratory counters of 1 to 2 cm. in diameter and 4 to 8 cm. in length, after shielding completely with a heavy iron shield and an additional 5 cm. of lead, the background is from 5 to 20 counts per minute, caused by cosmic radiation, and from natural radioactive material dispersed in matter.   To reduce secondary radiation the inside of the lead shielding is covered with aluminum.   A higher background often indicates contamination of the counter or the surroundings with radioactive material and a thorough cleaning should be undertaken.   Since some counters show photosensitivity, light-tight shielding should always be used.

The resolving time of the counter with the given equipment must be determined (3).   From the resolving time one can compute what fraction of counts are lost at the observed counting rate.   Even at relatively low counting rates such corrections are important if one seeks to obtain accurate results.   The counter and the counting assembly have a finite time of response.   In a certain time interval after each count the system is insensitive to incoming radiation.   Because of the random distribution of the received radiation from radioactive substances, some particles must follow each other so quickly that they are separated by a time interval shorter than the dead time of the counter. Since the probability of having short interval pulses is higher as the counting rate is increased the losses also increase.

In all radioactive measurements it is assumed that the decay of individual atoms is occurring at random, but that a definite number of particles decay in a long enough period of time in a large assembly of nuclei of the same kind. If this is the case the observed disintegration can be expressed by Poisson's law (48).

The probability (P_n) of observing (n) events in a random process when the average for a large number is (m) events, can be expressed by:

$$P_n = \frac{m^n}{n!} \cdot e^{-m}$$

This equation can be applied to compute coincidence losses of the counter equipment. Let the time interval in which the arrangement is insensitive to a successive pulse be (t_r), and the time interval for counting be (T). During that time the instrument counts only (n) particles giving an observed counting rate of $\frac{n}{T} = C$ whereas the true counting rate is $\frac{m}{T} = C_0$. One can derive from Poisson's equation: that $C_0 = C e^{c_0 t_r}$, which represents the relation of the true counting rate as a function of the observed counting rate and the resolving time.

If the true rate, C_0, increases, then the observed rate C is rising at first. However, it gradually passes through a maximum and later decreases. By differentiation the maximum value can be found at:

$$C_{\max} = \frac{1}{e t_r}$$

This equation gives the resolving time as:

$$t_r = \frac{1}{e C_{\max}}$$

If the counting is done well below the maximum counting rate as first approximation:

$$C_0 = C e^{c_0 t_r} \quad \text{is} \quad C_0 = C(1 + C_0 t_r)$$

thus
$$\frac{C_0}{C} = \frac{1}{1 - C t_r} = P$$

This is the usual expression used for computing the true counting rate from the observed rate and resolving time with sufficient accuracy for tracer assay. The function is represented in Fig. 13d.

For the determination of the resolving time, the method of maximum counting rate cannot be recommended, because the counter must be exposed to high counting rates, which are detrimental to its overall life time. By using two sources with true counting rates C_1 and C_2 as determined by direct counting if the samples are sufficiently weak, and finding the apparent counting rate C_{12} of the combined samples, t_r is given by

$$t_r = \frac{1}{C_1 + C_2} \cdot \ln \frac{C_1 + C_2}{C_{12}}$$

In the case when C_2 is α times stronger than C_1

$$t_r = \frac{1}{(\alpha + 1)C_1} \ln \frac{(\alpha + 1)C_1}{C_{12}}$$

The last expression can be used to advantage with liquid counters, where α is determined by the concentration. In case the two samples have approximately equal strength, the equation

$$t_r = \frac{2(C_1 + C_2 - C_{12})}{(C_1 + C_2)C_{12}}$$

can be used to compute t_r.

Since the resolving time is calculated from small differences, the individual counting rates must be known quite accurately. Resolving time corrections are applied before the background is subtracted.

Another factor to be determined is whether a counter counts double counts. Several reasons for close successive or spurious counts have been mentioned. The answer can be derived from several experiments. If one suspects some anomalous behavior of the counter a divergence coefficient can be determined, based on the randomicity of counts. By determining the counting rate (C) of a stable source (a) times the divergence coefficient is calculated as $W = \Sigma \frac{(C - \bar{C})^2}{aC}$ where $\bar{C}$ is the mean counting rate $\bar{C} = \frac{\Sigma C}{a}$. If the computed W is close to unity, there is a high probability that the data follow a Poisson distribution and therefore that the counter behaves properly. From statistics one obtains the fraction of counts which, within a certain number of counts, occurs in a predetermined time interval t. If this number is much higher than the calculated one, one can deduce that double counts were introduced by a single particle. An estimate of double counts can be made on the oscilloscope, usually permanently attached to the counter system, if at a low counting rate too many pulses in a given number of counts follow each other closely. For more accurate work special interval timers are constructed, (11, 44) or the individual counts are recorded on a moving tape.

The cathode ray oscillograph, together with a loud speaker, is a valuable aid for supervising the overall behavior of the counting equipment. A valuable test is to bring a source giving a high counting rate up to the counter. If this source is suddenly removed the counting rate should fall to a low value at once. If spurious counts are created, the higher rate will persist for a short time. Sometimes spurious counts can be decreased by counting on a lower portion of the plateau or by lowering the resistance to ground. Otherwise a counter has to be replaced if the spurious counts are produced by a defect in construction. Because spurious counts will increase with counting rate, the counting rate will be far from proportional to the received radiation and the obtained data from such a counter are of little value for quantitative measurements over a wide counting range.

For many practical purposes the efficiency of the counter should be known. The efficiency will depend on the construction and filling of the counter. Neglecting the absorption of the radiation by the wall of the counter at first, a beta particle, once finding itself in the sensitive volume, will trigger a discharge if it can produce secondary ions. The probability of such a process will depend on the specific ionization (ζ) of the gas at atmospheric pressure, the actual pressure (p) of the gas in the counter tube and the average distance (l) will be related to the cross-sectional area of the counters exposed to the radiation.

As the pressure (p) is lowered, the average distance (l) shortened, or gases used which have lower ionization efficiency, the counting efficiency will decrease and approach zero. On the contrary, on increasing these values the efficiency will gradually level off since it is necessary for only one collision to take place to release the discharge.

The counter efficiency (F) can be expressed by the relation

$$F = 1 - e^{\zeta l_p}$$

Since even beta rays produce several ion pairs when traveling 1 cm. in argon at 10 cm. Hg pressure, all argon filled counters, excepting only the very small ones, will be almost 100% efficient. A particle that entered the sensitive volume will be detected if its energy was not lowered by the absorption of the window below the ionization potential of the gas, and if it does not cross the counter tangentially so that its mean free path is larger than the distance traveled. If the same counter is filled with hydrogen at 10 cm. Hg pressure it will be only 60% efficient because of the much lower ionization efficiency of hydrogen.

Beta-ray counters can be tested for efficiency by counting a standard sample of solid potassium chloride or acetate, or a saturated solution of these salts in the case of liquid counters. A very convenient testing material for the bell type counter is a round piece of uranium glass the size of the sample or a piece of uranium glass tubing that can be slipped over the counter tube.   In this way the efficiency of different counters can be easily determined and compared.   Since the half life of these radioactive samples is long, the activity is constant, one can detect any change in counter behavior with time.   Quite different is the efficiency of a counter for gamma rays.   Many gamma rays will pass through the counter volume without creating a secondary electron, so that the efficiency is only about 1%.   The type of walls, solid or screen, its atomic weight and many other factors will improve the efficiency somewhat.   The gamma ray counters are tested best with radium standards.   The overall counting yield, the ratio of the number of disintegrations taking place in the sample to the number of disintegrations recorded, is affected by many more factors as will be discussed later.   Expressions can be derived for the sensitivity of a counter.   If the measured corrected counting rate be C_m and that of the background C_b then the relative activity of the sample is $C_m - C_b = C_s$.   The relative sensitivity of a counter for a given isotope can be defined as the necessary amount of radioactive material to give $\dfrac{C_s}{C_b} = 1$, or a counting rate of the sample equal to the background.

3.3.5. Preparation of Samples.   In the preparation of samples and the special technique of measurement to be used, the energy and energy distribution of the radiation emitted by the radioactive element is of primary importance.   This is true especially in the case of beta rays, because the absorption of the radiation must be taken into account.   Beta activity is by far the most dominant type of radioactivity that artificially produced radio elements possess.   The emitted beta rays of individual nuclei do not all have the same energy, so that from a large sample a continuous energy distribution will be observed.   The radioactive species are usually characterized by their maximum energy, but the most probable energy occurring in the spectrum might be considerably less than the indicated maximum energy.   Usually the average energy is only about one-third of the maximum energy.   The maximum energy of the emitted beta rays varies considerably from element to element.   Energies from less than 0.1 Mev to about 5 Mev are found.   The importance of energy, equivalent to the velocity of the particles, lies in the fact that they have a different range.   The range is defined as the distance the particle travels in matter before completely losing its ionizing property.   For more energetic beta rays above 0.6 Mev, the range (X) can be expressed closely by the formula:

$$X = 0.54V - 0.16$$

where X is given in thickness times density or mg./cm.^{2} and V in Mev. For energies below 0.2 Mev the range is given by an empirical equation: $X = \dfrac{V^{\frac{3}{2}}}{150}$ represented by an exponential curve.

Solid samples: The measurement of solid samples with counters and ionization chambers includes two cases. In the first case the radiation has to penetrate the barrier that separates the filling gas from the atmosphere. In the second case the energy of the emitted beta ray or of soft electromagnetic radiation resulting from orbit electron capture is insufficient to be transmitted through such windows. In that case the sample has to be introduced into the counter proper. A wide range of overlapping is possible and with rather strong samples and the thinnest windows the introduction of the sample into the counter can be avoided.

In all arrangements one is generally guided by the consideration that the largest fraction of the available radiation should enter the sensitive volume of the counter. There should be a minimum loss along the path of the particles from the origin to the place of registration. Because losses are unavoidable the geometrical arrangement should be designed for the highest degree of reproducibility.

The classical method of evaporating the sample from a liquid on to shallow platinum discs rarely gives satisfactory results when counting beta-ray activity because nonuniform deposits are obtained. The advantage of this method, however, is that one can use known analytical procedures, like ignition, heating to obtain stable precipitates, etc. Nonuniform deposits can be spread more evenly in a moistened state by a glass rod if the sample is rotated. Such samples are sometimes loosely deposited and care has to be taken not to contaminate the counter and surroundings. This method, therefore, will be used only in cases dealing with small amounts of solid, formed by complete evaporation of a solution which cannot otherwise be deposited.

If enough carrier material is present a convenient method is to deposit the sample uniformly on a polished aluminum disc of from 1 to 3 cm. in diameter (35). The disc forms the bottom of a cup made from a metal cylinder on which a heavier head can be screwed, which presses the disc liquid tight against the cylinder. The precipitate is suspended uniformly in alcohol, which prevents creeping and sticking to the container wall, so that all of the precipitate will eventually settle without the necessity of rinsing. Part of the liquid is sucked off; the rest can be evaporated by gentle heating. In this way uniform deposits with well defined areas are obtained.

Methods have been worked out to obtain uniform deposits of a standard area on filter paper (20). Any analytically useful precipitate is suitable. However, the many specific, sensitive, and insoluble precipitates with organic reagents offer many advantages. Such precipitates are often voluminous, easy to filter, and, since they are composed of low atomic weight elements, have a low absorption coefficient. Hardened filter paper is preferable. Ordinary filter paper, because of its texture does not give reproducible results. The use of hardened filter paper for depositing the radioactive precipitates is very convenient, since it can be easily disposed of after the measurements. The filter paper eliminates the tedious cleaning procedure when porous porcelain or fritted glass discs are used. In the latter case, after each cleaning the background counts of the filtering discs must be measured.

The deposition of the precipitate can be accomplished by filtration or by centrifugation. For larger amounts of precipitate the filtering apparatus shown in Fig. 10b can be used. The filter paper of the size of the outside vessel is placed on the flat fritted glass plate and a cylinder is pressed against it by springs. The substance is precipitated in a beaker, stirred up thoroughly, poured into the vessel, and suction applied. After washing the filter paper is taken out and dried. If the energy of the emitted radiation is sufficient the precipitate can be covered with a thin sheet of cellophane, which is fastened to the side of the filter paper by adhesive tape. An even better protection is obtained by spraying the precipitate with a few milliliters of a dilute collodion solution and drying. The filter paper can be wrapped in the same way around the counter tube as indicated in Fig. 10g and pressed tightly to the glass with a clamp. Since the precipitate is centered on the filter paper, and if the counter tube has paper sleeves as stops for wrapping, the same sensitive area of the counter is covered by the precipitate every time.

An apparatus indicated schematically in Fig. 10a can be recommended for smaller samples. The precipitate is made directly in the vessel in a horizontal position. After placing it perpendicularly and attaching to a suction bell, filtering and subsequent washings can be performed.

The precipitates are mounted on a table and pushed under the window of the bell type counter as shown in Fig. 10e. The deposits on metal discs are handled in the same way. By this arrangement the precipitate can be brought closer to the window of the counter than by sliding it from the side under the counter (Fig. 11b). In both cases good centering of the precipitate must be secured. For reasons of reproducibility the actual sample area should not exceed three-fourths of the window area. A similar arrangement as Fig. 10e has been described for automatic sample changing (40).

Because the fritted plate provides a uniform suction over the whole area defined by the glass cylinder precipitates of uniform thickness with

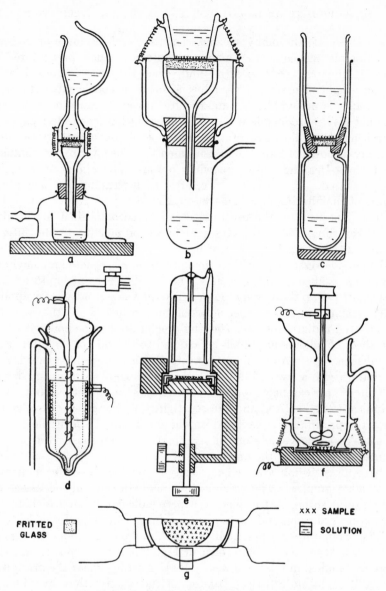

FRITTED GLASS ▨

××× SAMPLE

▤ SOLUTION

Fɪɢ. 10.   Equipment for sample preparation.
a. Fritted glass plate filtering apparatus for uniform deposition of small amounts of solid on filter paper
b. Filtering device for large volumes of liquid
c. Arrangement for the deposition of a precipitate on filter paper by centrifuging
d. Arrangement for electroplating the radioactive ions on the inside of a conducting cylinder
e. Sample holder for positioning the sample under a bell type counter
f. Apparatus for electroplating on a flat disc
g. Wrapping the filter paper with sample around a thin walled counter

476

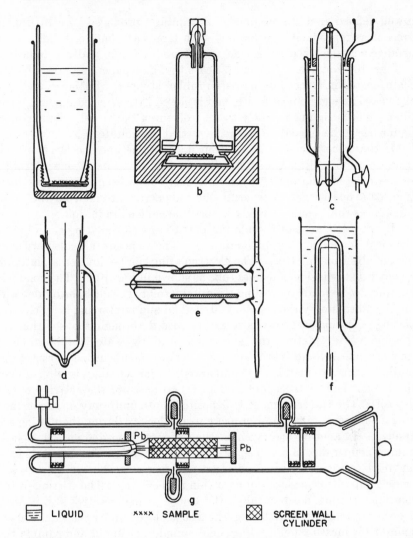

FIG. 11.   Counter constructions.
a. Centrifuging tube for deposition of radioactive material on filter paper or metal disc
b. Mounting of sample to be slipped under a bell type counter
c. Liquid jacket filling counter
d. Self draining and centering vessel for dipping counter
e. Side window pipette counter
f. Vessel for counting gamma activity of a liquid
g. Insertion counter for solids with screen wall cylinder

a well defined area are obtained.   Precipitates produced by centrifuging are not as reproducible, especially with larger amounts of solids.   Two arrangements for centrifugation were found suitable and are indicated in Figs. 10c and 11a.   In the first case the filter paper rests on a fritted plate, seated in a specially prepared rubber stopper.   In the second case the vessel is made out of lucite, and is closed by a screwed-on cap.   The filter paper is clamped tightly to the bottom of the vessel.   The mother liquor has to be sucked off from the settled precipitate.

If the tracer element is a cation it can sometimes be electroplated from solution (46).   The method is of special value if one attempts separate determinations of several radioactive species present in the solution, or if one wishes to separate the radioactive atoms from the other substances that would strongly absorb the emitted radiation.

By proper choice of the plating potential, electroplating can obviate chemical separation by precipitation.   The deposits are also without foreign absorbing matter.   The electroplating can be done on a platinum cylinder on the inside of a glass tube as shown in Fig. 10d.   The conducting ring can be made by sealing a platinum foil to the glass, or by depositing the platinum by the colloidal oil method and reinforcing it by electroplating.   During electrolysis a gas is passed through the solution for stirring.   After plating the gas is replaced by water for continuous rinsing while voltage is still applied.   Known microchemical procedures for depositing the metals can be followed.   The container is slipped over the narrow end of the counter (Fig. 7f) to measure the activity of the deposit.   The tracer element is deposited quite uniformly on a constant area if sufficient mixing and proper current density during the plating are applied.   In another arrangement the cation is deposited on a flat platinum or copper disc in a vessel, as shown in Fig. 10f.   The disc rests on a metal plate for electrical connection and forms the bottom of a vessel made tight with the glass top by a thin rubber ring.   The stirring of the solution is done mechanically, the anode being rotated also.   After deposition, washing, and drying, the disc is placed under the side window counter for measurement.   For small amounts of liquid and sample the deposition can be made on a straight platinum wire immersed in the plating solution.   A microplatinum crucible can serve as anode.   The counting is done by inserting the wire into the sensitive region of a counter shown in Fig. 7g.

For tracers where the emitted radiation is not sufficient to penetrate the counter window the sample must be put directly into the counter volume (6).   A convenient way to achieve this is to use the helium counter at atmospheric pressure.   Through a side arm helium is passed through the counter continuously (Fig. 12c) and escapes around the

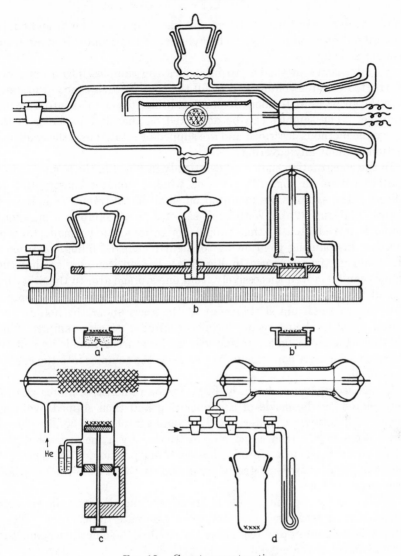

FIG. 12.   Counter constructions.

a. Insertion front window counter with samples moved into counting position
   by a magnet
b. Insertion side window counter with sample rotated into counting position
c. Continuous gas flow counter.
d. Arrangement for introducing a radioactive gas.

sample holder.   By this procedure various samples can be brought into the required position readily.   The cylinder of the cconter is made from a copper screen.

An alternative method is to introduce the samples into a specially constructed counter volume and to fill the counter each time.   Pumping down the air pressure to about 10 cm. Hg. brings the counter into working condition.   The samples can be deposited on the filter paper or metal disc by the methods described and are slipped or rotated into the counting position without any covering.

In the construction shown schematically in Fig. 12a the front window counter is used, in Fig. 12b the side window counter construction is utilized.   The samples are mounted on small metal frames as indicated in Figs. 12a[1] and 12b[1].   With each set of 8 to 10 samples a standard sample is introducted so that proper corrections can be made for the difference in counting yield owing to slightly changed filling conditions. The mounting frame shown in Fig. 12a[1], has an iron core so that the samples can be moved successively from one storage arm to the other by a small magnet.   A shallow impression on the bottom of the sample holder and a small pin sticking out in the glass under the hole in the counter cylinder helps secure proper centering of the sample.   The mounting of samples on a rotating disc actuated from outside by a stopcock is an even more convenient way to place the samples into the counting position.

In the arrangement shown in Fig. 11g the radioactive atoms can be electroplated on the inside of a copper ring and then slipped over the screen cylinder of the counter (32).   Several samples can be introduced at the same time.   Iron cored stops actuated by a magnet allow the sample to be fixed in a reproducible counting position.   The sensitive volume of the counter is protected by a lead partition from the radiation of the other samples.

In all cases where the sample is introduced directly into the counter extreme care is necessary so as not to contaminate the counter.   Even with the best standardized technique the results fall somewhat below the reproducibility of the outside sample method.

Liquid samples: In tracer investigations, a very suitable way to determine the radioactivity of the sample is to dissolve the precipitate in a liquid.   The main advantages are that the time necessary for preparation of uniform precipitates is eliminated and that reproducible solid angle conditions can be secured.   The method can be recommended where sufficiently penetrating radiation is emitted.

The immersion counter (Fig. 7f) that is dipped into the vessel containing the radioactive liquid is convenient to use (2).   The counter tube, if made of pyrex, can have a quite thin wall.   Care must be taken that the layer of liquid is not too narrow, otherwise variations in counting rate are observed because of eccentric location of the counter tube in the vessel and creeping of the solution along the walls.   Creeping can be partly eliminated by coating the counter with paraffin above the liquid level.   To avoid eccentric location, precise rack and pinion movement of the sample vessel, or of the counter, is used.   A self draining, self centering vessel (Fig. 11d) avoids the elaborate moving mechanism and the exact pipetting of the solution.   An alternate construction is the draining counter (Fig. 11c), where the vessel is permanently attached to the counter and the liquid is filled through a funnel into the spacing of the jacket (39).   The main disadvantage of both arrangements is the filling and the cleaning procedure after each measurement.   In case the solution contains a gamma-ray emitting substance, a satisfactory arrangement is shown in Fig. 11f.   The entire vessel, filled with liquid, is slipped over the counter tube.

A convenient way of determining the radioactivity of a liquid is to use pipette counters (27).   In one design (Fig. 7e) the jacket entirely surrounds the sensitive volume and has two side arms, one for filling and the other for suction.   The counter can be filled, emptied, cleaned, and rinsed with ease.   The completely enclosed arrangement prevents any spilling of radioactive liquid.   Also the counter can be permanently enclosed in a thick lead shell for protection against stray radiation.   The rigidly attached jacket automatically provides the same amount of liquid and liquid layer thickness in the same position with excellent reproducibility.   The outside heavy glass cylinder protects the fragile thin inside wall of the counter so that no particular care is needed in handling.   The arm for sucking up the solution can be provided with a sintered glass filter plate.   In this way solutions can be investigated that contain suspended radioactive solids that would interfere with the measurement.

For smaller amounts of liquids, below 1 ml., the pipette can be attached rigidly to the side window counter as indicated in Fig. 11e. Very thin glass windows sometimes crack under the action of the liquid. It is therefore more convenient to use a separate barrel pipette with a thin window on one side (33).   For very small amounts of liquids, below 0.1 ml., a counter was constructed where the central wire is replaced by a thin glass capillary as indicated in Fig. 7g.   The outside of the capillary is platinized.

Gaseous samples: If the radioactivity of a gas has to be determined the liquid jacketed counter (Fig. 7e) with a large volume can be used.   Both arms are now provided with stopcocks and means for evacuation, and a manometer for measuring the pressure of the gas must be provided.

Because of the lower self-absorption of radiation in a gas the thickness of the gas layer can be substantially increased.

If the radioactive gas is to be introduced directly into the counter, the arrangement of Fig. 12d will suffice. The radioactive gas is stored in a separate volume and the pressure measured. A small portion is trapped in the measuring volume between three stopcocks and then expanded into the counter previously filled for working conditions. Quantitative results often lack the desired reproducibility but the technique can be refined.

3.3.6. Corrections Introduced by the Sample. The measured counting rate is only a relative representation of the radioactive strength of the sample. Different losses occur that must all be evaluated for absolute measurements. In the following discussion it will be assumed that only one radioactive element is present, which decays into a nonactive nucleus. The measurements are made at constant temperature to avoid a change of the counter characteristic (24).

When radioactive atoms disintegrate the radiation emitted will be equally probable in all directions in space. If no magnetic or electrostatic field is acting to collimate the emitted charged particles, and if no collisions occur, the particles will travel on a straight path. Only those particles that travel in the direction of the measuring device in a solid angle given by its sensitive area can act as primary particles and be recorded. This fraction is called "the geometrical efficiency," or, "solid angle factor." The solid angle factor can seldom be computed with enough accuracy to be of any real value. Only in the case of a point source and known dimensions of the sensitive area can such calculations be made readily. For the bell shaped counter with a window radius r and the point source placed at a distance D from the center of the window, the geometrical efficiency E is given as the ratio of the area of a curved surface of a spherical segment of height $h = (D^2 + r^2)^{\frac{1}{2}} - D$ and radius $R_1 = (D^2 + r^2)^{\frac{1}{2}}$ and the surface of a sphere of the same radius, leading to:

$$E = \frac{1}{2} \frac{(1 - D)}{(D^2 + r^2)^{\frac{1}{2}}} \text{ or } \frac{1}{2} (1 - \cos \delta)$$

where δ is the angle between the sample and the effective diameter of the counter window. If (D) is large or the radius (r) small the area of the circle πr^2 can be compared directly to the surface $4\pi D^2$ of a sphere giving approximately:

$$E = \frac{1}{4} \left(\frac{r}{D} \right)^2$$

Since a disc radiator is used frequently integration from all points of the disc must be considered, leading to more complicated expressions. When

a. PULSE SHAPE

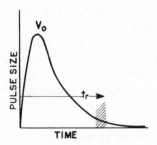

b. CHARACTERISTIC CURVE

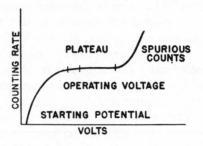

c. REGIONS OF COUNTER OPERATION

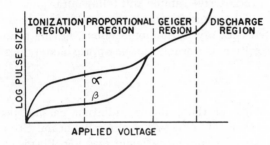

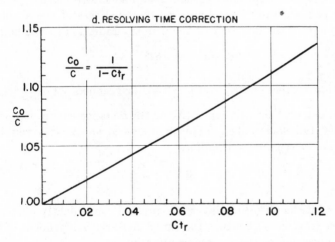

FIG. 13.

a. Typical pulse shape
b. Characteristic curve of a well working counter tube
c. Different regions in counter operation
d. Resolving time correction curve

the radiation is emanating from a monolayer of a circular area, small compared to the area of the counter window, and the sample is placed close to the window the geometrical factor is nearly one-half. Such a sample of known strength can then be used to determine the geometrical factor for any other arrangement, provided the radiation has a low absorption coefficient. This indicates that a strict standardization of sample area and counting arrangement is necessary to provide a constant geometry for all measurements.

The emitted radiation before reaching the counter has to traverse a distance filled with matter where interactions and absorption losses occur (19). It was experimentally verified that beta rays as well as gamma rays emitted from a radioactive sample will follow an exponential absorption curve closely. This empirical absorption law is mainly due to the fact that the emitted beta rays are inhomogenous, having a range of velocities. The absorption as a whole can be approximately described by the equation:

$$C = C_0 e^{-\mu d} \tag{1}$$

C_0 is the intensity of the primary radiation passing perpendicularly through an absorber of thickness d as a parallel beam with an absorption coefficient μ. The absorption coefficient (see Fig. 14a) is often expressed in terms of half absorptive thickness $d_{\frac{1}{2}}$, the thickness of the absorber necessary to reduce the intensity of the primary radiation to one half.

$$\mu d_{\frac{1}{2}} = \ln 2 = 0.693$$

For absorption corrections the ratio $\dfrac{C_0}{C} = Z$ is defined. For practical purposes one can consider the range (X) as the distance where the radiation intensity falls below 1%. This happens after about seven half thicknesses are interposed. Therefore

$$\mu X = 5 \quad \text{or} \quad \mu = \frac{X}{5}$$

The thickness of the absorbing layer is expressed conveniently in weight per unit area (mg./cm.²) because the range is nearly independent of the chemical composition of the absorbing material.

In the following section some solutions of important cases occurring frequently in tracer work will be given (31). The more rigorous solution of these problems involves the use of the exponential integral (50), leading to not easily evaluated equations. The complications arise because the radiation does not pass through the shortest thickness as a parallel beam but takes an oblique path at any angle. The equations should help in

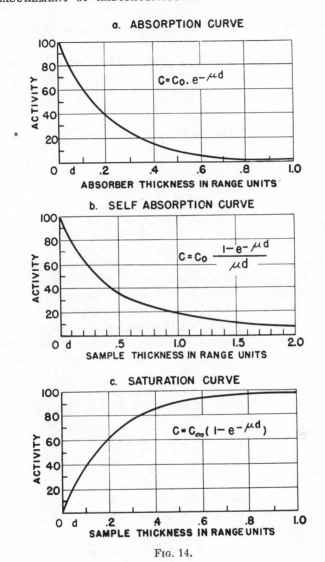

FIG. 14.

understanding the problem and can be used for numerical solutions if an accuracy of about 5% is sufficient.

Let the specific activity of a precipitate per unit weight be S. The measured counting rate of a flat sample of area A and uniform thickness d would be

$$C_0 = \frac{SAd}{2} \qquad (2)$$

if there is no absorption and the reflection of the radiation directed downward is neglected.

If an absorptive medium is present, assuming the experimental absorption curve, the measured activity will be

$$C = \frac{SA}{2} \int_0^d e^{-\mu x} \, dx$$

for

$$C_d = \frac{SA}{2\mu} (1 - e^{-\mu d})$$

$$\mu = \frac{5}{X}$$

Replacing

$$C_d = \frac{SAX}{10} (1 - e^{-5\frac{d}{X}}) \tag{3}$$

Using these equations several practical questions can be answered. The "self absorption factor" is given as the ratio between the number of particles leaving a sample to the radiation from a sample that would not absorb the radiation or that would consist only of a monolayer. This factor determines the radiation lost in the sample. It is obtained empirically by precipitating and counting samples of constant amount of radioactive atoms but with variable amounts of carrier element. Plotting the observed counting rate against the sample thickness, the curve illustrated in Fig. 14b is obtained. The activity decreases with increasing thickness (weight) of the precipitate. In order to obtain the activity of the undiluted sample the curve can be graphically extrapolated to zero thickness or the activity can be computed from the equation

$$C = C_0 \frac{1 - e^{-\mu d}}{\mu d} = C_0 \frac{1 - e^{-5\frac{d}{X}}}{5\frac{d}{X}}$$

obtained by dividing eqs. (2) and (3). Knowing μ or x and the actual thickness d the sample strength is obtained as

$$C_0 = C \cdot Q \qquad \text{where} \qquad Q = \frac{C_0}{C}$$

Closely related to the self absorption of a solid is the self absorption of a liquid due to different amounts of the solute in the solvent or to different densities of the solvent. To determine the absorption losses, the counting rate is plotted in a similar manner against the weight of the liquid.

The question arises, what is the activity of a sample of uniform activity, which is relatively thick. Such a sample is produced by piling up thin layers of the same material. C_∞ is given when $d \to \infty$. From eq. (2) it follows:

$$C_\infty = \frac{SA}{2} = \frac{SAX}{10} \tag{4}$$

A sample which has a thickness equal to the range of the particles in the solid will have only about one-tenth the activity it would have if the whole activity were concentrated in a monolayer.

It is often important to know what the activity of a uniform sample of various thicknesses is as compared to an infinitely thick sample. This can be derived from eqs. (3) and (4)

$$\frac{C_d}{C_\infty} = 1 - e^{-\mu d} = 1 - e^{-5\frac{d}{X}}$$

The equation represents the saturation curve, indicated in Fig. 14c. As expected the activity at first is increased with increasing thickness but eventually, at a thickness equal to the range, maximum activity is obtained. For correction purposes we define $\frac{C_\infty}{C_d} = H$.

The saturation curve has several practical implications. In order to compare precipitates of uniform activity and area directly one must eliminate the thickness factor. For practical purposes this can be achieved by counting precipitates that are thicker than the range or by using precipitates with a constant thickness (d) obtained by adding sufficient carrier element to make the total amount of precipitate constant. Only in cases of thin deposits is the activity of the deposits directly proportional to the number of radioactive atoms present. Knowing d, one can also calculate $C_\infty = C_d H$.

The same analysis can be applied to liquid counters. For the same counter, a radioactive solution of constant strength, and the same height of the liquid jacket, a similar counting efficiency curve is obtained as for a solid, by increasing the thickness of the liquid layer. It is apparent that the counting rate must level off with increasing thickness because more radiation coming from the outer layers is absorbed by the inner ones. The advantage of a liquid counter is that the absorbing layer can be kept constant all the time. This allows one to use a narrow spacing, thereby increasing the counting yield since a more concentrated solution can be made with the same amount of solid.

The radiation, on leaving the sample, has to penetrate a layer of air and the wall of the counter. By putting the counter with the sample into a bell jar and evacuating successively to lower pressures the "air absorption factor" can be evaluated. The factor also contains a scattering contribution due to the surrounding air. On the other hand by interposing sheets of known thicknesses of material from which the counter window is made the "window absorption factor" can be found, extrapolating again to zero thickness. Or knowing the window thickness, the amount of radiation transmitted by the window can be calculated from eq. (1) (Fig. 14a). However, these two factors are seldom considered if absolute values are not desired since they remain practically unchanged for a given counting arrangement.

A factor that increases the counting rate is the back scattering and secondary emission of the surroundings. Its magnitude is difficult to evaluate quantitatively and the effect can be kept constant only by keeping the position of any object in the vicinity of the counting apparatus unchanged during the measurements, and by using a base of constant dimensions for the support of the sample.

In evaluating the measurements one must consider the decay of radioactivity with time. If the measurements extend over an appreciable length of time compared to the half life of the substance, all the measured activities should be corrected to a given time, usually the start of the experiment.

From the known equation:

$$\frac{C_t}{C_{t_0}} = e^{-\lambda(t-t_0)}$$

the correction can be made if the decay constant (λ) is known. The decay constant is often given in terms of the "half life" $\lambda t_{\frac{1}{2}} = \ln 2$. In radioactive assay the counting interval is usually a small fraction of the half life of the sample. A constant source of radiation can therefore be assumed for the counting interval. Only in cases when the counting interval is extended over several percent of the half life, a correction for the decay of the source during measurements must be applied.

Frequently, due to methods of sample preparation from unseparated isotopic mixtures, the radioactive sample contains two or more radioactive isotopes of different half life and in unknown proportions. In this case a simple decay correction cannot be made. For such measurements and preferably in all the others, the radioactivity of the sample is compared to the radioactivity of a standard, which was prepared at the start of the experiment and is measured each time the sample is evaluated. This method is often called "piloting" the sample. It must be considered, however, that sometimes the radioactive element decays into another element which is also radioactive. While both would remain in the standard sample, the daughter substance could be completely eliminated by the process being investigated. In this case simple "piloting" would give erroneous results.   The pilot sample must undergo the same procedure of isolation as the true sample.

3.3.7. Statistics of Counting and Sample Strength.   Even if all of the errors of the counter and of the sample are known and corrected for, the measurements still have an uncertainty inherent to all measurements dealing with the counting of individual particles emitted by a radioactive substance.   Statistical fluctuations affect the accuracy of the measurements, dependent on the total number of particles recorded.   Weak samples must be counted considerably longer than samples with high counting rates.   Usually the results are expressed in terms of the probable error given as:

$$P = 0.67 \sqrt{N}$$

where N is the total number of counts taken.   This indicates that there is a probability of 0.5 that the true value will lie between $N \pm P$.

The number of counts which must be taken in order that the probable error is below a given percentage is shown in Table I.

TABLE I

Probable error (%)	Approx. number of counts
10	50
5	200
1	5,000
0.5	20,000
0.1	450,000

The probability that the measured error is greater than b times the probable error is given in Table II.

TABLE II

b	Occurrence
1	0.500
2	0.177
3	0.043

The probable error of the result is also affected by the probable error of the background.   If $N \pm n$ is the count of the sample and $M \pm m$ that of the background, the sum or difference of the two values is given by

$$(N \pm n) \pm (M \pm m) = N \pm M \pm (n^2 + m^2)^{\frac{1}{2}}$$

The combined error is the square root of the sum of the squares of individual errors.

Similarly the quotient of two counting sets is:

$$\left(\frac{N \pm n}{M \pm m}\right) = \frac{N}{M} + \frac{N}{M}\left[\left(\frac{n}{N}\right)^2 + \left(\frac{m}{M}\right)^2\right]^{\frac{1}{2}}$$

correlating the probable error of an operation often performed with counting rates. If the counting of the same sample was repeated under identical conditions a times, the standard deviation can be calculated from equation

$$\epsilon = \left[\frac{\Sigma(C - \bar{C})^2}{a(a - 1)} \right]^{\frac{1}{2}} \quad \text{where} \quad \bar{C} = \frac{\Sigma C}{a}$$

This procedure expresses best counting data of weak samples.

Ordinarily one does not count the background with the same probable error as the sample, since this would take an unnecessarily long counting time, but makes the ratio of the counting times of the sample to the background the same as their respective counting rates.

In radioactive tracer application the radioactive sample strength is rarely expressed in absolute units, i.e., grams of radioactive atoms present as calculated from the absolute number of disintegrations per minute and from the decay constant. The difficulty of such an undertaking can be seen from the fact that up to the present time, with the best available equipment, the standard of radioactive decay "the millicurie" is known only to about 4%. A "millicurie" is the number of alpha particles emitted per second by 1 mg. of pure radium element free of its radioactive disintegration products. One millicurie was defined by international agreement as 3.7×10^7 disintegrations per second. For practical measurements a standard has to be used, to which all other measurements are referred. As a beta-ray standard the β-ray emission of UX_2 can be utilized. A weighed quantity of U_3O_8 is spread on a base and covered with a 5-mil aluminum foil to filter out the alpha radiation. Since 3.5 g. of U_3O_8 correspond to one of UX_2 the strength of the standard sample is evaluated. In case of gamma-ray emission the sample can be expressed in radium equivalents, but it is becoming more customary to express gamma radiation in roentgen units.

To eliminate some of the difficulties in expressing the radioactive strength of artificially radioactive elements a new unit, the rutherford, "rd," was proposed (7). A microrutherford, "μrd," is defined as one disintegration per second. Any arrangement which would determine the total number of disintegrations per second would consequently directly determine the strength of the sample in "rd."

4. Special Analytical Procedures

4.1. General Assumptions and Procedures

In many of the experiments it is assumed that the radioactive isotopes, at least in solution, are homogeneously distributed among the nonactive ones. This implies that the ratio of active to nonactive species is constant in any volume element. Apart from minute statistical fluctuations this will always be the case if sufficiently fast diffusion takes place and if proper mixing and shaking of the sample is arranged after addition of the radioactive tracer to the bulk of the nonactive carrier isotope.

It is often taken for granted that the radioactive isotope behaves like the nonactive one. Since the radioactive isotope can differ by several mass units from the stable one, some differences may occur in procedures where mass plays a role.

The radioactive isotopes offer some special analytical procedures which can be used to advantage in some investigations. In many applications of radioactive tracers a great deal of data can be purely relative. In such cases the counting rate is determined with the given equipment for a standard geometrical arrangement, using samples of identical size and composition. Gamma-ray measurements can be directly compared if all other radiation that could reach the detecting device from the sample is screened off by a sufficiently thick aluminum or lead foil. Also, beta-ray emitters give relative results if the samples have at least the thickness of the range of the emitted radiation. Another necessary requirement is a homogeneous mixture of the radioactive atoms in the precipitates. In cases, when only limited amount of sample material is on hand, the self absorption correction is applied. With liquid counters that have a constant jacket spacing relative values are always obtained for the same tracer, as long as the density of the solution is unchanged. Relative counting rates are directly comparable among themselves or are correlated to the amount of carrier element present.

If measurements of an absolute character are desired, all the other factors affecting the counting yield must be quantitatively evaluated. The procedure of applying these corrections for a solid sample is usually as follows: The probable error of the counting rate is determined and the necessary number of counts taken in the required time interval. The counting rate is computed and the resolving time correction made by multiplying with the factor P. The background is now subtracted, giving the corrected counting rate.

In order to obtain the true activity of the sample the corrected counting rate is further adjusted for the counting yield Y, which is composed of several factors. It includes the solid angle factor (E) and the counter efficiency (F). From the known maximum energy the range of the radiation is computed. Now the self absorption factor (Q) can be evaluated. The absorption of the radiation by the counter window and by the air is corrected by the factor Z, the stray and back scattering by the factor (U). The counting yield is given by:

$$Y = (E) \cdot (F) \cdot (Q) \cdot (Z) \cdot (U).$$

Dividing the new counting rate by the total weight of the sample, the counting rate per unit sample weight is obtained. From the chemical composition of the sample the actual amount of carrier element is evaluated and the counting rate for 1 mg. of the element is computed. This value can be further expressed in "mC" or "rd" units. For liquid samples a similar procedure can be adopted.

The accuracy of the result will depend on how well the correction factors are known. Usually, under best conditions and care one can get the sample strength to within only several per cent of the true values.

The actual process of determination will depend largely on the energy of the emitted radiation, on the sample strength, and on the particular problem of investigation. In many cases it is a matter of choice whether to use an ionization chamber or counter equipment. Both instruments, at moderate radioactivities can give data with about equal accuracy. The electroscope is simple, inexpensive, and can be operated easily without close supervision. Modifications for the insertion of samples into the sensitive volume for weak energy beta-ray emitters or an adaptation for the determination of gases have been described (21). On the other hand, the advantage of the counter is its higher sensitivity at very weak intensities and also the adaptability for automatic timing and recording. The tiresome reading of the fiber position can be avoided through photoelectric timing of the fiber movement between certain marks. It should be mentioned that integrating roentgen dosimeters, fitted with a suitable ionization chamber can be used for tracer work, if stronger samples are available.

As to the actual sample technique, the adopted method will depend mainly on the energy of the emitted radiation and on the problem to be solved. The procedures described can well serve as a guide.

Isotopes with very weak beta radiation are best introduced in a gaseous form into the counter and mixed with the filling gas. For low activity the counter (Fig. 12d) can be quite large, because the background of the counter is proportional to the cross section of the counter cylinder whereas the counting rate of the sample is proportional to the volume. The system, after counting, must be throughly flushed. Strong samples must be diluted. This procedure is suitable for tritium. The sample is usually converted first to water and then reduced to hydrogen. Similarly carbon and sulfur can be converted to CO_2 and SO_2.

Excepting tritium, almost all other elements emitting low energy beta rays can be precipitated and the activity determined either by introducing the precipitate directly into the measuring device or passing the radiation through a thin window. It is a common experience, as already stated, that organic reagents are preferable because of their greater sensitivity and specificity.   They filter readily and make uniform deposits of low density, with good adherence to the paper base.   For these reasons it is advantageous to precipitate sulfate as benzidine sulfate instead of barium sulfate, copper with benzoin oxime instead of ferrocyanide.   Many metals can be electroplated or their activity determined while still in solution.

In the following table are given the half life and maximum beta rays, energy and range for some of the frequently used artificial radioactive tracers.

TABLE III

Isotope	A	Radiation	Half-life m = min. d = days y = years	Max. energy of radiation Mev
T	3	β^-	12 y	0.01
C	11	β^+	20.5 m	0.99
C	14	β^-	6400 y	0.15
N	13	β^+	10.1 m	1.24
F	18	β^+	110 m	0.60
Na	22	β^+, γ	3 y	0.58
Na	24	β^-, γ	14.8 h	1.40
Mg	27	β^-, γ	10.2 m	1.80
Si	31	β^-	170 m	1.80
P	32	β^-	14.3 d	1.69
S	35	β^-	87.1 d	0.17
Cl	38	β^-, γ	38 m	4.94
K	40	β^-	1.4×10^9 y	1.40
K	42	β^-	12.4 h	3.57
Ca	45	β^-	180 d	0.26
Fe	59	β^-, γ	47 d	0.46
Co	58	β^-	72 d	0.47
Cu	64	β^-, β^+	12.8 h	0.58
Zn	63	β^+, γ	38 m	2.36
Zn	65	β^+	250 d	0.35
As	74	β^+, β^-, γ	17.5 d	1.3
Br	82	β^-, γ	34 h	0.46
Sr	89	β^-	54 d	0.15
Sb	124	β^-, γ	60 d	1.60
I	131	β^-, γ	8 d	0.59
Pb	210	β^-, γ	22 y	0.02

4.2. Radiometric Titration

In addition to the chemical methods of determining the equivalence point in volumetric analysis the radioactive property of atoms, especially those artificially made, can be used successfully as endpoint indicators in precipitation reactions (27). In such a titration, where the readings of the activity indicator are proportional to the amount of radioactive atoms present either in the solution or in the precipitate, we should obtain three basic types of radiometric titration curves. Since the radioactivity measurement of the liquid phase can be done more accurately and more conveniently, the activity measurements of the liquid will be considered only.

If the substance in the solution to be titrated is mixed with a radioactive isotope and the reagent is inactive during the titration, the activity of the solution decreases due to the removal of the active substance as precipitate. At the endpoint only a small activity remains given by the background of the detecting device and the solubility of the precipitate. If, on the other hand, the solution to be titrated is inactive, but the reagent is radioactive, then during the first addition of the reagent, up to the equivalence point, almost no change in radioactivity is observed. Only after the endpoint is exceeded does the radioactivity increase by further addition of the reagent. If both the substance and reagent are radioactive one observes first a decrease, and, after the endpoint, an increase of the radioactivity in the solution.

If the measured activities are plotted against the volume of the added reagent, a break in the titration curve indicates the endpoint. Under favorable conditions of solubility and concentration straight lines are obtained (29).

It can be shown that the ideal titration curve in a simple precipitation reaction $A^{n+} + B^{n-} = AB$ solid, is represented first by a straight line given by the equation:

$$C = K_a A_0 + K_b B_x$$

where C = corrected counting rate of the solution,
A_0 = initial concentration of the substance A,
B_x = reagents added, and k_a and k_b are constants

for the radioactivity of A and B on the given detecting device. When B_x becomes $B_x S/A_0$, where S is the solubility product of AB given by $(A)(B) = S$, the titration curve is given by the equation:

$$C = \frac{k_a + k_b}{2} (A_0 - B_x) + \frac{k_a + k_b}{2} \sqrt{(A_0 - B_x)^2 + 4S}$$

which has the form of a hyperbola. The equivalence point $B_x = A_0$ is given as the intersection of the two asymptotes

$$C = k_a(A_0 - B_x)$$
$$C = k_b(A_0 - B_x)$$

If $S/A_0 < 10^{-3}$ the first straight part of the titration curve becomes negligible and the asymptotes coincide well with the tangents to the titration curve. Drawing the tangents is the usual way to determine the endpoints at their intersection. The different titration curves when $k_a = 0$, $k_b = 0$ or $k_a = k_b = 1$ are indicated in Fig. 15. The determination can be made with the pipette counter using a fritted glass filter on the immersed arm of the counter tube.

Activities can be measured either with a counting rate meter or with a mechanical counter and scaling circuit. The mechanical counter gives more accurate average values for weak activities. Correction for back-

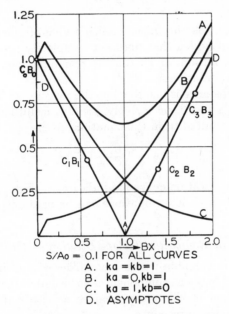

FIG. 15. Idealized radiometric titration curves under different conditions.

ground and volume change due to the added reagent should be applied. The volume change correction is taken into account by the equation:

$$C_{\text{cor}} = C_{\text{obs}} \frac{L + l}{L}$$

where L is the original volume of the liquid and l the volume of the liquid added. The equation can be used only if the solubility of the precipitate can be neglected.

The accuracy of such titrations is of the order of one to two per cent due to the scattered nature of the titration points and other errors caused by the relatively low activities at the endpoint. Therefore, if the counting is done for a limited time only, the titration lines are drawn to fit the points farther from the endpoint.

The sensitivity of the indicator can be adjusted by the concentration of radioactive isotopes. The method should prove of value where the total amount of carrier element has to be determined. It is not necessary to perform the whole titration curve, two points before or after the equivalent point are enough to find the amount of carrier present. From the equation of the asymptotes of the titration curve one can derive the amount A of the substance present by the relation

$$A = \frac{C_0 B_1}{C_0 - C_1}.$$

In this equation C_0 is the initial radioactivity of the solution, B_1 the amount of reagent added that does not completely precipitate the substance from the solution, and C_1 is the remaining counting rate of the solution after precipitation.

In case the substance is inactive but the reagent is radioactive and an excess B_2 and B_3 is added successively, yielding counting rates C_2 and C_3, then A can be computed from the equation

$$A = \frac{C_3 B_2 - C_2 B_3}{C_3 - C_2}$$

The points on the titration curve are indicated in Fig. 15. Many direct and indirect analytical determinations can be based on this and similar procedures (12).

4.3. Radioactive Isotope Dilution Methods

This method is valuable where a complicated multicomponent mixture is present and only one component is to be determined quantitatively (22). The isolation of this component in a pure state would require elaborate fractionation procedures.

Suppose there are A grams of a substance in a mixture and that B grams of the same substance with some radioactive atoms is added. Let the counting rate for one gram of B under standard conditions be C_B. After homogeneous mixing has taken place the counting rate C_{A+B} is determined for a small isolated part of the mixture. Since the relation holds:

$$C_{B+A} = \left(\frac{B}{B + A}\right) C_B$$

it follows that:

$$A = B\left(\frac{C_B}{C_{B+A}} - 1\right)$$

The unknown amount of substance A is determined from the amount of B added and the measured counting rates C_B and C_{B+A}.

On the other hand the amount of B might be unknown and a given amount A of the nonactive molecules is added.   In such a case:

$$B = A \; \frac{1}{\dfrac{C_B}{C_{B+A}} - 1}$$

It is often observed that when radioactive atoms are added to a system, for example to a suspension of a solid in a liquid, the radioactivity of the solution diminishes with time.   The uptake of the radioactivity by the precipitate can be caused by many processes such as occlusion, absorption, diffusion, and exchange reactions.   The rate and endpoint of such a process can therefore be followed by radioactivity measurements. In some cases analytical determinations can be based on such a procedure, closely resembling the isotope dilution method (28).

For example, suppose there are A grams of a given ion in an insoluble precipitate suspended in a solution to which we add B grams of the same species now dissolved in the solution.   Let the added ion be partly radioactive with an initial counting rate C_B.   After a certain time, due to the diffusion of the ions from the solution into the precipitate and vice versa, a homogeneous distribution of the radioactive ions throughout the whole system will result, so that the radioactivity of the solution will be:

$$C_{AB} = C_B \left(\frac{B}{B + A} \right).$$

This yields the same result as the isotope dilution method.   In the former case the mixing was molecular whereas now it is ionic.   Again the amount of the ion A in the solid compound can be computed from radioactive measurements and the known amounts of B added.   The process and the time necessary for a homogeneous distribution has to be established first. If the exchange of the radioactive atoms is restricted to the surface of a solid only, the specific area of the solid can be determined.

5. Protection Measures

In any radioactive tracer work it has to be realized that the emitted radiation is biologically active.   If sufficiently strong it has a destructive effect on the blood and tissue cells of the living organism.   Sufficient body shielding by lead barriers should be adopted.   The precipitates and solution must be handled with sufficiently long forceps and tongs, while the head can be protected with a several-centimeter thickness of lead glass without obscuring clear vision.   Frequent measurement of the radiation received by the body should be taken.   The tolerance dose of 0.3 r/week should not be exceeded.   At least once a year a blood analysis should be made. Any dangerous contamination of skin and clothing can be detected with available sensitive measuring devices. If the radio-activity handled reaches the limits where direct shielding becomes unmanageable, remote control of all operations must be adopted.

ACKNOWLEDGMENT

It is a pleasure to thank Dr. E. U. Condon, at present director of the National Bureau of Standards, for his deep interest in tracer work during my Westinghouse Research Fellowship in 1939–40.

GENERAL REFERENCES

Bale, W. F., and Bonner, J. F., Determination of Radioactivity in Physical Methods of Organic Chemistry. Interscience, New York, 1946, Vol. II.
Glasser, O., Medical Physics. The Year Book Publishers, Chicago, 1944.
Jaffey, A. H., Kohman, T. P., and Crawford, J. A., A Manual on the Measurement of Radioactivity. Declassified report M-cc-1602, M626.
Korff, S. H., Electron and Nuclear Counters. Van Nostrand, New York, 1946.
Lewis, W. B., Electrical Counting. Cambridge, London, 1942.
Meyer, St., and Schweidler, E., Radioaktivitat. Teubner, Leipzig, 1927.
Rasetti, F., Elements of Nuclear Physics. Prentice-Hall, New York, 1936.
Strong, J., Procedures in Experimental Physics. Prentice-Hall, New York, 1938.
Wilson, W. D., Nier, A. O. C., and Reimann, S. P., Preparation and Measurement of Isotopic Tracers. J. W. Edwards, Ann Arbor, Michigan, 1946.
Worthing, A. G., and Geffner, J., Treatment of Experimental Data. Wiley, New York, 1943.

REFERENCES

1. Bale, W. F., and Bonner, J. F. Jr., Rev. Sci. Instruments 14, 222 (1943).
2. Bale, W. F., Haven, F. L., and LeFevre, M. L., Rev. Sci. Instruments 10, 193 (1939).
3. Beers, Y., Rev. Sci. Instruments 13, 72 (1942).
4. Bradt, H., Gugelot, P. D., Huber, O., Medicus, H., Preiswerk, P., and Scherrer, P., Helv. Phys. Acta 19, 77 (1946).
5. Brown, B. W., and Curtiss, L. F., J. Research Natl. Bur. Standards 35, 147 (1945).
6. Brown, S. C., Phys. Rev. 59, 954 (1941).
7. Condon, E. U., and Curtiss, L. F., Phys. Rev. 69, 672 (1946).
8. Curtiss, L. F., J. Research Natl. Bur. Standards 30, 157 (1943).
9. Curtiss, L. F., and Brown, B. W., J. Research Natl. Bur. Standards 34, 53 (1945).
10. Copp, D. H., and Greenberg, D. M., Rev. Sci. Instruments 14, 205 (1943).
11. Davis, F. J., and Curtiss, L. F., J. Research Natl. Bur. Standards 29, 405 (1942).
12. Ehrenberg, R., Physikalische Methoden der Analytischen Chemie. Akademische Verlagsgesellschaft, Leipzig, 1933, Vol. I, p. 333.
13. Evans, R. D., and Mugele, R. A., Rev. Sci. Instruments 7, 441 (1936).
14. Frey, P., Helv. Phys. Acta 19, 41 (1946).
15. Geiger, H., and Müller, W., Physik Z. 29, 839 (1928).
16. Getting, I. A., Phys. Rev. 53, 103 (1938).
17. Good, W. M., Kip, A., and Brown, S. C., Rev. Sci. Instruments 17, 262 (1946).
18. Hamilton, T. G., Radiology 39, 541 (1942).

19. Hendricks, R. H., Brynes, L. G., Thomas, M. D., and Ivie, J. O., *J. Phys. Chem.* **47**, 496 (1943).
20. Henriques, F. C. Jr., Kistiakowsky, G. B., Margnetti, C., and Schneider, W. G., *Ind. Eng. Chem., Anal. Ed.* **18**, 349 (1946).
21. Henriques, F. C. Jr., and Margnetti, C., *Ind. Eng. Chem., Anal. Ed.* **18**, 415, 417, 420 (1946).
22. Henriques, F. C. Jr., and Margnetti, C., *Ind. Eng. Chem., Anal. Ed.* **18**, 476 (1946).
23. Keston, A. S., *Rev. Sci. Instruments* **14**, 293 (1943).
24. Korf, S. A., Spatz, W. D., and Hilberry, N., *Rev. Sci. Instruments* **13**, 127 (1942).
25. Kip, A., Bousquet, A., Evans, R. D., and Tuttle, W., *Rev. Sci. Instruments* **17**, 323 (1946).
26. Lifschutz, H., and Duffendack, O. S., *Phys. Rev.* **54**, 714 (1938).
27. Langer, A., *J. Phys. Chem.* **45**, 639 (1941).
28. Langer, A., *J. Chem. Phys.* **10**, 321 (1942).
29. Langer, A., and Stevenson, D. P., *Ind. Eng. Chem., Anal. Ed.* **14**, 770 (1942).
30. Lauritsen, C. C., and Lauritsen, T., *Rev. Sci. Instruments* **8**, 438 (1937).
31. Libby, W. F., *Ind. Eng. Chem., Anal. Ed.* **19**, 2 (1947).
32. Libby, W. F., Lee, D. D., *Phys. Rev.* **55**, 245 (1939).
33. McKay, H. A. C., *Rev. Sci. Instruments* **12**, 103 (1941).
34. Montgomery, C. G., and Montgomery, D. D., *J. Franklin Inst.* **229**, 585 (1940).
35. Montgomery, C. G., and Montgomery, D. D., *J. Franklin Inst.* **231**, 447, 509 (1941).
36. Neher, H. V., *Rev. Sci. Instruments* **10**, 29 (1939).
37. Neher, H. V., and Harper, W. W., *Phys. Rev.* **49**, 940 (1936).
38. Neher, H. V., and Pickering, W. H., *Phys. Rev.* **53**, 316 (1938).
39. Olson, A. R., Libby, W. F., Long, F. A., and Halford, R. S., *J. Am. Chem. Soc.* **58**, 1313 (1936).
40. Peacock, W. C., and Good, W. M., *Rev. Sci. Instruments* **17**, 255 (1946).
41. Penick, D. B., *Rev. Sci. Instruments* **6**, 115 (1935).
42. Reich, H. J., *Rev. Sci. Instruments* **9**, 222 (1938).
43. Regener, V. H., *Rev. Sci. Instruments* **17**, 185 (1946).
44. Roberts, A., *Rev. Sci. Instruments* **12**, 71 (1941).
45. Rosenblum, C., and Flagg, J. A., *J. Franklin Inst.* **228**, 471, 623 (1939).
46. Ross, J. F., and Chapin, M. A., *Rev. Sci. Instruments* **13**, 77 (1942).
47. Ruark, A., *Phys. Rev.* **53**, 316 (1938).
48. Schiff, L. I., *Phys. Rev.* **50**, 88 (1936).
49. Seaborg, G. T., *Chem. Rev.* **27** (1940).
50. Soddy, W. M., and Russell, A. S., *Phil. Mag.* **19**, 725 (1910).
51. Strajman, E., *Rev. Sci. Instruments* **17**, 232 (1946).
52. DeVault, D., *Rev. Sci. Instruments* **12**, 83 (1941).
53. Weltin, H., *Rev. Sci. Instruments* **14**, 278 (1943).
54. Yankwich, P. E., Rollefson, C. K., and Norris, T. H., *J. Chem. Phys.* **14**, 131 (1946).

Statistical Analysis*

By

J. SHERMAN

Philadelphia Naval Shipyard, Philadelphia, Pennsylvania

CONTENTS

* The opinions expressed in this chapter are those of the author, not of the Navy Department.

When any scientific conclusion is supposed to be proved on experimental evidence, critics who still refuse to accept the conclusions are accustomed to take one of two lines of attack. They may claim that the *interpretation* of the experiment is faulty, that the results reported are not in fact those which should have been expected had the conclusion drawn been justified, or that they might equally well have arisen had the conclusion drawn been false. Such criticisms of interpretation are usually treated as falling within the domain of statistics.—*The Design of Experiments*, R. A. Fisher

1. STATISTICAL ANALYSIS APPLIED TO SPECTROGRAPHIC MEASUREMENTS

1.1. Introduction

This chapter will be concerned with the statistical approach to the evaluation of the precision of controlled physical measurements or experiments. The problem will be considered as being twofold; (1) to express precision in an objective form, usable for prediction and (2) the use of precision estimates as a guide for a methodical procedure to evaluate the contributions of the various experimental factors to the total "error." It is impractical to develop a rigorous statistical theory in this discussion. What will be presented should be considered as a kind of justification or explanation of the general arithmetical methodology. No mathematical proofs or derivations will be given. While the symbols will be given denotations peculiar to spectrography and spectrographic procedures, it should be clear that any other consistent and analogous set of meanings will do equally well.

1.2. Generalities

1.2.1. Theory of Probability and Random Variate. The concepts of probability and of the random variable have undergone many transformations in their historical development and undoubtedly are still unsatisfactory to many minds.   On the one hand there is the intuitive approach in which probability is considered as having the connotation of "chance" or "expectation." Thus probability has been defined as the measure or degree of rational belief. The random variable has been similarly associated with the notion of haphazardness, or randomness, such as is observed in the usual affairs of life or in the erratic fluctuations in repeated physical measurements. This behavior is contrasted with the strictness of the relation between the variables in an algebraic formula say in an exact law of dynamics or in the law of constant proportions in chemistry, despite the observed fluctuations in any measurements based on these laws.   Somehow or other, the ever-present fluctuations were associated with human fallibility, and considered, in physical science, as necessary, unpleasant concomitants to the search for truth, all efforts to minimize them notwithstanding. Indeed one would rather not discuss them, except as something to be abolished.   While these concepts may be esthetically satisfying, they are hardly capable of quantitative formulation.   A less subjective concept of probability is that of frequency, in the sense of vital statistics.   Certain regularities are observed in the behavior of large numbers of similar biological individuals, considered as a group: such as height, weight or longevity even though little may be definitely asserted about an individual.

During the 18th century, a mathematical theory of probability was developed by extending the notion of regularity of averages of large numbers, particularly to the problems connected with the ordinary games of chance.   In these games, the results that are *a priori* possible may be arranged in a finite number of cases supposed to be perfectly symmetrical, such as the cases represented by the 6 sides of a die, the 52 cards in an ordinary pack of cards, etc., and the results of any event analyzed according to combinatorial theory.   These considerations led to the famous principle of "equally possible cases" which was explicitly stated and extensively developed by Laplace.   According to this principle, a division into "equally possible" cases is conceivable in any kind of observations, and the probability of an event is the ratio between the number of cases favorable to the event and the total number of possible cases.   The weakness in this concept is apparent.   There is no indicated mechanism to decide whether two cases are equally possible or not.   Moreover it seems difficult, and to some minds even impossible, to form a precise idea just how a division into equally possible cases could be made with respect to observations not belonging to the domain of games of chance, or to apply the principle to experimental or physical observations.

On the other hand, the modern mathematical approach, influenced by the general tendency to build any mathematical theory on an axiomatic basis, makes a clean break with intuition at the very beginning. The practical justification of the approach is based on the power and usefulness of the derived results. Even the postulation of the existence of definite limits to frequency ratios is avoided and the probability of an event is considered simply as a number associated with the event. The axiomatic development leads to a theory of probability that is essentially a theory of measure in some special sort of function space. For example, consider a set function $P(S)$ defined for sets, S, in that space and satisfying the following three conditions:

(a) $P(S)$ is non-negative; $P(S) \geq 0$
(b) $P(S)$ is additive:
$P(S_1 + S_2 + \cdots = P(S_1) + P(S_2) + \cdots$ (for disjoint sets, S, i.e., $S_u S_v = 0$, $u \neq v$)
(c) $P(S)$ is finite for any bounded set, S.

Hence if, for S_1 contained in S_2,

$$P(S_1) \leq P(S_2) \text{ and } P(0) = 0,$$

then, to any set function $P(S)$ defined as above, there corresponds a non-decreasing point function, $F(x)$, such that for any finite or infinite interval (a, b),

$$F(b) - F(a) = P(a < \xi \leq b)$$

If $P(R) = 1$, where R is the entire space under consideration, then P is termed a probability function, F a distribution function, and ξ a random variable. The mathematical theory develops from there on.

It is indeed a far step from such abstract concepts to intuitive probability However, analogously, while for purposes of elementary trigonometry and surveying, or other simple engineering needs, it is sufficient to define sin θ as the ratio of the side opposite the angle θ, in a right-angle triangle, to the hypothenuse, for analytical purposes a more appropriate definition is $\sin \theta = \theta - \dfrac{\theta^3}{3!} + \dfrac{\theta^5}{5!} - \dfrac{\theta^7}{7!} + \cdots$. It is also difficult to see the right-angle triangle in this expression, yet the defined function reduces to that chosen for the triangle.

1.2.2. Statistical Inference. Extensive application has been made of probability theory to that section of statistical inference that is of interest in this discussion, namely the theory of errors. It is a matter of common experience that repeated measurements under apparently identical conditions are not identical, for example the measurement of $\Delta \log I$ of a certain line pair under closely controlled conditions. Indeed, if the measurements were identical, or even within the least count of the measuring instrument (densitometer) there would be no statistical problem. The connotation of "error," then, is not that of a mistake, either objective or subjective, but of an unavoidable fluctuation in repetitive measurements. These fluctuations are called random, in spite of the fact that we are unable to give a precise physical interpretation to the term. This situation is not entirely incompatible with a deterministic point of view, since it is realized that slight, undetectible changes in the initial or intermediate conditions of an experiment may show up in an exaggerated form as fluctuations in the terminal result. On the other hand, there is no question of essential theoretical indeterminancy as in the quantum theory. However, in spite of the irregular behavior of individual results, the average values of long sequences of repeated "random" measurements show striking regularities. Accordingly, the conjecture is made that to an event E connected with a random experiment (deviation of $\Delta \log I$ from the true value), it is possible to ascribe a number P such that in an infinitely long series of repetitions of the random experiment, the frequency of E will be equal to P. This conjecture is of course not capable of mathematical or even experimental proof, since it is impossible to perform an infinitely long sequence of measurements. However, the assumption is the typical form of statistical regularity which constitutes the empirical basis of statistical theory.

Then, in an extended series of measurements, under controlled conditions, on the $\Delta \log I$ of a certain line pair, the frequency of the errors, or deviations from the true value, for any range of deviations will approach a fixed value. It should be noted that the application is made to a range of deviations since P is a set function, and not to a single or individual value of the derivation. Indeed, the value of P for any individual value of the deviation is zero, on the assumption of the continuity of the values of the error. This may be concealed in any physical measurement due to the least count of the measuring instrument, δ, since then a single measurement really corresponds to the range of $\pm \delta$.

It is now further assumed, in keeping with general physical evidence, that the errors of spectrographic measurements approximately follow a normal or Gaussian distribution. While the precise specific formulation of this distribution is not important it may be stated that it implies that the errors are symmetrically distributed around the true value or zero, and that large errors occur less frequently than small ones. Explicitly,

$$P = P(|\xi - m| > \lambda) = \frac{2}{\sigma\sqrt{2\pi}} \int_\lambda^\infty e^{-\frac{(x-m)^2}{2\sigma^2}} dx$$

where ξ is the random variate, i.e., error, m is the true value of the variable, (here $m = 0$), σ is a measure of the spread of the errors (standard deviation), defined as follows, $\sigma^2 = \lim_{n=\infty} \frac{1}{n} \sum_{i=1}^n (\xi_i - m)^2$ where n is the number of measurements, and (λ, ∞) is the range of the variate considered. It is to be noted that the function P is completely determined, for any λ, if two parameters, m and σ are known.

However, the formulation of the distribution, even if only assumed, does not lead very far in itself. The parameters m, σ are not known and indeed can never be known as the results of any finite experiment no matter how extended. Accordingly, any experiment is considered to be a sample of all possible measurements, or population, of the kind under consideration. Actually even an infinite series of measurements would not be quite enough, since the normal distribution assumes that the average or arithmetic mean of the measurements, $\lim_{n=\infty} \frac{1}{n} \sum_{i=1}^n \chi_i$ is the true value, and any knowledge of the difference between m and the true value is extra-experimental and cannot be detected. However, neglecting this point, it may be seen that the problem is really that of estimating m and σ from the results of experiments of finite length. This is quite a difficult problem considered either from experimental or theoretical aspects. One must be assured of the representation of the sample, i.e., whether it is truly random or biased. It appears almost too much to expect that any experiment of reasonable magnitude will contain the true proportionality of elementary disturbing factors, consequently a major part of the theoretical effort must be devoted to tests for randomness or quality of representation of the sample experiment. Sampling theory is divided into two parts, that of large samples and small samples. In large sample theory it is assumed that the experiment exhibits an effectively true and complete state of affairs, in miniature, and the parameters may be computed directly as if the entire infinite population were available. Then, after the parameters have been estimated, tests may be devised to see whether the distribution is truly normal, or whether another type of distribution would fit the facts more precisely. It may reasonably be assumed that large samples, in this sense, will not be available in spectrographic procedures. The theoretical problem in small samples is the relation between the parameters as computed from the samples, or statistics, and the parameters of the assumed infinite parent population or true values of the parameters. In other words, the problem is that of the distribution of sample statistics, the samples being taken from a population of an assumed normal character. It will be evident that if a sample is not random and nothing precise is known about the nature of the bias operating when it was chosen, very little can be inferred from it about the parent population. Certain conclusions of a trivial kind are indeed always possible, for instance, if one were to take 10 turnips from a population of 100 and find that they weigh 10 pounds altogether, the mean weight of turnips in the pile must be greater than $\frac{1}{10}$ of a pound; but such information is rarely of value, and estimations based on biassed samples remain very much a matter of individual opinion and cannot be reduced to exact and objective terms.

Let it be considered what is meant by estimation in general. It is known or assumed as a working hypothesis that the parent population is distributed in a form which would be completely determined if the value of some parameter θ were known (in the one dimensional case). A sample of values $\{X_1, \ldots, X_n\}$ are given. It is required to determine, with the aid of the X's, a number which can be taken as the value of θ, or a range of numbers which can be taken to include that value. Now a single sample, considered by itself, may be rather improbable and any estimate based on it may therefore differ considerably from the true value of θ. It appears, therefore, that one cannot expect to find any method of estimation which can be guaranteed to give a close estimate of θ on every occasion and for every sample. One must be content with the formulation of a rule which will give good results "in the long run," or "on the average," or which has "a high probability of success," phrases which express the fundamental fact that one has to regard the method of estimation as generating a population of estimates and to assess its merits according to the properties of this population. As a rule the estimates are given as functions of n, the size of the sample, and all that is to be expected is that the estimate will converge to the true value (that of the parent population) as n increases indefinitely. Even the problem of convergence is intricate. Convergence is an analytical sense has been quite well understood since the time of Cauchy, but in probability theory the classical notion must be modified, since for a random variate ξ, ξ_n cannot be expressed as a function of n. Indeed, a probability $P = 0$ does not mean the event never occurs since it is a characteristic of the integration process (Lebesgue) that a set of measure zero may be arbitrarily added or subtracted from the set of the independent variable, n. $P = 0$ means only that the event will occur, say, no more than in a few isolated instances in an infinite run. A similar condition prevails with regard to certain occurrence when $P = 1$, i.e., the event may not occur in a few isolated instances in an infinite run. (The term few is used in a relative sense.) While the discussion has been concerned with a one parameter, or one dimensional distribution, the extension to more dimensions is, at least, logically clear.

NOTE: A logical objection has sometimes been expressed concerning the applicability of the normal distribution to error theory, since, it is argued, very large errors are theoretically feasible although they are certainly not practically possible. The argument is really concerned with the conceptual difficulty in the application of the limit of an infinite mathematical process to empirical data and simultaneously considering the application of the process in a term-wise manner. Discussion of difficulties of this type go back at least to the time of Zeno. All that need be said at this time is that very large errors are very improbable, the larger the error the greater the improbability, and that any mathematical process must be a convergent one, in some sense, before it can be used.

1.2.3. Tests of Significance and the Null Hypothesis. From what has been said before, it is seen that the central problem in sampling theory is not only to estimate the population parameters from the sample statistics but also to estimate the closeness of the estimations. The two most important parameters to be estimated, particularly for normal distributions, are the mean or average value and the spread of the values around the average. The spread is to be measured by the dispersion or variance, i.e., $\sigma^2 = \frac{1}{n} \sum (Y_i - \bar{y})^2$ where $\bar{y}$ is the mean and Y_i the individual observation. For ordinary functional relations, the two parameters y and σ^2 would be estimated from two sets of independent observations, i.e., samples. However, this simple procedure is not sufficient for probability theory.

It has been emphasized that no mathematical theory deals directly with objects of immediate physical experience. The mathematical theory belongs entirely to the conceptual sphere and deals with purely abstract objects. The theory is, however, designed to form a model of a certain group of phenomena in the physical world and the abstract objects and propositions of the theory have their counterparts in certain observable things and relations between things. The concept of mathematical probability has its counterpart in certain observable frequency ratios. Accordingly it is required that, whenever a theoretical deduction leads to a definite numerical value for the probability of a certain observable event, the truth of the corresponding frequency interpretation should be borne out by observation. Thus, when the probability of an event is very small, it is required that in the long run the event should occur at most in a very small fraction of all repetitions of the corresponding experiment. Consequently, one must be able to regard it as practically certain that, in a single performance of the experiment, the event will not occur. Similarly, when the probability of an event differs from 1 by a very small amount, it must be required that it should be practically certain that, in a single performance of the corresponding experiment, the event will occur. In a great number of cases, the problem of testing the agreement between theory and fact presents itself in the following form. One has at one's disposal a sample of n observed values of some variable, and it is required to test whether this variable may reasonably be regarded as a random variable associated with a certain distribution. In some cases the hypothetical distribution will be completely specified, for example a normal distribution with $m = 0$ and $\sigma^2 = 1$. In other cases, it is required to test the hypothesis that the sample might have been drawn from a population with this distribution. One begins by assuming that the hypothesis to be tested is true. It then follows that the distribution function, F^*, of the sample may be expected to approximate the distribution function of the population, F, when n is large. Let some non-negative measure of the deviation of F^* from F be defined. This may, of course, be made in various ways, but any deviation measure D will be some function of the sample values and will thus have a determined sampling distribution. By means of this sampling distribution, one may calculate the probability $P(D > D_0)$ that the deviation D will exceed any given number D_0. This probability may be made as small as one pleases by taking D_0 sufficiently large. Let D_0 be chosen so that $P(D > D_0) = \epsilon$, where ϵ is so small that one is prepared to regard it as practically certain that an event of probability ϵ will not occur in a single trial. The value of D is then computed from the actual sample values. Then if $D > D_0$, it means that an event of probability ϵ has presented itself. However, the hypothesis was that such an event ought to be practically impossible in a single trial, and thus one must reach the conclusion that the hypothesis has been disproved by experience. On the other hand, if $D \leq D_0$, one should be willing to accept the hypothesis as a reasonable interpretation of the data, at least until further evidence is presented. If in the actual case, $D > D_0$, it is said that the deviation is *significant*. Tests of this general character are called *tests of significance*. The probability ϵ, which may be arbitrarily fixed, is called the *level of significance*, and the higher the probability ϵ the lower the significance level. In the case where the deviation measure D exceeds the significance level one may regard the hypothesis as disproved by experience, a condition by no means equivalent to logical disproof. Even if the hypothesis were true, the event $D > D_0$, with a probability ϵ, may occur in an exceptional case. However, when ϵ is sufficiently small, one may be practically justified in disregarding this possibility. On the other hand, the occurrence of a single value $D \leq D_0$ does not provide a proof of the truth of the hypothesis. It only shows that, from the point of view of the particular test, the agreement between theory and observation is satisfactory. Before a statistical hypothesis can be regarded as practically established, it will have to pass repeated tests of different kinds.

Let a sample of spectrographic measurements, $\Delta \log I$ for a certain line pair be given. It is required to justify the hypothesis that the deviations or errors are normally distributed, say around zero. It has been seen how this question may be answered by a properly chosen significance test. On the other hand, let it be supposed that the general character of the distribution is known from previous experience and information is required concerning the values of some particular characteristics of the distribution. For example, let a comparison be made between effects of two electrode shapes on the error. The error distributions, i.e., the probability or frequency of an error or deviation within a certain range, are assumed known for each sample form and they are assumed to be nonidentical. Then the question may be asked whether the difference is due to random or sampling fluctuations or is significant, i.e., indicative of a real difference between the probabilities. In such cases it is often useful to begin by considering that there is *no* difference between the two cases (electrode shapes), so that in reality all the sample observations come from the same population. This is called the null hypothesis. This being assumed, it is often possible to construct significance tests for the difference between the means, or other characteristics. If the differences exceed certain limits, they will be regarded as significant and one may conclude that there is, practically, a real difference between the cases, i.e., effect of electrode forms; otherwise the differences will be ascribed to random or sample fluctuation. It should be borne in mind that a significant difference merely disproves the null hypothesis at a certain probability level in a logical sense, and does not logically prove the existence of a factual difference between the effects of the two cases.

There are two kinds of errors or incorrect conclusions that may be drawn concerning the significance of a difference in effect, to carry out the previous example, of the electrode forms. Let the null hypothesis be indicated as H_0, i.e., the difference between the electrodes is merely a random or sampling effect, and let H_1 be an alternative hypothesis that need not be specified. Then an error of the first kind is committed when

H_0 is rejected when it is true, i.e., it is decided that "the difference between the electrode forms is random" is not true when it actually is. An error of the second kind is committed when H_0 is accepted when H_1 is true. The probability of an error of the first kind may be indicated by α and that of an error of the second kind by β. The choice of tests should be of course in the direction of minimizing both α and β. Under most practical conditions, it is impossible to make them both arbitrarily small, and the decision is usually made by choosing α, then devising a test to minimize β. For a fixed sample size, under certain mathematical conditions, β is a single-valued function of α, and if α is small, $\beta(\alpha)$ is in general large, and if α is large $\beta(\alpha)$ is small. The choice of α or β should be influenced by the relative importance of the two kinds of errors.

1.3. Practical Applications

1.3.1. Design of Experiment. Fortunately, at least for the sake of expediency, a theoretical development such as discussed above is not necessary for the application of the statistical methods to experimental data that will be considered. It may simply be assumed that mathematical tests of significance have been devised and, more or less, generally accepted. However, it should be realized that in order to apply these tests in a proper manner, it is often necessary that the experimental data be obtained in a certain way. The arrangement of the course of an experiment so that statistical tests or computations may be subsequently performed on the data may be called the design of an experiment. It is important that an experiment be carefully considered from this point of view before the data is accumulated or measurements made.

Accordingly, the practical course of a statistical study may be divided into three parts; (a) arrangement, or design of the experiment, with regard to the variables or factors being studied, (b) computation of certain statistics and (c) determination of significance by reference to certain tables.

The general approach will be that of variance analysis, with and without reduction for regression, while significance will be determined by reference to the "F" or chi-square test (the exact meaning of these terms will be developed later). It will be observed that the computation is purely arithmetical, and may be rather extensive so that a modern electrical computing machine with automatic multiplication and division is practically a necessity. Some parts of the computation will yield results useful in themselves, independent of their significance, for example, the slope of a calibration or working curve, the equivalence point, etc. The tables for determining significance may be used in a similar manner. In all cases, they will associate the value of the statistic with the probability that it is as large as it is purely as random happening due to sampling, i.e., based on the null-hypothesis. While the choice of significance levels is more or less arbitrary and a matter of personal judgment, for the sake of uniformity it will be assumed that

(a) $P > .05$, definitely when $P > .10$, will be interpreted as non-significant,

(b) $P < .01$, definitely when $P < .001$, will be considered significant.

Intermediate values, i.e., $.01 < P < .05$ will be considered indecisive and judgment reserved until further experimentation has been effected. It need hardly be repeated, but the significance determined from these tables is a statistical, not a physical or engineering, test and that evaluation from the experimental side is always necessary.

In concluding these general remarks it may be stated that not all significance tests are equally good since consideration must be given to the rapidity of their convergence (in probability) with increasing n or decreasing $1/n$ (efficiency), and to the dispersion or spread of their distribution functions around their central or limiting value. It is suggested that the reader consult the references for a full mathematical treatment of the preceding discussion.

1.3.2. Factorial Experiments. Interaction

(1) Introduction. In order to understand fully the reasoning governing the differences between suitable and unsuitable arrangements of an experiment it is of course necessary to understand the manner in which the computations on the experimental data are to be performed, and *vice versa.* However, since a beginning must be made, a few general statements, introducing the subsequent treatment, will be a sufficient introduction.

Let Y represent the dependent variable, that is Y_i is the ith measurement or estimation of the density of a line, the $\Delta \log I$ of a line pair or the per cent of an element in some material being analyzed. Then Y_i is a function of recognized main experimental factors, $Y_i = Y_i(P, Q, R, S, \ldots)$, where the independent arguments P, Q, R, S may, for present purposes represent such factors as photographic plates, the various components of an excitation system, electrode shape, line pairs, densitometer sensivity, etc. The error in Y_i, $Y_i - \bar{y}$ where $\bar{y}$ represents the true value of Y, depends on the combined result of the errors or uncontrollable fluctuations in the response of $P, Q, R, S, \ldots$. It will be assumed, until proved otherwise in some manner, that the random fluctuations or errors attributable to each of P, Q, R, S, follow a normal distribution law. There are several reasons for assuming a normal distribution for the errors in the parent population (of the independent arguments). In the first place, for error theory, the normal law is nearly always an excellent approximation. Furthermore, investigations on non-normal populations have shown that even considerable departures from normality do not produce appreciable changes in many important deductions based on the normal law. It has also been established that statistics such as the mean, computed from samples drawn from a non-normal parent population are often much more normal than the population itself. The degree of necessity for normality in the parent population really depends on the character of the distribution of the significance tests employed. In general, for present purposes, any bell-shaped distribution with a hump in the middle and tapering off at both sides will be satisfactory as a good approximation. There are some very important consequences of this assumption of normality. In the first place, it follows, rigorously, that the errors in Y are normally distributed. Let $\bar{y}$ stand for the true value of Y, then the measure to be used for the spread, or error, in a number of measurements of Y will not be, for example, $\frac{1}{n} \sum |Y_i - \bar{y}|$, but the variance, $\sigma^2 = \frac{1}{n} \sum (Y_i - \bar{y})^2$. The square root of this quantity, σ, is called the standard deviation. It follows from the normal law, if no systematic errors are present, that the mean of the parent population would be the true value of the quantity being measured. (The effect of a systematic error would be to displace the mean of the parent population of observations to one side or the other of the true value, and the correction, if ever isolated, can be added to the mean of the parent population to give the true value. The effect of a systematic error cannot be isolated or even detected by the theory of the random variable.) It also follows that the sample mean is the best approximation to the population mean. It may be shown that the variance of sample means, $\sigma_{\bar{y}}^2 = \frac{1}{n} \sigma^2$, where $\bar{y}$ will from now on indicate the mean value, $\sigma_{\bar{y}}^2$ the variance of the $\bar{y}$ (as a sample statistic) and σ^2 is the variance of the individual measurements. The improvement in precision involved in the use of a mean of multiple measurements has long been recognized. Indeed there are only two ways intuitively used to improve the otherwise unsatisfactory precision of measurements: (1) to modify or improve the experimental conditions and (2) to use the mean of repeated observations. Particular attention should be paid to the condition of independence of $P, Q, R, \ldots$ In the model of the mathematical theory of probability, independence has the following meaning. If the distribution functions of the random variables Q and R are $Q_1(u)$ and $R_1(v)$, then the distribution of $Y(u, v) = Q_1(u)R_1(v)$. For a normal distribution this implies $\sigma_y{}^2 = \sigma_{Q_1}{}^2 + \sigma_{R_1}{}^2$. Empirically, independence may be assumed for two factors Q and R if one can be changed without affecting the other. If the conditions of successive random experiments are strictly uniform, the probability of any specified event, for example the magnitude of error, connected with the nth experiment cannot be supposed to be in any way influenced by the $n - 1$ preceding experiments. This implies that the distribution of the random variable associated with the nth experiment is independent of any hypothesis made with respect to the value assumed by the combined preceding $n - 1$ variables. A sequence of repetitions of a random experiment showing a uniformity of this character will be denoted as a sequence of independent repetitions. When nothing is stated to the contrary, it will always be assumed that any sequence of repetitions considered will be of this type.

The purpose of a considered arrangement of the factors in an experiment, or experimental design, is to insure as efficient an independent repetition of the effects of the principal factors, or main effects, in order to make full use of the improvement in precision involved in the use of the mean of multiple observations and as far as possible, to cancel out systematic errors.

(2) *Factorial Experiments.* The classical ideal of experimentation is to have all independent variables but one constant. It is frequently not recognized that this may sometimes be far from ideal, for in order to obtain a fair assessment of the effects of varying the particular variable selected one must also allow the others to vary over their full normal range. If they were to be held constant, it would necessarily be at arbitrary value. Thus, varying factor Q, say secondary voltage, from its normal value, Q_1, to another value Q_2, may affect one change in the dependent variable Y, when factor R, say electrode form, is at R_1, but may quite conceivably induce another change when factor R is at R_2. This is not incompatible with the notion of independence, but introduces a new variable, namely the interaction of Q and R, written as $Q \times R$. The factorial experiment is designed to detect this type of effect as well as for maximum efficiency, i.e., to give the maximum amount of information about the system being experimented upon for a given amount of effort. It is ideally suited for experiments whose purpose is to map a function, Y, in a preassigned range of values of the independent variables.

(a) Three factor experiment:

Consider an experiment to investigate Y as dependent on three factors, $Y(P, Q, R)$. (For specific meanings, $Y \equiv \Delta \log I$, $P \equiv$ photographic plate, $Q \equiv$ some excitation condition, and $R \equiv$ electrode shape.) It may be considered adequate, for the example or as a first attempt, to restrict the range of P, Q, and R to two values or levels. It should be noted that there may be no numerical measure of the difference between the two levels, for example R_1 may be rods with conical top while R_2 may be a flat surface with a graphite counter electrode. Let the normal value be $Y_1 = Y(P_1, Q_1, R_1)$. The classical experiment, that of changing one variable at a time, would be to obtain four observations, namely

1. $Y(P_1, Q_1, R_1)$,   2. $Y(P_2, Q_1, R_1)$,   3. $Y(P_1, Q_2, R_1)$,   4. $Y(P_1, Q_1, R_2)$.

The effect of the change in P, i.e., $(P_1 - P_2)_Y$ would be obtained from the first two measurements, the change in Q, $(Q_1 - Q_2)_Y$ would be obtained from a comparison of the first and third observation, while the change in R would be obtained from a comparison of the first and fourth observation. Now it is important to observe, that each of these observations would have to be repeated not less than once, for with use of less than two observations at constant conditions, it is quite impossible to form any estimate of the non-reducible experimental error, i.e., σ^2, that of a single observation, which would serve as a basis for comparison. Without such a basis, it would be impossible to decide whether the observed, or apparent, difference in Y due to a change in, say, P, is real i.e., significant, or due to the errors of experiment. The complete set will, then, consist of four measurements repeated once, or eight measurements in all. Each level of each effect or factor will be given by two observations, i.e., comparisons will be between one mean of two observations and another mean of two observations. No information will be given by this type of experiment concerning the possible interaction between effects. For example $(P_1 - P_2)_Y$ at $R = R_1$ may be appreciably different from $(P_1 - P_2)_Y$ at $R = R_2$.

On the other hand in a factorial design, one would carry out all combinations of P, Q, R, at all levels, namely, eight observations:

(1) (P_1, Q_1, R_1),   (2) (P_1, Q_1, R_2),   (3) (P_1, Q_2, R_1),   (4) (P_1, Q_2, R_2)
(5) (P_2, Q_1, R_1),   (6) (P_2, Q_1, R_2),   (7) (P_2, Q_2, R_1),   (8) (P_2, Q_2, R_2)

The number of observations is then the same as in the classical design.

It may make it easier to grasp the meaning of the above set of combinations if they are represented as points in the three component vector space of P, Q and R One may obtain an estimate of $(P_1 - P_2)_Y$ by comparing the average of the P_1 plane with the average of the P_2 plane, for although Q and R vary in each plane, the variations are equal and at least to a first approximation, cancel out. The other main effects, $(Q_1 - Q_2)_Y$ and $(R_1 - R_2)_Y$ are obtained similarly as differences in the averages of the corresponding planes.

The first advantage of the factorial design is that the main effects are obtained as the difference between the means of sets of four observations.   In the classical design, these effects were obtained as differences between means of sets of only two observations.   Hence the variance of the means has been cut in half with no increase in total effort.

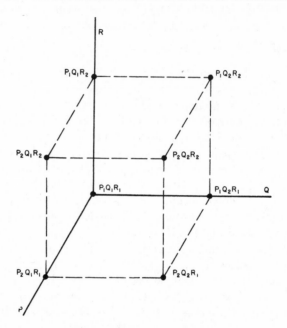

The second advantage of the factorial design is that it provides an estimate of the possible interactions between the main effects.   To obtain the interaction, for example, of P and R, i.e., $P \times R$, one averages over Q for each $P_i R_j$, and thus obtains four means,

$$Y(P_1, R_1, *), \qquad Y(P_2, R_1, *)$$
$$Y(P_1, R_2, *), \qquad Y(P_2, R_2, *)$$

where the * in place of Q indicates a mean with respect to Q.   Hence, the difference between the values in the top row gives $Y(P_1 - P_2)$ at $R = R_1$ while the difference between the values in the bottom row gives $Y(P_1 - P_2)$ at $R = R_2$.   The difference between these differences is a measure of the interaction of P and R.   Interactions between the other effects, i.e., $P \times Q$, $Q \times R$ may be estimated in a similar fashion.   An interaction is symmetrical with respect to the component effects, i.e., $P \times R = R \times P$.

Another viewpoint may help further to clarify the concept of inter-action.   Consider the observations averaged over Q as before.   Then $Y(P_i, R_j, *) = \bar{P}_i + \bar{R}_j + P_i \times R_j$ where $\bar{P}_i$ and $\bar{R}_j$ are the means of the respective classifications.   If there were no interaction, then $Y(P_i, R_j)$

would equal $\bar{P}_i + \bar{R}_j$. Hence $P_i \times R_j$ may be considered as a kind of discrepance. Dispensing with the restriction of two levels, consider the tabular values of an experiment $P^5R^4(Q^x)$. The Q multiplicity is of no moment since the effect is averaged out

	P_1	P_2	P_3	P_4	P_5	Σ	(Mean R)$\bar{R}$
R_1	4	18	26	38	44	130	26
R_2	3	19	25	35	43	125	25
R_3	6	18	24	28	39	115	23
R_4	7	13	21	31	38	110	22
Σ	20	68	96	132	164	480	
(Mean P)$\bar{P}$	5	7	24	33	41		

Grand mean $= 24$

Transforming the values into deviations from the mean:

	p_1	p_2	p_3	p_4	p_5	Σ	Mean r ($\bar{r}$)
r_1	−20	−6	2	14	20	10	2
r_2	−21	−5	1	11	19	5	1
r_3	−18	−6	0	4	15	−5	−1
r_4	−17	−11	−3	7	14	−10	−2
Σ	−76	−28	0	36	68		
$\bar{p}$	−19	−7	0	9	17		

Considering the interaction $P \times R$ as a discrepance

$$p_i r_j = p_i + r_j + p_i \times r_j$$

and one obtains the interaction table

	$P \times R$					
	P_1	P_2	P_3	P_4	P_5	Σ
R_1	−3	−1	0	3	1	0
R_2	−3	1	0	1	1	0
R_3	2	2	1	−4	−1	0
R_4	4	−2	−1	0	−1	0
Σ	0	0	0	0	0	

If there were no interaction the entries in the last table would be all zeros. For example, the expected value of p_2r_3 would be the sum of $p_2 + r_3 = (-7) + (-1) = -8$. Since the value of p_2r_3 is -6, the interaction term $P_2 \times R_3 = 2$.

(b) Higher factorial experiments:

The extension to a four-factor experiment is logically clear. If the factors are still to be investigated at two levels each, $P^2Q^2R^2S^2$, $2^4 = 16$ observations will be required. The main effects will be given by differences between means of eight observations. There will be six possible first order interactions, i.e., interactions of two main effects as previously discussed, namely, $P \times Q$, $P \times R$, $P \times S$, $Q \times R$, $Q \times S$ and $R \times S$. To obtain them one averages over the factors not indicated in the symbol; thus, to obtain $P \times Q$, one averages over R and S. These interactions are determined as differences between means of sets of four observations. In addition it is possible to obtain higher or second order interactions namely $P \times Q \times R$, $P \times Q \times S$, $P \times R \times S$, and $Q \times R \times S$. The interpretation of these is simply an extension of that of the first order reaction, thus $P \times Q \times R$ may be considered as the interaction of $P \times Q$ and R. Interactions of any order are symmetrical with respect to the component effects.

The nearest equivalent classical design would be to carry out the set of five combinations

$$
\begin{array}{llll}
P_1 & Q_1 & R_1 & S_1 \\
P_2 & Q_1 & R_1 & S_1 \\
P_1 & Q_2 & R_1 & S_1 \\
P_1 & Q_1 & R_2 & S_1 \\
P_1 & Q_1 & R_1 & S_2
\end{array}
$$

with a double repetition of each set, or 15 observations in all. The main effects would be determined as differences between means of sets of only three observations with no information given concerning the interactions. In the classical design, only $P_1Q_1R_1S_1$ is used several times, while any other term contributes information concerning only one effect; for example $P_2Q_1R_1S_1$ contributes information only concerning P, and adds nothing to the knowledge of the other factors (and of course interactions). In the factorial design, on the other hand, every observation is used many times over, in a different manner each time.

1.3.3. Types of Design

(1) Balanced Complete Randomized Blocks. The design of experiment implicitly considered in the preceding section is known as that of balanced complete randomized blocks. The meaning of this is as follows: A block is considered as the main unit of the experiment and replication of the block furnishes the measure of unassigned experimental error. For spectrographic purposes, unless otherwise indicated, a plate will represent a block. The experiment is called balanced if the various levels of the factors are repeated an equal number of times and complete means that each block, or plate, contains a full set of combinations of all levels of the factors. The term randomized refers to the random placement of the combinations within the block, or plate; however this aspect will

be of little significance for spectrographic work since, neglecting the very edges of the plates, there are no preferred systematic arrangements within the plate. For example, if one wished to investigate the effect of electrode form at four levels, E^4, and excitation condition at five levels, C^5, one would have to put $5 \times 4 = 20$ spectra on each plate, $C^i E^j$, with plate replication to an adequate amount.

This design is comprehensive and yields information concerning all main effects and their interactions. There are certain difficulties and criticisms, however, of this design that are not trivial. First, the size of the block may become too great. If many effects and many levels for each effect are necessary, the number of combinations may become too large to put on one plate. For example, $C^5 E^4 M^5$, where M represents material types, implies the use of 100 spectra, which obviously cannot be put on a single plate. Secondly, it has been found that higher order interactions, say greater than the second, usually are difficult to interpret in a physical sense and it may be felt that the effort to compute them is largely useless. More important than the computational effort, however, is the consideration that the effort could be more profitably made, in the design, to yield more precise estimates of the main effects and then interactions of lower order. The third criticism is still more serious. Certain experimental factors, particularly those involving a time-like effect simply cannot be combined in a complete manner.

For example, suppose it is desired to estimate the stability of the source with respect to time. One might use two spectrographs, expose two plates simultaneously at T_1 ($T \equiv$ time) and then interchange the plates and expose them at T_2. The experiment would be of the form $P^2 T^2 S^2$ ($P \equiv$ plate, $T \equiv$ time and $S \equiv$ spectrograph). (It is assumed that only one plate may be used in a spectrograph at a time.) Then the balanced complete set of observations would be eight in all, and arranged as follows:

(1) $P_1 T_1 S_1$ (2) $P_1 T_1 S_2$ (3) $P_1 T_2 S_1$ (4) $P_1 T_2 S_2$
(5) $P_2 T_1 S_1$ (6) $P_2 T_1 S_2$ (7) $P_2 T_2 S_1$ (8) $P_2 T_2 S_2$

Obviously (1) and (2) are an impossible pair, since one cannot expose one plate simultaneously in two spectrographs. It is clear that the possible arrangements are (1), (6) and (7), (4).

One need not be restricted to the denotation of plates for block. For example, in a time study, one may consider all observations on one day as the block, or all observations on a given material, excitation condition, electrode form, etc.

(2) *Balanced Incomplete Blocks.* Accordingly, the experiment design may necessarily require modification so that while the combination of effects and levels are still equally frequent, the blocks are not complete

and will no longer be exactly alike in their treatments. It is really necessary to understand the consequent mode of computation in order to discuss the possible designs in a critical manner, but some consideration will be clear. The important point to consider is that this design depends too much on the combinatorial properties of the numbers of combinations of effects × levels, or treatments, and too many repetitions may be necessary to obtain balance.

If v treatments, i.e., effect × levels, are to be compared in blocks (assumed to be plates) of K spectra per plate, ($K < v$), the arrangement must be such that every two treatments occur together in the same number (λ) of plates. If r is the number of repetitions, and b the number of blocks or plates, the number of spectra is $rv = bk$ and $\lambda = \dfrac{r(k-1)}{v-1}$. Arrangements satisfying the required conditions are clearly provided by taking all possible combinations of the v treatments, k at a time, but if v is at all large, the number of repetitions required will be very large. Tables are available for those arrangements requiring less than 10 repetitions. Generally v^2 treatments will require $(v+1)$ repetitions, which may be considered too many. However, sometimes this design may be put to effective use. Consider an experiment of form $C^5E^2R^2$, where C = excitation conditions, E = electrode form and R = repetition. Let it be assumed that 16 spectra may be put on one plate. The plate is assumed to represent the block and it is known that plates are not uniform in their response. Hence the experiment is really of the form $P^xC^5E^2R^2$, and a suitable set of combinations is $K = 16$, $v = 10$, $b = x = 5$, $\lambda = 4$ and $r = 8$ (two repetitions on each of four plates). The arrangement may be tabulated as follows (each entry represents two spectra as repetitions).

P_1	P_2	P_3	P_4	P_5
C_1E_1	C_1E_1	C_1E_1	C_1E_1	C_1E_2
C_1E_2	C_1E_2	C_1E_2	C_2E_1	C_2E_1
C_2E_1	C_2E_1	C_2E_2	C_2E_2	C_2E_2
C_2E_2	C_3E_1	C_3E_1	C_3E_1	C_3E_1
C_3E_2	C_3E_2	C_3E_2	C_3E_2	C_4E_1
C_4E_1	C_4E_1	C_4E_1	C_4E_2	C_4E_2
C_4E_2	C_4E_2	C_5E_1	C_5E_1	C_5E_1
C_5E_1	C_5E_2	C_5E_2	C_5E_2	C_5E_2

This arrangement merits some study. Every treatment is compared with every other treatment on three plates, any combinations of two levels of C are on one plate, E is repeated four times on each plate etc.

(*3*) *Lattice Squares.* In order to avoid the restriction to the peculiar properties of combinations of numbers, a lattice square arrangement may be made. The combinations of treatments are arranged in a table and the rows and columns used as block units. For example, in the experiment C^3E^4, the treatments are tabulated

$$
\begin{array}{cccc}
C_1E_1 & C_1E_2 & C_1E_3 & C_1E_4 \\
C_2E_1 & C_2E_2 & C_2E_3 & C_2E_4 \\
C_3E_1 & C_3E_2 & C_3E_3 & C_3E_4
\end{array}
$$

The rows and columns are put on plates (seven) with a suitable number of replicates (say two). The design is not balanced, since some combinations, for example C_1E_1 and C_1E_2 are not compared in the same block or plate. However satisfactory comparisons are possible through intermediates, and with appropriate algebraic treatment the design is very efficient.

(*4*) *Latin Squares.* This design may be illustrated as follows. Consider the previous example on determination of source stability, and let the arrangement be as follows:

$$
\begin{array}{cc}
P_1 & \qquad P_2 \\
S_1T_1 & \qquad S_2T_1 \\
S_2T_2 & \qquad S_1T_2
\end{array}
$$

Comparison of the rows will estimate the main effect T, the columns will give P, while the diagonals will give S. It is to be seen that the interactions are confounded, thus T and $P \times S$ are not distinguishable. If the interactions are considered unimportant, this is a very efficient design for the main effects.

(*5*) *Other Designs. Sequential Designs.* It should not be considered that the investigation of design of experiment is a completed subject. On the contrary new concepts are constantly being introduced and the forms improved. The important point is the care to be taken, in design other than the balanced complete blocks, not to lose or *confound* a desirable or important main effect or interaction even though some loss of information is inevitable. Consider an experiment of form $P^5C^5E^4R^4$. Then, one design may be considered as follows:

$P_1,$ C_1	$P_2,$ C_2	$P_3,$ C_3	$P_4,$ C_4	$P_5,$ C_5
$E_1:4\times$	$E_1:4\times$	$E_1:4\times$	$E_1:4\times$	$E_1:4\times$
$E_2:4\times$	$E_2:4\times$	$E_2:4\times$	$E_2:4\times$	$E_2:4\times$
$E_3:4\times$	$E_3:4\times$	$E_3:4\times$	$E_3:4\times$	$E_3:4\times$
$E_4:4\times$	$E_4:4\times$	$E_4:4\times$	$E_4:4\times$	$E_4:4\times$

This arrangement is particularly bad, since P and C are confounded, the blocks or plates are not complete, the treatments are badly unbalanced, interactions involving C or P are not obtainable, etc.

A factorial experiment is useful, much more so than the classical forms, in that its interpretation is simple and efficient in the sense of giving more information for a given number of observations, particularly so when the interactions are not significant. It is interesting to note that the non-existence of interactions presupposes that the dependent variable Y can be expressed as a sum of a sequence of functions of the independent variables or factors separately considered, i.e., $Y(C, E, T, P, \ldots)$ $= Y_1(C) + Y_2(E) + Y_3(T) + \cdots$ where the explicit functional forms Y_i are not relevant.

The factorial design, in general, is ideally suited for experiments whose purpose is to map a function, $Y = \log I$, in a preassigned range of values of the independent variables or factors. The fact that the region is preassigned means that it is feasible to lay out the design completely and specifically in advance of the experiment; the fact that the behavior of the function is desired for all possible combinations of the independent variables means that the experiment must represent all important combinations in some way. However there are certain deficiencies in the factorial design:

(1) It devotes observations to exploring regions that may, in the light of the results, be of no interest.

(2) Because it seeks to explore a given region comprehensively, it must either intensively explore only a small region, or explore a large region superficially. Critical values or regions, if they are small, may be easily overlooked or their importance obscured by the mass of other data.

(3) It neglects the fact that some of the variables are continuous and have numerical significance and some are discrete and merely ordered or given a lexicographical designation.

These deficiencies of the factorial design suggest that an efficient design for study of critical regions ought to be sequential, that is, ought to adjust the experimental program at each stage in the light of the results of prior stages. A general scheme designed to determine, say, utmost precision or stability of $\Delta \log I$ with regard to factors, C, E, and L (line pair), for example, may be outlined as follows:

(1) Select some particular combination of C, E, and L either on basis of general experience or as a consequence of a factorial study.

(2) Arrange the factors and their levels in some order.

(3) Make tests at the starting point and a series of other levels of only one independent variable, the others being held fixed.

(4) Holding the first variable fixed at the optimum value, repeat the experiment varying the second factor and then in sequence, hold the first and second at the optimum value and vary the third to obtain its optimum value.

(5) After all the variables have been varied, the whole process is repeated, except that the original starting point is replaced by the combination of values of the variables reached at the end of the first round, etc. Statistical significance tests. have been devised to determine reality of improvement and to distinguish it from random sampling fluctuations.

Considerable effort is being spent in improving this sequential design, particularly by the Columbia University Group, but for the present the following discussion will be restricted to the factorial designs.

The particular advantage in a sequential design in the economy of effort in selecting a critical region. Consider a simple $5 \times 3 \times 3 \times 3$ factorial design. It will require 135 observations, without providing for repetition or replications. A single round of the sequential design would require only 14 observations, disregarding repetitions. It should be realized however, that the information obtained from a factorial design is so broad that the other observations are certainly not useless. They provide information about the behavior of the function in regions removed from the critical, about the relative importance of the variables, their interactions and even to reveal regions in which critical values may be found.

1.4. The Interrelation of Two Variables

1.4.1. Introduction. The use of curves or graphs to correlate two variables is a common procedure in physical experimentation; indeed the procedure is so wide spread that usually no doubts are raised concerning its validity. One normally plots a sequence of points using one variable as the x and the other as the y coordinate in a Cartesian frame, and if a smooth line, not too intricate in shape may be drawn more or less closely between the points then it is assumed that the relationship does exist, if it is not too much opposed to physical intuition based on previous experience or established theory. The principal problem is a determination of the form of the relationship or functional connection between the variables, usually conditioned by the desire to have it conform to some theoretical considerations. An extensive mathematical discipline has been developed for this purpose, namely, the theory of interpolation.

The theory of the random variate, on the other hand, presents added intrinsic difficulty, because the question is raised whether the line so drawn is real or merely the result of a random or chance effect due to sampling from a population. Hence the correlation of two variates in the theory of probability sets a twofold problem, (1) the determination of the significance of the line on the basis of the null hypothesis, i.e., assuming the line to be a spurious or random effect, to determine the probability of such an assumption and (2) to determine the best form of the line. For example, just as a single measurement can give no information concerning the error involved, so two points cannot be used to determine the significance of a straight line connecting them, or three points cannot be used to determine the significance of a circle passing through them, because two points can always be connected by a straight line, or three points by a circle. It is only by the accumulation of many points that one can determine the significance of their correlation, just as many are needed to determine the significance of a mean value. The general problem in a statistical correlation of n sets of variables is complex and the computational efforts laborious. A great simplification is effected if suitable transformations can be devised to make the correlations linear.

Fortunately, the application of the theory to spectrographic data needs only the simplest statistical procedures and computations. There are essentially only three lines or relationships of interest and all of them may be assumed linear by simple transformations. It is to be understood that this assumption, namely, of linearity, is based on laboratory experience and the significance of the linearity will be tested only from the viewpoint of error theory. Another simplification to be assumed is that the lines are plane, i.e., only two variables are involved.

The lines of interest, accordingly, may be listed as the following relationships:

(1) between the density, or $\log I$ of one spectrum line and another,
(2) between the densities of a set of spectrum lines and their corresponding $\log I$, i.e., plate calibration,
(3) between the $\Delta \log I$ of a line pair and the log per cent of the corresponding element in the electrodes, i.e., the "working" or analytical curve in the method of internal standard or internal comparison.

It will be repeated, that the assumption of the functional form as a straight line, indeed, even of the existence of the functional relationship, under appropriate condition, is empirical and the use of statistical methods is in connection with the theory of errors.

The statistical analysis may be divided into two parts, namely, (1) one variable random and the other free of errors due to the experimental factors under consideration and (2) both variables random.

1.4.2. The Straight Line with Random Dependent Variate. This is the simplest case. Let $Y_i \equiv \Delta \log I$, of a certain line pair and let X_i = the log per cent of the associated element in a certain material, (in the method of interval comparison) Y_i is a random variate, while X_i is assumed known without error. Then it is assumed on the basis of extensive laboratory experience, that the curve of Y_i vs. X_i, for a restricted range of both variables, is a straight line of positive slope. The observed points will in general, of course, not lie exactly on a straight line, but the fit is usually quite good, in an intuitive serve. A straight line may be drawn through the points by eye or computed in many ways. However, on the assumption of the normality of the distribution of errors, a definite method of computation is used. This is the method of least squares, namely, the line is so computed that the sum of the squares of the deviations of the points, in a direction parallel to the Y-axis, is minimum. It may be seen that the computation of the line is entirely independent of any probability theory, but this method is chosen because the significance of the various deviations may be easily determined as consequences of the normal distribution law.

Let $Y_i \equiv$ the ith observation of $\Delta \log I$ of a line pair, the random and dependent variate, $X_i \equiv$ the log per cent of the associated element, the independent variable assumed to be free not only of errors associated with the experimental factors under consideration but with errors of any kind.

Then the general straight line may be written as

$$\hat{Y}_i = a + bX_i$$

where $\hat{Y}_i \equiv$ the expected or computed value of Y_i.

$(\hat{Y}_i - Y_i)$ is defined as the residual or error.

The theory of least squares then implies the computation or adjustment of a and b, the undetermined parameters of the line so that $\Sigma(\hat{Y}_i - Y_i)^2$ is minimum. The process is the familiar one in the elementary calculus of determining the minimum of a function, $\phi(a, b) = \Sigma(\hat{Y}_i - Y_i)^2 = \Sigma(a + bX_i - Y_i)^2$ where the summation extends over all readings. The conditions are $\partial\phi/\partial a = \partial\phi/\partial b = 0$. Omitting the algebra, the solution may be exhibited as follows,

$$\hat{Y}_i = \bar{y} + b(X_i - \bar{x})$$

where $\bar{y}$ and $\bar{x}$ are the means of the Y_i and X_i respectively. Hence the straight line passes through the mean of both the y and x set of values, a condition intuitively seen to be somehow in accord with the normal distribution theory. The slope $b = \Sigma xy/\Sigma x^2$, where again the summation extends over all observations, and $y_i = Y_i - \bar{y}$, $x_i = X_i - \bar{x}$. $\frac{1}{n}\sum xy$ is known as the covariance of y and $x (\Sigma xy = \Sigma(X_i - \bar{x})(Y_i - \bar{y})$ $= \Sigma x_i(Y_i - \bar{y}) = \Sigma(X_i - \bar{x})y_i = \Sigma yx)$. It should be noted that $\hat{Y}_i$ depends on X_i, not on Y_i.

The total spread of the set of Y_i is measured by the variance $\frac{1}{n}\sum y^2$, while the total "sum of squares" is Σy^2. Regression reduced the sum of squares by $\Sigma^2 xy/\Sigma x^2$, that is, the sum of squares reduced for regression of Y on X is $\sum y^2 - \frac{\Sigma^2 xy}{\Sigma x^2} = \sum y^2 - b \sum xy$. A significance test applied to this reduction is called testing the significance of the regression coefficient, b, being different from zero. Evidently a and b are examples of statistics computed from observations in the sample experiment and are to be considered as estimates of α and β, the corresponding parameters in the parent infinite populations of errors of all possible observations of this kind. As sample statistics they are associated with probability distributors, which have been computed on the basis of normal theory with the following results. If σ^2 is the error variance of an individual observat on in the parent population n the size of the sample, i.e., the number of *pairs* of observations then:

(1) estimate of σ^2 is $\dfrac{1}{n-2}\left(\sum y^2 - \dfrac{\Sigma^2 xy}{\Sigma x^2}\right) = S'_{y \cdot x}$

(2) estimate of α is $\bar{y} = a$; estimate of error variance of a is $V_a = \dfrac{1}{n}S^2_{x \cdot y}$

(3) estimate of $\beta = b$; estimate of error variance of b is $V_b = \dfrac{S^2_{y \cdot x}}{\Sigma x^2}$

It may be proved that estimates are unbiased and that the variances are independently distributed or as they are usually called orthogonal; hence the estimate of the error variance of a single observation may be derived (since $\sigma^2(u + k) = \sigma^2(u)$ where k is a constant and $\sigma^2(ku) = k^2\sigma^2(u)$) to be

$$\sigma^2_{yi} = S^2_{y \cdot x} + \frac{1}{n}S^2_{y \cdot x} + x^2_i \frac{S^2_{y \cdot x}}{\Sigma x^2}$$

i.e., the sum of the error variance of an individual observation, plus the error variance of the mean of the set of Y's used to determine straight line, plus $(X_i - \bar{x})^2$ times the error variance of the regression coefficient.

A few remarks should be made concerning the conditions underlying this theory. It was assumed that any X_i is free of all error. If this is not true, i.e., if the chemical composition of the sample (or standard) is not known or given exactly, the error will behave as if it were a systematic error as previously discussed and normal statistical theory can not get rid of the bias. The variance of b is strongly diminished by the increase or spread in the values of X_i.

It will have been noticed that the line was determined as the regression of Y on X, i.e., assuming that X_i is known. But, except when standards are used, it is exactly this value of X_i that is to be determined and it may be asked why the line was not computed as X on Y, i.e., $\hat{X}_i = a' + b'Y_i$. The answer involves consideration of distribution theory. Attention is called to the fact that the least square solution of the problem was based on minimizing $\Sigma(\hat{Y}_i - Y_i)^2$. No meaning can be attached to minimizing $\Sigma(\hat{X}_i - X_i)^2$, since the values of X_i are not randomly distributed. This is obvious when standards are used. In general, as will be discussed later, if both variables are random, there is no choice between minimizing the x or y residuals, and indeed the regression lines will not be the same if computed first with one variable and then the other as the choice of independent coordinate. A thorough discussion of this point will be found in the references. However, the essence of the solution of the inversion problem is contained in the following relation. Consider $\hat{Y} = \bar{y} + b(X_i - \bar{x})$ and $\hat{X}_i = \bar{x} + b'(Y_i - \bar{y})$, where x is the independent, nonrandomly distributed variable while Y is the dependent, randomly distributed variable. Then the best estimate of b' is $1/b$, as follows from ordinary algebra. But for purposes of determination of significance of error, the difference between the algebraic and stochastic inversion (i.e., according to the theory of the random variate) in the role of independent and dependent variable largely depends on the difference between $\dfrac{1}{b}$ and $\dfrac{1}{b - \dfrac{t^2}{b}\dfrac{S_{y \cdot x}}{\Sigma x^2}}$, where t is Students' t function at the selected significance level. While it is true that in all instances observed by the writer, the differences for spectrographic data are entirely negligible, it is considered advisable to proceed along rigorous lines, i.e., the proper choice of dependent and independent variable, and to make an algebraic inversion later. Besides, and this is by no means to be considered as a justification, the proper choice, particularly in an application to be considered in connection with spectrographic data, simplifies the arithmetic computation to a marked degree.

1.4.3. The Straight Line with Independent Variate Determined Experimentally. In the method of plate calibration using sets of iron lines and corresponding log E values determined from spectrographic measurements, as previously discussed, it may be assumed that the log E values were obtained as the means of extensive series of observations, made under varied conditions over a long period of time. Hence it may be assumed that the error variance of the assigned log E values is very much less than the error variance in the density values of the lines on a given plate, which may be determined either as single observations or at most as means of sets of few observations. In general, if both variables are subject to error, there is little justification in minimizing the sum of squares of the residuals in the direction of the Y-axis. The direction of the residuals, it is felt, should somehow be associated with either the values of σ_y and σ_x (known from extra-experimental sources) or at least with their ratio, $c = \sigma_y/\sigma_x$. The expression for the slope of a straight line, minimizing the squares of the residuals *normal* to the regression line is

$$b = \frac{c\Sigma y^2 - \Sigma x^2 + \sqrt{(c\Sigma y^2 - \Sigma x^2)^2 + 4c\Sigma^2 yx}}{2c\Sigma xy}$$

However, use of this relation and assuming that $4 < \sigma_y/\sigma_x < 5$, i.e., that the error in the density observations is only between four and five times as great as the error in the log I (perhaps due to source variations) gave regression lines not significantly different than if the log I were assumed known free from all error.

1.4.4. The Straight Line with Both Variates Random. This is the most difficult case and no altogether satisfactory solution is available. An instance where this situation may arise would be in the determination of the relation of the densities of two lines. It is evident to all experimenters that it is practically impossible to produce spectra such that two selected lines have identical densities from spectrum to spectrum, even if they are on one plate. Hence the question may arise whether the Δ log I of these line pairs is really independent of the density level. This question may be answered by computing the regression line connecting the observations as plotted with the density of one line as the X coordinate and the density of the other as the Y coordinate. If the slope is 1, and the computation valid the answer would be immediate and acceptable. If the slope is not 1, it would be necessary to estimate the significance of the difference from 1 in view of the general experimental error. There is obviously no rational choice to decide the density of which spectrum line should be considered as the independent and dependent variable, respectively, for a least square solution.

The older procedure would have been to compute the correlation coefficient, $r = \Sigma xy/\sqrt{\Sigma x^2 \Sigma y^2}$, and say that the closer it is to 1 the closer the linear connection between the densities of the spectrum lines and the less difference it makes which variable is chosen as the independent one for a least squares solution. However, present tables only indicate the significance of r being different from zero, which is not at all satisfactory. Spectrographic observations of even indifferent quality may give values of r, in experiments of this type, as high as .995+. In addition r measures only the relation of variances and gives no information concerning the desired mean values, say of b. On the other hand one could compute a least square line, assuming the error variances equal in the observations of the density of either line, and minimizing the sum of squares of the residuals normal to the regression lines. The slope would be represented by

$$b = \frac{\Sigma y^2 - \Sigma x^2 + \sqrt{(\Sigma y^2 - \Sigma x^2)^2 + 4\Sigma^2 xy}}{2\Sigma xy}$$

Many objections may be raised against this method. First there is no justification for the direction chosen for the residual or deviate and second, the straight line is not invariant under transformation of the coordinate system. It is clear that a satisfactory method should give results which do not depend on the choice of a particular coordinate system. Wald, in the reference noted (9), has devised a method of computation which, under certain assumptions, enables one to compute the straight line with no *a priori* assumptions (independent of the observed values) regarding the standard deviations of the errors. Also the standard deviations of the errors can be well estimated by means of the observed values, with the precision of the estimate increasing with the number of observations.

The basic assumptions are that the two random error variables, in the X and Y sets, have the same distributions within themselves and are uncorrelated with each other, and that a single linear relation holds between the true values of X and Y, that is $(\hat{Y}_i = \alpha \hat{X}_i + \beta)$. The computation of the slope of the regression line is logically simple. The sets of Y and X are split into corresponding two parts, i.e., $\{Y\}_1$, $\{Y\}_2$ and $\{X\}_1$, $\{X\}_2$. Then $b = \dfrac{\{Y\}_1 - \{Y\}_2}{\{X\}_1 - \{X\}_2}$, and consequently it is necessary to assume that the limit inferior of the mean value of $\{X\}_1 - \{X\}_2$ is positive (> 0) for the population of all sample observations. To determine significance it is necessary to assume that the division of the sets of Y and X values is made independent of the value of the error. The limitations are rather severe, since for almost any spectrum line pair it is not certain that the errors are uncorrelated, and if the errors and the X values are normally distributed it is difficult to select a split in the X and Y sets that would be certain to be independent of the errors.

1.5. Analysis of Variance.   Computation

1.5.1. Introduction. All the previous discussion has been prepared to clear the way for a treatment of the central problem in the analysis of spectrographic data, namely, (1) the determination of the contribution of the various experimental factors to the general or over-all error, (2) the computation of an objective, usable estimate of precision and (3) the manner in which this estimate can be used for the prediction of precision of future observations under similar but not necessarily identical conditions. This treatment will be divided into two parts; (1) computation based on the data and (2) estimates of significances of various appropriate kinds. It should be emphasized that the computation of data is of a purely arithmetic character, similar to the process of substituting numbers into an algebraic formula, with no consideration given to statistical or probability theory. Of course, the computations are designed for the application of significance tests although certain results derived from the computation will be useful without further consideration.

While the symbols will be given denotations peculiar to spectrographic procedures, any other appropriate sets of meanings will serve equally well. The numbers used to indicate levels are only indicative; there is clearly no loss of generality in writing P_1, P_2, P_3 rather than $P_1, P_2, \ldots , P_n$ and it may be much clearer, as long as no use is made of the peculiar properties of the number 3. After all, the generality implied by a series of dots, . . . , is often overrated. Actual numerical illustrations will be given in a later section as specific examples.

1.5.2. Complete Balanced Experiment for Means. Consider an experiment of form $P^4Q^3R^2S^6$, where the following meanings may be attached:

$P \equiv$ photographic plates; four levels, or four plates used

$Q \equiv$ excitation condition; three levels

$R \equiv$ repetition in immediate succession; two levels

$S \equiv$ specimen; at six levels

The dependent variable, or observation is taken to be the $\Delta \log I$ of a line pair corresponding to an element common to all samples and a line of the matrix element; 36 spectra may be placed on a plate by appropriate masking.

The connotations peculiar to the factors are different   Plates, P, may be considered the block unit. Evidently plates may be used only once, and for present purposes are considered indistinguishable except for a serial-like designation or dictionary ordering. Q, the excitation conditions may or may not have a quantitative graduation; thus the differences between the Q_1, Q_2, Q_3 may be that of known secondary voltage, capacitance, or even exposure times. R, the repetition factor, is assumed indistinguishable between R_1 and R_2; that is, R_1 on P_1 does not in any peculiar way correspond to R_1 on P_2 rather than to R_2 on P_2. The sample factor, S_1 is not taken to indicate a different composition between the levels but some other characteristic, electrode size for example. The influence of differences in composition will be treated later under regression.

The set of data, i.e., the set of $\Delta \log I$ observations or measurements is arranged as is illustrated in Table I. One proceeds to compute various

TABLE I

	P_1					P_2					P_3					P_4				
	Q_1		Q_2		Q_3		Q_1		Q_2		Q_3		Q_1		Q_2		Q_3		Q_1		Q_2		Q_3
	R_1	R_2	R_1	R_2	R_1	R_2	R_1	R_2	R_1	R_2	R_1	R_2	R_1	R_2	R_1	R_2	R_1	R_2	R_1	R_2	R_1	R_2	R_1	R_2
S_1																								
S_2																								
S_3																								
S_4																								
S_5																								
S_6																								

sums of squares of deviations from the mean. The computations in general are apt to be laborious unless performed in a methodical manner. First, a general simplification in the computation will be indicated. For any set of numbers, the sum of squares (of deviations) i.e., $\sum\limits^{N} (Y_i - \bar{y})^2$, summed over all values of i will be computed by means of the formula,

$$\sum_{}^{N} (Y_i - \bar{y})^2 = \sum_{}^{N} Y_i^2 - \frac{(\Sigma Y_i)^2}{N},$$

an algebraic identity that may be easily proved:

$$\sum_{}^{N} (Y_i - \bar{y})^2 = \sum Y_i^2 - 2\bar{y} \sum Y_i + N\bar{y}^2$$
$$= \sum Y_i^2 - \frac{2\Sigma Y_i \Sigma Y_i}{N} + N \left(\frac{\Sigma Y_i}{N}\right)^2$$
$$= \sum Y_i^2 - \frac{(\Sigma Y_i)^2}{N}$$

The latter form is easily computed on modern computing machines with automatic multiplication, since in the process of squaring, the sum of Y_i appears on one dial and the sum of squares, $Y_i{}^2$, on another. The following symbols will be used hereinafter: ΣP_1 will mean the sum of all observations on P_1; $\Sigma P_1 Q_1$ means the sum of all measurements on $P_1 Q_1$ etc.

There are $4 \times 3 \times 2 \times 6 = 144$ observations in all, i.e., $N = 144$. Compute $(\Sigma Y)^2/144$; this quantity will be called the correction factor for the mean, or simply the correction factor and will be indicated by the symbol cf. The following computations are now made: $\{ \Sigma^2 P \equiv (\Sigma P)^2 \}$

(a) (*Total*) sum of squares: $\sum\limits^{144} Y^2 - cf$

(b) (*P*) sum of squares: $\dfrac{\Sigma^2 P_1 + \Sigma^2 P_2 + \Sigma^2 P_3 + \Sigma^2 P_4}{36} - cf$

(c) (*Q*) sum of squares: $\dfrac{\Sigma^2 Q_1 + \Sigma^2 Q_2 + \Sigma^2 Q_3}{48} - cf$

(d) ($P \times Q$) sum of squares:
$$\dfrac{\Sigma^2 P_1 Q_1 + \cdots + \Sigma^2 P_3 Q_3 + \cdots + \Sigma^2 P_4 Q_3}{12}$$
$- cf - (P)$ sum of squares (Q) sum of squares

(e) (*S*) sum of squares: $\dfrac{\Sigma^2 S_1 + \cdots + \Sigma^2 S_6}{24} - cf$

(f) ($P \times S$) sum of squares: $\dfrac{\Sigma^2 P_1 S_1 + \cdots + \Sigma^2 P_4 S_6}{6} - cf - (P)$
sum of squares $-$ (*S*) sum of squares

(g) ($Q \times S$) sum of squares: $\dfrac{\Sigma^2 Q_1 S_1 + \cdots + \Sigma^2 Q_3 S_6}{8} - cf - (Q)$
sum of squares $-$ (*S*) sum of squares

(h) ($P \times Q \times S$) sum of squares: $\dfrac{\Sigma^2 P_1 Q_1 S_1 + \cdots + \Sigma^2 P_4 Q_3 S_6}{2}$
$- cf - (P)$ sum of squares $- (Q)$ sum of squares $- (S)$ sum of squares $- (P \times Q)$ sum of squares $- (P \times S)$ sum of squares $- (Q \times S)$ sum of squares

(i) (ΣR) sum of squares: Remainder, i.e., the difference between the *total* sum of squares and all the sums previously computed.

It should be noted that the divisor, i.e., the number in the denominator of the above fractions, is the number of observations used in the summation of each of the terms in the numerator.

The computed values may be exhibited in an *Analysis of Variance Table*.

TABLE II
Analysis of Variance

Source of variation	Degrees of freedom (df)	Mean square (V)	Components of variance
Total	$144 - 1 = 143$	$\dfrac{(Total)}{143}$	
P	$4 - 1 = 3$	$\dfrac{(P)}{3}$	$\sigma^2_0 + 2^2\sigma_{PQS} + 12^2\sigma_{PQ} + 6^2\sigma_{PS} + 36^2\sigma_P$
Q	$3 - 1 = 2$	$\dfrac{(Q)}{2}$	$\sigma^2_0 + 2^2\sigma_{PQS} + 12^2\sigma_{PQ} + 8^2\sigma_{QS} + 48^2\sigma_Q$
S	$6 - 1 = 5$	$\dfrac{(S)}{5}$	$\sigma^2_0 + 2^2\sigma_{PQS} + 6^2\sigma_{PS} + 8^2\sigma_{QS} + 72^2\sigma_S$
$P \times Q$	$3 \times 2 = 6$	$\dfrac{(P \times Q)}{6}$	$\sigma^2_0 + 2^2\sigma_{PQS} + 12^2\sigma_{PQ}$
$P \times S$	$3 \times 5 = 15$	$\dfrac{(P \times 5)}{15}$	$\sigma^2_0 + 2^2\sigma_{PQS} + 6^2\sigma_{PS}$
$Q \times S$	$2 \times 5 = 10$	$\dfrac{(Q \times S)}{10}$	$\sigma^2_0 + 2^2\sigma_{PQS} + 8^2\sigma_{QS}$
$P \times Q \times S$	$3 \times 2 \times 5 = 30$	$\dfrac{(P \times Q \times S)}{30}$	$\sigma^2_0 + 2^2\sigma_{PQS}$
ΣR	Remainder $= 143$ $-71 = 72$	$\dfrac{\text{Remainder}}{72}$	σ^2_0

Referring to the Analysis of Variance Table, the first column, headed "Source of Variation" lists the main effects P, Q, S their first order interaction $P \times Q$, $P \times S$ and $Q \times S$, and their second order interaction $P \times Q \times S$. The effect R and all its interactions, i.e., R, $R \times P$, $R \times Q$, $R \times S$, $R \times P \times Q$, $R \times Q \times S$ and $R \times P \times Q \times S$ are pooled into one term ΣR, with the corresponding df equal to the sum of the df of the pooled terms, i.e., $1 + 3 + 2 + 5 + 6 + 15 + 10 + 30 = 72$. This procedure is mathematically permissible, since it may be proved[3]that for independent factors, the comparisons obtained above are independent or *orthogonal*, and their sum of squares and df are linearly additive, respectively, to give a combined sum of squares and a combined df corresponding to the combined or pooled effects. The physical reason for the pooling of the R terms, as has been stated before is that R_1 and R_2 are indistinguishable when compared in any classification larger than the cell $P_iQ_jS_k$. In a similar fashion, if the entire experiment were to be repeated over several days, introducing a new effect, D, since the various P levels within each day have only a serial difference, P would have to be pooled with its D interactions, i.e., $P + P \times D$ would be the least combination that would have physical meaning.

The second column, headed "Degrees of freedom (df)," is derived as follows: degrees of freedom has the connotation of the number of observations or levels corresponding to an effect minus the number of constraints. In this example the constraint is the use of the mean. However in keeping with the formalistic attitude assumed throughout this discussion, df is to be considered as a number computed from the data to be used in entering tables of statistical significance. The rule for computing this number is as follows: (a) the df of the *total* is $N - 1$, where N is the number of observations, (b) the df of a main effect is the number of levels of that effect minus 1, for example, $df(P) = 4 - 1 = 3$, and (c) the df of an interaction is the product of the df of the component main effects entering into the interaction, for example, $df(P \times Q) = 3 \times 2 = 6$.

The third column, headed "mean square (V)," is the quotient of the corresponding sum of squares by the associated df.

The fourth column, headed "Components of variance," indicated by σ^2 with various subscripts on line with the various sources of variation may be computed step wise, starting at the bottom. It is to be noted that the coefficients of the various components is the number corresponding to the multiplicity of the effect corresponding to the subscript, except σ_0^2. The interpretation of these components is intimately connected with their significance and will be discussed later.

NOTE: The above computation procedure may be easily adapted to experiments that have unequal class numbers, for example a different number of observations or repetitions in S_1 than in S_2, by an arithmetical adjustment of the divisors, which will still remain the number of terms used in forming the sums in the numerators separately considered. However details of this modification and its influence on significance, particularly interactions, and other refinements will be omitted. The interested reader is advised to consult the references for complete discussions.

1.5.3. Complete Balanced Experiment, for Regression (Covariance) Analysis. Qualitative Interpretation of Effects. The previous computation, to anticipate a later discussion, was designed to estimate the significance of differences of mean values between various classifications of the data due to the various effects. However, spectrographic data is largely concerned with establishing a line or relation between two variables. The most common example is the relation between the $\Delta \log I$ of a line pair corresponding to an element and matrix line with the log per cent of that element in the sample, S. The relation, of course, need not be limited to that mentioned for it could easily be that of the $\Delta \log I$ of a sample and the secondary voltage in the effect Q, for example. Or, to be sure, the experiment may be designed to yield, simultaneously, two lines; one line correlating $\Delta \log I$ with per cent and the other correlating

$\Delta \log I$ with voltage. However, the discussion will be restricted to the determination of one line, assumed straight, namely, that correlating $\Delta \log I$ with log per cent.

Consider the previous experiment $P^4Q^3R^2S^6$. To each sample S_i, there corresponds an independent, known variable, not subject to error, namely the log per cent, X_i. S_1 is always associated with X_1, S_2 with X_2 etc, i.e., the samples or standards are the same throughout the entire experiment. It will simplify the computations if the log per cent values are transformed into deviations from the mean, i.e., $X_i = X_i - \bar{x}$; otherwise, when computing $\Sigma x_i Y_i$ it will be necessary to subtract another correction factor, i.e., $\sum y = \sum y = \sum y - \dfrac{\Sigma x \, \Sigma y}{N}$ where N is the number of paired observations.

The introduction of the new condition, i.e., correlation of $Y(S_i)$ $(= \Delta \log I \ (S_i))$ with x_i introduces some new and important considerations. Consider R at only 1 level, i.e., $P^4Q^3S^6$, then a regression line will be obtained within each P_iQ_j combination or twelve regression lines in all. These regression lines, as may have been apparent, are least square solutions and hence will pass through $(\bar{x}, \bar{y})$; with $\bar{y}$ determined within each P_iQ_j cell. The regression lines in general will not be identical, but will move around in the (x, y) plane. Kinematical considerations indicate the generalized motion of a line to be resolvable into two independent components, namely (1) a translation and (2) a rotation about some point. Since $\bar{x}$ is fixed for all combinations of P_iQ_j the translation of the line will become a motion along the Y-axis corresponding to the different values of $\bar{y}$ in the P_iQ_j cell while the rotation will be reflected in the different value of b_n. This may also be seen from the equations. The twelve regression lines will be of the form $\hat{Y} = \bar{y} + b_n\bar{x}$, $n = 1, 2, \cdots$ 12. Consequently, the analysis of variance reduced for regression should distinguish three main varieties of error, namely: (1) the error due to the variation in $\bar{y}$ or means (this has been analyzed in the previous computation of the analysis of variance), (2) the error due to the variation in b_n, in regression coefficient, or the variation in *slopes;* this will be called covariance or regression analysis, and (3) the error due to the points not lying immediately on the line or the error due to *deviations.*

Accordingly, reconsidering the original experiment, it is seen that while it is still of the form $P^4Q^3S^6R^2$ there is an added important modification, namely the set S_1 to S_6 is a recognizable class correlated with the six independent variables, x_1 to x_6.

The computation may be divided into three parts, namely: (1) means, (2) slopes or regression (covariance analysis) and, (3) deviations. The procedure may well be arranged as follows.

Prepare a covariance table (Table III), that is, compute $\Sigma xy = \Sigma xY$ for every P_iQ_j combination, summing $Y_{ijk}(R_1) + Y_{ijk}(R_2)$ in each combination to obtain the Y for each S, as illustrated. For easy reference it is suggested that the values of the covariance be exhibited in a manner similar to that shown in the table. To facilitate the computation it is suggested that the values of x_i be entered in a margin along the column of S_i in Table I, so that the multiplication and summation for each P_iQ_j may be directly performed on the computing machine. It is to be remembered that the x_i are not the values of log per cent, but the devia-

TABLE III
Covariance

	P_1	P_2	P_3	P_4
Q_1	$\Sigma_{xy}(P_1Q_1)$	$\Sigma_{xy}(P_2Q_1)$	$\Sigma_{xy}(P_3Q_1)$	$\Sigma_{xy}(P_4Q_1)$
Q_2	$\Sigma_{xy}(P_1Q_2)$	$\Sigma_{xy}(P_2Q_2)$	$\Sigma_{xy}(P_3Q_2)$	$\Sigma_{xy}(P_4Q_2)$
Q_3	$\Sigma_{xy}(P_1Q_3)$	$\Sigma_{xy}(P_2Q_3)$	$\Sigma_{xy}(P_3Q_3)$	$\Sigma_{xy}(P_4Q_3)$

Example: $\Sigma_{xy}(P_3Q_2) = x_1\{Y(P_3Q_2S_1R_1) + Y(P_3Q_2S_1R_2)\} + \cdots + x_6\{Y(P_3Q_2S_6R_1) + Y(P_3Q_2S_6R_2)\}$

TABLE IV
Covariance

	P_1	P_2	P_3	P_4
Q_1	$\Sigma_{xy}(P_1Q_1R_1)$ $\Sigma_{xy}(P_1Q_2R_2)$	— —	— —	— —
Q_2	— —	— —	$\Sigma_{xy}(P_3Q_2R_1)$ $\Sigma_{xy}(P_3Q_2R_2)$	— —
Q_3	— —	— —	— —	— —

tions from the mean value, $\bar{x}$, i.e., $x_i = X_i$ (log per cent of S_i) $- \bar{x}$. It may easily be shown that

$$\Sigma xy(P_iQ_j) = \Sigma x\{Y(P_iQ_jR_1) + Y(P_iQ_jR_2)\} = \Sigma xY(P_iQ_jR_1) + \Sigma xY(P_iQ_jR_2)$$

Care must be given to use the proper sign of x_i, since approximately half of them will be negative. (The symbol $\Sigma xy(P_1)$ represents the sum of the covariance in P_1, $\Sigma xy(P_2Q_3)$ the sum of the covariance in P_2Q_3, etc.)

Compute the sum of squares of the x_i, $\Sigma x^2 = x_1^2 + \cdots + x_6^2$.

Sum all the covariances, i.e., the entries in Table III, and represent this quantity by $\sum xy$ (total) $= \sum\sum xy$. Compute $\dfrac{(\Sigma\Sigma xy)^2}{24\Sigma x^2} = \dfrac{\Sigma\Sigma^2 xy}{24\Sigma x^2}$

and call this quantity the sum of squares reducible for regression, with the symbol rf. This quantity is analogous in its use to cf. It is to be noted that the denominator in the above fraction, as well as in the similar fractions to be used below, is the product of Σx^2 into the number of sets of S that are used in the summation of the covariance represented by each term in the numerator.

The analysis of covariance reduced for regression, of Y on $X(S)$, may now be performed along lines quite parallel to the previous analysis of variance.

(1) *Means.* Compute, according to the previously indicated procedure for the analysis of variance, the sum of squares corresponding to the *total* and the various effects, i.e., $P, Q, P \times Q, \Sigma R, S, P \times S, Q \times S, P \times Q \times S$ and total. Represent the terms as follows:

Sum of squares for the mean: (P mean), (Q mean), ($P \times Q$ mean);
(ΣR)
(S), ($P \times S$), ($Q \times S$), ($P \times Q \times S$), and
Total.

(2) *Slopes, Regression or Covariance Analysis.*

(a) Total sum of squares reduced by regression of Y on $xSS^2{}_{y \cdot x} =$ Total $- rf = \Sigma Y^2 - cf - rf = \Sigma y^2 - rf$

(b) (P reg) sum of squares: $\dfrac{\Sigma^2 xy(P_1) + \cdots + \Sigma^2 xy(P_4)}{6 \Sigma x^2} - rf$

(c) (Q reg) sum of squares: $\dfrac{\Sigma^2 xy(Q_1) + \Sigma^2 xy(Q_2) + \Sigma^2 xy(Q_3)}{8 \Sigma x^2} - rf$

(d) ($P \times Q$ reg) sum of squares: $\dfrac{\Sigma^2 xy(P_1 Q_1) + \cdots + \Sigma^2 xy(P_4 Q_3)}{2 \Sigma x^2}$
$- rf - (P \text{ reg}) - (Q \text{ reg})$.

(3) *Deviation Analysis.*

(a) (S dev) sum of squares $= (S)$ sum of squares $- rf$
(b) (P dev) sum of squares $= (P \times S)$ sum of squares $-$ (P reg) sum of squares
(c) (Q dev) sum of squares $= (Q \times S)$ sum of squares $-$ (Q reg) sum of squares
(d) ($P \times Q$ dev) sum of squares $- (P \times Q \times S)$ sum of squares $-$ ($P \times Q$ reg) sum of squares.

(4) *Analysis of Replication.* If R is still retained as a mere repetition factor for individual spectra, for example if spectrum $P_1 Q_1 S_1 R_1$ is followed immediately by spectrum $P_1 Q_1 S_1 R_2$ and similarly throughout the entire experiment, no further analysis is possible. On the other hand, if the unit of repetition is the set of six spectra ($P_1 Q_1 S_i R_1, i = 1, \cdots, 6$),

for example a set of six spectra, R_1, one for each specimen, is exposed in succession and after a time lapse the other set of six for R_2, is exposed, or perhaps the first set is exposed for each combination of P_iQ_j for all twelve combinations of and then the series repeated to expose the second set, R_2, the repetitions will be distinguishable within each P_iQ_j if not between them. For example, the two sets in P_2Q_3 are distinguishable as R_1 and R_2, where the subscripts have only a serial relationship, and no peculiar correspondence or relationship is implied between set R_1 in P_2Q_3 to R_1 in any other P_iQ_j as opposed to correspondence of R_1 in P_2Q_3 to R_1 *or* R_2 in any other P_iQ_j. To repeat, the repetitions are distinguishable *within* P_iQ_j but not *between* them.

Under this assumption of the nature of the repetitions, the analysis may be extended as follows.

The covariance Table III is extended, using Table I, so that the covariance is computed explicitly for each $P_iQ_jR_k$ set, or $4 \times 3 \times 2 = 24$ numbers. These numbers may be exhibited in a manner similar to Table III, but with two entries in each $P_iQ_jR_k$ cell, one for R_1 and the other for R_2 as indicated in Table IV. However the R_1 and R_2 values are not to be distinguished by any index common between the different P_iQ_j.

The following sums of squares may now be computed in addition to those previously obtained.

(a) (ΣR) Sum of squares: (computation independent of any "remainder" process)

$$\sum Y^2 - \frac{\Sigma^2 P_1 Q_1 S_1 + \cdots + \Sigma^2 P_4 Q_3 S_6}{2}$$

or, equivalently:

$$\sum y^2 - \left\{ \frac{\Sigma^2 P_1 Q_1 S_1 + \cdots + \Sigma^2 P_4 Q_3 S_6}{2} - cf \right\}$$

Note: There are $4 \times 3 \times 6 = 72$ terms in the numerator.

(b) (ΣR means) Sum of squares:

Compute twelve numbers similar to the one indicated for all P_iQ_j and sum

$$\frac{\Sigma^2 P_1 Q_1 R_1 + \Sigma^2 P_1 Q_1 R_2}{6} - \frac{\Sigma^2 P_1 Q_1}{12}$$

or, in one operation:

$$\frac{\Sigma^2 P_1 Q_1 R_1 + \cdots + \Sigma^2 P_4 Q_3 R_2}{6} - \frac{\Sigma^2 P_1 Q_1 + \cdots + \Sigma^2 P_4 Q_3}{12}$$

(c) (ΣR reg) Sum of squares:

Compute, in a parallel fashion, twelve numbers similar to the one indicated, for all P_iQ_j and sum:

$$\frac{\Sigma^2 xy(P_1Q_1R_1) + \Sigma^2 xy(P_1Q_1R_2)}{\Sigma x^2} - \frac{\Sigma^2 xy(P_1Q_1)}{2\Sigma x^2}$$

or, in one operation:

$$\frac{\Sigma^2 xy(P_1Q_1R_1) + \cdots + \Sigma^2 xy(P_4Q_3R_2)}{\Sigma x^2} - \frac{\Sigma^2 xy(P_1Q_1) + \cdots + \Sigma^2 xy(P_4Q_3)}{2\Sigma x^2}$$

(d) (ΣR dev) Sum of squares:

(ΣR) sum of squares $-$ (ΣR means) sum of squares $-$ (ΣR reg) sum of squares

This treatment of the R factor, when feasible, is very useful and will be considered the normal manner unless otherwise indicated.

The computed values for the entire analysis may be exhibited as follows:

TABLE V

Analysis of Variance Reduced for Regression. $N = 144$

Source of variation	Degrees of freedom (df)	Mean square (V)
Total	$144 - 2 = 142$	Total reduced for regression / 142
Means		
P means	3	(P means)/3
Q means	2	(Q means)/2
$\times Q$ means	6	($P \times Q$ means)/6
ΣR means	12	(ΣR means)/12
Σ Means	23	(Σ means)/23
Regression		
P reg	3	(P reg)/3
Q reg	2	(Q reg)/2
$P \times Q$ reg	6	($P \times Q$ reg)/6
ΣR reg	12	(ΣR reg)/12
Regression	23	(Σ reg)/23
Deviations		
S dev	4	(S dev)/4
P dev	$3 \times 4 = 12$	(P dev)/12
Q dev	$2 \times 4 = 8$	(Q dev)/8
$P \times Q$ dev	$3 \times 2 \times 4 = 24$	($P \times Q$ dev)/24
ΣR dev	$12 \times 4 = 48$	(ΣR dev)/48
Σ dev	96	(Σ dev)/96

Or, if one wishes to summarize the three principal types of errors, one may prepare condensation as follows:

TABLE V(a)

Source of variation	Degrees of freedom	Mean square
Means	23	$(\Sigma$ Means$)/23$
Regression	23	$(\Sigma$ Reg$)/23$
Deviations	96	$(\Sigma$ Dev$)/96$
Total	142	Total reduced for regression 142

Tables V and V(a) should be carefully considered. The second column lists degrees of freedom, df, not quite the same as those in Table II; 1 df, for regression, is lost from the total, hence the total $df = N - 2 = 142$. The df for means and regression is the same as in Table II, that is, for main effects, P and Q, the df is the number of levels minus 1, and the df of $P \times Q = df(P) \times df(Q)$. Since there are twenty-four repeated sets (of S), there are $24 - 1 = 23$ df, respectively, for both means and regression. Since the regression is around S, the S effect loses 2 df, one for the mean and one for regression; hence the df $(S$ dev$) = 6 - 1 - 1 = 4$. On account of its linear properties, the df of a deviation effect, say P, may be derived from the mode of computation of P, namely $df(P$ dev$) = df(P \times S) - df(P$ reg$) = 15 - 3 = 12$. Or else, one may consider P dev as equal to the interaction of $P \times S$ dev and the $df(P \times S$ dev$) = 3 \times 4 = 12$, by the usual rule.

NOTE: It may be perhaps unnecessary to remark that in an analysis of this type the sum of squares as well as the covariance or regression factors for all effects and interactions are non-negative numbers.

Although the full quantitative meaning of the various mean squares will be only appreciated after the discussion on significance, the following discussion may be considered as an introduction to their qualitative meanings. The viewpoint will be that of the null-hypothesis.

Total: If the total (variance) mean square were zero it would mean that all twenty-four observations on each of the six samples, S_i, are identical and that they all lie immediately on the regression line (analytical curve) drawn through the six points $(x_1y_1,\ x_2y_2,\ x_3y_3,\ x_4y_4,\ x_5y_5,\ x_6y_6)$ where each point is the identical location of the twenty-four observations. This composite condition, involving slopes, means, deviations, plates, excitation condition and repetitions is admittedly on the improbable side. Consequently, it may be assumed that the *total* (variance) mean square, after reduction for regression, is not zero.

There are twenty-four individual regression lines (analytical curves), one line for each $P_i Q_j R_k$ cell or combination. The equations of these lines are all of the form $\hat{Y} = a + bx$, where $a = \bar{y}$ and b is the slope, i.e., $\Sigma xy / \Sigma x^2$, for the cell under consideration. Thus, let $a(P_1 Q_3 R_1)$ represent the mean value of Y in $P_1 Q_3 R_1$, and $b(P_1 Q_3 R_1)$ represent $\dfrac{\Sigma xy (P_1 Q_3 R_1)}{\Sigma x^2}$. Extend the meaning of the symbols to include an averaging process to be indicated by a bar over the symbol for the factor, i.e., $a(\bar{P}_1)$ is the average over P_1, i.e., $\dfrac{\Sigma Y (\overline{P_1})}{36}$, $b(\overline{P_2 Q_2}) = \dfrac{\Sigma xy (P_2 Q_2)}{2 \Sigma x^2}$; $b(Q_3) = \dfrac{\Sigma xy (Q_3)}{8 \Sigma x^2}$ etc. In addition, let $a_0 = \dfrac{\Sigma Y}{144}$ and $b_0 = \dfrac{\Sigma xy \text{ (total)}}{24 \Sigma x^2}$, i.e., the overall averages of the Y and the slopes, respectively. If $Y_2 (P_2 Q_3 R_1)$ for example, represents the calculated value of $\Delta \log I$ for S_2 in $P_2 Q_3 R_1$, i.e., $\hat{Y}_2 = a(P_2 Q_3 R_1) + b(P_2 Q_3 R_1) x_2$ then the corresponding deviation is $\{ Y_2 (P_2 Q_3 R_1) - \hat{Y}_2 (P_2 Q_3 R_1) \}^2$, i.e., the square of the difference between the observed and calculated value.

The qualitative interpretations of the effects may be tabulated under their implications with regard to a, b and deviations, under the null hypothesis.

Hypothesis   Implication

Means $= 0$ $a(P_i Q_j R_k) = a_0$

Regression $= 0$ $b(P_i Q_j R_k) = b_0$

Dev $= 0$ $\Sigma \{ Y_n (P_i Q_j R_k) - \hat{Y}_n (P_i Q_j R_k) \}^2 = 0$ $\begin{cases} i = 1, 2, \cdots, 4 \\ j = 1, 2, 3 \\ k = 1, 2 \\ n = 1, 2, \cdots, 6 \end{cases}$

P means $= 0$ $a(\bar{P}_1) = a(\bar{P}_2) = \cdots = a(\bar{P}_4) = a_0$

P reg $= 0$ $b(\bar{P}_1) = b(\bar{P}_2) = \cdots = b(\bar{P}_4) = b_0$

P dev $= 0$ $\Sigma \{ Y_n (P_1) - \hat{Y}_n (P_1) \}^2 = 0$, $n = 1, 2, \cdots, 6$

                            Similarly for P_2, P_3, P_4

Q means $= 0$ $a(\bar{Q}_1) = a(\bar{Q}_2) = a(\bar{Q}_3) = a_0$

Q reg $= 0$ $b(\bar{Q}_1) = b(\bar{Q}_2) = b(\bar{Q}_3) = b_0$

Q dev $= 0$ $\Sigma \{ Y_n (Q_1) - \hat{Y}_n (Q_1) \}^2 = 0$, $n = 1, 2, \cdots, 6$

                            Similarly for Q_2, Q_3

S dev $= 0$ $\Sigma \{ \bar{Y}_n - (a_0 + b_0 x) \}^2 = 0$, $n = 1, 2, \cdots, 6$

i.e., the sum of the squares of the differences of average $\Delta \log I$ for each S_i from the calculated values, using the overall regression line is zero.

$P \times Q$ mean $= 0$ $\quad \{a(\overline{P_iQ_j}) - a_0\} = \{a(\bar{P}_i) - a_0\} + \{a(\bar{Q}_j) - a_0\}$, i.e.

$$a(\overline{P_iQ_j}) = a(P_i) + a(Q_j) - a_0$$

$P \times Q$ reg $\quad = 0$ $\quad\quad\quad b(\overline{P_iQ_j}) = b(\bar{P}_i) + b(\bar{Q}_j) - b_0$

$P \times Q$ dev $\quad = 0$ $\quad \Sigma\{Y_n(\overline{P_iQ_j}) - \hat{Y}_n(\overline{P_iQ_j})\}^2 = \Sigma\{Y_n(\bar{P}_i) - \hat{Y}_n(\bar{P}_i)\}^2$

$$+ \Sigma\{Y_n(\bar{Q}_j) - \hat{Y}_n(\bar{Q}_j)\}^2$$

R means $\quad = 0$ $\quad\quad\quad a(P_iQ_jR_1) = a(P_iQ_jR_2)$

R reg $\quad\quad = 0$ $\quad\quad\quad b(P_iQ_jR_1) = b(P_iQ_jR_2)$

R dev $\quad\quad = 0$ $\quad \Sigma\{Y_n(P_iQ_jR_1) - \hat{Y}_n(P_iQ_jR_1)\}^2 = \Sigma\{Y_n(P_iQ_jR_2)$

$$- \hat{Y}_n(P_iQ_jR_2)\}^2$$

$\Sigma R \quad\quad\quad = 0$ $\quad\quad\quad Y_n(P_iQ_jR_1) = Y_n(P_iQ_jR_2)$

1.6. Computation. General Procedure for Orthogonal Comparisons. Reduction to Single Degrees of Freedom

1.6.1. Introduction. While the computational procedure presented in the preceding section is an efficient method it is limited, sometimes severely, by two conditions, namely, (1) the experiment design must be balanced and complete and (2) the various levels of the main effects, and consequently their interactions, are confounded even though there may be some valid physical reason for distinguishing between them. These restrictions may be illustrated by an example. Consider the previous experiment $P^4Q^3R^2S^6$. A close consideration of the previous computational procedure will show that it is not valid unless the effects are balanced and each block, or plate, is complete. For example if the experiment were of the form

P_1	P_2	P_3	P_4
Q_1, Q_2 R^2S^6	Q_1, Q_3 R^2S^6	Q_2, Q_3 R^2S^6	Q_1, Q_2, Q_3 R^2S^6

the P would not be complete and the meaning of the P effect dubious.

On the other hand, suppose the blocks are complete, but the P_i are not quite identical in connotation, i.e., suppose P_1 and P_3 were exposed and developed on a humid day (a condition which may have some influence) while P_2 and P_4 were treated on a cool dry day. The computation already presented is unable to provide for some estimation of this effect. It may appear as if this could be remedied by introducing a new factor, namely weather at 2 levels and the experiment considered to be of the type $W^2\hat{P}^2Q^3R^2S^6$. However, the comparison of $W_1\hat{P}_1$ and $W_2\hat{P}_1$, i.e., P_1 and P_2 is not meaningful, for there is no reason for comparing $W_1\hat{P}_1$ with $W_2\hat{P}_1$ rather than $W_1\hat{P}_1$ with $W_2\hat{P}_2$. Similar conditions were met in the discussion of replicates. This type of difficulty is particularly troublesome in an experiment similar to the one discussed for determining the stability of the source or excitation using two spectrographs.

The computation procedure to be presented is a general one and will enable any factorial experiment to be analyzed. On account of the amount of paper required to present the necessary tabulations the levels in the effects to be presented will be held at a low number, and should not indicate a lack of generality.

1.6.2. Orthogonal Comparisons. Consider an experiment of type Q^3, that is, observations on three levels of factor Q and for initial simplicity, without any repetitions. From the computation that has been presented, the data may be analyzed for effect Q with 2 *df*, i.e., $\Sigma Q_i^2 - \dfrac{(\Sigma Q_i)^2}{3}$.

But what if the qualitative connotations of the three levels are not quite alike in some respect or other, how can one make any further decomposition, say into single degrees of freedom?

Consider, for purposes of analogy, that the set of observations represents a point in the three-vector space, with three components Q_1, Q_2, and Q_3, and let the problem of decomposition be considered as that of resolving the resultant-vector into three orthogonal vectors one of which must be somewhat associated with the origin, or mean value. (The analogy need not be pushed too far. The mathematical treatment is perfectly rigorous and involves the theory of matrices and positive definite quadratic forms.) It is to be recalled that necessary and sufficient conditions for orthogonality of two vectors is the vanishing of their scalar product; that is if $\vec{A} = \Sigma a_i \vec{\delta_i}$, $\vec{B} = \Sigma b_i \vec{\delta_i}$, where δ_i are the unit orthogonal vector components, then vectors $\vec{A}$ and $\vec{B}$ are orthogonal if and only if $\Sigma a_i b_i = 0$. Consider the following array,

Q_1	Q_2	Q_3
1	1	1
1	-1	
1	1	-2

The symbols in the top row represent the observations, and should indicate the factors and levels involved in the observations. The rest of this table, and others similar to it, consists of a number of rows of coefficients, with the number of such rows equal to the number of observations. The first row is a sequence of 1 under each observation. Let any coefficient be indicated by the double index symbol K_{ij}, where the first index represent the row and the second the column, for example in the above table K_{23}, the coefficient in the second row and third column, $= 0$, $K_{33} = -2$, $K_{22} = -1$, $K_{31} = 1$ etc. Then the following rules govern the permissible choice of coefficients: each row is to represent a vector, with components in the "direction" of Q_1, Q_2, Q_{31}, which is orthogonal to the first row-vector, i.e., $\sum_j K_{1j}K_{ij} = 0$ for every value of i; this makes every vector orthogonal to the sum. To make the vectors, or rows, orthogonal to each other, the other rule is $\sum_j K_{mj}K_{nj} = 0$, for every pair of $m \neq n$. Since the first row is always a sequence of 1, i.e., $K_{1j} = 1$ for all values of j, it is usually omitted and the permissible coefficients are chosen according to the rules.

Rule 1. (1) For every row i, $\sum_j K_{ij} = 0$; i.e., the sum of coefficients is zero.

(2) For any pair of rows, $m \neq n$, $\sum_j K_{mj}K_{nj} = 0$, i.e., the sum of products of the two coefficients in each column of the two rows is zero.

Each row represents a comparison associated with $1df$. When rule (1) only is satisfied, the comparison is said to be orthogonal to the sum; and when, in addition, rule (2) is satisfied for two pair of rows, the corresponding comparisons are said to be orthogonal to each other and to the sum. When both rules are satisfied for any pair of rows, the set is said to constitute a complete orthogonal set of comparisons, each associated with $1df$.

The procedure for computing the sum of squares, or variance mean square for any comparison, since each $df = 1$, is as follows:

Rule 2. (1) Multiply the observation by the coefficients in the comparison or row.

(2) Compute the algebraic sum of the products.

(3) Square the sum.

(4) Divide by the sum of squares of the coefficients.

The two sets of rules as given above are sufficient for the variance analysis of any factorial experiment, while the decomposition or partitioning of the variance has been brought down to comparisons of single degrees of freedom.

The application of rules 1 and 2 will be illustrated by examples of the computation of experiment designs of varying intricacy.

(1) One effect at multiple levels R^3. ($Y \equiv$ the observation.)

		$Y(R_1)$	$Y(R_2)$	$Y(R_3)$
1		1	1	1
2	R'	1	-1	
3	R''	1	1	-2

(The discussion is relevant for any permutation of the indices of R.)

Row 1 sum of squares is $(Y_1 + Y_2 + Y_3)^2/3 = (\Sigma Y_i)^2/3 = (\Sigma Y_i)^2/N$. This is recognized as cf, or the correction for the mean. Since this quantity is always introduced, it is usually not considered explicitly, hence the df for Σy^2 is said to be $N - 1 = 3 - 1 = 2$, where N is the number of observations in the general case. This reduction is said to be accompanied by loss of $1df$ for the mean.

Row 2, R', and Row 3, R'', sum of squares are $(Y_1 - Y_2)^2/2$ and $(Y_1 + Y_2 - 2Y_3)^2/6$ respectively. It is to be observed that no subtraction of cf is involved in this mode of computation and the sum of the sum of squares of row 1 and row 2 is equal to the $R(2df)$ sum of squares as computed by the previous method, i.e., $R' + R'' = R$.

Row 2 is a comparison between R_1 and R_2. Row 3 is essentially a comparison between the mean of (R_1 and R_2) and R_3. Thus

$$\frac{1}{\frac{1}{4} + \frac{1}{4} + 1} \left(\frac{1}{2} Y_1 + \frac{1}{2} Y_2 - Y_3\right)^2 = \frac{2}{3} \left(\frac{Y_1 + Y_2}{2} - Y_3\right)^2 = \frac{1}{6} \left(Y_1 + Y_2 - 2Y_3\right)^2$$

It may be seen that multiplying the coefficients in any row by a constant leaves the sum of squares invariant for that comparison. This operation may be considered equivalent to that of "clearing of fractions" and may be performed only after the complete set of coefficients in every row has been computed in order not to confuse the determination of orthogonality between comparisons in the general case. It may be verified by trial, that the above partition "of the sum of squares" is a complete orthogonal set and no other partition is possible. A rather common error, unfortunately, may be illustrated. Considering the observations as replicates, the following comparisons have been reported:

	R_1	R_2	R_3
R'	1	-1	
R''	1		-1
R'''		1	-1

i.e., the three differences between all sets of two observations. These are evidently not orthogonal between themselves. While there can be no objection, in some cases even valid justification, for including sets partitions or comparisons some of which are not orthogonal between themselves, every partition must be orthogonal to the sum, and only orthogonal partitions may be compared with each other.

With the increase in the number of levels of the effect there is a corresponding increase in the number of possible choices of coefficients. The actual choice in any specific experiment will necessarily depend on the interpretations involved. The relative magnitude of the coefficients may be considered as the relative weight or importance attached to the observations, which may or may not be desirable. The following two partitions are characteristic.

	R_1	R_2	R_3	R_4
R'	1	1	-1	-1
R''	1	-1	1	-1
R'''	1	-1	-1	1

This is a particularly effective partition applicable whenever the number of items is a power of 2, i.e., 2, 4, 8, 16, etc. All the observations are used for each comparison and all observations are given equal weight. Another point should be noticed, namely, R''' may be considered as the *interaction of $R' \times R''$*, that is, the coefficients of R''' are the products of the coefficients of R' and R'' in the corresponding columns. The interpretation of *interaction*, in a physical sense, is precisely the meaning previously described. However it should be noticed that R''' is an interaction of sub-effects within a main effect, rather than the previously discussed interaction between main effects. This type of interaction was completely lost in the first mode of computation. The importance of this interaction of course depends on the physical connotation of the terms. It is clear that what has been said of R''' holds for R' and R'' by a permutation of indices.

A general mode of partition, that at least, may be used to compute permissible comparisons, may be called the diagonal partition, for example:

	R_1	R_2	R_3	R_4	R_5
R^{I}	1	-1			
R^{II}	1	1	-2		
R^{III}	1	1	1	-3	
R^{IV}	1	1	1	1	-4

This is a completely asymmetrical system, each comparison involves a different number of terms, and only the last comparison utilizes all observations; all but the first observation are given different weights in the successive comparisons. However, due to its generality it may well be used in investigating various experiment designs.

1.6.3. Two Effects. Interactions. The analysis of a two effect design, P^3Q^3 may be readily computed.

TABLE VI

	$P_1,$ Q_1	$P_1,$ Q_2	$P_1,$ Q_3	$P_2,$ Q_1	$P_2,$ Q_2	$P_2,$ Q_3	$P_3,$ Q_1	$P_3,$ Q_2	$P_3,$ Q_3
cf	+	+	+	+	+	+	+	+	+
P'	+	+	+	−	−	−			
P''	+	+	+	+	+	+	−2	−2	−2
Q'	+	−		+	−		+	−	
Q''	+	+	−2	+	+	−2	+	+	−2
$P' \times Q'$	+	−		−	+				
$P' \times Q''$	+	+	−2	−	−	+2			
$P'' \times Q'$	+	−		+	−		−2	+2	
$P'' \times Q''$	+	+	−2	+	+	−2	−2	−2	+4

$(+) = +1. (-) = -1.$

Although the effects are balanced, this is of no significance to the procedure. The interactions are obtained as indicated in the preceding example, that is by multiplying the coefficients in corresponding columns. It is suggested that the reader verify that $P' + P'' = P(2df)$, $Q' + Q'' = Q(2df)$ and that $P' \times Q' + P' \times Q'' + P'' \times Q' + P'' \times Q'' = P \times Q(4df)$, (considering the sums of squares). Symmetry in all the coefficients can be obtained if 4 plates are used.

1.6.4. Latin Square. This mode of computation is directly applicable to Latin Square designs. Consider an experiment in which two plates are exposed simultaneously exposed to the arc, in two spectrographs, at T_1, and then the plates are interchanged and re-exposed at T_2, simultaneously. The form of the experiment is $P^2S^2T^2$ ($P \equiv$ plates, $S \equiv$ spectrographs, $T \equiv$ time), but instead of eight observations there are only four, i.e.,

	$P_1S_1T_1$	$P_2S_2T_1$	$P_2S_1T_2$	$P_1S_2T_2$
P	+	−	−	+
S	+	−	+	−
T	+	+	−	−

It is evident that $P = S \times T$, $S = T \times P$ and $T = P \times S$. The efficiency of this design for main effects is apparent.

1.6.5. Regression or Covariance Analysis. For purpose of analysis, the values of the independent variable, measured from the mean, may be considered merely as a set of weights attached to the observations. Consider the experiment measuring $Y \equiv \Delta \log I$ on six samples S^6, of varying composition $x_i = X_i - \bar{x}$. The analysis may be displayed as follows.

	Y_1	Y_2	Y_3	Y_4	Y_5	Y_6
cf	1	1	1	1	1	1
rf	x_1	x_2	x_3	x_4	x_5	x_6

Since $\Sigma x_i = 0$, *rf* is a permissible comparison. The corresponding sum of squares, for 1*df*, is $\dfrac{\Sigma^2 xy}{\Sigma x^2}$, which is the formula obtained from the least square solution and the analysis is $S^2{}_{x \cdot y} = \Sigma Y^2 - cf - rf = \Sigma y^2 - \dfrac{(\Sigma Y)^2}{6} - \dfrac{\Sigma^2 xy}{\Sigma x^2}$. $S^2{}_{x \cdot y}$ is to be associated with $6 - 1 - 1 = 4df$. The question may then be asked how to partition the 4*df* for the Remainder ($= S^2{}_{x \cdot y}$) into single degrees. The answer is involved for the x_i are arbitrary numbers as far as the mathematical solution of the problem is concerned. One suitable answer is to consider this as a problem of curvilinear regression of a special type, namely, to fit the six points by means of orthogonal polynomials up to the 5th degree, since it is known that a polynomial of the mth degree may be passed exactly through $m + 1$ points. If certain types of polynomials, the so-called orthogonal polynomials, are used, it may be shown that the coefficients may be computed *independently* of the points to be fitted if the X_i are spaced at *equal* intervals. For example, for six points the coefficients are as follows:

	Y_1	Y_2	Y_3	Y_4	Y_5	Y_6
cf	1	1	1	1	1	1
rf (i.e. linear $= x_i$)	−5	−3	−1	1	+3	+5
Quadratic	+5	−1	−4	−4	−1	+5
Cubic	−5	+7	+4	−4	−7	+5
Quartic	+1	−3	+2	+2	−3	+1
Quintic	−1	+5	−10	+10	−5	+1

When the x_i are not spaced at equal intervals (say for standards prepared in such a manner that the difference in log per cent of the element to be analyzed is constant along the sequence of samples), the coefficients must be computed by general methods.

However, since linear regression is all that will be necessary for the analysis of spectrographic data, the df associated with S, and within its interactions, will be pooled into a common effect, i.e., deviations, the meaning of which has already been discussed.

The extension to multiple regression, i.e., multiple sets of independent variables, say X_i for S, and Z_i for E, may be treated in an extension of the indicated method.

1.6.6. Latin Square with Regression. Consider the experiment as follows: four samples (S^4) exposed on two plates (P^2) simultaneously in two spectrographs (C^2) and then the plates are interchanged and similarly exposed, i.e., exposures at two times (T^2). The samples are of varying composition and a regression is determined of $Y = \Delta \log I$ for each sample S_i on the log per cent element $x_i = X_i - \bar{x}$. The experiment is of form $P^2C^2T^2S^4$ or 32 for a complete balanced design. However only sixteen observations were actually made, eight on each plate, hence it is to be expected that not all effects or interactions will be obtainable. If the design were of the complete balanced type, one could analyze the data as follows (the number after the symbol represents the degrees of freedom):

Means: $P1, C1, T1; P \times C1, P \times T1, C \times T1, P \times C \times T1$; $7df$
Regression: $P1, C1, T1; P \times C1, P \times T1, C \times T1, P \times C \times T1$; $7df$
Deviations: $S2, P2, C2, T2; P \times C2, P \times T2, C \times T2, P \times C \times T2$; $16df$

Total $30 = 32 - 2$

However, only sixteen observations were made, hence the total $df = 14$; and the individual comparisons may be computed as in Table VII.

The P, C, T means and P, C, T reg may be computed as indicated. The S effects and the indicated interactions may be computed as indicated, pooled to give $S3$, $P \times S3$, $C \times S3$ and $T \times S3$, then subtracting $rf\,1$, P reg 1, C reg 1 and T reg 1, respectively, to give effects, (deviations) S dev 2, P dev 2, C dev 2 and T dev 2.

It is suggested that the reader verify that no additional comparisons can be obtained.

1.7. Computation. Miscellaneous

1.7.1. Discriminant Functions. Consider the experiment, S^2R^n, in which observations are made on the log I of a spectrum line pair, one line for the element being analyzed and the other line for the matrix element, on each of two samples with many, n, repetitions. As cus-

TABLE VII

Analysis of Latin Square
$$P^2C^2T^2S^4$$

		P_1								P_2							
		S_1	S_2	S_3	S_4	S_1	S_2	S_3	S_4	S_1	S_2	S_3	S_4	S_1	S_2	S_3	S_4
	cf	+	+	+	+	+	+	+	+	+	+	+	+	+	+	+	+
	rf	x_1	x_2	x_3	x_4	x_1	x_2	x_3	x_4	x_1	x_2	x_3	x_4	x_1	x_2	x_3	x_4
Means	P	+	+	+	+	+	+	+	+	−	−	−	−	−	−	−	−
	C	+	+	+	+	−	−	−	−	+	+	+	+	−	−	−	−
	T	+	+	+	+	−	−	−	−	−	−	−	−	+	+	+	+
Reg	P	x_1	x_2	x_3	x_4	x_1	x_2	x_3	x_4	$-x_1$	$-x_2$	$-x_3$	$-x_4$	$-x_1$	$-x_2$	$-x_3$	$-x_4$
	C	x_1	x_2	x_3	x_4	$-x_1$	$-x_2$	$-x_3$	$-x_4$	x_1	x_2	x_3	x_4	$-x_1$	$-x_2$	$-x_3$	$-x_4$
	T	x_1	x_2	x_3	x_4	$-x_1$	$-x_2$	$-x_3$	$-x_4$	$-x_1$	$-x_2$	$-x_3$	$-x_4$	x_1	x_2	x_3	x_4
S	S'	+	+	−	−	+	+	−	−	+	+	−	−	+	+	−	−
	S''	+	−	+	−	+	−	+	−	+	−	+	−	+	−	+	−
	S'''	+	−	−	+	+	−	−	+	+	−	−	+	+	−	−	+
$P \times S$	$P \times S'$	+	+	−	−	+	+	−	−	−	−	+	+	−	−	+	+
	$P \times S''$	+	−	+	−	+	−	+	−	−	+	−	+	−	+	−	+
	$P \times S'''$	+	−	−	+	+	−	−	+	−	+	+	−	−	+	+	−
$C \times S$	$C \times S'$	+	+	−	−	−	−	+	+	+	+	−	−	−	−	+	+
	$C \times S''$	+	−	+	−	−	+	−	+	+	−	+	−	−	+	−	+
	$C \times S'''$	+	−	−	+	−	+	+	−	+	−	−	+	−	+	+	−
$T \times S$	$T \times S'$	+	+	−	−	−	−	+	+	−	−	+	+	+	+	−	−
	$T \times S''$	+	−	+	−	−	+	−	+	−	+	−	+	+	−	+	−
	$T \times S'''$	+	−	−	+	−	+	+	−	−	+	+	−	+	−	−	+

tomary, it is assumed that the measurements are not identical. The observations may be classified as follows:

	Element line	Matrix line
Sample S_1 = A	Y_{1A}	Y_{2A}
Sample S_2 = B	Y_{1B}	Y_{2B}

The differences between Y_{1A} and Y_{1B} or Y_{2A} and Y_{2B} may perhaps be due to differences in concentration of the element in A and B, or due to the fact that Y_1 is an arc line and Y_2 a spark line, etc. Whatever the physical reason for the difference, the problem is to determine a linear function of the observations, so chosen that the chances of misclassifying a specimen from observation of Y_1 and Y_2 are minimized. That is to say, knowing that the given specimen is a sample of either class A or class B, and making the observation Y_1 and Y_2, what linear combination of these two observations will furnish the best discrimination between classes A and B, taking due account of the variation of the observations within the classes, or in still other words, what linear combination of Y_1 and Y_2 will minimize the variation within classes A and B and maximize the differences between them.

The linear function of Y_1 and Y_2, i.e., $Y = \lambda_1 Y_1 + \lambda_2 Y_2$ so chosen is called a discriminant function. It is computed as follows:

Let

$$Y = \lambda_1 Y_1 + \lambda_2 Y_2$$
$$d_1 = \bar{Y}_{1A} - \bar{Y}_{1B}$$
$$d_2 = \bar{Y}_{2A} - \bar{Y}_{2B}$$
$$D = \lambda_1 d_1 + \lambda_2 d_2$$

Then

$$\lambda_1 \Sigma y_1^2 + \lambda_2 \Sigma y_1 y_2 = d_1$$
$$\lambda_1 \Sigma y_1 y_2 + \lambda_2 \Sigma y_2^2 = d_2$$

From these equations λ_1 and λ_2 may be computed by simple algebra.

If the total number of observations is $2n$, i.e. $n/2$ observations for each spectrum line, and n observations in each class A and B, the sum of squares of Y, Σy^2, may be analyzed as follows:

Source of variation	df	Sum of squares
Between classes	2	$\dfrac{n}{2} D^2$
Within classes	$2n - 3$	D
Total	$2n - 1$	$D\left(1 + \dfrac{n}{2} D\right)$

The statistical significance of the discrimination is determined as in an analysis of variance.

As may be seen from the equations, the important consideration is not the value of (λ_1, λ_2) but their ratio, λ_1/λ_2. When the difference between the two classes, A and B, is associated with a difference in concentration of the element to be analyzed in the two samples, that is to say, when the difference is to be associated with the covariance of Y and X_1 the ratio $\lambda_1/\lambda_2 = -1$, i.e., that $Y = \log I$ (element) $- \log I$ (matrix) or $\Delta \log I$, would furnish a statistical or empirical justification of the use of $\Delta \log I$ as a measure of the dependent variable. This has been indeed found to be the case in all instances computed by the writer.

That the ratio λ_1/λ_2 should be -1 is not to be considered intuitively apparent. For example, if an arc line-spark line combination were to be used in the line pair, the statistically appropriate measure, i.e., discriminant, could very well be, $\Delta' \log I = \log I$ (element) $- \alpha \log I$

(matrix), with $\alpha \neq 1$. It is to be noted that the discriminant function with the independant variable, or log per cent, is another and quite separate problem, already treated under covariance analysis.

1.7.2. Dilution Correction.   The use of dilution corrections or similar compensations for compositional differences has been discussed in the appendix to the chapter on Analysis.   The computation for these corrections is apparent, since they almost always involve modifications of the x_i, i.e., the log per cent.   The procedure is then to transform the x_i into a new set x_i', the transformed set may be log ratio per cent, log atomic per cent or any other function that appears advisable, and then to compute a new regression (i.e., covariance) and deviation analysis.   Significance criteria will quickly indicate whether a real gain in precision has been made or not.

1.8. Tests of Significance

After the computations have been made it is necessary to interpret the statistics by use of appropriate tables, the most frequently used of which will be of (1) the normal deviate, (2) "Student's" t, (3) chi square and (4) Snedecor's "F."   The tables are to be used in testing the null hypothesis, as considered in section 2.3, as follows:

(a) a statistics, D, is computed from the sample, with the associated df;

(b) The appropriate table is entered with the df and the desired probability level, and the tabular value D_0 noted, then

(c) If $D > D_0$ the null hypothesis has not been proved and the fact that D is as large as it is cannot be ascribed to sampling fluctuations.

Or, alternately, and equivalently

(a) the appropriate table is entered with the df and the probability noted for which D_0, the tabular value, is closest to D.   For present purposes the following evaluations will be given (of course in a purely conventional manner), if the probability, (Prob) is in the following ranges:

Prob $> .05$—no significance, i.e., the null hypothesis is not disproved and the statistic may be as great as it is merely as a result of sampling fluctuations;

$.05 >$ Prob $> .01$—almost significant or indecisive, indicated by ($\checkmark$);

$.01 >$ Prob $> .001$—significant, indicated by (*)

$.001 >$ Prob—highly significant, indicated by (**).

By "significance" is understood that the null hypothesis is disproved and the statistic is as great as it is *not* as the result of sampling fluctuations from a certain known or assumed per cent population. The precise application of significance tests may involve a high degree of subtlety, but the procedures to be indicated are considered adequate for spectrographic purposes.

The general test of significance involves a test ratio, T, defined as follows—

$$T = \frac{S - h}{\sigma_s}$$

where S is the sample value of a statistic, h is the parameter value by hypothesis and σ_s is the standard deviation of the sampling distribution of the statistic. Many times the significance of the difference between statistics as estimated from two samples is desired, in which case the general formula becomes

$$T = \frac{(S_a - S_b) - (O_h)}{\sigma(S_a - S_b)} = \frac{d}{\sigma_d}$$

where $S_a - S_b = d$ is the difference between the statistics (usually the difference between sample means), $\sigma(S_a - S_b) = \sigma_d$ is the standard deviation of the difference; the hypothetical difference, or difference between population parameters in zero, since that is the real meaning of the significance test. When the number of observations, or samples, is large enough the distribution of the statistics to be used in this discussion may be assumed to be normal. However when the number of observations is small, tables specially computed for the relevant sampling distributions involved must be consulted.

1.8.1. The Normal Deviate. This is the ratio of the deviation of the sample value (mean) from the hypothetical mean of the normal population or assumed true value, to the standard deviation of the sample mean. It has been remarked that for spectrographic data, it may be assumed that sample means are normally distributed, with standard deviation $\sigma_0/\sqrt{n}$, where n is the size of the sample and σ_0 the standard deviation of an individual measurement. The value of σ_0 is assumed known or derived from a sufficiently extended sequence of observations, so that it can be considered as derived from a large sample.

1.8.2. "Student's" t. When the sample available for the determination of σ_s is small (i.e., the determination of the standard deviation of the mean of a small sample), the distribution of the small-sample means is not normal and consequently another table, namely, that of student's t has to be consulted. The df associated with the "t" is that of the standard deviation, or variance, involved, i.e., $n - 1$. When n is more than 30, t may be treated as a normal deviate without serious inaccuracy.

1.8.3. Chi-Square, χ^2. The sample is divided into a number of categories or classes and the frequency of occurrence of the sample values within each class is compared to the theoretical frequency. The exact form of the ratio is as follows:

$$\chi^2 = \sum \frac{(f_s - f_h)^2}{f_s}$$

where f_s is the sample frequency, f_h is the expected of hypothetical frequency and the summation is over n classes or categories. As may be expected, the df of χ^2 is closely associated with the number of classes minus the number of constraints. Thus, if the entire sample is divided into a set of independent, mutually exclusive classes, the constraint is the total number of observations and the df is $n - 1$. When the number of classes, or df, is more than 30, $\sqrt{2\chi^2} - \sqrt{n - 1}$ may be treated as normal deviate (that is, normally distributed about means equal to zero and standard deviation equal to 1).

The χ^2 test may be used in many forms by suitable transformations. However, for present purposes, two applications will be important, namely (1) to test the agreement of the errors of spectrographic data with the normal distribution low and (2) to test the data for "homogeneity of variance" as a necessary condition for the application of the "F" test.

The use of χ^2 as a significance test should be limited to the cases in which enough observations are available. For best results, the number of categories should be about 30, with the expected frequency not less than 10 in each category. In any event one should not use this test for less than 100 observations total, and classes in which the expected occurrence is less than 10.

1.8.4. "F," "Z," or Variance Ratio Test. This is merely the ratio of two variance mean squares as displayed in column 3 of either Table II or Table V. The ratio is always taken so that it is *greater than 1*, that is *the larger variance mean square is always in the numerator*. There are two df values associated with this test, $n_1 \equiv$ the df of the numerator, i.e., the larger variance mean square, and $n_2 \equiv$ the df of the denominator. These df are shown in the second columns of the analysis of Variance Tables II or V on the same line as the mean squares. There are two forms of tables for using this ratio. The F or Snedecor "F" table exhibits the ratio directly while the "Z" or Fisher "Z" table uses the transformation $F = e^{2z}$, or $Z = \frac{1}{2} \log_e F$. Hence if only a Z table is available, one must enter it by taking one half the natural logarithm of the ratio.

Referring to the published significance tables, their forms may be described as follows.

The c or normal deviate table is a one-way table. That is, under the heading of probability is given the value of c, thus at Prob .05, $c = 1.96$ or approximately 2.

The t and χ^2 tables are similarly constructed and are two-way tables. The top row or column headings are the probability values while in the left margin or column is arranged, in increasing order, the values of the df, sometimes indicated by N. Sometimes the bottom row of the t table is written for ∞ df, that is, the values of c.

The F or Z tables are three-way tables, i.e., must be entered by use of three numbers, n_1, n_2 (or N_1, N_2) and the probability or significance level; hence the tables cannot be displayed in their entirety in one listing. Snedecors "F" table usually displays n, or N_1 (the df of the larger variance mean square) in the top row or column headings, and the df of the smaller variance mean square, n_2 or N_2, in the left margin. The Roman type gives the F values at Prob $= .05$ (or 5%) and the bold-face type (dark) at Prob $= .01$ (or 1%). The Z tables are usually displayed as separate tables, each headed by the probability (.20, .05, .01 and .001 are common values) with N_1 in the top row and N_2 in the left margin.

A difficulty may arise in the use of the t or c tables, in that the indicated probability in one set may be twice that of another. This is accounted for as follows: if one considers the algebraic deviate, i.e., the difference between the sample mean and true mean with proper algebraic sign the value of the probability is one half of that when only the numerical difference is considered. As a guide, when the *numerical* difference is considered, the value of c, or of t for ∞ df, is approximately 2 (1.96) at Prob .05 ($c = t_\infty = 2$ for Prob 1/20).

NOTE: The four tests, c, t, χ^2 and F were developed for different purposes and at different times, and it is not surprising that their interrelations have tended to be obscured. They are essentially ratios of two variances, or standard deviations, although these ratios may be subject to transformations. The relations of c, t, and χ^2 may be easily explained in relation to F. As has been noted F is a three-dimensional table involving N_1, N_2 and P ($\equiv$ probability). t^2 is a variance ratio whose numerator has always $1df$, i.e., $N_1 = 1$. χ^2 is a variance ratio whose denominator is fixed by hypothesis, which is equivalent to its having ∞ df, i.e., $N_2 = \infty$. c has a numerator with $1df$ and a denominator fixed by hypothesis, i.e., $df = \infty$. Hence c is a special case of both t and χ^2.

For example:

The value of F for $N_1 = 1$, $N_2 = 10$, $P = .05$ is 4.96 and the value of t for $N = 10$, $P = .05$ is 2.228; hence $t^2 = 2.228 \times 2.228 = 4.96 = F(1, 10)$.

The value of F for $N_1 = 10$, $N_2 = \infty$, $P = 05$ is 1.83, and the corresponding $\chi^2/10$ is $18.31/10 = 1.83$. The relation between t and c has already been stated, namely $c = t_\infty$.

1.9. Interpretation of the Analysis of Variance

The tests of significance will now be applied to the various parts of the analysis of variance as displayed in Tables II and V.

1.9.1. Total Mean Square. The total mean square (V_y) or mean square reduced for regression of y on x $(S^2_{y \cdot x})$, is to be considered as an estimate of the population of deviations or errors in the spectrographic data. The corresponding standard deviations will be indicated by σ_y (standard error) and $S_{y \cdot x}$ or $\sigma_{y \cdot x}$ (standard error of estimate). It will be assumed that the number of observations in the total, or total df, is large, at least 100.

Normality of the Population. While the strict normality of the error population is not necessary for the application of the significance tests, it is advisable to investigate whether the population is approximately normal. It is known that χ^2 is an linearly additive function and that it is more indicative if larger numbers are available. Consider the experiment to determine an analytical curve, and compute the $S_{y \cdot x}$. The observations may be classified in mutually exclusive sets in many ways, but since the connotation of the random variate is that of an error. and since one is normally interested in the frequency of the larger errors, the following division is suggested. Compute the significant differences, $d_i = c_i S_{y \cdot x}$, choosing the values of c_i:

Per cent included	70	80	90	
c	1.04	1.28	1.64	Remainder

That is, the deviations of the observed content of the standard samples from the known value are list and classified according to the value of c_i, i.e., in the first cell are all values contained within $(x_1 \pm 1.04S_{y \cdot x})$, $(x_2 \pm 1.04S_{y \cdot x})$, . . . , $(x_n \pm 1.04S_{y \cdot x})$ and so on for the other values of C. The theoretical frequency is given in the top line. A table is illustrated, for the results obtained in the analysis of a certain type of stainless steel for the eight listed elements. χ^2 is computed according to the formula and summed.

If one considers each row as a sample of an infinite population, $1df$ is lost for the finite sample and the sum of χ^2 is 16.3 for $24df$, which is quite non-significant (80%). If, on the other hand, each row were to be considered as drawn from a restricted universe with a standard deviation equal to the sample value (the mean or true value is fixed), $2df$ are lost in each row, and there are 16 available df. The χ^2 is still non-significant, for $\chi^2 = 16$ for $16df$ has a significance level of 40%.

One may treat the frequences almost as a variance table and sum each column, and compute a pooled χ^2. This is 5.8, which is non-significant for 2 or $3df$.

The conclusion is that the errors may be considered as being normally distributed.

TABLE VIII

Chi Square Test for Normality of Error Distribution
Stainless Steel

Element	N	70%		80%		90%		Remainder		χ^2
		Theor.	Obs.	Theor.	Obs.	Theor.	Obs.	Theor.	Obs.	
V	260	182	190	26	21	26	23	26	26	1.659
Cu	500	350	355	50	50	50	40	50	55	2.571
Mo	200	140	145	20	15	20	18	20	22	1.828
Sn	260	182	174	26	23	26	30	26	33	3.199
Pb	110	77	83	11	7	26	30	26	9	2.286
Cr	240	168	177	24	19	24	24	24	20	2.190
Mn	200	140	148	20	16	20	20	20	16	2.057
Ni	240	168	173	24	22	24	22	24	23	.524
		1407	1445	201	.73	201	188	201	204	16.314
										5.8

$$Example: \text{V}: \chi^2 = \frac{(190 - 182)^2}{182} + \frac{(26 - 21)^2}{26} + \frac{(26 - 23)^2}{26} + \frac{(26 - 26)^2}{26}$$

$$= \tfrac{64}{182} + \tfrac{25}{26} + \tfrac{9}{26} = 1.659$$

1.9.2. Comparison of Mean Squares. The total mean square, as has been stated, is to be considered as an estimate of the variance of the parent population of errors. It may be desired to compare the total mean squares, or the square root of that quantity, called the total standard error, as they are obtained from repetitions of experiments similar to those analyzed in Table II or Table V.

Let σ_0^2 represent the mean square, determined from an extensive series of observations, that is to be used as the reference value and let σ_1^2 represent the mean square as determined from a new experiment of n_1 observations. Then it may be concluded that σ_1^2/σ_0^2 is significantly ≤ 1 whenever $\dfrac{\sigma_1^2}{\sigma_0^2} \leq \dfrac{\chi_\alpha^2(n_1)}{n_1}$ where $\chi_\alpha^2(n_1)$ is the value of χ^2 for $n_1 df$ at the α level of significance, and conversely, $\dfrac{\sigma_1^2}{\sigma_0^2}$ is significantly > 1 when

$$\frac{\sigma_1^2}{\sigma_0^2} > \frac{\chi_\alpha^2(n_1)}{n_1}$$

This test is equivalent to considering $\sigma_1{}^2/\sigma_0{}^2 = F(n_1, n_0)$ at the desired level and determining the significance of F, for $(n_1, n_0)df$, from the F table. A more critical discussion of this test will be found in the references.

1.9.3. Homogeneity of Variance. The homogeneity of variance is a mathematically necessary condition for the validity of the F test. This may be explained as follows: The F, or variance ratio, is designed to test the significance of the differences between the mean values within an effect. Referring to the experiment $P^4Q^3R^2S^6$, Table II, it is assumed that the mean values of P_1, P_2, P_3, P_4 for example, are not identical and the significance of the differences between the means is estimated by the F test; in a similar fashion one may test the significance of the differences between the Q_1, Q_2, Q_3 means, or between the twelve $P \times Q$ means etc. However the F test is valid only if the variances within P_1, P_2, P_3, P_4 or the Q_i, or the P_iQ_j are not significantly different, that is, statistically identical. An entirely satisfactory homogeneity of variance test has not yet been devised. The usual test is known as Bartlett's test, which considers the natural logarithm of the ratio of the arithmetic mean to the geometric mean of the variances within classes is distributed approximately as χ^2.

The precise formulation is as follows: Let $m \equiv$ the number of mutually exclusive classifications of the data ($4P$, $3Q$, $12P \times Q$, or $6S$, for example), $f \equiv$ the df within each class (assumed equal for every P, Q, $P \times Q$, or S), $(SS) \equiv$ the set of sum of squares within the selected classes, and $(V) \equiv$ the set of mean squares within the selected class. Then Bartlett's test states that

$$\chi^2{}_{(m-1)} = 2.3026 \, f.m. \, \log_{10} \frac{\text{arithmetic mean of } (SS)}{\text{geometric mean of } (SS)}$$

$$= 2.3026 \, f.m. \, \log_{10} \frac{\text{arithmetic mean of } (V)}{\text{geometric mean of } (V)}$$

For computational purposes it is perhaps simpler to determine

$$V_0 = \text{arithmetic mean of } (V) = \frac{\Sigma SS}{\Sigma f}$$

and

$$\chi^2{}_{(m-1)} = 2.3026 \log_{10} [(\log V_0) \Sigma f - \Sigma (f \log V)]$$

where $\chi^2(m - 1)$ is χ^2 for $(m - 1)$ degrees of freedom.

The selection of a suitable division into classes cannot be decided for for all experiments. It is not advisable to choose classes with only few observations within them. If regression is not to be considered, P (plates) may be a suitable classification. If regression is important, as in determining a working curve, the group of standards should be a suitable classification if, and this is important, many standards are used.

When only a few standards, say three or four, are used, the test is apt to be misleading.

This test may be unsatisfactory in its application to spectrographic data for two reasons:

(1) If the variances are not proved homogeneous, there is no satisfactory alternative. The best one can do is to consider the rational subgroups that have physical interest and try to decide just what has happened.

(2) While in many other applications, Bartlett's test may be disturbed by some class having an unduly large variance, thus increasing the value of the arithmetic mean, the writer has found that spectrographic data almost always present a difficulty of the opposite sort; that is, some class, whether it is a plate, or group of standards almost invariably has a very low variance, for example, the points may lie too close to the analytical curve. This will make the geometric mean very low and consequently, the χ^2 is much too high. Thus if only three standards are used, it is not unusual to find in an extended investigation that one group of three, and it does not take more than one, lies immediately on the analytical curve. Consequently, that set or class has a zero variance, thus the geometric mean of the variances of the entire experiment is zero and χ^2 becomes infinite. In this case, or others approximately similar, the spectrographer must use his judgment whether to discard the offending set or the entire test.

1.9.4. "F" Test (Table V). The use of this test is really the purpose behind the construction of Table V, and consequently will be considered at some length.

The ratio of two independently distributed variances,

$$F = \frac{\text{larger mean square}}{\text{smaller mean square}},$$

is called the F ratio or F value, and tables have been computed correlating the F value, the df of the mean squares involved, and a probability. The meaning of these tables involves the null hypothesis, that is, it is assumed that there is no significant reason for the F ratio being as large as it is other than that of chance or sample fluctuations. If the probability is high the null hypothesis is tenable; otherwise, if the probability is low, the null hypothesis must be taken as unwarranted. As an illustration, let it be assumed that a comparison is made between P means and Q means (any other two terms could have been selected) and that the P means mean square is the greater. The question is whether the contribution of P means (i.e., the differences between the mean values of the plates) to the total variance is really greater than that of Q means, i.e., is actually based on some physical difference in the effect of P means compared to Q means, or whether the higher value of the mean square of P means may be ascribed to a random effect, or sampling fluctuations, in view of the available df. The null hypothesis assumes the difference is random, and the table furnishes the probability that a value of F at least as large as the one obtained or specified will occur by chance. It may be considered unfortunate that the hypothesis is a negative one, that is, that there is no physical significance and consequently the answer does not have the force if a positive hypothesis were made. However, on the basis of the null hypothesis if the probability is high, say .20, one may assume that the differences between the mean value of P means compared to the differences between the mean values of Q means, even though greater, has one chance in five of being a random effect. If on the other hand, the probability is low, say .001, meaning that the chance of the F ratio being as high as it is merely as a consequence of sample fluctuation is only 1:1000, one may reasonably conclude that there is a physical significance to the differences between the mean values of P_i means compared to the differences between the mean values of Q_j means. It is a clear logical step from a high or significant difference between the mean values of P_i means to a high significant contribution of the effect to the total variance.

It should be noticed that significance has been determined only as a mutual relationship between effects or *comparisons* as they may now be called. However, almost any practical investigation involves more than two comparisons and it is desirable to establish one of these as a measure or reference for the comparison of all the others. In some instances, there seems to be a logical choice. For example, if the investigation involved replicates (R), then it may appear reasonable to consider the R effect as a non-reducible source of error, and to pool it together with its interactions into a ΣR term and call it the error term. When such a comparison is not available, it is customary to pool all the higher order interactions into an *error* term (considering interaction as a discrepancy) particularly if no clear physical meaning can be found for these terms. If such a logical choice is not available, then each investigation must be considered independently to see whether it is reasonable to select some other common comparison. If such a choice is still not available, then only mutual comparisons are possible. In that case the tabular probability should be doubled, since presumably either of the terms may have been larger than the other. Some analysts pool all non-significant terms into a common *error* term, but the logical justification for the procedure is not too evident.

1.10. Prediction. Precision

The analysis of the data of an experiment has proceded along rigorous lines, but it should be emphasized that the interpretations and significances pertain only to the data on hand. However, the experimenter is usually particularly interested in extending the interpretations to future results. The extension is delicate. As an analogy, if one were given a sample of an ingot or of a carload of metal to analyze, no matter how carefully the analysis of the sample were made, the results of the analysis would still be valid only for the sample; the extension of the data to the ingot or carload would depend entirely on the extra-experimental evaluation of the representation of the sample. Unless one knew something about the uniformity of the ingot or the homogeneity of the contents of the carload the extension is quite meaningless. The present situation is quite similar. The extension of significance to future experimental results depends entirely on the judgment of the spectrographer. A few guide lines are available. It is known that the standard deviation of a mean square, $\sigma_0{}^2$, as obtained in the analysis of variance with f degrees of freedom may be estimated as follows;

$$\sigma(\sigma_0{}^2) = \sqrt{\frac{2}{f}}\,\sigma_0{}^2$$

This may be too high in the general case for any precise prediction unless f, the number of degrees of freedom, is large. Hence, the use of small samples is still unsatisfactory for prediction, even though the analysis of results already obtained is on a sound basis. This follows, because if one were interested only in the results already on hand, one could consider them as reliable a sample of a hypothetical population as one desires.

Another difficulty presents itself in the estimation of overall precision, i.e., the total mean square. A factorial experiment may have been performed over factors of varying orders of significance or importance. For example (Table II), the experiment $P^4Q^3R^2S^6$ yields a total mean square equal to $\dfrac{Total\ Sum\ of\ Squares}{143}$. But suppose P were a highly significant effect and R of very low significance. Then if an experiment of form $P^2Q^3R^4S^6$ were performed, still with 144 observations, the total sum of squares would be expected to be much less, consequently the total mean square, which would still be equal to $\dfrac{Total\ Sum\ of\ Squares}{143}$ might well be significantly less than the first value. This difficulty may be avoided by the use of variance components, column 4 in Table II. To predict the results of a variance analysis, based on $P^4Q^3R^2S^6$, of an experiment of another form, $P^iQ^jR^kS^l$, one may compute the various variance components of the first experiment, i.e., σ^2_0, σ^2_{PQS}, σ^2_{PQ}, σ^2_{PS}, σ^2_{QS}, σ^2_P, σ^2_Q, σ^2_s, and then combine them using coefficients derived from (i, j, k, l) instead of $(4, 3, 2, 6)$ to yield a mean square: $\sigma^2 = \sigma^2_0 + k\sigma^2_{PQS} + kl\sigma^2_{PQ} + kj\sigma^2_{PQ} + ik\sigma^2_{QS} + ijk\sigma^2_s + ikl\sigma^2_Q + jkl\sigma^2_P$. It is apparent how this procedure may be used to redesign a new experiment that would emphasize the factors previously determined to be significant.

The application of this procedure to experiments involving regression is more involved. As has been stated, the variance of a single determination, where regression is involved, may be written as

$$\sigma y^2_i = S^2_{y\cdot x} + \frac{1}{n} S^2_{y\cdot x} + x^2_i \frac{S^2_{y\cdot x}}{\Sigma x^2}$$

i.e., $\sigma^2_{y_i}$ is the sum of the total variance reduced for regression, plus the variance of the *means* plus x_i^2 times the variance of regression coefficient, or the variance of *reg*. This form shows the danger of extrapolation, since the factor x_i^2 increases rapidly with x_i, i.e., the distance between X_i and the mean. In order to predict an average or over-all variance, one may use the form

$$\sigma^2_{x\cdot 0} = S^2_{y\cdot x} \left\{ 1 + \frac{1}{n} + \frac{M^2}{3\Sigma x^2} \right\}$$

where M is the maximum x_i, $\left(\text{since } \dfrac{1}{M} \displaystyle\int_0^M x^2 dx = \dfrac{M^2}{3} \right)$. Since in the use of standards there is an inversion in the roles of Y and X one may compute

$$\sigma_{\ell\cdot y} = \frac{1}{b^2} \sigma_{0\cdot x}$$

where b is the slope of Y on X. To estimate the standard error of a new experiment one may pool the error due to *deviations* as a non-reducible error and compute the changes in the errors of the *means* and *reg* according to the new sets of levels using the data as presented in Table V. In general, the standard errors will accumulate so rapidly, if the effects are significant, that the estimate will hardly be precise or close enough for practical use. A more practical procedure would be to arrange standardizing experiments in the form in which the actual analyses are performed, for example with one replicate and one excitation condition (including electrode form) on one plate with many replications over many plates in one day and over many days.

However one condition peculiar to analytical work may be discussed, namely the use of repetitive measurements. It is, or has been, a rather commonly-spread notion that analyses in duplicate, or triplicate will decrease the error of the mean of the repeated observations to one-half or one third the error of a single observation. This notion may now be recognized as false. Considering the statistical analysis into variance components, it can be seen that increasing the levels of R, i.e. using R^3 instead of R^1, will merely alter the value of σ_0^2; that is the new non-reducible error is $\sigma_0'^2 = \sigma_0^2/3$. Indeed the effect on the error variance of repetition or replication to any extent can be predicted by the use of appropriate divisors in the formula exhibiting the total error variance as the sum of its various components. It has been widely observed that R (Table II) for spectrographic procedure is almost always the least significant of all effects; hence decreasing it will affect almost no increase in precision. On the other hand, if the observations were truly replicated entirely, that is, repeated observations made with new plates, new excitation conditions (although nominally the same), new electrodes, new densitometer readings, etc., then the mean of replicated readings would have an error reduction proportional to the square root of the number of observations, i.e., $\sigma_0' = \sqrt{\sigma_0^2/n}$. Mandel, has introduced a measure for this relationship and called it the coefficient-of-improvement, $(CI)_N$. It is defined as follows $(CI)_N = n'$ and means the following: n' is the number of true replicates required to give the improvement in precision obtained by using N repetitive observations. The ratio n'/N may be called the efficiency of improvement. To one who has not measured these quantities, the low efficiency of improvement by repetitive observations, in spectrographic analyses at least, may be very surprising. Some numerical values will be given in the following section.

An important use of variance components is in the estimation of the expected improvement by changing experimental conditions. Thus if Q = electrode form, and σ_Q^2 is highly significant, it would be apparent that an investigation into the closer control or a more suitable electrode form would be likely to bring about a marked improvement.

Estimations of precision are based on the formula

$$d = t\sigma$$

or if the degrees of freedom are sufficiently high,

$$d = c\sigma$$

where d is the interval extended in both directions from the mean or true value which contains the proportion of the population of values indicated by the probability level of t. Or, d may be defined as the least difference between single observations which would be considered significant at the indicated probability level; σ is the standard error of the population. If, instead of single observations, the means of n replicated observations (*not* repeated ones) were considered, the least significant difference would be $d = t \dfrac{\sigma}{\sqrt{n}}$.

Tables may be prepared, based on the experimental value of σ, arranged either for a scale of values of d (say 1%, 5% of content, etc.) or for a scale of probability values (say 95%, 90%, 80% etc.).

Least significant differences may be also be used as an aid in the analysis of variance in the following manner. Suppose, in the analysis Table II, it develops that P is a significant effect and it is desired to locate just what plate, or plates, are the main contributor to the significance even though the variances are homogeneous. Since the experiment is of the form $P^4 Q^3 R^2 S^6$, there are $3 \times 2 \times 6 = 36$ observations on each plate, and the standard error of a plate mean is $\sigma/\sqrt{36} = \sigma/6$, and the standard error of a difference between plate means is $\sigma' = \sqrt{2}\,\dfrac{\sigma}{6}$. Hence the plate means are arranged in increasing order, for example. P_1, P_2, P_3, P_4 and the least significant difference computed as $d' = t_\alpha \dfrac{\sqrt{2}\,\sigma}{6}$ where α is the selected significance level. One can then determine, by comparison of the observed differences with d', which plates are significantly different. The procedure may, of course, be applied within any effect or interaction.

It should be noted, that since in the regression analysis, the curve was computed as a regression of $\Delta \log I$ on log per cent, for actual use it is necessary to invert the role of independent and dependent variables. Hence if b is the slope of the regression line as computed, $1/b$ is the slope of the working curve (log per cent $= Y$, $\Delta \log I = X$) and the above formula becomes $d = t \dfrac{S_{\hat{y}\cdot x}}{b}$.

1.11. Conclusion

Before considering some numerical examples, it should be pointed out how easily one may arrive at misleading estimates of precision prepared in an intuitive manner. The use of too small a sample as a basis for estimation is a common fault; for example, an analytical curve based on three standards, or three plates (notoriously a non-uniform factor) and so on. It is also difficult to see how quantitative measures of the contributions of various factors to the total error can be easily estimated, for statistical significance is quite independent of physical significance or importance. A procedure with low total physical error may still have statistically significant effects, and *vice versa.*

It is the opinion of the writer that in establishing an analytical curve, for example, great care should be taken to have it based on many observations. Spot or daily checks should be considered only as indications whether the conditions or factors of the experiment are in normal control, allowing for fluctuations to be expected of small samples. If the check results are not satisfactory, the experimental conditions should be investigated for sources of error or lack of control and the results of a few observations should not be used as the basis for a new analytical curve. However, even this statement should not be considered too restrictive. For example, if plates are found to be a very highly significant source of variations, even a spot adjustment for each plate, poor as it may be, may still effect a significant improvement in precision. However, such a condition suggests the need for closer investigation to insure greater stability.

A final caution should be given before considering a computation. The discontinuous nature of measurement has nothing to do with the "law of error," which is the specification of the parent population. The step or least count of the instrument, being finite, simply has the effect of grouping the observations into class intervals. Such a grouping must always be accomplished before a frequency curve, or frequency polygon can be constructed; if the instrument did not attend to this, the computer would have to do it.

It might be expected that the computed values of n measurements would vary somewhat as the least count and zero of the measuring scale are changed, and such, in fact, is the case. This effect has been carefully investigated by statisticians and corrections to be applied to the various derived quantities on account of the finite width of the class intervals have come to be known as "corrections for continuity" or "Sheppard's corrections." (These are not to be confused with the transformation used to analyze a sequence of measurements that are merely ordinal classifications, a type of observation usually not met with in spectrographic data.) The corrections serve to bridge the gap between the continuous law of error and the discontinuous nature of measurement. Such investigations have served to show that the least count of the instrument should be small enough so that when a large number of readings (well over 100) are taken, there will be a variation in the significant terminal digits of around 20 units, for otherwise a considerable portion of a set of observations is, in effect, scrapped. An astonishingly large number of observations may be required to overcome the damage done by unnecessarily coarse reading or graduation of the scale, or else the handicap of the coarse scale if a finer scale is not possible, in an experimental sense. Unfortunately, suitable continuity corrections have not been devised for the analysis of variance; hence the computer must be particularly careful to avoid attaching too much significance to interpretations of the computations if this source of error cannot be remedied.

2. NUMERICAL EXAMPLE

The interpretation, in physical terms of the experiment, of the various parts of an analysis of variance is the final and justifying step of the entire statistical procedure. Obviously no general method of interpretation can be developed that will be applicable to all problems. It will be considered sufficient to present the analyses of typical investigations, to serve both as an indication of the power and guide for the computation of the statistical procedures. One example, the determination of an analytical curve, will be presented with full details while the others will be illustrated by summaries.

2.1. Determination of—Manganese in Stainless Steel (CRS)

The detailed experimental conditions are not particularly relevant. The electrodes were ¼-inch diameter rods, in a synchronously interrupted spark excitation (35000 volts, 0.016 microfarads capacity, 10.5 turns inductance). Since the densities of the lines (Mn 2809.106, Fe 2827.46)

TABLE IX
Chemical Analyses of Samples

	% Mn*	% Ni	% Cr	% (Residuals)	% Fe
S_1	3.35	8.7	17.5	2.	68.45
S_2	3.55	9.2	18.35	2.	66.90
S_3	4.10	9.75	20.0	2.	64.15
S_4	4.23	9.85	20.10	2.	63.80
S_5	4.58	10.05	20.75	2.	62.60
S_6	4.87	10.15	20.85	2.	62.15

* Element to be considered

For sake of convenience the original data are given as delta densities × 1000. This makes no difference in the computations, since the densities are on the straight line portion of the emulsion calibration curve (density × log I coordinates, slope (gamma) 1.75) and multiplication of the densities by 1000 merely moves the decimal point three places to the right. The transformation to delta log I must be made in the general case.

were above 0.500, the densities of the lines were used directly, without conversion to log I. The only difference from ordinary procedure was that each plate was masked and used on four separate days. The experiment form is of the complete balanced type with each set of standards representing a unit for replication.

TABLE X

Analysis of Variance
Mn in CRS
$P^4D^4S^6R^3$

Y = Density Differences X = log per cent

Mn = 2809.106 A.	Fe = 2827.434 A.

A

$\bar{x} = 610.5$		P_1				P_2			
x		D_1	D_2	D_3	D_4	D_1	D_2	D_3	D_4
−85.5	S_1	−130	−115	−135	−100	−110	−150	−115	−110
−60.5	S_2	− 90	− 75	− 90	−115	−100	−120	− 80	− 90
2.5	$R_1 S_3$	− 5	0	− 15	45	10	− 20	5	0
15.5	S_4	15	5	35	15	20	20	20	0
50.5	S_5	75	65	70	75	• 75	70	60	45
77.5	S_6	110	105	120	100	100	100	140	105
−85.5	S_1	−140	−160	−120	−130	−140	−160	−100	−130
−60.5	S_2	−100	−105	−105	− 70	−100	− 80	− 70	−100
2.5	$R_2 S_3$	0	40	− 25	− 20	− 20	− 20	− 40	− 5
15.5	S_4	30	35	10	− 5	20	25	− 10	20
50.5	S_5	90	20	60	60	65	80	70	75
77.5	S_6	120	105	135	120	100	125	120	105
−85.5	S_1	−115	−130	−125	−105	−120	−170	−115	−150
−60.5	S_2	−105	− 85	− 95	− 85	− 85	−110	−100	−100
2.5	$R_3 S_3$	− 10	0	− 5	0	10	20	0	− 40
15.5	S_4	10	10	20	30	0	55	5	25
50.5	S_5	85	70	50	70	50	70	65	50
77.5	S_6	135	135	135	115	100	110	120	105

		P_3				P_4			
		D_1	D_2	D_3	D_4	D_1	D_2	D_3	D_4
−85.5	S_1	−110	−150	−125	−120	−140	−110	−120	−115
−60.5	S_2	− 80	−115	− 80	−100	−100	−100	−100	−125
2.5	$R_1 S_3$	20	− 25	− 25	− 20	− 10	20	ʻ5	− 15
15.5	S_4	40	0	− 10	− 10	30	10	25	30
50.5	S_5	80	45	55	55	65	40	60	35
77.5	S_6	125	90	80	60	90	105	90	100
−85.5	S_1	−120	−135	−140	−115	−140	−115	−145	−130
−60.5	S_2	−110	−110	−100	−110	−100	− 85	−100	−100
2.5	$R_2 S_3$	− 10	20	− 40	0	0	0	0	− 25
15.5	S_4	− 10	− 20	0	0	− 15	35	10	10
50.5	S_5	40	70	40	55	45	80	30	25
77.5	S_6	70	80	120	80	70	110	90	60
−85.5	S_1	− 80	−120	− 90	−115	−150	−115	−125	−155
−60.5	S_2	− 70	− 90	− 70	− 85	−100	− 90	−110	−125
2.5	$R_3 S_3$	20	0	− 5	10	− 20	15	− 15	− 35
15.5	S_4	50	10	20	0	0	35	− 10	− 15
50.5	S_5	95	80	75	60	50	85	55	15
77.5	S_6	130	90	120	80	95	90	125	60

TABLE X.—*(Continued)*

B

ΣY

		D_1	D_2	D_3	D_4	Σ	
	S_1	−385	−405	−380	−335	−1505	
	S_2	−295	−265	−290	−270	−1120	
P_1	S_3	− 15	40	− 45	− 65	− 85	
	S_4	55	50	65	40	210	
	S_5	250	155	180	205	790	
	S_6	365	345	390	335	1435	
		− 25	− 80	− 80	− 90		−*275*
	S_1	−370	−480	−330	−390	−1570	
	S_2	−285	−310	−250	−290	−1135	
P_2	S_3	0	− 20	− 35	− 45	− 100	
	S_4	40	100	15	45	200	
	S_5	190	220	195	170	775	
	S_6	300	335	380	315	1330	
		−125	−155	− 25	−195		−*500*
	S_1	−310	−405	−355	−350	−1420	
	S_2	−260	−315	−250	−295	−1120	
P_3	S_3	30	− 5	− 70	− 10	− 55	
	S_4	80	− 10	10	− 10	70	
	S_5	215	195	170	170	750	
	S_6	325	260	320	220	1125	
		80	−280	−175	−275		−*650*
	S_1	−430	−340	−390	−400	−1560	
	S_2	−300	−275	−310	−350	−1235	
P_4	S_3	− 30	35	− 10	− 75	− 80	
	S_4	15	80	25	25	+ 145	
	S_5	160	205	145	75	585	
	S_6	255	305	305	220	1085	
		−330	10	−235	−505		−*1060*
	Σ	−400	−505	−515	−1065	**−2485**	

TABLE X.—(*Continued*)

C

ΣY

	D_1	D_2	D_3	D_4	Σ
S_1	−1495	−1630	−1455	−1475	−6055
S_2	−1140	−1165	−1100	−1205	−4610
S_3	− 15	50	− 160	− 195	− 320
S_4	190	220	115	100	625
S_5	815	775	690	620	2900
S_6	1245	1245	1395	1090	4775

D

P	D	R_1	R_2	R_3	Σ
1	1	− 25	0	0	− 25
	2	− 15	− 65	0	− 80
	3	− 15	− 45	− 20	− 80
	4	− 70	− 45	25	− 90
2	1	− 5	− 75	− 45	−125
	2	−100	− 30	− 25	−155
	3	30	− 30	− 25	− 25
	4	− 50	− 35	−110	−195
3	1	75	−140	145	80
	2	−155	− 95	− 30	−280
	3	−105	−120	50	−175
	4	−135	− 90	− 50	−275
4	1	− 65	−140	−125	−330
	2	− 35	25	20	10
	3	− 40	−115	− 80	−235
	4	− 90	−160	−255	−505

The purposes of this experiment are specifically then, a) to determine a mean working curve, with mean slope and intercept; b) to determine the relative importance of plates (P), days (D), samples (S) and replicates (R) as contributing factors to the overall error; c) to obtain an objective and meaningful measure of the error or precision; d) to obtain an estimate of the likely increase in precision if certain experimental factors were to be more closely investigated and controlled.

Statistical Analysis

Plates (P) 4 Samples (S) 6

Days (D) 4 Replicates (R) 3

TABLE XI
Mn in CRS

			A			
			Σxy			
			$\Sigma x^2 = 19773$			
P	D	R_1	R_2	R_3	Σ	
1	1	29092.5	32330	31070	92492.5	
	2	25867.5	29822.5	30410	86100	
	3	30327.5	30197.5	29720	90245	
	4	27165	27552	27032.5	81749.5	*350587.5*
2	1	27327.5	29312.5	25702.5	82342.5	
	2	31630	32585	34152.5	98367.5	
	3	28875	24365	28542.5	81782.5	
	4	25260	29387.5	29825	84472.5	*346965.0*
3	1	28642.5	24180	26772.5	79595	
	2	28967.5	27672.5	26875	83515	
	3	24287.5	29240	25315	78842.5	
	4	23532.5	25465	24230	73227.5	*315180.0*
4	1	28717.5	25485	28712.5	82915	
	2	25817.5	28082.5	27125	81025	
	3	26715	27092.5	29615	83422.5	
	4	27340	23170	25902.5	76412.5	*323775*
					1336507.5	

	B		
D_1	D_2	D_3	D_4
337345	349007.5	334292.5	315862.5

The enumeration and various summations of the data (as delta density) are exhibited in Table X: A, B, C, and D. The covariance is exhibited in Table XI: A and B. Table XII exhibits the analysis of variance of density differences reduced for regression. A few illustrations of the computations will be given.

(1a)
$$cf = \frac{(-2485)^2}{288} = 21442$$

(2)
$$P_m = \frac{(-275)^2 + (-500)^2 + (-650)^2 - (1060)^2}{72} - 21442 = 4554$$

(3) $\quad D_m = \dfrac{(-400)^2 + (-505)^2 + (-515)^2 + -(1065)^2}{72} - 21442 = 3759$

(4) $P \times D_m = \dfrac{(-25)^2 + (-80)^2 + \cdots + (-125)^2 + (-155)^2 + \cdots + (-505)^2}{18}$

$\qquad\qquad\qquad\qquad - 21442 - 4554 - 3759 = 9696$

(5) $\displaystyle\sum R(PD)_m = \dfrac{\text{Sum of squares of entries in Table X (D)}}{6}$

$\qquad\qquad\qquad\qquad - 21442 - 4554 - 3759 - 9696 = 19103$

(1b) $\qquad\qquad rf = \dfrac{(1336507.5)^2}{48 \times 19773} = 1882041$

(14) $\quad P\ \mathrm{reg} = \dfrac{(350587.5)^2 + (346965)^2 + (315180)^2 + (323775)^2}{12 \times 19773} - 1882041$

$\qquad = 3801$

TABLE XII

Analysis of Variance of Density Differences
$P^4 D^4 S^6 R^3$

Source of variation	df	SS	V
I. Translation or means			
1. (a) cf	1	21442	
(b) rf	1	1882041	
2. P_m	3	4554	1518
3. D_m	3	3759	1253
4. $P \times D_m$	9	9696	1077
5. $\Sigma R(PD)_m$	32	19103	597
6. Σ means	47	37112	789.6
7. Total	287	1979533	
8. S	5	1886241	
9. $S \times P$	15	7703	
10. $S \times D$	15	8310	
11. $S \times P \times D$	45	10653	
12. $\Sigma SR(PD)$	160	29514	
13. Total reduced for regression	286	97492	$340.9 = S^2_{y \cdot x}$
II. Slope or regression coefficient			
14. P reg	3	3801	1267
15. D reg	3	2383	794
16. $P \times D$ reg	9	3283	365
17. $\Sigma R(PD)$ reg	32	6729	210
18. Σ reg	47	16196	344.6
III. Deviations			
19. S dev	4	4200	1050
20. $P \times S$ dev	12	3902	325
21. $D \times S$ dev	12	5927	494
22. $P \times D \times S$ dev	36	7370	205
23. $\Sigma SR(PD)$ dev	128	22785	178
24. Σ dev	192	44184	230
25. Σ replicates	192	48617	253.2
26. Σ Effects	94	48875	519.9

The analysis of variance will now be considered.

(1) *General Characteristics.* Of the 286 available df, 192, or $\frac{2}{3}$ of the total, are associated with replicates. Since Σ effects ($94df$) are by far the more significant contributors to the total variance, it should be associated with the greater df in order to obtain a more precise estimate. Insofar as this is not feasible, the completely balanced experiment is wasteful of otherwise useful experimental effort. A saving grace is that the ΣR is not entirely confounded but may be broken up into three parts associated with means, regression coefficients, and deviations, respectively. Again there is an unfavorable division of the df as may be seen from a comparison (lines 5, 17, 23) of the df and mean squares of the replicate variance due to means, reg and dev respectively.

(2) *Significance of Regression.* Even though there are strong physical grounds for the significance of regression, i.e., the meaningful existence of a positive correlation, or even a functional relation between Y_k and X_k a statistical test is enlightening.

	df	SS	V	F
Total ($\Sigma_y{}^z$)	287	1979533		
Reducible for regression (rf)	1	1882041	1882041	5520
Deviation from regression	286	97492	341	

A straight line, in the selected coordinates, is therefore a good fit to the measurements.

(3) *Normality of the Distribution of Deviation.* Using $d = tS_{y \cdot x}$, values of d are computed for selected probability levels of t. The observed frequencies of the measurements are then compared with the computed ones.

$$S_{y \cdot x} = \sqrt{340.9} = 18.46 \qquad b_0 = \frac{1336507.5}{48 \times 19773} = 1.4082$$

$$\hat{Y}_k = \bar{Y} + b_0 x_k = -8.628 + 1.4082 x_k$$

	S_1	S_2	S_3	S_4	S_5	S_6
Y	−129.0	−93.8	−5.1	13.2	62.5	100.5
Selected probability level of t	.95	.90	.80	.70	.60	.50
$d = tS_{y \cdot x}$	36.2	30.3	23.6	19.2	15.5	12.4
Observed frequency	.95	.89	.79	.67	.64	.50

The deviations from expected values are evidently normally distributed, especially the important ranges of the larger deviates.

(4) *Homogeneity of Variance.* The data were divided into $16P_iD_j$ cells, which are mutually exclusive, and the sum of squares determined within each cell.

	P_1	P_2	P_3	P_4
D_1	145850	116200	115500	118050
D_2	132000	167750	121650	113500
D_3	140500	121000	111100	120500
D_4	118150	123350	92600	103800

The $\log_{10}$ arithmetic mean is 5.08847,
The $\log_{10}$ geometric mean is 5.08455, and
The log ratio is .00392.
There are 16 cells ($m = 16$), each of which associated with $17df$ ($f = 17$). Hence $\chi_{(15)}^2 = 2.3026 \times 16 \times 17 \times .00392 = 2.45$, which is not significant, even at the .90 level.

(5) *Analysis of Variance—Table XII.* The various items in Table XII may now be interpreted into physical terms of the experiment. It should be emphasized that the possible comparisons are for the estimation of the significance of the differences between the *means* of the levels within one effect compared to the differences within the same effect. The difference between means is of course measured by mean square and the significance by the F test.

Since the effects are orthogonal, any effect may be compared to any other. Main effects have their usual interpretation and interaction effects may be considered as measures of parallel response or discrepancies. However, following usual experience, in this particular experiment, the interpretation of some interactions may seem unnatural and forced. A systematic elimination procedure will be followed in comparing plates and days.

1. F $(Pm, Dm) = 1.21$; F $(Pm, P \times Dm) = 1.41$; F $(Dm, P \times Dm) = 1.16$

2. F $(P \text{ reg}, D \text{ reg}) = 1.60$; F $(P \text{ reg}, P \times D \text{ reg}) = 3.47$; F $(D \text{ reg}, P \times D \text{ reg}) = 2.18$

3. Disregarding S dev for the present, $P \times S$ dev, $D \times S$ dev, $P \times D \times S$ dev yield low F values for all comparisons.

All the above F values indicate *no significant difference between plates compared to days.* Hence there is no valid physical reason why Table XII should not be simplified by pooling the P and D effects into a new effect, P'.

TABLE XIII

Simplified Analysis of Variance

Source of variation	df	SS	V	F
Total (reduced for reg.)	286	97492	340.88	
A				
I. Translation or means				
P_m'	15	18009	1201	2.01
$\Sigma(R + R \times P')_m$	32	19103	597	
II. Slope or regression coefficient				
P' reg	15	9467	631.	3.00**
$\Sigma(R + R \times P')$ reg	32	6729	210	
III. Deviations				
$\Sigma(S + P' \times S)$ dev	64	21399	334	1.88**
$\Sigma(R \times S + R \times P' \times S)$ dev	128	22785	178	
B				
Means	47	37112	789.6	3.43**
Regression	47	16196	344.6	1.50
Deviations	192	44184	230.	
C				
Effects	94	48875	520	2.05**
Replicates	192	48617	253.2	
D				
Means + Reg.	94	53308	567	2.46**
Deviations	192	44184	230.	

(6) *Analysis of Variance—Table XIII.* The total (reduced for regression) mean square, 340.88, represents the square of the mean deviation of the measurements, Table X, A from the mean analytical curve passing through $(\bar{x}, \bar{y})$ with the slope b_0. However, this variance is partly due to the variation of the mean curves around each $P_i'(P_iD_j$ set) that pass through different $(\bar{y}_{ij})$ with different slopes b_{ij}, as well as to the points within each P_i' fitting their particular curve with different degrees of exactness.

The various $\bar{y}_{ij}$ and b_{ij} are presented:

	P_1	P_2	P_3	P_4	
			y_{ij}		
D_1	−1.38	−4.4	−4.4	−5.0	
D_2	−6.94	−8.61	−1.38	−10.83	
D_3	−4.4	−15.5	−9.75	−15.27	
D_4	−18.3	.5	−13.05	−28.05	$\bar{y} = -8.628472$
			b_{ij}		
D_1	1.55924	1.38813	1.34181	1.39778	
D_2	1.45147	1.65828	1.40790	1.36592	
D_3	1.52135	1.37869	1.32913	1.40634	
D_4	1.37813	1.42404	1.23447	1.28816	$b_0 = 1.408178$

Table XIII, A indicates

$F(P_m', R + R \times P_m')$ is the comparison of the difference between the mean values around each P' or plate-day combination with the average difference between the mean values of each replicate within each $P_i D_j$ set. F is not significant.

$F(P' \text{ reg}, R + R \times P' \text{ reg})$ is the comparison of the difference between the slopes around each P' or plate-day combination with the average difference between the slopes of each replicate within each $P_i D_j$ set. F is significant.

$F(S + S \times P', R \times S + R \times P' \times S)$ is the comparison of the average difference between the deviation of the individual points from the curve drawn around each $P_i D_j$ set with the average difference of the measurements between the deviation of the points from the curves drawn around each replicate within each $P_i D_j$ set. F is significant.

It is questionable whether a verbal description as just given really clarifies the symbolic results, even in this simple instance. The three values of F are obtained in similar fashions and have similar connotations. Each is a measure of a comparison of the effects due to differences in means, slopes or deviations, respectively, between and around replicates within each P_i' or $P_i D_j$ set.

Table XIII, B indicates that the deviations from the curve drawn around each replicate set contributes the least to the total variance. Compared to it the differences in *means* are highly significant.

Tables XIII, C and D indicate that the variances due to *replicates* is of the same order as that due to *deviations* (not an orthogonal comparison). *Effects* and (*means + reg*) are significantly greater than *replicates* and *deviations*, respectively.

The following conclusions may be summarized:

(a) *Plates* and *days*, and their interaction, are not significantly different in any intercomparison.

(b) *Deviations* (difference of average deviation of a point from the curve around its own replicate set) is the least of the three main categories. This is practically a necessary condition for a quantitative procedure.

(c) *Replicates* and *deviations* are of the same order of magnitude and each may be considered the experimentally irreducible variance.

(d) *Translation* or *means* is the significant effect. No comparison within this category is significant (either in Table XII or Table XIII, A).

(e) Although differences of plate slopes and plate deviations are significant compared to differences of replicate slopes and deviations, respectively, the categories themselves are not significant. Conclusions (d) and (e) reveal a lack of experimental control.

Although *means* is the significant contributor to the overall variance or "error" there is no apparent way to apply an adjustment or correction, since the difference between replicate means within a plate is not significantly less than the difference between plate or day means. And, although plate slopes and deviation may be adjusted by determining a mean slope or deviation through replicates for each plate or day, the improvement in "error" would not be significant. The entire experiment indicates that a drastic re-examination of the experimental set up is necessary in order to effect a marked or significant improvement in precision.

(7) *Inversion.* The difference between the algebraic and stochastic inversion of $\hat{Y}' = \bar{y} + b(X - \bar{x})$ into $\hat{X} = \bar{x} + \frac{1}{b}(Y - \bar{y})$, i.e., the change in role of independent and dependent variable, largely depends on the difference between $\frac{1}{b}$ and $\dfrac{b}{b^2 - t^2 \frac{S_{y \cdot x}}{\Sigma x^2}}$ (approximately). Using the determined experimental values at the .95 level, $t^2 \dfrac{S_{yx}}{\Sigma x^2} = \dfrac{4 \times 18}{48 \times 19773}$ = .00007, which may be neglected. Hence, the expected mean values of the standards, i.e., the values directly on the regression line, may be determined as a simple algebraic computation. The comparisons are presented:

	S_1	S_2	S_3	S_4	S_5	S_6
Chemical (% Mn)	3.35	3.55	4.10	4.23	4.48	4.87
Mean Spectrographic (% Mn)	3.365	3.535	4.092	4.225	4.566	4.900

The differences are responsible for the S sum of squares.

The mean value of the set is 4.121 per cent Mn and the equivalence point, the value for which delta density is zero, i.e., $X(0)$ is 4.136 per cent Mn. This is an important factor. The critical spectrographer might argue that since the analytical curve rotates around $(\bar{x}, \bar{y})$ while variations of the plate or emulsion calibration curve would effect a rotation about $(\bar{x}, 0)(Y =$ delta log $I)$, any difference between $\bar{Y}$ and zero would reflect itself in a translation of the plate means. However, the extremely close coincidence of the two values, i.e., 4.12 and 4.14 per cent precludes any such considerations. The effect of variation in the *means* must be held to be independent of changes in the plate gamma.

(*8*) *Precision.* Although the previous tables are given in terms of delta density, no transformation to delta log I need be made since the plate calibration curve is a straight line. This is shown as follows:

Let γ be the slope of the plate calibration curve, then

$$\frac{S_{y \cdot x}}{\gamma} \text{ (density)} = S_{y \cdot x} \text{ (intensity)}$$

$$\frac{b_0}{\gamma} \text{ (density)} = b_0 \text{ (intensity)}$$

$$d = t \frac{S_{y \cdot x}}{b} \text{ (intensity)} = t \frac{S_{yx}}{\gamma} \cdot \frac{\gamma}{b} \text{ (density)} = t \frac{S_{y \cdot x}}{b} \text{ (density)}$$

Using the value of $S_{y \cdot x} = \sqrt{.00034088} = .01846$ (after restoration of the decimal point), and the formula $d = t \frac{S_{yx}}{b}$ for t at the 95 per cent level,

$$d = \frac{1.95996}{1.408178} \times .01846 = .02569 \text{ in terms of log per cent.}$$

This may be converted to 6.1 per cent of content, which is the precision estimate based on this experiment.

(*9*) *Estimation of Expected Precision.* It will be assumed, for purposes of estimation, that the experiment is a representative sample of an infinite population of similar experiments on similar sets of samples. Based on the results of this sample experiment, computations may then be made of the expected precision of similar experiments, which may, however, differ in design or in the assumed control of selected physical conditions. It should be pointed out, however, that these refined statistics are subject to rather severe sampling fluctuations and that the factual information should be tempered by the knowledge that it is based on a small sample (4 plates, 6 specimens, etc.). For sake of uniformity, estimates of precision will be given in terms of per cent of content, at the 95% probability level.

(a) Control of physical conditions:

The contribution of the various factors, or combination of factors, to the overall "error" may be estimated from the analysis of variance. It will be assumed that certain controls or physical conditions can be modified to such an extent that the contribution of some selected factors can be made highly nonsignificant, or even non-significantly different from zero. The experiment will then be considered to have been repeated, in the same design $P^4D^4S^6R^3$ under the modified conditions with the unmodified contributors unaltered. The consequent improvement in precision will then estimate the desirability of the effort to effect such controls. Whether the physical results are feasible or not is, of course, a non-predictable matter; but at least the various directions of effort will be indicated and estimated.

TABLE XIV

Controlled factors	$S^2_{y \cdot x}$	Precision
Original conditions	340.9	6.1
Pm and P reg (adjustment of mean differences between plates)	244	5.2
Means or translation	211	5.2
Regression coefficient or slope	284	5.5
Deviation	186	4.5
Replicates	171	4.3
Plates and replicates	14.7	1.2

(b) Statistical design:

By improvement of precision due to statistical design is meant the improvement due to the use of the means of multiple measurements or observations. The manner in which the multiplicity is obtained is controlled by the design of the experiment.

Considering the sample experiment to be of the form $P^{16}S^6R^3$ variance components may be computed, approximately, as follows: $\sigma^2_R = 253$, $\sigma^2_{PS} = 11.3$, $\sigma^2_S = 15.9$, $\sigma^2_{P\,reg} = 19.1$ and $\sigma^2_{Pm} = 50.8$.

(The component $\sigma_S{}^2$ is computed on the assumption that the average lots of future samples will be similar to the set considered in the present experiment. The theory of regression indicates that the variance of a sample varies directly with its deviation from the mean. However, the high degree of homogeneity of the S variances and the close agreement between chemical and spectrographic analyses, justify the assumption that the differences in variance within the indicated range of Mn content are not significant.)

The variance of the mean of a given sample measured in p plates with r replicates, i.e., and experiment of the form $S^1 P^p R^r$ is estimated by

$$S^2_{y \cdot x} = \frac{\sigma^2_R}{pr} + \frac{\sigma^2_{P \, reg} + \sigma^2_{Pm}}{p} + \frac{\sigma^2_{PS}}{p} + \sigma^2_s$$

For $p = r = 1$, i.e., for a single measurement, $S^2_{x \cdot y} = 350.1$ with a precision of 6.2 per cent.

It is interesting to compute the effect of using the mean of repetitive measurements, i.e., multiple exposures in immediate succession on the same plate. The interpretation is facilitated by computation of coefficient of improvement of N repetitions $(CI)_N$, defined as follows:

$$(CI)_N = \frac{\text{variance of a single determination}}{\text{variance of the mean of } N \text{ repetitive measurements.}}$$

$(CI)_N$ may be considered as the number of truly replicated measurements that are equivalent to N repetitive measurements. For this experiment

$$(CI)_N = \frac{350.1}{97.1 + \dfrac{253}{N}}$$

N	2	3	4	5	. .	∞
$(CI)_N$	1.56	1.93	2.18	2.37	. .	3.6

It should be noted that an indefinitely large number of repetitions will yield an *estimated* improvement in precision equivalent to the use of between three and four true replicates. On the other hand the mean of two repetitions will furnish quite a satisfactory and economical gain in precision.

It will be instructive to compare the estimate precision with those observed in the experiment. This will serve principally as an indication of the extent to which the physical variables satisfy the mathematical assumptions.

		$S^2_{y \cdot x}$	Precision
Estimated	Single observation	350.1	6.2
Observed	Single observation	340.9	6.1
Estimated	Mean of three repetitive observations	181.4	4.4
Observed*	Mean of three repetitive observations	173.3	4.3
Estimated	Mean of three replicate observations	116.7	3.5

* Table, XIII, C. The three repetitions are assumed to be equal to their mean value. Hence there are three parallel experiments, $3 \times P^{16}S^6$ for $282 df$, and the mean square $= 48875/282 = 173.3$.

Assuming the experiment to be six independent sub-experiments of the form $P^{16}R^3$ the following statistics may be computed to illustrate sampling fluctuation.

	S_1	S_2	S_3	S_4	S_5	S_6
Observed mean	−126.0	−96.0	−6.6	13.0	60.4	99.6
Expected mean	−129.0	−93.8	−5.1	13.2	62.5	100.5
Observed precision around expected mean	6.2	4.6	6.0	5.8	6.0	7.1
Observed precision around observed mean	6.1	4.6	6.0	5.8	6.0	6.9
Variance components about observed mean						
σ_P^2	122	16	41	14	88	206
σ_R^2	235	184	300	300	248	248
Estimated precision of one determination	6.2	4.6	6.1	5.8	6.1	7.1
$(CI)_2$	1.5	1.8	1.8	1.9	1.6	1.4

Perhaps a more instructive comparison may be obtained by considering the experiment of the form $E^e R^r$ (Table XIII, C), $e = 96$, $r = 3$. This will serve to present a kind of average of the above values.

The expression for $(CI)_{N'}$ may be transformed into

$$(CI)_{N'} = \frac{1 + D}{1 + \dfrac{N}{N-1}\left(\dfrac{1}{N} - \dfrac{1}{N'}\right) D}$$

where N is the number of repetitions in the original experiment (3); N' is the number of repetitions in the future experiment; D is $\dfrac{e-1}{e}$ $\dfrac{SS(R)}{SS(E)} = \dfrac{95}{96} \times \dfrac{48617}{48875} = 0.9843$. Confidence limits, at the 1 per cent level, may be computed for D through the relations $D/D_1 = F_0$ and $D_2/D = F_0'$ (since $F \geq 1$) where F_0 and F_0' are the F values, at the 1 per cent level, for $(e(r-1), (e-1); df)$ and $((e-1), e(r-1); df)$ respectively. In this case F_0 (192, 95; df) = 1.51 and F_0' (95, 192; df) = 1.48. The computations yield the following estimates:

N'	2	3	4	6	∞
$(CI)_{N'}$	1.59	1.98	2.26	2.63	3.91
Efficiency	.80	.66	.56	.44	0
Confidence Interval at $Pr = .98$ $\left\{\vphantom{\begin{matrix}a\\b\end{matrix}}\right.$	1.4	1.6	1.8	2.0	2.5
	1.8	2.4	3.0	3.9	9.0

The various values of $(CI)_{N'}$, computed under different assumptions, should be compared to appreciate the order of variations in estimates.

Appendix. Orthogonal Partition into Single Degrees of Freedom

There are four days involved in the experiment, with $3df$. A question might be raised whether the days are truly replicates of each other. For example, a question might be raised concerning the permanency of the latent image in the emulsion and the validity of experimental comparison of images developed after various days exposure. The experimental data for *day* means (Table X, B) are: -400, -505, -515 and -1065. There appears to be a progression.

The statistical procedure to investigate this question is to partition the $3df$ of *days* into three sub-effects of $1df$ each, in an appropriate fashion. There are many ways of effecting this partition, one of which is illustrated. The D effect is partitioned into three parts, of $1\ df$ each, as described in Section 1.6.2. That is, instead of having one main effect D for $3\ df$ we now have three effects, D', D'', D''' for $1\ df$ each. The manner of effecting this partition (not uniquely, to be sure), consequent summation of experiment data, computation of covariance and final analysis of variance are displayed in Tables XV and XVI. Their similarity to Tables X and XII is apparent. While the arithmetical similarity is close, there is quite a difference in physical connolation.

The physical interpretations of the sub-effects are as follows:

$D' \equiv$ the mean difference between successive days;

$$\frac{1}{2}\left(\frac{D_1 - D_2}{2} + \frac{D_3 - D}{2}\right)$$ i.e., the mean effect due to difference of one day.

$D'' \equiv$ the mean difference between alternate days;

$$\frac{1}{2}\left(\frac{D_1 - D_3}{2} + \frac{D_2 - D_4}{2}\right),$$ i.e., the mean effect due to difference of two days.

$D''' \equiv$ an interaction or cross term, the difference between the sum of the extreme days and the sum of the middle period.

The sum of the sum of squares of $D' + D'' + D'''$ is of course equal to the sum of squares of D.

The experiment values are as follows:

TABLE XV
Mn in CRS
Orthogonal Decomposition of D

A

	D_1	D_2	D_3	D_4
D'	1	−1	1	−1
D''	1	1	−1	−1
D'''	1	−1	−1	1

B
$S \times D$

	ΣY	D	D	D
S_1		155	−195	115
S_2		130	0	− 80
S_3		− 30	390	−100
S_4		− 15	195	− 45
S_5		110	280	− 30
S_6		305	5	−305
		655	*675*	*−445*

C
$P \times D$

	ΣY	D	D	D
P_1		65	65	45
P_2		200	− 60	−140
P_3		460	250	260
P_4		− 70	420	−610

D
$P \times D$

	$\Sigma_{x.y}$	D'	D''	D'''
P_1		14887.5	6597.5	− 2102.5
P_2		−18715	14455	−13335
P_3		1695	11040	− 9535
P_4		8900	4105	− 5120
		6767.5	36197.5	−30092.5

TABLE XVI
Sub-effects of D

Source of variation	df	SS	V
Means			
D'	1	1490	1490
D''	1	1582	1582
D'''	1	687	687
$P \times D'$	3	2131	710
$P \times D''$	3	1845	615
$P \times D'''$	3	5720	1907
Regression			
D'	1	48	48
D''	1	1381	1381
D'''	1	954	954
$P \times D'$	3	2707	902
$P \times D''$	3	268	89
$P \times D'''$	3	308	103
Deviation			
$S \times D'$	4	1528	382
$S \times D''$	4	3424	856
$S \times D'''$	4	975	244
$S \times P \times D'$	12	2926	244
$S \times P \times D''$	12	1823	152
$S \times P \times D'''$	12	2621	218

There are no apparent physically meaningful or statistically significant comparisons.

2.2. Discriminant Functions.   Nickel in CRS

Three samples of steel (CRS) were each exposed 216 times on many plates and the densities of lines Ni 2303.86 and Fe 2308.77 measured. The Ni content averaged about 10 per cent (9, 10, and 11 per cent). A discrimination test was computed to determine the values of λ_1, and λ_2 in the linear form $D = \lambda_1 \times$ (density of Ni line) $+ \lambda_2 \times$ (density of Fe line) that would furnish the least chance of misclassifying a sample. It is clear that only the ratio λ_1/λ_2 is necessary. The following values were obtained.

Comparison	λ_1/λ_2	Significance level of difference from -1.000
$S_1:S_2$	-1.0436	.40
$S_3:S_2$	-1.0323	.50
$S_1:S_3$	-1.0141	.75

The values of λ_1/λ_2 may be considered a statistical or experimental proof that, at least in this experiment, the use of Δ density (or equivalently $\Delta \log I$) is the optimum linear combination.

2.3. Regression. Two Random Variates. Method of Wald

A number of spectra of CRS specimens were obtained on many plates and the densities of a line pair for Ni measured (2303.86 Ni, 2308.77 Fe). Computations were made to determine whether the difference in density between the lines, both of which were on the straight line portion of the calibration curve, is independent of the density, that is to say, whether the slope of the regression line of (density of Ni line) $\times$ (density of Fe line) is significantly different from 1. The density of neither line can be assumed to be free from error, and since the investigation is for the "structure" of the relation rather than for purposes of prediction, the ordinary regression method is not suitable. The densities of the iron line were arranged in order of magnitude and divided into two parts at the median. It is reasonable to assume that the division is not correlated to the error. The computations were made as indicated in the reference and the following results obtained.

n = Number of observations.
a = Observed slope computed from the data.
α = Estimated slope of the population.
δ = Least significant difference in slope.
P_r = Significance level.

Sample	n	a	α	δ	Pr
1	216	0.9948	0.9949	0.0133	0.33
2	216	1.0434	1.0445	0.0218	0.05
3	216	1.0548	1.0546	0.0415	0.05
All	648	1.0288	1.0294	0.0307	0.33

It seems that a further investigation of this line pair is called for since the expected slope is significantly different from 1 in two samples.

2.4. Comparison of Microphotometer and Repetition Error

A number of repeated spectra were exposed and a line pair was remeasured after a lapse of time, and the errors compared as in a two-factor experiment, $M^i R^j$ (M = microphometer effect, R = repetition effect). The measurements were of density differences.

A. Mn in CRS

Source	df	Sum of squares	Mean square	F
ΣR	840	253115	201.33	3.13**
ΣM	1056	101732	96.33	

The significant value of F at .01 probability is about 1.15.

B. Ni in CRS

ΣR	342	44790	130.96	2.18**
ΣM	432	25937	60.4	

The significant value of F at .01 probability is about 1.20.

Evidently the microphotometer error can be made highly nonsignificant, if due care is taken in the measurement process.

2.5. Plate Calibration

Many investigations may be made on plate calibration. The following experiment is rather involved, but is a good example of the use of variance analysis.

The experiment may be described as follows. A pair of mild steel pins were excited and two spectra, without changing electrodes, were exposed simultaneously onto two plates in two prism spectrographs. The plates were interchanged in the spectrographs and the exposures repeated. Both spectrographs were readjusted into another optical condition, and the entire experiment repeated (on the same plates). Thus three optical adjustments were made in all, corresponding to position 5, 6, and 8 on the Bausch and Lomb large Littrow spectrograph. Eight of the nine iron lines used for plate calibration were measured, and the data analyzed for the effect of regression, i.e., plate calibration and deviation, since in this work the means, or over-all density of the spectra, has no significance.

The experiment form is $P^2R^2C^3T^3S^2L^8$, where

$P \equiv$ plates,

$R \equiv$ replicates, i.e., between two new pins and two used pins,

$C \equiv$ optical adjustment, i.e., positions 5, 6, 8,

$T \equiv$ comparison of simultaneous exposure and successive exposure,

$S \equiv$ spectrographs (S_1 = Bausch and Lomb, S_2 = Hilger), and

$L \equiv$ iron spectrum lines.

The data were analyzed as follows:

$$P^2R^2C^3T^3S^2L^8 \qquad n = 192$$

	df	Sum of squares	Mean square
Total	190	439772	
Σ means	23	0	
Reduced total	167	439772	
Σ reg	23	346672	15073**
Σ dev	144	93100	646
Reg			
P	1	89	89
S	1	158604	
T	3	1064	355
C	2	137220	
C × S	2	43680	21840
Interactions	2	1496	
ΣR	12	4519	376
R	1	41	
Deviations			
L	6	30.853	
P	6	3170	528
S	6	5461	910
T	18	4971	276
C	12	11538	961
C × S	12	24348	2029
Interactions	12	4109	342
ΣR	72	8750	120
R	6	2003	334
Σ'R	66	6647	147

Values of γ		
Position	S_1 B & L	S_2 H
5	1.988	1.498
6	2.048	1.814
8	2.135	2.001

Many conclusions may be drawn concerning what happened, the most important of which are:

(1) The apparent gamma of a plate depends on the spectrograph, on its optical arrangement.

(2) The changes in gamma are not alike for the individual spectrographs.

(3) The apparent change in gamma due to the use of new or used pins is not significant (R).

(4) The source is stable in the sense that the change in gamma as determined from simultaneous or successive exposures (T) is not significant compared to repetition (ΣR).

The P effect should not be considered too seriously since it is based only on two plates.

As far as deviations go, i.e., the fit of the points on the calibration curves, most of the significant effects are connected with spectrographs or optical position. The change in deviations due to new or used pins is significant compared to the change in gamma. However the stability of the source still shows up to be good ($T = 276$, compared to $R = 334$ or even $\Sigma'R = 107$).

The effect of the spectrograph on contrast of intensities of radiation has been observed before, particularly in the comparison of prism and grating instruments. Indeed the effect, i.e., change in contrast, has been observed in optical instruments other than the spectrographs. The importance of this effect on the comparison of methods between laboratories is apparent.

2.6. Effect of Excitation on Analytical Curve

The following experiment is given for its formal value rather than an estimate of the substantive factors involved since only 80 observations are involved.

Source of variation	Sum of squares			
	df	C_1	C_2	$F(\ )$
P means	3	569	1019	
$\Sigma(R + R \times P)$ means	4	147	780	
Σ means	7	716	1799	2.5
P reg	3	14	534	
$\Sigma(R + R \times P)$ reg	4	30	226	
	7	44	760	17.***
Σ deviations	24	640	3453	5.4**
Total	38	2540	13028	5.1***
Precision: Least significant difference at .05 probability in terms of per cent of content		4.7	12.2	

Five samples were used to determine an analytical curve for the determination of Mn in steel, ($S_1 = 0.65$, $S_2 = 1.00$, $S_3 = 1.31$, $S_4 = 1.56$

and $S5 = 1.77$ per cent Mn). Two excitation conditions (C) were used on the same plate: $C_1 \equiv$ synchronous interrupted spark, 0.016 mf., 10.5 turns, 5.1 ohms primary resistance, and $C_2 \equiv$ high frequency spark, 0.004 μf., 10.5 turns, 11 ohms primary resistance, five breaks per half cycle. The electrodes were $\frac{1}{4}$-inch diameter pins, ground to a 150° cone on top for C_1 and flat for C_2.

The experiment was of the complete balanced type $S^5P^4R^2C^2$, but each level of C is computed separately.

Significance is determined between excitation conditions rather than within them, and it may be seen that C_1 is by far the more precise set of conditions.

2.7. Source Stability

The use of an arc-spark line comparison to estimate source stability has been frequently suggested. The lines used in this experiment are Fe 2813.29 and Fe 2813.61, and the following $\Delta \log I$ were observed on one instrument (synchronous excitation).

Capacity in μf.	0.009	0.001	0.013	0.015
Inductance = 10.5 turns	128	89	58	31
= 42.5 turns	306	302	288	285

Two experiments were made, twelve plates each, using two spectrographs and thus simultaneous and successive spectra (T) were obtained. The plates were coupled in succession. Exposures were made using freshly prepared pins (R'), pins excited a second time (R'') and excited a third time (R'''). The experiments were of forms $P^{12}R^3(S^2T^2)$, where S = spectrograph and T = time were arranged in a Latin square. The results obtained are as follows:

Source of variation	df	Sum of squares	Mean square
Total	287	30573	
Experiments	1	2050	
S	1	102	102
ΣP	22	1065	48.4
ΣT	24	1506	62.7
Σ interactions	46	2810	61.1
R'	1	2	2
R''	2	11429	5715
R'''	1	6766	6766
ΣR	188	4836	25.7

The results show no significant difference between plates and (simultaneous vs. successive exposures = T). The $\Delta \log I$ of the line pair is very sensitive to the condition of the electrode. The T effect is significant compared to repetitions, after the effects due to electrode conditions have been removed.

In general one may venture the prediction, that on the basis of this line pair, the source is not significantly worse than plates but it is not as stable with regard to time fluctuations, i.e., the difference between simultaneous and successive exposures is greater than the difference between immediately successive exposures on the same plate.

REFERENCES

1. Brownlee, K. A., Industrial Experimentation. H. M. Stationery Office, London, 1946.
2. Cramer, H., Mathematical Theory of Statistics. Princeton Univ. Press, Princeton, New Jersey, 1946.
3. Eisenhart, C., Hastay, M. W., and Wallis, W. A., Techniques of Statistical Analysis. McGraw-Hill, New York, 1947.
4. Fisher, R. A., Statistical Methods for Research Workers. Oliver & Boyd, London, 1941.
5. Fisher, R. A., The Design of Experiments. Oliver & Boyd, London, 1941.
6. Kendall, M. G., Advanced Theory of Statistics. Griffin, London, 1946.
7. Mather, K., Statistical Analysis in Biology. Interscience, New York, 1947.
8. Rider, P., Modern Statistical Methods. Wiley, New York, 1939.
9. Wald, A., *Annals of Mathematical Statistics* **11**, 284 (1940).
10. Wilks, S. S., Mathematical Statistics. Princeton Univ. Press, Princeton, New Jersey, 1943.
11. Mandel, J., *Ind. Eng. Chem., Anal. Ed.* **18**, 280 (1946).
12. Mood, A. F., Introduction to the Theory of Statistics. McGraw-Hill, New York, 1950.
13. Mann, H. B., Analysis and Design of Experiments. Dover, New York, 1949.

Chromatographic Analysis

WALTER G. BERL

The Applied Physics Laboratory, Johns Hopkins University, Silver Spring, Maryland

CONTENTS

I. Introduction

Chromatographic analysis includes separation techniques based on differential partition of solutes between a moving and a stationary phase. Included are liquid-solid, gas-solid and liquid-liquid systems. The difference between chromatographic analysis and the well-known adsorption from solution and partition between solvents is in the modification of experimental techniques whereby adsorption and desorption and partition are repeated a large number of times. Thus, chromatographic analysis can be compared to fractional distillation or crystallization.

Chromatographic analysis is primarily a separation technique. Since it can be readily applied to microgram quantities of material and often permits almost quantitative recovery of the starting substances, it has become an extremely powerful tool in the separation and identification of complex mixtures. Under favorable circumstances, positive identification of particular compounds in a mixture and quantitative estimates of their concentration can be made. This is particularly useful when dealing with members of homologous series (sugars, amino acids) (41, 43).

Meinhard (34) has given a schematic outline and classification of possible interactions between a mobile fluid containing mixtures that are to be resolved and a stationary phase on which fractional separation proceeds. By choosing four physical states in which the solutes can be found in the mobile or immobile phase, sixteen types of interactions are deduced. Some of these are recognized as well established techniques. Others are either in an early stage of development or are not expedient for use. The classification into four major sections is not strictly precise. However, the outline serves to separate the field of adsorption analysis into a number of logical groups.

TABLE I

Type of Competitive Interaction

Primary mode of action	Class	Mobile phase	Solid phase	Representative phenomena
Ionic: (solubility product, instability constant, etc.)	1	Ions	Ions	Ion exchange
	2	Complex	Ions	Ion exchange
	3	Ions	Complex	Inorganic chromatography
	4	Complex	Complex	(Not reported)
	5	Ions	Dispersion	Fractional decomposition methods
	6	Complex	Dispersion	Fractional decomposition methods
	7	Dispersion	Dispersion	Diffusion of colloids, macromolecules
	8	Ions	Association	Electrokinetics
	9	Dispersion	Ions	(Not reported)
	10	Dispersion	Complex	(Not reported)
Nonionic: H-bonding: dipole, and/or induced dipole; geometry of molecules (partition coefficients)	11	Association	Association	Organic (and partition) chromatography
	12	Association	Dispersion	Catalytic polymerization
	13	Association	Ions	Catalytic dissociation
	14	Association	Complex	(Not reported)
	15	Complex	Association	(Not reported)
	16	Dispersion	Association	Salting-out adsorption

In Table I the following definitions apply:

Ion: A solute particle having a definite electrical charge and characterized by a simple structure and subcolloidal dimensions.

Complex: The product of a reversible interaction between a solute particle of simple structure and a complexing agent to form a new species.

The combination usually involves linkages of an auxiliary, or coordinate, character. The complex may itself be a simple structure (charged or uncharged), or it may be a relatively large and complicated aggregation of particles appearing as a colloidal dispersion, as a precipitate, or as an immobile deposit on the solid phase.

Dispersion: The product of a reversible interaction of a solute with another solute, or with the solvent itself, to produce a species having a decreased association with the solvent. This decrease in association becomes evident in the aggregation of particles to form a colloidal dispersion or a visible precipitate. In this discussion the term dispersion is not intended to include those dispersions arising from a process of complexing as described in the preceding paragraph. It does, however, include dispersions of proteins, silicates, soaps, dyes, organic polymers, and other particles which may or may not be ionically charged, depending upon pH, adsorption or occlusion of ions, presence of dissociable groups, etc.

Association: A mutual attraction between a solute particle and another substance (either in the liquid or solid phase, or both), or between two solute particles of the same species, which does not involve the establishment of fixed bonds. This interaction is characterized, rather, as a loosely bound complex of indeterminate composition arising from the geometry of the molecules involved, from dipole and induced dipole interactions, from resonating electrostatic attractions, or from other imperfectly understood factors. The "bond energies" involved, insofar as this term may be applied here, lie in the neighborhood of two to eight kilocalories per mole, as contrasted with the much greater bond energies involved in the types of aggregation discussed previously.

2. THEORY OF CHROMATOGRAPHY ANALYSIS

The chromatographic analysis that depends on differences in adsorption of solute between phases (gas-solid, liquid-solid) can be divided into three groups: (1) frontal analysis; (2) elution analysis; (3) displacement analysis. In frontal analysis solutes and solvent are passed through the column containing the adsorbent and the effluent is continuously analyzed for the appearance and concentration of components. In elution analysis solutes and solvent are introduced into the column where a preliminary separation may take place as in frontal analysis. Subsequently, one or several solvents of different eluting properties are added to the top of the column and a further separation of solutes is effected thereby. It is not necessary in this case to elute until the solutes appear in the effluent provided means are available to locate the bands into which the various solutes are separated. The theoretical treatment of this type of separation has been discussed in detail by Wilson, De Vault, Weiss and Glueckauf (14, 17, 18, 19, 20, 40, 52, 53, 57). These theories have been of great assistance in unravelling the various factors that influence the resolution of a mixture. The main factors entering into the discussion are type of adsorption between solute and adsorbent (i.e. Langmuir, Freundlich, sigmoid isotherm, etc.), mutual competition between solutes for adsorption sites, influence of incomplete equilibrium, diffusion and pore space between adsorbent particles. In displacement analysis solutes are added to the column as in elution analysis and are developed by a solvent containing an additional solute more strongly adsorbed on the column than any of the components already present.

2.1. Elution Analysis

Glueckauf has developed a detailed theory of the differential equations that can be set up for a system of multiple components in elution analysis. The simplest case of separation of two solutes obeying Langmuir's adsorption law is presented here. Separation is brought about by differential rates of movement of solutes when eluted with pure solvent.

The bands formed originally are of constant intensity. On addition of pure solvent the various zones begin to move. The rate of movement of the forward edge (Fig 1b) is given by

$$x_u = (v + v^0)c_2^0/f_{2(c_1^0c_2^0)} + \alpha c_2^0 \tag{1}$$

where $\quad x =$ distance from top of column (expressed in grams of adsorbent)

$v^0 =$ volume of solvent in which solutes at concentration c_1^0 and c_2^0 are contained.

$v =$ amount of solvent added for development

$\alpha =$ pore volume/gram of adsorbent

$f_{2(c_1c_2)} = q_2 =$ equilibrium amount of substance 2 adsorbed on one gram of adsorbent in presence of concentration c_1 and c_2

$f_{2(c_1c_2)} + \alpha c_2 =$ amount of solute 2 contained in volume filled by one gram of adsorbent if local concentrations of solutes in the solvent are c_1 and c_2

As development proceeds, the regions of constant composition are changed into regions of varying concentration. In these regions, movement of fronts proceeds according to

$$x = v/(\alpha + f_1'_{(c_1c_2)}) = v/(\alpha + f_2'_{(c_1c_2)})$$

A general equation for multiple solutes following Langmuir's isotherm can be developed. For two solutes

$$f_{1(c_1c_2)} = q_1 = a_1c_1/(1 + a_1\beta_1c_1 + a_2\beta_2c_2)$$
$$f_{2(c_1c_2)} = q_2 = a_2c_2/(1 + a_1\beta_1c_1 + a_2\beta_2c_2)$$

where a = adsorption coefficient

β = amount of adsorbent required so that one mole of solute covers surface in a mono molecular layer.

From (2) and (3)

$$f_1'_{(c_1 c_2)} = a_1(1 + b_2 c_2 - b_2 c_1 \cdot dc_2/dc_1)(1 + b_1 c_1 + b_2 c_2)^2 \tag{2a}$$
$$f_2'_{(c_1 c_2)} = a_2(1 + b_1 c_1 - b_1 c_2 \cdot dc_1/dc_2)(1 + b_1 c_1 + b_2 c_2)^2 \tag{3a}$$

where $b = a\beta$

$\delta = (a_2 - a_1)/a_1$

At any point f_1' and f_2' are equal and relation between coexisting concentrations of the two solutes can be calculated.

$$a_2 b_1 c_1 = a_1 b_2 c_2 \lambda - (a_2 - a_1)\lambda/(1 + \lambda) \tag{4}$$

where λ is an integration constant.

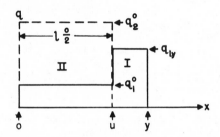

FIG. 1a. Band of two solutes before development.

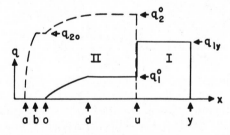

FIG. 1b. Initial development of a band of two solutes. Original concentration preserved in forward part of the band.

2.1.1. *Formation of Bands.* Let v_0 of solvent containing c_1^0 and c_2^0 of solutes 1 and 2 be added to the column to give a band as shown in Fig. 1a. The following relations can be written:

$$x_u = l_2^0 = v^0 c_2^0/f_2(c_1^0 c_2^0) = v_0((1 + b_1 c_1^0 + b_2 c_2^0)/a_2$$
$$q_1^0 = f_1(c_1^0 c_2^0) = a_1 c_1^0/(1 + b_1 c_1^0 + b_2 c_2^0)$$
$$q_2^0 = f_2(c_1^0 c_2^0) = a_2 c_2^0/(1 + b_1 c_1^0 + b_2 c_2^0)$$

Let m_1 and m_2 be the total quantities of solute added. The amount of solute 1 between o and u is

$$m_{1,o-u} = m_2 q_1^0/q_2^0 = m_1 a_1/a_2$$

and the separated quantity of 1

$$m_{1,u-y} = m_1(a_2 - a_1)/a_2$$

The concentration of 1 rises sharply at x_u to

$$c_{1y} = c_1^0(1 + \lambda_1)/\lambda.$$

From (4)

$$q_{1y} = a_1 c_{1y}/(1 + b_1 c_{1y})$$

and from (1)

$$x_y = v^0(1 + b_1 c_{1y})/a_1$$

2.12. Development. If a further volume v of solvent is added to the column the bands, dissolving from the top end and moving down the column undergo changes.

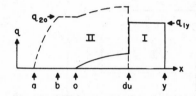

Fig. 1c. Full development of the mixed band. Separated band I has its original concentration.

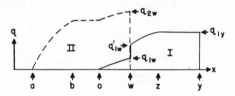

Fig. 1d. Further development and spreading of bands I and II.

At first, the concentration in the forward section remains unchanged, followed by a section in which the concentration of both solutes decreases, the less adsorbed going to zero. This is followed by a constant section of the more strongly adsorbed solute, followed by a variable section (Fig. 1b).

The position of the various points of concentration change are:

$$c_{2o} = \delta/b_2(1 + \lambda)$$
$$x_a = v/f_2'(c_2 = 0) = v/a_2$$
$$x_b = v/f_2^1(c_{2o}) = v(1 + b_2 c_{2o})^2/a_2$$
$$x_v = (v + v^0)c_2^0/f_2(c_1^0 c_2^0) = (v + v^0)(1 + b_1 c_1^0 + b_2 c_2^0)/a_2$$
$$x_y = (v + v^0)c_{1y}/f_1(c_1 y) = (v + v^0)(1 + b_1 c_{1y})/a_1$$

x_b cannot reach x_0 since $\dfrac{x_o}{x_b} = 1 + \dfrac{\delta\lambda}{1 + \lambda + \delta}$. This band shift persists until x_d overtakes x_v, when the development of solute 2 is complete. After 2 is fully developed its frontal concentration c_{2w} begins to decrease.

$$c_{2w} = \sqrt{m_2/b_2v(1 + \lambda)}$$

The concentration of front of solute 1 is

$$c_{1w} = \lambda(a_1b_2/a_2 - b_1)\sqrt{(m_2/b_2v(1 + \lambda))} - \lambda(a_2 - a_1)/a_2b_1(1 + \lambda)$$

The concentration of solute 1 on the other side of the discontinuity is

$$c_{1w}' = -\lambda_2^1(a_2 - a_1)/(1 + \lambda_2^1)a_2b_1 = c_{1w} = (1 + \lambda_1)/\lambda_1$$

After the band of solute 2 has been fully developed, the concentration of pure solute 1 also changes (Fig. 1c).

2.1.3. Complete Separation. Development will continue with further addition of solvent, the frontal concentration of 1 becoming continually smaller (Fig. 1d).

Volume V required for complete separation

$$V = m_2b_2(1 + \lambda)/\delta^2$$

2.2. Frontal Analysis

The theory of frontal and displacement analysis has been developed by Claesson (8, 9, 10).

Consider a column filled with adsorbent, saturated with pure solvent. The solution to be analyzed is then added and the effluent analyzed continuously for content of solute.

The volume of pure solvent leaving the column before the appearance of solute is the retention volume $(v)_a$, after correction for the pore space between the solid particles and for tube losses, such as volume change of solid due to adsorption of solutes. The retention volume divided by the weight of adsorbent is the "specific retention volume (v^0)".

Let a = amount of solute adsorbed

c = concentration of solute in solution

then $a = vc$, or, per gram of adsorbent:

$a^0 = v^0 c.$

If a^0 is plotted against c one obtains the adsorption isotherm, since a^0 is in equilibrium with solution of concentration c.

Let $f(c)$ = adsorption isotherm/gram adsorbent, then

$a^0 = f(c) = v^0 c.$

If the isotherm is curved toward the abscissa, then $v^0 = \dfrac{f(c)}{c}$ will decrease as c increases. An isotherm of this kind allows establishment of a sharp front within the column. If the front is disturbed (by variation in column packing density, for example) a bulge will form giving rise to sideways concentration gradients. The concentration of this diffused material is less than that in the undisturbed solution and the front will move more slowly and be overtaken eventually by the main front. Irregularities in the rear, on the other hand, will tend to amplify. For isotherms curved away from the abscina the arguments are reversed.

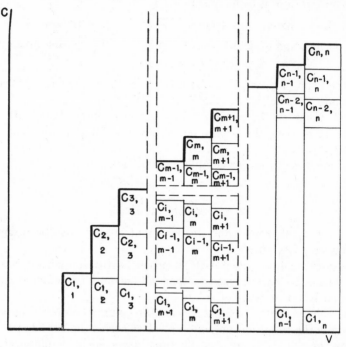

Fig. 2. Volume-concentration diagram for n components in frontal analysis.

If two solutes are present in solution two steps will be observed in the effluent if the isotherms of the two substances are not identical. The height of the steps is not a direct measure of concentration due to mutual competition of solutes for adsorption sites.

Let a_1^0 = amount of substance 1 adsorbed per gram from solution of concentration c_1 of solute 1 and concentration c_2 of solute 2,

and a_2^0 = amount of substance 2 adsorbed from the same solution,

then $a_1^0 = f_1(c_1, c_2)$

$a_2^0 = f_2(c_1, c_2)$

The adsorption isotherm $f(c_1)$ for the case of one solute only is larger than $f(c_1, c_2)$ for the same solute in presence of another substance. Thus, in frontal analysis, the concentration of substance 1 in the first step will be greater than in the original solution due to the substance 2 partly displacing substance 1 from the adsorbent. For two solutes, a_1 and a_2 can be calculated from the experimental data, $a_2 = v_2c_2$, since the solution passes unchanged through the adsorbent after the second step. The amount of solute 1 adsorbed equals $a_1 = v_2c_1 - (v_2 - v_1)c_1$, where the second term expresses the amount of solute 1 adsorbed in the first step. In case of three or more solutes it is not possible to determine the adsorbed amounts from frontal analysis and isotherms cannot be derived from analysis of effluent alone.

For the general case of a solution containing n solutes in concentration c_1, c_2, c_3, ... c_n, the amount a_i^0 of solute per gram of adsorbent is a function of all components. $a_i^0 = f_i(c_1, c_2, c_3 \ldots c_n)$ where the function f_i is the adsorption isotherm for substance i in presence of substances $1, 2, 3 \ldots, c - 1, c + 1, \ldots n$. In most cases f_i increases with c_i, but decreases when $c_j(j \neq i)$ increases, or when an additional solute, $n + 1$ is added. A schematic composition diagram for the case of n solutes is shown in Fig. 2.

Consider the section of a column where S represents the position of a front which on leaving the column would cause the step having a retention volume v_{m+1} (Fig. 3). At the lower boundary, L_1, the concentration

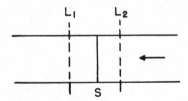

FIG. 3. Schematic cross section through chromatographic column.

of the different components in solution between the particles is $c_{1,m}$, $c_{2,m}$, ... $c_{m,m}$, and at the upper boundary L_2, the concentrations are $c_{1,m+1}$, $c_{2,m+1}$ ... $c_{m+1,m+1}$. Below S the amounts adsorbed are

$$a_{i,m}^0 = f_i(c_{1,m}c_{2,m+1} \cdots c_{m,m})$$

Above S

$$a_{i,m+1}^0 = f_i(c_{1,m+1}c_{2,m+1} \cdots c_{m+1,m+1})$$

Let a small volume v be forced into the column. The amount of substance i transported across the boundaries L_1 and L_2 is $\Delta vc_{i,m}$ and $\Delta vc_{i,m+1}$. The amount of material added to the section between L_1 and L_2 is $\Delta v(c_{i,m+1} - c_{i,m})$. As a consequence the front S moves a distance Δx downwards.

If there are M_0 grams of adsorbent and x the empty volume per unit length

$$\Delta v(c_{i,m+1} - c_{i,m}) = \Delta x M_0 [f_i(c_{1,m+1}c_{2,m+1} \cdots c_{m+1,m+1}) -$$
$$f_i(c_{1,m}c_{2,m} \cdots c_{m,m})] + \Delta x \alpha(c_{1,m+1} - c_{1,m})$$

and

$$\frac{\Delta v}{\Delta x} - \alpha = \frac{M_0 f_i(c_{i,m}c_{2,m} \cdots c_{m,m}) - f_i(c_{1,m+1}c_{2,m+1} \cdots c_{m+1,m+1})}{c_{i,m} - c_{i,m+1}}$$

$\Delta \dfrac{v}{x}$ is the volume of solution to move front S one centimeter down the column. For every component i

$$v_{m+1}{}^0 = \frac{f_i(c_{1,m}c_{2,m} \cdots c_{m,m}) - f_i(c_{i,m+1}c_{2,m+1} \cdots c_{m+1,m+1})}{c_{i,m} - c_{i,m} + 1}$$

For components $m + 1$, giving rise to front S and found only above S

$$v_{m+1}{}^0 = \frac{f_{m+1}(c_{1,m+1}c_{2,m+1} \cdots c_{m+1,m+1})}{c_{m+1,m+1}}$$

In order to get results applicable in practice, the isotherm must be known. If components $1, 2 \cdots i - 1, i + 1 \cdots n$ are present

$$a_i = f_i(c_1, c_2 \cdots c_n) = \frac{\beta_i c_i}{1 + \displaystyle\sum_{j=1}^{n} l_j c_j}$$

so that

$$c_{m+1,m+1} v_{m+1}{}^0 = \frac{k_{m+1}c_{m+1,m+1}}{1 + \displaystyle\sum_{j=1}^{n+1} l_j c_{j,m+1}}$$

2.3. Partition Chromatography

The chromatographic analysis that depends on separation by partition of solutes between two phases is carried out by immobilizing one phase within a solid framework. This framework itself should have no or very limited adsorptive powers for the solutes. The simplest case is a column filled with a porous solid containing water or organic solvent as the fixed phase. Solutes having the larger distribution coefficient for the stationary phase will be retained in the upper part of the column. Instead of granular materials (silica gel (12, 31), starch (36)) cellulose in form of paper sheets saturated with the stationary solvent can be used (33, 51) (Paper Chromatography). The theory of separation by partition assumes the existence of "theoretical plates," in analogy with liquid-vapor fractionation theory (32). The height equivalent of a theoretical plate (HETP) is defined as the width of a layer of column so that the solution leaving it is in equilibrium with the mean concentration of solute in the non-mobile phase within this layer. It is further assumed that no diffusion of solute takes place between plates and that the distribution ratio of one solute between two phases is independent of its absolute concentration and of the presence of other solutes.

Let R = height equivalent of a theoretical plate

$\quad A$ = column cross section ($A = A_L = A_s = A_I$)

$\quad A_s$ = non-mobile phase cross section

$\quad A_L$ = mobile phase cross section

$\quad A_I$ = inert solid cross section

$\quad v$ = volume of solvent used in development

$\quad \alpha$ = partition coefficient = $\dfrac{\text{grams solute in non-mobile phase}}{\text{grams solute in mobile phase}}$

$\quad V = h(A_L + A_s)$

$\quad r$ = serial number of plate as measured from top

$\quad Q_r$ = total quantity of solute in plate r

$\quad R$ = movement of position of maximum concentration of solute, divided by simultaneous movement of surface of developing fluid in empty part of column above solid

Let unit mass of a single solute be contained in the first plate. Pure solvent is used for development. Table II shows the quantity of solute in each plate after successive infinitesimal volumes dv of mobile phase have passed through the column.

TABLE II

Volume of mobile phase nv	Serial number of plate			
	1	2	3	4
0	1	0	0	0
1	$1 - v/V$	v/V	0	0
2	$(1 - v/V)^2$	$2(1 - v/V)\dfrac{v}{V}$	$\left(\dfrac{v}{V}\right)^2$	0

The concentration of solute in each plate can be expressed by the binomial expansion $\left[\left(1 - \dfrac{\partial v}{V}\right) + \dfrac{\partial v}{V}\right]^n$, so that after passage of n volumes

$$Q_{r+1} = n! \left(1 - \frac{\partial v}{V}\right)^{n-r} \left(\frac{\partial v}{V}\right)^r \Big/ r!(n - r)!$$

where n is large

$$Q_{r+1} = \frac{1}{r!} \left(n \frac{\partial v}{V} \right)^r e^{-n\partial v/V}$$

but

$$n\partial v = V$$

therefore

$$Q_{r+1} = \frac{1}{r!} \left(\frac{v}{V} \right)^r e^{-v/V}$$

For $r > 10$, by Stirling approximation

$$Q_{r+1} = \frac{1}{\sqrt{2\pi r}} \left(\frac{v}{rV} \right)^r e^{r-v/V}$$

Q_{r+1} is a maximum and equal to $\dfrac{1}{\sqrt{2\pi r}}$ when $\dfrac{v}{rV} = 1$, so that the position of maximum concentration has moved a distance $\dfrac{hv}{V}$, directly proportional to volume v of developing liquid.

In terms of movement of solvent in the unobstructed part of the tube

$$R = \frac{vh/V}{v/A} = \frac{Ah}{V} = \frac{A}{A_L + A_s \alpha} = \frac{A_L + A_s + A_I}{A_L + \alpha A_s}$$

A useful term in paper chromatography is R_F, the ratio of the distance of movement of maximum concentration of solute divided by the distance of movement of the developing solvent in the column.

$$R_F = R \frac{A_L}{A}$$

In actual operation the assumption of zero diffusion between plates will not be valid for low flow velocities. Apart from this, HETP is proportional to flow velocity and to the square of particle diameter. Diffusion rate in the solvent is also important, particularly in case of large molecules of low diffusivity. The assumption of constancy of distribution ratio with concentration is usually not strictly true, decreasing with increase in concentration. This leads to sharpening of the front boundary and weakening of the rear, since the concentrated part of the mixture moves more rapidly. Mutual interaction of solutes often leads to improved separation, the more strongly adsorbed eluting the less.

The presence of inorganic salts in the mixture may lead to complications due to ion exchange on the cellulose, giving rise to zones of high and of low p_H. These zones may interfere with subsequent developing procedures. If the sample is sufficiently large the salts of strong acids can be removed by electrodialysis. When this procedure is inapplicable due to the number and smallness of the samples the developing procedure must be adequate to overcome these disturbing influences. In separation of amino acids obtained from hydrolyzed material, chemical development with ninhydrin produces a yellow spot in the glycine-alanine region caused by an inorganic alkaline zone. The alkaline spot interferes with color development of neighboring amino acids. By use of acidified ninhydrin this interference can be minimized (13).

Distribution maps have been prepared giving the approximate location of members of homologous series (amino acids, sugars (42)) in two dimensional chromatograms. Extensive tables of R_F values for a variety of compounds are also available (sugars (25), pterins (21)). Positive identification is best carried out by parallel development of unknowns, the probable pure substance and mixture of the two. If the position of the spots after development are identical, particularly from two different solvent pairs, the identification is certain with a high degree of probability.

One of the most adequate supports for the stationary liquid phase (water) is cellulose in form of filter paper. For most compounds the adsorption effects are small and partition between mobile and stationary phase the predominant factor. No supporting tube is necessary for small scale experiments, the paper hanging from a trough filled with eluant within a large container. The latter is saturated prior to the chromatographic analysis with water and solvent vapor. Large scale separations on paper are possible by packing paper strips on top of one another in a suitable container.

The unknown is added to the top of the paper as a single drop. After elution is complete the solvent is evaporated and the position of the constituents located by suitable chemical or physical reactions. If for a given solvent pair some of the constituents of a complex mixture are not resolved, it is possible to provide further separation by eluting with a different solvent at right angle to the first paper chromatogram. For this purpose, a square paper is suitable with the initial drop placed in one corner. After chromatographing with one solvent pair in the usual manner the solvents are removed by drying, the paper turned through 90° and elution with the second solvent pair commenced.

Quantitative evaluation of paper chromatography depends to a large degree on the nature of the substances. The location of the position of the various constituents can be determined by carrying out two parallel elutions, developing one by a suitable method and using the pattern to locate the corresponding spots in the parallel chromatograph. These spots are separated and tested individually by a suitable procedure.

Resolution is difficult if R_F values differ by less than 10%. Reproducibility for duplicate analysis is better than 4% in the R_F values.

3. BASIC EXPERIMENTS

A foundation has been laid in the theoretical understanding of chromatographic analysis by emphasizing the essential importance of the adsorption isotherms and the mutual influence of multiple solutes on one another. Thus, it is possible, in principle, to predict the separation behavior if sufficient information is available on the type and magnitude of the adsorption isotherms.

A very important prerequisite for the understanding of the chromatographic process is the elucidation of the forces responsible for the interaction between solute and adsorbent. This is particularly true since the usefulness of chromatographic analysis lies in the fact that it makes use of very small differences in physical properties between closely related compounds. In physical adsorption, one can distinguish two essential factors that influence the magnitude of the effect, the operation of oriented forces between solute and adsorbent and a geometrical "fit." The detail understanding of these two factors for any but the simplest molecules is still in its infancy. For this reason the accumulation of a considerable body of experimental information is necessary in guiding the understanding. Regarding the interaction between adsorbent and solute a close parallel exists with problems encountered in heterogeneous catalysis where the orientation and binding forces are of paramount importance in the subsequent reactions. Comparatively few systematic experiments have been carried out to establish the primary factors responsible for adsorption. These can be considered from the standpoint of a) adsorbent, b) structure of solute, c) medium effects.

a) The types of adsorbents useful in chromatographic analysis will be discussed more fully in Section 5. They comprise the field of polar hydrophylic solids, principally oxides, hydrated oxides and salts. For some applications, organic adsorbents (sugars, polysaccharides) are useful. In contrast to ion exchange, the bond between adsorbent and adsorbate is of addition adsorption type and depends on the lattice structure of the adsorbent and the polarizability of the solute.

The influence of structure of the solute is based on either chemical or stereochemical considerations. Brockmann (4), by varying the side chains on azobenzene has determined the sequence of separation indicated in Table III.

The Roman numerals express the activity of the aluminum oxide adsorbent. Pairs in the same horizontal row cannot be separated using benzene as solvent. This difficulty, however, can be overcome by small changes in the solvent composition. Thus cyclohexane-ethylacetate (9:1) will separate p-amino azobenzene from the p-acetoxy azobenzene.

TABLE III

1.	RCOOH
V	
2.	ROH
IV	
3.	RNHCOCH₃
III	
4.	RNHCOC₆H₅
III	
5.	RNH₂, ROCOCH₃
III	
6.	RCHO
II	
7.	ROCOC₆H₅
II	
8.	RN(CH₃)₂, RNH₂
I	
9.	ROCH₃
I	
10.	RCl, RCH₃, RH

R = azobenzene skeleton.
Roman numerals = degree of activity of aluminum oxide adsorbent,

The following deductions are possible: Side chains contribute to adsorption in the order —COOH, —OH, —NH₂, —CO, COOCH₃, CH₃O. Esterification of a hydroxyl group decreases adsorption. Carbonyl groups, whether in aldehydes, ketones, esters show approximately the same adsorptive effect, —NO₂ groups are not effective.

Under favorable conditions compounds of varying hydrocarbon chain length can be separated cleanly if the chain differs by one CH₂ group only. Thus the p-phenyl phenacyl esters of straight chain fatty acids from acetic through caproic have been separated on silica gel. In the higher fatty acids partial separation of palmitic (16C) from stearic acid (18C) was achieved. Unsaturation permits separation of compounds of the same chain length from the equivalent saturated compound. An increase in the number of functional groups generally represents an increase in the strength of adsorption.

The importance of structural factors is indicated by the fact that optical isomers can be separated under favorable circumstances. Cis-trans isomers of azobenzene are instructive in pointing out an empirical rule by Berl and Wachendorff, that the strength of adsorption on a hydrophylic solid (silica gel) is larger if the solvent is hydrophobic and vice versa (2). In comparing the adsorption of cis and transazobenzene by alumina and charcoal it is found that the cis compound is adsorbed most strongly by Al_2O_3 from petroleum ether, less strongly from methyl alcohol. The trans compound is adsorbed more strongly on carbon from methyl alcohol. Thus, the more hydrophylic solute (cis isomer) is adsorbed more thoroughly by hydrophylic adsorbents (Al_2O_3) in a hydrophobic medium (petroleum ether). The hydrophylic nature of the cis isomer is indicated by its greater water and alcohol solubility.

Isomeric molecules containing the same number and kinds of functional groups are adsorbed on polar solids roughly proportionally to the magnitude of the dipole moment of the structure (1). For example, nitrophenols or nitroanilines are adsorbed in the order para-meta-ortho, in agreement with change in dipole moment. However, this argument cannot be extended to a comparison of compounds having a differing number of functional groups. Picric acid is more strongly adsorbed on Al_2O_3 than nitrophenol even though the latter has the larger dipole.

The strength of adsorption may vary from practically irreversible adsorption through reversible adsorption to no adsorption. In the case of irreversible adsorption, elution with solvent will not lead to movement along the column and can only be overcome by choice of different adsorbents or a more active solvent.

The nature of the solvent or eluant is of very great importance in successfully carrying out a chromatographic analysis (4). The competition between solvent and solute for the various adsorption points on the solid adsorbent and the dependence of distribution coefficients between immiscible solvents determine the effectiveness of separation to a considerable extent. For hydrophylic adsorbents the order of solvents in the direction of increasing eluting power is: Petroleum ether (saturated hydrocarbons)—benzene—chloroform—diethyl ether—ethylacetate—acetone—propyl alcohol—ethyl alcohol—methyl alcohol—water—pyridene. This order which runs parallel to the dielectric constant of the liquids and their heats of wetting, has been determined for the adsorption or elution of one solute. In the case of multiple solute separation, however, inversions in the adsorption sequence are often observed. Comparatively small changes in the properties of the solvent give rise to different adsorption sequences on similar columns. This points up the importance of effect of mixed solutes on the adsorption isotherm of each component.

Proof of purity of a substance as determined by behavior on chromatographic columns must as a consequence be determined by adsorption on a variety of adsorbents and from a number of solvents. The reversing of position is of advantage in frontal analysis where only the first component appears pure in the eluate or in elution chromatography in which the bands are not completely separable. In either case the least adsorbed component will be separated in high state of purity from the other components.

Structural effects and overall shapes are of great importance in the field of long-chain polyene hydrocarbons (60). Isomerization can be induced in carotenes whereby the all-trans configuration is converted into mixtures of stereoisomers containing mono-cis and di-cis configurations. The location of the cis linkage is important with regard to the adsorption sequence. If centrally located, so that the entire carotene structure assumes a bent configuration, the strength of adsorption decreases remarkably. Cis-linkages near the end of the molecule adsorb above the all trans configuration. Poly-cis configurations lead generally to substantial weakening in adsorptive strength.

4. APPARATUS (50)

The apparatus necessary in chromatographic analysis is very simple, consisting of circular or straight sided tubes in which the adsorbent is maintained. Following a suggestion of Claesson, the volume of the tube is conveniently expressed in multiples of π (pi). Straight sided tubes are used when the position of adsorbed bands is to be observed by the technique of total reflection. When ultraviolet light is used for observation of band position, the tube material should be quartz.

It is essential in the preparation of columns to introduce the adsorbent as uniformly as possible to avoid cracks and inclusion of air pockets. Support for the adsorbent can be either a dense fritted glass support or a perforated porcelain plate. The chosen solvent is introduced and the adsorbent added in a fine stream and allowed to settle with repeated tapping. Excess solvent is run off by opening the stopcock (greaseless) in case of the porcelain plate assembly or by applying pressure on the fritted glass column until the adsorbent is barely covered with solvent. The excess is reintroduced at the top and allowed to run through several more times until the adsorbent is thoroughly settled. An accurately cut piece of filter paper and some cotton are added to the top of the adsorbent to prevent disturbance on subsequent use and excess solvent is removed to the point where the top of the adsorbent remains covered with liquid.

Under no circumstance should the column be allowed to dry out since cracks are bound to develop. Therefore, when the column is not being used a tight stopper must be employed to prevent solvent evaporation. To obtain adequate flow rates it is preferable to apply positive pressure rather than suction.

5. ADSORBENTS

In view of the pronounced effect of adsorbent structure on the shape of the adsorption isotherm, adequate quantitative information of the structure of the substance is desirable. Activities may vary widely due to variation of surface structure and chemical composition. Reproducible results can be obtained only by strictest maintenance of uniformity of the adsorbent. As in preparation of catalysts, the manipulation's during manufacture of the adsorbent must be closely controlled.

It is found convenient to establish a relative scale of activity of adsorbents. Highly active aluminum oxide preparations can be deactivated stepwise by controlled addition of water or exposure to water vapor (37). This results in a preferred adsorption of water on the adsorbent surface having maximum degree of unsaturation adsorption strength. By employing test solutions consisting of a group of azo dyes with different functional groups, the degree of activity can be established rapidly by observing the behavior of different adsorbents under conditions of uniform adsorption and elution. This test gives no indication of the rate of zone movement which is determined by the number of active adsorption sites per unit volume of adsorbent, but gives a valuable clue concerning the strength of bond established between solute and adsorbent.

Test solutions are made up of a series of azo dyes with similar skeleton

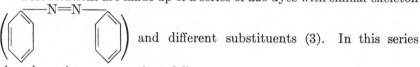 and different substituents (3). In this series

the adsorption sequence is as follows:

       p-hydroxyazobenzene
       p-aminoazobenzene
       Sudan red
       Sudan yellow
       p-methoxyazobenzene
       azobenzene

The experimental procedure consists in standardized adsorption and elution experiments with pairs of the azo dyes. The activity of the adsorbent is measured by the extent to which test pairs are adsorbed and eluted from the column. Table IV shows the empirical separation of aluminum oxides with 5 degrees of activity. Other adsorbents, like silica gel, magnesium oxide, calcium sulfate, can be ranked in comparison to alumina on a similar scale by making use of the same test substances (4).

Adsorption activity decreases in the order of oxides, sulfate, carbonate, oxalate. As pointed out, however, the order of adsorption is not only a function of the adsorbent structures but of the solvent medium. Particularly for solutes differing only slightly in adsorption inversion in order may occur.

Heat of wetting (38, 39) supplies quantitative data of surface character while the adsorption of azo dyes will provide relative rates of band

TABLE IV

Degree of activity	I	II		III		IV		V
		a	b	a	b	a	b	
Position of test dyes								
In column	*p*-methoxy azobenzene	*p*-methoxy azobenzene	Sudan yellow	Sudan yellow	Sudan red	Sudan red	*p*-amino azobenzene	*p*-oxy azobenzene
In column		azobenzene	*p*-methoxy azobenzene		Sudan yellow		Sudan red	
In filtrate	azobenzene			*p*-methoxy azobenzene		Sudan yellow		*p*-amino azobenzene

motion. Heat of wetting may be determined directly calorimetrically or from the temperature dependance of adsorption isotherms. The temperature effect is a function of the heat of wetting of the surface and heat of adsorption of the solvent. The latter quantity is strikingly influenced by the presence of small amounts of polar impurities. Measurements of this kind, are not sufficient to specify the adsorption behavior of non-homogeneous mixtures of adsorbents, where, for example, extremely active particles are diluted with completely non-active material. However, in the preparation of graded alumina specimen the calorimeter procedure is very adequate to indicate the degree of deactivation by water or other polar solvent.

An important technique of characterization of adsorbents is the measurement of actual rates of movement of bands along a column (28, 29). Under steady flow conditions an adsorbent can be specified by three terms: S = length of column containing one unit volume of solvent/length of unfilled tube required to contain same volume of solvent; V_c = rate of flow of the developing solvent through the column (mm/min); R_f = rate of movement of adsorbate zone (mm/min)/rate of flow of the solvent (V_c). T_o = time in seconds required for a solvent to penetrate 50 mm into an initially dry 9 × 75 mm column. S expresses a packing term of the column (% of tube occupied by adsorbent = $100(S - 1)/S$) and is a function of the technique with which columns are prepared, as well as particle size and shape. V_c is a function of pressure drop through the column and driving force and can be calculated from Darcey's Law.

$$V_c = k(A/700\alpha)\, P/yL$$

where k is permeability in Darceys, y is the viscosity in centipoise, α is the interstitial volume of the column, L is length of column in centimeters and A the cross section in square centimeters. $KA/760\alpha$ is most conveniently measured by determining V_c for one set of conditions for a standard set of packing.

The values of V_c, T_{50}, and R that are found generally useful are $V_c = 10 - 50$ mm/min, $T_{50} = 20$ to 100 sec; $R = 0.10$ to 0.30.

All methods discussed are to be considered guides in the selection of adsorbents, permitting general reproducibility of results when different specimen of adsorbents are to be used.

It has been shown by Dickey that the activity of an adsorbent can be decidedly influenced in favor of high specificity by its preparation in the presence of the substance to be adsorbed (15). Experiments on silica gel precipitated in the presence of methyl orange and its derivatives indicated that the structure of the silica gel was sufficiently modified by the presence of the dye to yield noticeably increased adsorption. This property proved to be very specific as shown in Table V.

TABLE V

	Adsorptive power for			
	Methyl orange	Ethyl orange	Propyl orange	Butyl orange
Control gel	84	80	240	320
Specific adsorbent	300	740	5000	5000

6. IDENTIFICATION OF SOLUTES

The identification of adsorption zones can be carried out in the following manner:

1) Direct visual inspection
2) Fluorescence in ultraviolet light (27)
3) Color change in stationary indicator (45, 46)
4) Marking of colorless substances with indicators (radioactive) (6)
5) Fluorescence quenching of adsorbent (4, 49)
6) Optical techniques in the effluent
    a. Refractive index (9)
    b. Interferometer (9)
    c. Thermal conductivity (9, 44)
7) Coupling to form colored derivatives (47)
8) Optical total reflection (11)

If the components of interest are colored no identification problem exists. Similarly if the adsorbed substances fluoresce in ultraviolet light, identification of zone position can be accomplished in a light tight box with suitable ultraviolet light sources. This technique was first used by Karrer and Schopp (27).

The use of indicators present in the column prior to adsorption of the unknown belongs more properly into the field of partition chromatograph, where the indicator is part of the stationary aqueous phase. Thus, the aliphatic acids (C_1-C_{10}) have been separated on silica gel columns using a stationary phase to which bromocresol green has been added (45, 46).

The use of indicators having the same adsorption isotherms as the compound under investigation applies almost entirely to the use of isotopes that can be detected by characteristic radiations. Location of zones in columns is not convenient. However, absence or appearance of a compound in effluent can be conveniently measured. In cases where purification is desired, the addition of a radioactive substance in dilution sufficient for identification is an extremely delicate tool. Removal of undesirable ions by an exchange column can be followed with ease. Likewise, estimates of the probable contamination of the eluate are made possible. Auto-radiographic techniques, wherein the emitted radiation is used to expose a photographic plate is of very considerable value in paper chromatography which lends itself exceedingly well to the mounting of plate and development paper. This method is of greatest value in determining rapid physiological processes in living organisms by permitting insight in the fate of particular radioactive substances under controlled experimental conditions (6).

The conversion of colorless compounds into colored derivatives is a measure that should be of use in those cases where none of the other methods for detection of colorless compounds are applicable. The p-phenyl azobenzoyl esters of mono-, di-, and trisaccharides on silica and magnesol columns, 2, 4, dinitrophenyl hydrazones of aldehydes and ketones and azobenzoic acid derivatives of amino acids are typical examples of colored derivatives.

If the adsorbent is made fluorescent by adsorption of a fluorescing dye or washing with fluorescing pigment, the presence of strongly adsorbed bands will usually produce a weakened fluorescence emission at the point of fixation. This is due to a blanketing effect of the adsorbed substances which will adsorb a fraction of the incident ultraviolet light making it unavailable for reemission. The part of the column containing the adsorbed substance appears as dark band. Another mode of action is that the adsorbed substance quenches the fluorescence of the adsorbed dye (4, 49).

Fluorescence can be produced in the following ways: The adsorbent is prepared according to the techniques of luminous phosphors by incorporating in it a small amount of a metallic activator. For the more common adsorbents this has been accomplished for aluminum oxide where the addition of thallium produces a light yellow fluorescence. A more adequate technique is to add a fluorescent dye which will not react with the solute and not be eluted by the solvents used in subsequent analyses or to mix mechanically a fluorescent solid which by itself has no adsorptive capacity. Morin on aluminum oxide, calcium carbonate and magnesium oxide gives yellow fluorescence, diphenyl fluorindin sulfonic acid red fluorescence. Berberine is satisfactory on silica gel. For maximum sensitivity the spectral range of the lamp should match the adsorption maxima of the compound being adsorbed.

Characteristic color reactions can be carried out in order to locate the position of the bands after colorless substances have been separated and the column is removed from its glass envelope. In the identification of sugars a thin line of permanganate drawn along the column will indicate the position of oxidizable bands. The method suffers from the difficulty of not permitting observation of separation during elution and of requiring removal of adsorbent from the column (30, 31).

If the analysis is carried out by frontal or displacement analysis, the identification of the appearance of bands in the eluate can be carried out by any physical method which is sufficiently sensitive and specific. The eluate can be measured continuously for changes in refractive index, density, electrical conductivity, light adsorption, and in the cases of gases by thermal conductivity determinations. In order to correlate the physical constants with the volume of liquid that has passed through the adsorption column it is advisable to make the measuring cell as small as possible. A weighing device allows the determination to become entirely automatic.

7. Reactions with Adsorbents

An undesirable interference in chromatographic analysis is the possibility of irreversible reactions taking place on the adsorbent. On the other hand reversible changes in configurations are possible in which the adsorbed substance undergoes a structural change which reverts to the original state upon elution.

Triarylmethyl halides in benzene solution are colorless. They are known to form colored double salts with $ZnCl_2$, $AlCl_3$, etc. similar in structure to the heteropolar colored triarylmethyl nitrates, perchlorates, etc. If the colorless halides are brought in contact with well dried silica gel or alumina similar color formation is obtained. Elution with solvents containing small amounts of alcohol, acetone or water restores the aryl derivatives to its colorless form. Thus, the bond with the adsorbent acts similarly as the complex formation with inorganic halides. The behavior is common to a large number of similar classes, as for example, unsubstituted and substituted triphenyl carbinols, as well as a large family of dyes containing chromophoric groups (C=O, =NR, —C=N,

$$-N=O, \quad -N{\overset{\displaystyle O}{\underset{\displaystyle O}{\diagdown\kern-0.6em\diagup}}}\Big)$$ connected by conjugation to auxochrome groups,

like —NR_2, —OR, —SR. Their color is strongly dependent on the nature (dielectric constant) of the solvent. Adsorption on silica gel or alumina generally leads to deepening of color in the same sense as is due to the presence of a polar solvent (alcohol). Elution with alcohol or acetone eliminates the color on the column (54, 55, 56).

The effect of the adsorbent is not confined to organic molecules only. Colored pseudo salts, composed of colorless ions, are decolorized by adsorption. Mercuric iodide vapor, intensely yellow above 120°, forms a colorless addition complex on silica gel, which on addition of water is converted back to the colored form. That very considerable polarization forces exist is demonstrated by the observation that when adsorbent and the polarisable substance are crushed together dry, the typical adsorption colors are developed. For example, the green p-nitroso dimethyl

aniline, forms a yellow brown quinonoid hydrochloride,

An aqueous solution has a similar yellow brown color, due to

formation of the ion . A similar yellow color is formed if the green

benzene solution is adsorbed on alumina or silica gel. Addition of water or alcohol regenerates the green color in solution.

In contrast to the simple pseudo salt color changes, the color assumed by the types of compounds consisting of chromophores and auxochromes can assume a number of forms depending on the particular resonance structures that are most stable. Thus tetramethyl diamino fuchsone, $C=O$, is orange in benzene, red in alcohol, olive green on silica gel, brown on air dried alumina, violet on well dried alumina.

Similar results are obtained on various adsorbing clays (7). Sudan red B, from diazotized o-amino azotoluol and β naphthol, gives red solution in absence of acids, changing to green in presence of concentrated sulfuric acid. On alumina, calcium carbonate and air dried natural clays the dye is adsorbed moderately strongly from benzene. However, acid treated bleaching earths (frankonite, floridine), bind it strongly with green color. That this is not due to presence of unbound mineral acid is shown by the fact that water, which does not elute the dye from adsorbents due to its lack of solubility therein, does not affect the color complex. The color tint depends on the water content of the clay, the rate of salt formation increasing with decrease in non-chemically bound water.

Irreversible changes have been observed particularly on adsorbents of high activity (48). Polymerization, isomerization, ring closure, splitting off of water are possible reactions. Floridine, heated to 325°C., polymerizes all ethylene derivatives of the constitution $R(R')C\!\!=\!\!CH_2$ and $R(R')C\!\!=\!\!CHR''$ at room temperature. Singly or symmetrically substituted ethylenes are not polymerized. Similarly dehydrated frankonite initiates vigorous reaction with ring systems containing unsaturated bands (limonene, pinene) (7). Weakly adsorbed solvents do not prevent this reaction, in the presence of methanol or acetone the polymerization is entirely suppressed.

Easily deesterified esters are hydrolyzed on alumina (5). However, carotene isomerizations suspected to be due to the action of alumina columns were shown to be due to spontaneous reactions on standing, the column merely resolving the mixture into its components (58, 59).

There is no doubt that very sensitive substances may undergo irreversible changes on active adsorbents. It is possible in nearly all cases to overcome this difficulty by proper choice of adsorbent or solute so that the chemical activity of the adsorbent is reduced to negligible contribution.

8. Resolution of Optical Isomers

For the separation of the two forms of a racemic mixture by chromatographic analysis two techniques have been employed. By forming the diastereo isomerides by combination with pure dextro or levo compound selective adsorption on non-active adsorbents will take place. due to the different adsorption isotherms of the diastereo isomerides (26). Jamison and Turner were able to partially separate dl-mandelic acid through their menthyl esters on alumina columns from petroleum ether. Much poorer separations are reported on calcium sulfate, dextrose and magnesium oxide from benzene (22).

Complete separation of a dl mixture on an optically active adsorbent has been accomplished with p-phenylene bisimino camphor on columns of lactose from petroleum ether-benzene (4:1) (23, 24). The separation was carried out by multiple elution of partially separated mixtures. The d-amino camphor is the more strongly adsorbed isomer on D-lactose. Prolonged contact with lactose or the use of a highly purified sugar adsorbent leads to compound formation, probably the p-phenylene bisimino derivative.

In view of this demonstration of detectable differences in adsorption isotherms of optical antipodes, Martin and Kuhn suggested an amplification by superimposing on the adsorption a thermal diffusion gradient and circulation (35). In the presence of an optically active adsorbent and in presence of a temperature gradient the more strongly adsorbed substance (with the higher heat of adsorption) will tend to be desorbed more strongly at the higher temperature than at the lower. In this way a concentration gradient in the liquid phase is set up with diffusion of the more strongly adsorbed antipode toward the cold boundary. If at the same time the liquid is circulated perpendicularly to the temperature gradient a multiplication of the separation factor can be expected. Using a wool band containing asymmetric amino acids and an aqueous solution of *dl* mandelic acid a partial resolution of the racemate was observed. This would tend to confirm the requirement that the temperature coefficient of adsorption of optical antipodes is not the same on a given adsorbent.

REFERENCES

1. Arnold, R. T., *J. Am. Chem. Soc.* **61**, 1611 (1939).
2. Berl, E. and Wachendorff, E., *Kolloid Z.*, Special No., **36** (1925).
3. Brockmann, H. and Schodder, H., *Ber.* **74**, 73 (1941).
4. Brockmann, H., *Angew. Chem.* **59**, 199 (1947).
5. Cahn, R. S. and Phipers, R. F., *Nature* **139**, 717 (1937).
6. Calvin, M. and Benson, A. A., *Science* **109**, 140 (1950).
7. Carlsohn, H. and Mueller, G., *Ber.* **71**, 858, 863 (1938).
8. Claesson, S., *Arkiv. Kemi.* **A20**, No 3 (1945).
9. Claesson, S., *Arkiv. Kemi.* **A23**, No 1 (1946).
10. Claesson, S., *Arkiv. Kemi.* **A24**, No 7 (1946).
11. Claesson, S., *Nature* **159**, 708 (1947).
12. Consdon, R. A., Gordon, A. H. and Martin, A. J. P., *Biochem. J.* **41**, 590, 596 (1947).
13. Consdon, R. and Gordon, A. H., *Nature* **162**, 180 (1948).
14. De Vault, T., *J. Am. Chem. Soc.* **65**, 532 (1943).
15. Dickey, F. H., *Proc. Nat. Acad. Sci.* (Washington) **35**, 227 (1949).
16. Freundlich, H. and Heller, W., *J. Am. Chem. Soc.* **61**, 2228 (1939).
17. Glueckauf, E., *Nature* **156**, 205 (1945).
18. Glueckauf, E., *Proc. Roy. Soc.* (*London*) **A186**, 35 (1946).
19. Glueckauf, E., *J. Chem. Soc.* 1947, 1308, 1315, 1321.
20. Glueckauf, E., *Discussions Farad. Soc.* No 7, 12 (1949).
21. Good, P. M. and Johnson, A. W., *Nature* **163**, 31 (1949).
22. Hass, H. B. and DeVries, T., *J. Am. Chem. Soc.* **65**, 1486 (1943).
23. Henderson, G. M. and Rule, H. G., *Nature* **141**, 917 (1936), 142, 163 (1938).
24. Henderson, G. M. and Rule, H. G., *J. Chem. Soc.* 1939, 1568.
25. Hirst, E. L. and Jones, J. K. N., *Discussions Farad. Soc.* No 7, 268 (1949).
26. Jamieson, M. M. and Turner, E. E., *J. Chem. Soc.* 1942, 611.
27. Karrer, P. and Schoepp, K., *Helv. Chim. Acta* **17**, 693 (1934).
28. LeRosen, A. L., *J. Am. Chem. Soc.* **67**, 1683 (1945).
29. LeRosen, A. L., *Anal. Chem.* **19**, 189 (1947).

30. Lew, B. W., Wolfrom, M. L. and Goepp, R. M., *J. Am. Chem. Soc.* **67,** 1865 (1945).
31. McNeely, W. H., Brinkley, W. W. and Wolfrom, M. L., *J. Am. Chem. Soc.* **67,** 527 (1945).
32. Martin, A. J. P. and Synge, R. L. M., *Biochem. J.* **35,** 1358 (1941).
33. Martin, A. J. P., *Ann. N.Y. Acad. Sci.* **49,** 249 (1948).
34. Meinhard, J. E., *Science* **110,** 387, (1950).
35. Martin, H. and Kuhn, W., *Z. Elektrochem.* **47,** 216 (1941).
36. Moore, S. and Stein, W. H., *J. Biol. Chem.* **176,** 337, 367 (1948), **178,** 53, 79 (1949).
37. Moore, S. and Stein, W. H., *Ann. N.Y. Acad. Sci.* **49,** 265 (1948).
38. Mueller, B. P., *Helv. Chim. Acta* **26,** 1945 (1943).
39. Mueller, B. P., *Helv. Chim. Acta* **27,** 404 (1944).
40. Offord, A. C. and Weiss, J., *Discussions Farad. Soc.* **No 7,** 26 (1949).
41. Partridge, S. M., *Nature* **158,** 270 (1946).
42. Partridge, S. M. and Westall, R. G., *Biochem. J.* **42,** 238 (1948).
43. Partridge, S. M., *Discussions Farad. Soc.* **No 7,** 296 (1949).
44. Phillips, C. S. G., *Discussions Farad. Soc.* **No 7,** 241 (1949).
45. Ramsey, L. L. and Patterson, W., *J. Assoc. Offic. Agric. Chemists* **31,** 139 (1948).
46. Ramsey, L. L., *J. Assoc. Offic. Agric. Chemists* **28,** 644 (1945), 31, 164 (1948).
47. Reich, W. S., *Biochem. J.* **33,** 1000 (1939).
48. Reichstein, T. and Shoppee, C. W., *Discussions Farad. Soc.* **No. 7,** 305 (1949).
49. Sease, G. W., *J. Am. Chem. Soc.* **69,** 2242 (1947).
50. Strain, H. H., Chromatographic Adsorption Analysis, Interscience Publishers, New York, 1945.
51. Synge, R. L. M., *Analyst* **71,** 256 (1946).
52. Weiss, J., *J. Chem. Soc.* 1943, 297.
53. Weiss, J., *Nature* **156,** 570 (1946).
54. Weitz, E. and Kissel, M., *Angew. Chem.* **59,** 164 (1947).
55. Weitz, E. and Schmidt, F., *Ber.* **72,** 1740, 2099 (1939).
56. Weitz, E., Schmidt, F. and Singer, J., *Z. Elektrochem.* **46,** 272 (1940), 47, 65 (1941).
57. Wilson, J. N., *J. Am. Chem. Soc.* **62,** 1583 (1940).
58. Zechmeister, L. and Tuzson, P., *Biochem. J.* **32,** 1305 (1938).
59. Zechmeister, L. and Sandoval, A., *Science* **101,** 585 (1945).
60. Zechmeister, L., *Discussions Farad. Soc.* **No 7,** 54 (1949).

Author Index

Numbers in parentheses are reference numbers. They are included to assist in locating references in which the authors' names are not mentioned in the text. Numbers in italics refer to the page on which the reference is listed at the end of each article.

Example: Abraham, K., 39 (5), *48*, indicates that this author's article is reference 5 on page 39 and is listed in the bibliography on page 48.

A

Abraham, K., 39 (5), *48*
Achmatov, A., 316, *331*
Acree, S. J., 138, 141 (2), *150*, *151*
Adam, N. K., 291, *301*, 308, *331*
Adams, 318, 321, *331*
Adams, L. H., 56 (28), *103*
Adams, N., 237 (24), 240 (25), *254*
Adinoff, B., 262 (2), *301*
Airs, R. S., 86, *102*
Alexander, B., 357 (77), 361 (77), *382*
Alexander, L., 357, 358, 360, *381*
Allen, N., 146 (1), *150*
Ammerman, E., 203, 205, 207, *227*
Anderson, P. A., *381*
Andreas, J. M., 324, 325, *331*
Anhorn, V. J., 334 (1), 338 (1), 339 (1), 341, 342 (1), 350 (1), 353 (1), *380*
Archer, C. T., 392 (2, 35, 36), 394 (1, 34), *435*, *436*
Archer, R. M., 350 (44), *381*
Aristarkhova, M., 372, *381*
Armbruster, M. H., 269, *301*
Armstrong, G., 144 (9), *150*
Arnold, E., 160, *227*
Arnold, R. T., 606 (1), *616*
Ashley, S., 357 (42), 358 (42), 360 (42), 363 (26), 364, *381*
Aston, J. G., 380 (46), *381*
Atchison, G. J., 379 (50a), *381*
Auer, H., 249 (1), *253*
Austin, J. B., 269, *301*

B

Baeckström, S. A., 135, *151*
Bailey, A. J., 354 (47), *381*

Bakr, A. M., 268, *303*
Baldwin, R. R., 350 (47a), *381*
Bale, W. F., 466 (1), 480 (2), *498*
Balfe, M. P., 86, *102*
Bangham, D. H., 289, 292, *301*
Barham, H. N., 354 (66), *382*
Barott, H. G., 434 (3), *435*
Barr, W. E., 341 (1), 338 (1), 339 (1), 341, 342 (1), 350 (1), 353 (1), *380*
Barrer, R., 372, *381*
Barrett, H. M., 268, *301*
Basford, P. R., 262 (8), *301*
Bashford, 318, 321, *331*
Bastien, P., 307, *331*
Bates, L. F., 232 (2, 3), 237 (4), 240 (25), 244 (39), *253*, *254*
Bates, R. G., 141, *150*
Bauman, R., 157 (3), *227*
Bawden, A. T., 136, 137, *150*
Baxter, J., 376 (49), *381*
Bayliss, L. E., 434 (4), *435*
Bazin, E. W., 434 (69), *437*
Bazzoni, C. B., 353 (50), *381*
Beach, A. L., 359, *383*
Beamer, W. H., 379 (50a), *381*
Beard, H. C., 142, *152*
Beckwith, J. B., 269 (9), *301*
Beebe, R. A., 269, *301*
Beeck, O., 353, *381*
Beers, Y., 469 (3), *498*
Belcher, D., 118, *151*
Bencowitz, I., 58 (2), *102*
Bengough, G. D., 58 (3), *102*
Benson, A. A., 612 (6), *616*
Benson, S., 372, 380 (53), *381*
Berezický, S., 42 (12), *48*
Berg, H. H., 425 (5), *435*
Bergin, M. J., 372, *383*

619

Subject Index